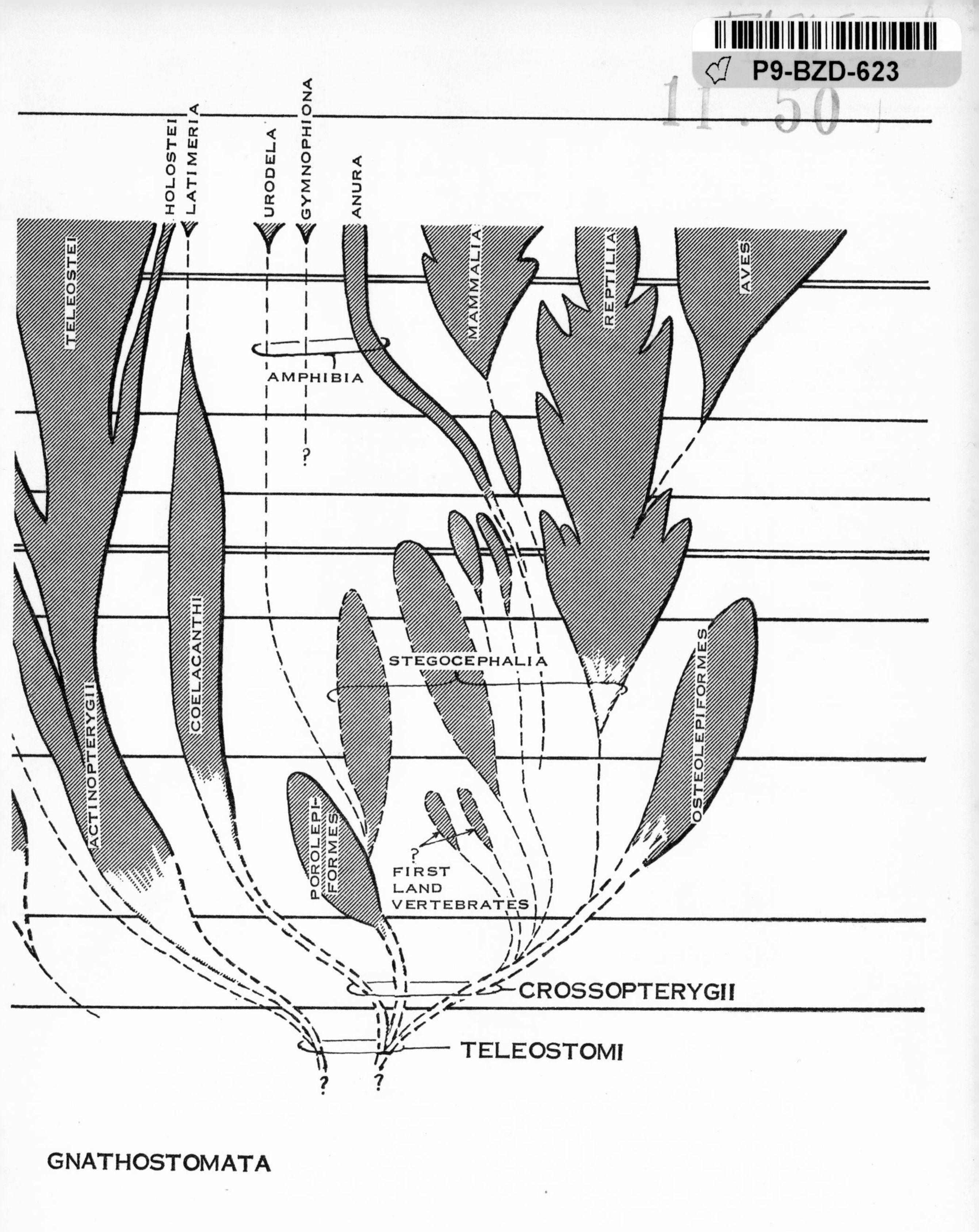

THE VERTEBRATES

COMPARATIVE
AND

THE RONALD PRESS

ANATOMY
EMBRYOLOGY

William W. Ballard
DARTMOUTH COLLEGE

COMPANY • NEW YORK

2 V

Library of Congress Catalog Card Number: 64–13945

PRINTED IN THE UNITED STATES OF AMERICA

Preface

The biology curriculum cannot stand still in the midst of a flood of new knowledge. Courses with the traditional names "Comparative Anatomy" and "Vertebrate Embryology" are still available to most American undergraduates, but their diversity increases with the multiplication of information: there are more and more baffling choices as to what to include in the syllabus and what to omit. At the same time, courses in new fields of molecular and environmental biology are crowding into the curriculum. The question is more frequently being raised whether these two traditional courses, which are interpenetrating parts of the wider field of vertebrate morphology, should not be merged for economy. Whatever is novel in this book is a response to this mixed lot of challenges.

Comparative anatomy and embryology both contribute to an understanding of gross body form. It was an accident of history rather than logical design that there should be separate undergraduate courses with these two names. There has never been agreement as to which should be studied first, and never any reason except tradition or expediency why they could not be united in a continuous exposition. In over-all plan this book is an *anatomy* for those who find it logical to approach adult structures through their developmental history, and an *embryology* for those who will not be satisfied until the story of development has been projected to its climax in mature animals. A main goal was to show how these two conventional subjects complement each other. In fact the book developed out of an effort at Dartmouth College to design an integrated course in *vertebrate morphology*.

There are no sharp boundaries to any scientific subject. Vertebrate morphology —or comparative anatomy and embryology—is a product of molecular interactions in the infinitesimal structure of living substance, and of the reaction of cells to each other, and of the interplay between tissues and organs and their products. The structures achieved by these elements are themselves infinitely complex and their description requires a formidable vocabulary. For an introductory course then, one must boldly make arbitrary boundaries where none really exist. For practical reasons the older descriptive aspects of the subject must predominate, but newer insights from analytical experimentation must be included as guides to the frontiers of current research. Practically, too, one must proceed from what can be seen with the naked eye to what is revealed with light microscopes. Reluctantly one excludes much exciting new morphological information from research at the ultrastructural and molecular levels because the students are not yet prepared for it. The choices are hard, and it is the author himself who claims priority for dissatisfaction with what has finally been selected.

In texts of comparative anatomy and vertebrate organogenesis, there is a long tradition behind the device of disengaging the parts of an animal and presenting them separately as "the muscular system," "the nervous system," etc. It is always recognized that important aspects of the animal's structure, and indeed of his life, unavoidably disappear in such a procedure. To temper this defect somewhat, certain chapters of this book focus rather upon regions, or discrete functional apparatus, and in these the relationships between the local representatives of the various organ systems are set forth. For instance, parts of the skeletal, muscular, nervous, and vascular systems, though described separately, are brought together in Chapter 16 to throw light on the development and the functional anatomy of the mandibular and hyoid segments. Chapter 17 similarly integrates the elements which make functional units of the post-otic pharyngeal segments, the tongue and the throat. Again, the student is encouraged to see the more meaningful developmental and functional interrelations of the "systems' in the locomotor apparatus, first in Chapter 20 for trunk and tail, and then in Chapter 21 for paired appendages. Nervous and endocrine systems are brought together at the last to show their interplay in the integrative functions.

Other chapters are more conventional in scope. For instance there are separate accounts of the digestive and the urinary systems. But even in the several chapters which are assembled on a regional basis in order to capture important functional relationships, the teacher who prefers to follow the organ-system arrangement throughout may do so by selecting from the subheadings, or rearranging their sequence.

Each new step in an elementary text must be prepared by, and be projected from, the last one. Therefore Parts I and II of this book lead off with basic ideas and an inclusive but general vocabulary. Also in Part II a theme is developed which progressively unfolds and ties the whole work together. Thus, the common structural heritage of tissues and organs is sketched in with a broad brush for all vertebrates in Chapters 4 and 5, particularly with a novel demonstration that a common basic plan of anatomy exists in all vertebrate embryos at the stage—called here the "pharyngula"—when their pharyngeal pouches and clefts are first fully displayed. Part III then shows how the processes of early embryology make sense in terms of this basic structural pattern; one can speak of it as the goal toward which they all proceed. Parts IV to VI subsequently show how the basic design of the little pharyngula is developed and specialized toward adult structure by the various classes of vertebrates, each after its own fashion.

In this way the anatomies of adult vertebrates are shown to differ as the result of trends discoverable in comparative embryology. Their similarities are traced to the common heritage of a basic design that has, *mirabile dictu,* stood relatively unchanged through the biological continuum of half a billion years and more.

It is often insisted that a science textbook should shun the unknown and the debatable, yet this produces a wholly inadequate impression of the most powerful and dramatic attribute of science, that it is *a way of finding out things.* Therefore, this text raises some questions that have not yet been answered, and refers to some current hypotheses or methods of investigation that may sometime furnish good answers—or, as the case may be, prove fruitless. Education in science is useless or dangerous unless it is carried to the point where the student demands proof, and must and will ask meaningful questions. He also needs to learn to recognize questions that are operationally meaningless, and to see where answers may profitably be sought. The asking of questions is where science begins, but the ability to ask *good* questions is developed only with practice, starting with a background of reliable information. The science teacher's greatest challenge is to help the student to the basic information without giving him the disastrously false notion that the edifice is complete. If the student who reads this book can be encouraged to meet every described fact in it with the irrepressible question "Why should this be so?" and if his teacher can help him with the provisional rudiments of a testable answer, or consider with him how such a hypothesis could be set up and refined, the great new frontiers will come into sight. The old descriptive sciences of comparative anatomy and embryology are an inexhaustible reservoir of problems for the new experimental phase of morphology, and people should discover this as undergraduates.

I must express deep gratitude to William Osburn, who with skill and patience produced the illustrations for this book, to friends for their encouragement and counsel, and to my wife who took care that I should survive this effort.

W. W. BALLARD

Hanover, New Hampshire
February, 1964

Contents

COMPARATIVE ANATOMY AND EMBRYOLOGY

1

Introduction

One cannot plunge into the vast field of **vertebrate morphology** without a careful plan. There are scores of thousands of kinds of vertebrates, whose differences can be suggested by mention of eels, toads, whales, and humingbirds in one breath. Encyclopedic reference works exist in the field, but they are not for the beginner. O. Hertwig's *Handbuch* [1], published in 1906, covered the early embryology of the vertebrates in nine fat volumes, but the store of information has probably been multiplied by 30 since then, and no similarly detailed summary can ever again be made. Ruthless selection is required. The field of comparative anatomy was concisely sampled by sixty collaborators in the 1930's in a *Handbuch* [2] that runs to more than 6,000 pages of text in seven volumes. The Grassé *Traité de Zoologie* [3], which is now in process of publication, will attempt to compress its vertebrate section into six huge tomes, of which the one on fishes alone runs to 2,700 pages.

Obviously, an introductory course can concern itself with only the principal groups of vertebrates, and can select only structural and developmental relationships that carry the broadest significance. But even here, the beginner at morphology is presented at once with an inescapable dilemma. He cannot understand anatomy without a previous knowledge of embryology, nor can he study embryology with much comprehension unless he has some background in anatomy. Where to begin? One can only begin with boldness at some point or other, survey the subject broadly, and then make a final conscientious review of the whole field in perspective.

However, some paths are better than others. Something is gained if each step is sufficiently prepared by what has gone before, and is itself designed to help explain the next one. Because of the elaborate way in which the parts of a vertebrate are knitted together in space, and are gradually prepared for new functions in time, picking a path requires some little maneuvering. In fact, the course charted in this text will involve some abrupt changes in tack, and the student will be wise if he spends a moment now looking across the whole map of it. He should also review, at the end of each chapter, where he has arrived, and where he will be going from there.

To begin with, it is necessary to examine a representative array of vertebrates and understand their classification (Chapter 2). As another essential preliminary, certain broad concepts and fundamental terms of spatial relationship in anatomy must be introduced (Chapter 3). Next, some of the general patterns assumed by the living cells of vertebrate tissues and organs are reviewed (Chapter 4), together with some of the most commonly recurring arrangements of organs in the body (Chapter 5). These constitute the *theme* of vertebrate structure; the rest of the book is taken up with *variations* on it.

The forthright study of morphology might be expected to start with the consideration of the events by which each new individual comes free from his parents' gonads and begins to demonstrate his own anatomical potentialities. It would seem logical to study the stages in such an individual's development consecutively, comparing the different kinds of vertebrates at each level of organization. However, their structures make sense functionally only after they have been completed. Also, confusion is introduced by the fact that different groups of vertebrates come from very different kinds of eggs and by quite remarkably different processes. The comparison of some early embryonic stages of vertebrates is as difficult as the comparison of their adult anatomies.

Experience with these facts has shown that it is easier not to follow the daily-newspaper practice of reporting events in their order of normal occurrence, but to set things in historical perspective with early benefit from hindsight. Therefore we do not begin with the fertilized egg but with the anatomy of a middle-embryonic stage, here named the **pharyngula** (Chapter 5). This stage is developed far enough that the embryo shows the rudiments of most of the organ systems in their relatively standardized topographical relations to each other, but it does not yet show the great range of adaptive specializations that so complicate the comparative anatomy of the adult.

The pharyngula stage follows the gastrula and neurula stages. It is named from its most characteristic and constant feature, the appearance of clefts or deep grooves which carve the lateral walls of the pharynx into segments. With some variations, the pharyngula stage may be easily recognized in all the vertebrates. It could be called the limb-bud stage or the tailbud stage, but these structural characters occur with less regularity than the pharynx segments.

Once the basic pattern of the pharyngula has been established, the puzzling diversities of early embryology can be more easily related to a common theme, namely how the anatomy of the pharyngula comes into being (Chapter 6). This is a story of convergence from different sorts of eggs through different maneuvers, into a comparable structural pattern.

In later sections of the book, the tissues and the organ rudiments of the relatively similar pharyngula stages of vertebrates are followed along divergent lines toward the remarkably different specializations of the adults in the different classes and orders.

The student will need to keep in mind this pedagogical strategy, the outline of which can be seen in the list of chapter headings.

Vocabulary

Vertebrates, as distinguished from many plants and some animals, have their organs disposed along a main head-to-tail axis and in rather definite symmetrical arrangements. It is the morphologist's task to recognize such anatomical relationships, and it will be necessary to assume the student's familiarity with the following terms that describe them:

Dorsal and **ventral.** "Dorsal" refers to the backbone side, "ventral" to the belly side. E.g., the vertebral column comes nearest to the surface in the mid-dorsal line, whereas the heart, umbilicus, and anus generally lie in the midventral line. Your mouth is ventral to your ears, your shoulder blade is dorsal to your collarbone.

Cranial and **caudal.** "Cranial" has to do with the head end of the animal, "caudal" with the tail end. Your lungs are cranial to your kidneys. Legs are caudal to arms.

Anterior and **posterior,** as used in this text, are synonymous with the terms cranial and caudal respectively. It is important to note that some texts of human anatomy still define "anterior" as the front (i.e., ventral) side, and "posterior" as the back (i.e., dorsal) side. In relation to a fish or a four-legged animal, such meanings for these terms would be nonsensical, and the terms "superior" and "inferior" (synonymous with "cranial" and "caudal," as in human anatomy) are equally inappropriate. Terms that are defined in relation to the body axis have a wider usefulness than those determined by posture, and they are now being generally adopted even in human anatomy.

Medial and **lateral.** Medial structures are relatively close to, or at, the midline, i.e., the longitudinal axis of the animal. Lateral structures are farther to the side. Your eyes are medial to your external ears, but lateral to the bridge of your nose. Lungs are medial to the ribs but lateral to the heart.

Proximal and **distal.** Proximal structures are relatively close to the center of the body or the point of attachment, and distal ones are relatively farther away. The wrist is proximal to the fingers but distal to the elbow.

Other pairs of spatial terms, whose meanings are opposite to each other but hardly need definition here, are **central** and **peripheral,** and **deep** and **superficial.** It would be difficult to describe the anatomy of any surgical operation without these terms. The relation of brain to skull can be described with either pair.

Adverbs are commonly made from any of the above adjectives by changing the ending **-al** to **-ad.** Thus, food normally passes **caudad** through the human neck, a spear which passes **dorsad** through the breast would enter the chest cavity, a flea crawling up your sleeve goes **mediad** (or **mesad**). In dissection, one follows nerves **centrad** after picking them up in the periphery.

For descriptive purposes, the animal, whether embryonic or adult, may be thought of as intersected by the following sectional planes of reference (Fig. 1–1):

Transverse: Any plane dividing the individual into a cranial and a caudal part, but usually one at right angles to the longitudinal axis rather than oblique.

Frontal: Any plane dividing the individual into a dorsal and a ventral part, but usually parallel to the longitudinal axis. Originally named for its relation to the front or face side of a human embryo, it is often replaced by the term **horizontal plane** in reference to a fish or four-legged animal. The still persistent use of the term "horizontal section" in human anatomy, to describe what is defined above as a "transverse section," is another of the confusions that follow from defining terms by posture rather than by reference to the body axis.

Sagittal: Any plane dividing the individual into right and left parts. Strictly speaking there can be only one **midsagittal** plane, which divides it into halves which are mirror images of each other, containing the same structures except for a few such non-symmetrical organs as stomach and spleen. All other planes parallel to the midsagittal may be specified as **parasagittal** if necessary.

If a vertebrate's body axis is not bent or twisted (Fig. 1 A), its midsagittal plane lies at right angles to the frontal, but both these are longitudinal, and both are at right angles to all true transverse planes. However, bends or twists usually occur, and as a result these terms have to be used with some caution. Many embryos are bent like a letter C (Fig. 1 B), and serial sections cut through them in parallel planes may be transverse at mid-trunk but frontal in head and tail regions—or vice versa.

Antimere. Many organs of the vertebrate body occur in right and left pairs, each of which may be defined as the antimere of its fellow of the opposite side.

Synonyms in Morphology

Morphology deals with a world of visible things, parts, processes, and relationships, and no way has ever been found to bring order into such a world without naming all of them to begin with. It is sufficiently burdensome when there is one name for each. But most students, and even hardy professionals, become restless when, for example, it turns out that twelve different anatomists, describing the same single frog muscle, have given it twelve different names.

International committees, appointed by various national societies of anatomists, have several times revised and consolidated the terminology of adult human anatomy. The latest of these name lists, the *Nomina Anatomica Parisiensia* or PNA[4], was adopted in Paris in 1955, and further amended by the International Anatomical Nomenclature Committee in New York, 1960. Such terms, though adopted only for human anatomy and approved

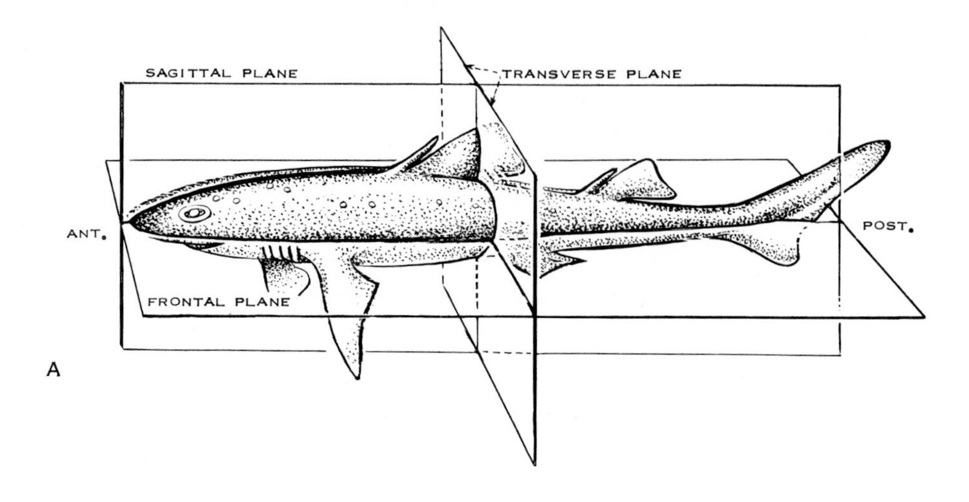

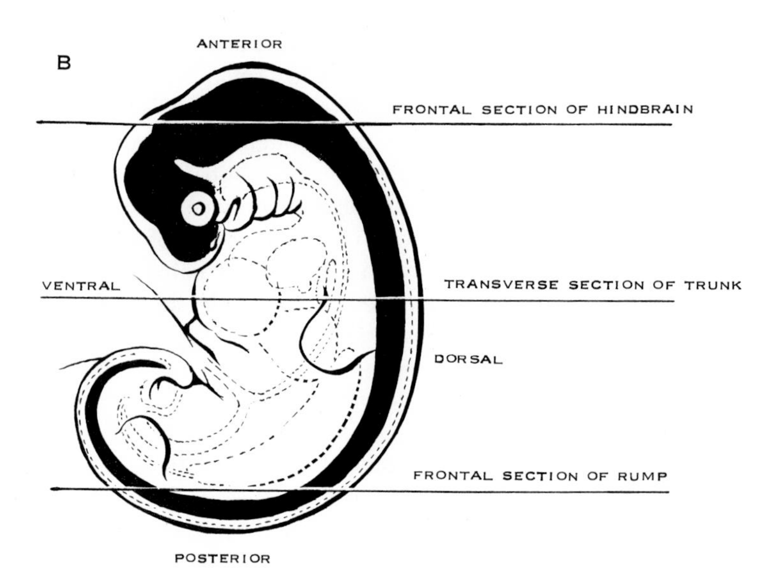

Fig. 1–1. Scheme for orientations.

only in their Latin form, are directly translated and used throughout this book for general vertebrate anatomy where such a procedure is not clearly nonsensical, in an effort to reduce synonymy. Where the PNA terms differ from the names previously selected at Basel (BNA 1895) or Jena (JNA 1936), attention is called to this in the text by specifying (PNA). Few of the 1960 IANC revisions have pertinence for comparative anatomy.

No such agreements have been reached for reducing synonymy in the fields of general comparative anatomy, or even in human embryology or histology. This text will follow the PNA practice of outlawing eponyms, i.e., memorial or gravestone names like Eustachian tube and Müllerian duct since the PNA equivalents or their English translations (tuba auditiva, ductus paramesonephricus) have anatomical significance. Some eponyms are extremely hardy perennials in zoology, and though they have been weeded out of the text, it has seemed proper to include them in the index, with reference to their preferred synonyms.

REFERENCES

1. Hertwig, O. (ed.), 1906. *Handbuch der vergleichenden und experimentellen Entwicklungslehre der Wirbeltiere.* G. Fischer, Jena, Germany.

2. Bolk, L., E. Göppert, E. Kallius, and W. Lubosch (eds.), 1931–1938. *Handbuch der vergleichenden Anatomie der Wirbeltiere.* Urban u. Schwarzenberg, Berlin.

3. Grassé, Pierre-P. (ed.). *Traité de zoologie.* Masson, Paris. This massive work covers anatomy, embryology, systematics, and general biology. The general volume on Vertebrates (Tome XII) appeared in 1955, the three volumes on fishes (Tome XIII) in 1958, the one on birds (Tome XV) in 1950, and the first of two on mammals (Tome XVI) in 1955. Tome XIV will cover amphibians and reptiles.

4. Knese, K.-H. (ed.), 1957. *Nomina anatomica,* 5 Auflage. G. Thieme, Stuttgart, Germany. This compares the Basel, Jena, and Paris nomenclature lists in parallel columns. The IANC revision of the PNA list has been published by Excerpta Medica Foundation, Amsterdam, 1963.

Part I

CLASSIFICATION AND BASIC CONCEPTS

2

Classification of Vertebrates

For descriptive purposes the animal kingdom is divisible into a number of phyla, on the basis of morphological resemblances. All but an insignificant fraction of one per cent of all known animals fall easily into one or another of about twenty phyla as now defined. With the advance in knowledge of the last two hundred years, the definitions and arrangements of the phyla have been revised many times, and one must assume that knowledge still to be gained will force still further changes. Nevertheless the main features of our system of classification are beginning to be stabilized.

Each phylum may be defined in terms of a list of *similar organs, similarly arranged* in the adults and *similarly developed* in the embryos of its species. It may be expected that these characteristics will be shared more or less as a common heritage by all the members of the phylum, but hundreds of millions of years of adaptive radiation have produced exceptions and variations within each group. If lists are drawn up of the diagnostic structures or developmental processes that belong to each of the phyla, certain items or certain combinations of them in any one list may be expected to occur only in that phylum.

I. COMMON HERITAGE OF THE VERTEBRATES

The group of vertebrates includes some very different creatures: man and trout, for instance, sea gulls, snakes, frogs, swordfish, bats, woodpeckers, and giraffes. In spite of the diversity of the group, it may be precisely defined. The members are considered to be relatives of each other because they possess in common certain structural features and developmental stages not shared by animals of other phyla.

For instance, all vertebrates have an internal axial skeleton of cartilage or bone, composed of a **skull** and a string of **vertebrae.** In special cases these may be only faintly developed, but they are always present. Nothing of the sort is found in clams (Phylum Mollusca) or bees (Phylum Arthropoda) or the Protozoa. Inside this skeleton the vertebrates all have a **central nervous system** consisting of a **brain** and a **spinal cord,** from which a long and bilaterally symmetrical series of nerves arises. In other phyla which have structures at all comparable to these, nearly all the central nervous system lies ventral to the gut, whereas in vertebrates it always lies dorsal. The vertebrate brain receives stimuli from **three pairs of major sense organs,** the olfactory, the optic, and the auditory. If comparable sense organs are present in members of other phyla—and in general they are not—they differ in their structure or their arrangement or their method of embryonic development (and usualy in all three of these).

Vertebrate blood bears **corpuscles,** most of which are loaded with red hemoglobin. It is pumped by a ventrally located **heart** composed of a series of chambers which beat in sequence. In other phyla there may be no heart, no blood, or no hemoglobin, but one can generalize that the particular combination of characters listed here for vertebrates does not occur in any other group. The blood from the capillaries of the digestive viscera is returned to the heart by way of an extra set of capillaries in the vertebrate **liver,** and this arrangement is not found in any other phylum. Among the few phyla which possess **pairs of lateral appendages,** the vertebrates are unique in having only *two* pair, and these with an **internal** skeleton of cartilage or bone.

One can make a considerable list of the structures and tissues found only in the vertebrates and present in almost every one of them. It would include cartilage, true bone, the special sense organs, the endocrine glands, the liver, the lymphatic system, the autonomic nervous apparatus, etc. There are several kinds of vertebrates which have a remarkable *superficial* resemblance to worms, both in their habit and their structure. Only a quick dissection is needed, however, to determine their true phylum.

II. THE CHORDATES

As the zoologists of the last century enlarged their collections and improved their systems of classification, it became known that certain lowly marine invertebrates showed undeniable resemblances to the vertebrates and could not be fitted into other previously recognized phyla. All of them shared with the vertebrates, at least in their early life history, three constant and fundamental structural features not found elsewhere in the animal kingdom. It was therefore necessary to define a larger phylum including both the true vertebrates and these related invertebrates. The three diagnostic features of the new phylum are:

1. A **central nervous system** with the special qualities of being hollow and lying dorsal to the gut;
2. An anterior section of the gut called the **pharynx,** which contains **paired lateral pouches** that generally lead through **clefts** to the outside;
3. An axial skeletal rod of special cellular texture, called the **notochord.**

The name of the larger assemblage of animals is taken from this last structure. We belong to the phylum Chordata.

This text deals primarily with the subphylum of vertebrates, and the lower chordate subphyla will be mentioned only briefly.

A. The Lower Chordates

1. **Subphylum Urochordata.** The urochordates (or tunicates) are small soft creatures, commonly found attached to rocks or weeds a little below the surface along the shores of most marine waters. Some species drift in the open ocean. The alternate name of the group refers to their only protective device, a leathery outer *tunic* strengthened with cellulose. There is almost as much anatomical diversity within the group as there is in the whole array of vertebrates, but in most of them the largest organ is a baglike **pharynx** pierced by a great many lateral **clefts** (Fig. 2–1). It serves as a filter, allowing the inhaled sea water to escape while retaining food particles. Most species develop from the egg to a tadpolelike larva which has a clear-cut **notochord** confined to the tail region (hence the name Urochordata) and a dorsal tubular **central nervous system** with a diminutive brainlike enlargement and sensory spots.

Excepting some pelagic species, the tunicate tadpole swims actively for only a few minutes or hours after hatching, and then settles down and glues itself to whatever solid object it may touch. The notochord and the nervous system then suddenly disintegrate, the whole anatomy is swiftly reorganized into a creature of almost totally different pattern. Such an anatomical revolution is called a **metamorphosis.** When a tunicate tadpole metamorphoses (Fig. 2–1), practically all its resemblance to a vertebrate vanishes.

Most adult tunicates, after attaching themselves permanently to a substrate, actively repro-

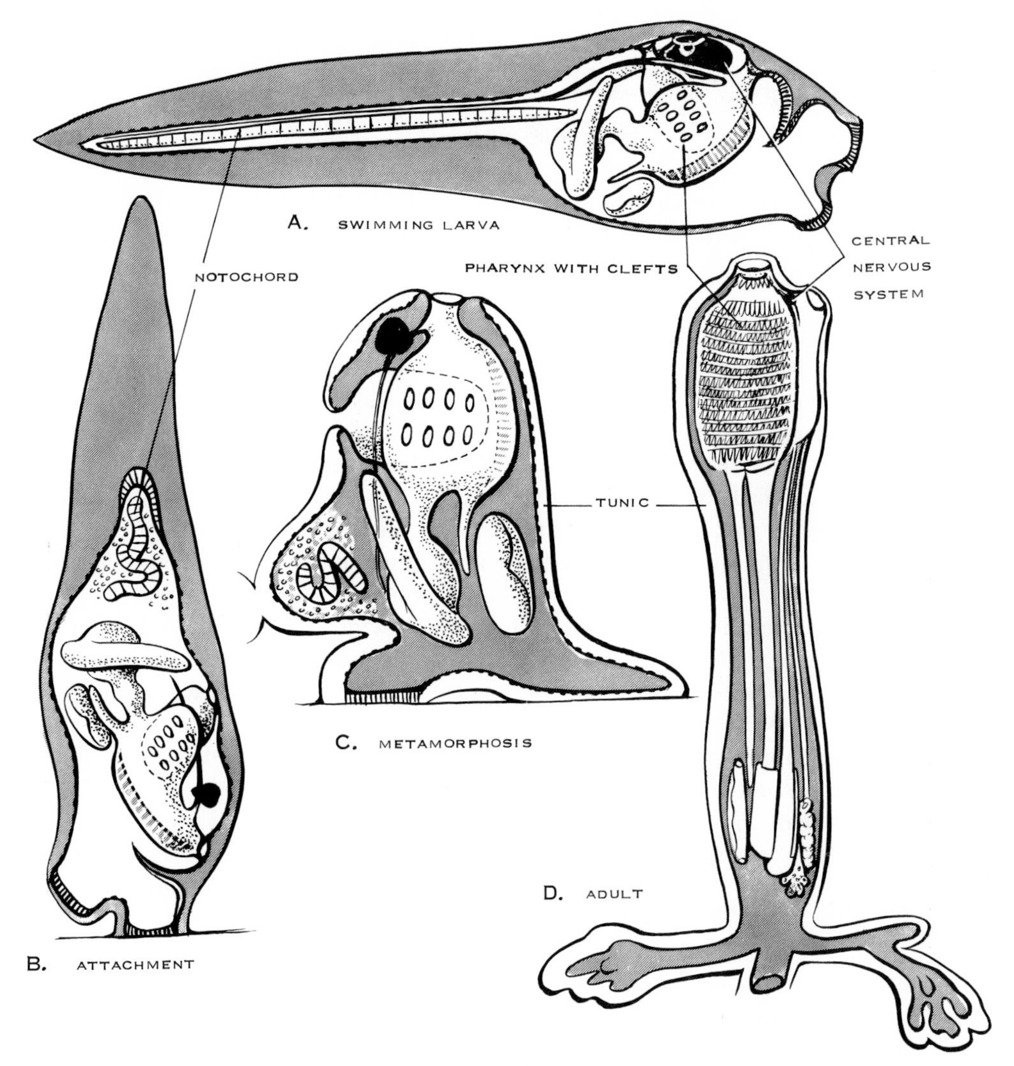

Fig. 2–1. Larva, metamorphosis, and adult of the tunicate *Clavelina*.
(After Brien, 1948, in Traité de Zoologie, by permission of Masson et Cie.)

duce themselves by asexual budding processes which are quite unlike the embryonic development of a fertilized egg but achieve the same adult anatomy. Large colonies of attached individuals are thus formed from a single metamorphosed tadpole, and all of these may then reproduce sexually, their drifting tadpoles serving to scatter the species throughout its possible range during their brief unattached phase. In the asexually produced colonies, the blood flows casually from one individual to another through a common system of vessels inside a common tunic. The heart of each individual has the interesting habit of reversing its direction of beat periodically. Only the individuals that are produced by the union of egg and sperm go through a tadpole stage, and only in the tadpoles are the chordate affinities of the urochordates briefly reaffirmed.

2. **Subphylum Cephalochordata.** These animals are likewise marine, soft and small, but in contrast to the Urochordata they are anatomically uniform and restricted to a few genera. Cephalochordates are best known through the

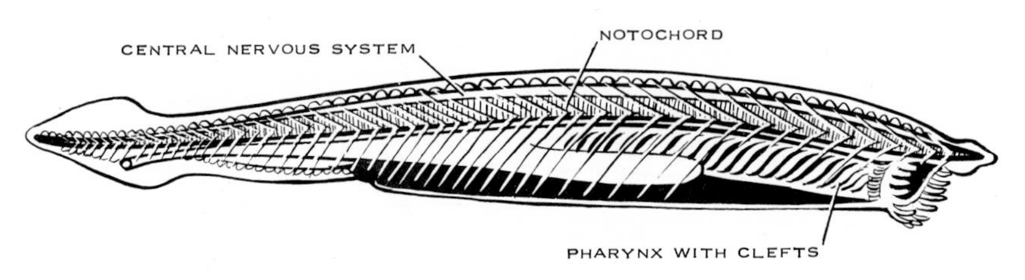

Fig. 2–2. The Amphioxus.
(After Drach, 1948, in Traité de Zoologie, by permission of Masson et Cie.)

classical studies on the famous amphioxus (*Branchiostoma*) at the *Stazione zoologica* in Naples, but similar species exist along the eastern coast of the United States from Chesapeake Bay southward, and in many other warm seas.

A strong, springy **notochord** extends from tip to tip of the animal (Fig. 2–2). The **pharynx** section of the gut is long and slotted with numerous lateral **clefts.**

The **central nervous system** is dorsal and hollow, but there is no brain development. Amphioxus anatomy is comparable with that of vertebrates so far as it goes, but there are no skull, vertebrae, paired appendages, eyes, ears, nose, etc. The kidneys are more like those of certain archaic annelids than like those of vertebrates.

B. Lower Chordates and the Origin of Vertebrates

The beautiful geometric quality of the amphioxus, in both its adult anatomy and its early development, hardly needs to be simplified for textbook diagrams. This has long tempted zoologists to assume that it is somehow closely related to the unknown original vertebrate stock. Its simplicity has been variously held to be primitive and ancient, or secondary and degenerate, but in the utter absence of any information on its past history these are only guesses.

Affinities of the urochordates are equally obscure. Lucky finds in recent years [1] leave a lingering hope that the history of both groups may some day be revealed in the fossil record. In the meantime, most guesses as to the relationships of the urochordates are based on the ephemeral appearance of the three chordate characteristics in their larvae.

There are small groups of queer marine worms called the Hemichordata, which contain structures at least somewhat suggestive of the three criteria of chordates. Perhaps assigning to these debatable structures an exaggerated value, some taxonomists have included the hemichordates among the chordates. Others prefer to segregate them in a phylum of their own. Certain species of hemichodrates have a larval stage called the **tornaria,** which shows a remarkable resemblance to the dipleurula larvae of certain echinoderms. Most of them have a direct development, skipping the tornaria stage altogether.

The most that this and other evidence can do is suggest that the phyla of chordates, echinoderms, and hemichordates are more closely related to each other than to other phyla, for instance those of the annelids, molluscs, or arthropods.

The question of the origin of vertebrates has been much discussed [2]. Most of the major phyla except the chordates are represented by fossils from the Cambrian period. Since the pre-Cambrian fossil record is so scanty as to be practically useless for the purpose, the only knowledge of how the phyla arose consists merely of disciplined guesswork. Comparative anatomical studies led earlier investigators to suggest that the chordates might have arisen from arthropods, annelids, or various other invertebrate phyla, but embryological considerations favor a common origin with the echinoderms. Current interest centers on such speculations as that (a) the echinoderms gave rise to the chordates through a hemichordate-like stage, or that (b) both the echinoderms and the chordates arose from a sessile, filter-feeding hemichordate-like stock. There are no facts inconsistent with these hypotheses, nor any fossil evidences bearing them out. The role of possible ancestors like the amphioxus, or urochordate tadpoles, in the evolution of genuine vertebrates continues to be the subject of widely divergent speculations.

III. CLASSIFICATION OF THE VERTEBRATES

One cannot say how many species of vertebrates are alive today, for a great deal of exploration and analysis remains to be done. The number is probably greater than 40,000. These have descended from other thousands of extinct species whose fossils are yet being discovered, or which have disappeared without a trace. The production of new lines of adaptation and specialization in vertebrates has been directed by the forces of natural selection for at least half a billion years, during which time some similar groups have become divergent from each other, and different lines have converged into confusing similarity. The sorting out of these relationships by means of the available morphological evidence has been a most intricate and specialized task.

The classification schemes now favored by zoologists are in the form of genealogical trees projected against a time scale of earth history. They are based on the study of known species, both in respect to the similarities and differences of their morphology and also to their time of existence on earth. It is important to remember that these classifications are theoretical constructions, ideas rather than observable facts. Like other ideas, they undergo changes from time to time, as new morphological and paleontological information becomes available.

The way classification schemes have evolved is instructive. First it was recognized that there were unbridgeable gaps between groups of animals (called **species**) in terms of structure or interfertility or location or way of life, each specific group being unique in some combination of these characteristics. Today it is widely recognized that the gaps between some species groups are not unbridgeable. One theoretical consequence of this discovery is that the species concept can no longer be rigorously defined. Another is, that speciation as an evolutionary process is becoming better understood [3].

Once the common species were described and named, they were cataloged in little groups or **genera** on the basis of close special resemblances: cats with lions and tigers for instance. (Here one must note that such a genus does not exist in nature: it is a symbol for observed resemblances, and exists only as an idea in the human mind.) Then the genera were assembled in larger groups or **families** (dogs with wolves and foxes), the orders into **classes** (all hairy animals together), and the classes into a phylum (hairy animals with birds and fish).

In place of this old-fashioned boxes-within-boxes classification, the whole scheme has been rearranged into a supposed hereditary sequence, making use of the paleontologist's knowledge of extinct species, and of the distribution of the groups in geologic time. Classes are represented as the principal branches of a trunk that stands for the phylum itself. Smaller and smaller branches represent the less and less inclusive groupings: the orders, families and genera. In such a model, the cloud of growing buds on the outer green part of the imaginary tree may be identified with species, while the supporting trunk and branches represent collections of species extinguished in the more or less distant past. The thickness of the branches may even be modeled to suggest the relative abundance of the known fossil types at successive periods. It is a queer sort of tree, for only the buds at the ends of the twigs are alive, and all the rest has disappeared except for a few fossilized scraps. In fact, it is not a thing like a tree; it is an idea, a symbol of an understanding of a collection of observations.

The tree-of-life scheme is both a classification and a history. Like all scientific theory it is a tissue of interrelated and relatively consistent guesses, adopted for pragmatic reasons until something better is offered. (See inside front cover.)

The alert student will soon discover that schemes of classification, either of the box type or the tree type, are seldom identical in any two textbooks. Between two books dealing with such schemes printed as much as ten years apart, the differences may be striking. There are several simple reasons for this divergence. First, authorities in different nations or schools frequently prefer different names for the same class, order or family. Nomenclature of the vertebrate fish groups in particular suffers from such duplication at present. Secondly, needed information on the morphology of extinct groups is often lacking or difficult to interpret, so that decisions on relationships are necessarily subjective and therefore variable. Thirdly, the advance in knowledge is now very rapid, and frequent revision has to follow the discovery of error or the gaining of new facts. Many special problems have still to be solved, and many new discoveries will be made, before the classification of vertebrates can be stabilized in a condition of maximum usefulness.

Some of the principal groups of the subphylum Vertebrata will now be listed and commented upon.

A. Superclass Agnatha

Among all the living fishes, two groups stand out strangely and fundamentally different from all the rest, and indeed from each other: the lampreys and hagfishes.

The lampreys (Fig. 2–3) are mostly marine, but ascend rivers to breed, and have made themselves at home in various inland waters. By way of the Welland Ship Canal they have penetrated the upper Great Lakes in recent decades, causing disaster to long-established fisheries there, and requiring very expensive control measures. They have no jaws (hence the name Agnatha: *gnathos* means jaw), but their round mouth is surrounded by a thick thorny sucker with which they attach themselves to other fishes (B, C, Fig. 2–3). In the center of the mouth there is a protrusible rasping device, and their food is flesh and blood torn and sucked from the living victim. When not feeding, they spend their time innocently enough attached to rocks, swaying with the current and breathing water in and out of their numerous gill pores.

Lampreys deposit their eggs in pebble nests in shallow streams. The eggs develop into a larval form which is so different from the adult that it was called *Ammocoetes* and thought to be an entirely different kind of animal until its origin was discovered. The ammocoete larva lives for some years in the mud before its metamorphosis, and during this stage it has a suckerless mouth covered by a hood, lacks the rasping apparatus, and is a filter-feeder like the lower chordates (cf. Fig. 2–3). It has certain other anatomical peculiarities reminiscent of the amphioxus,

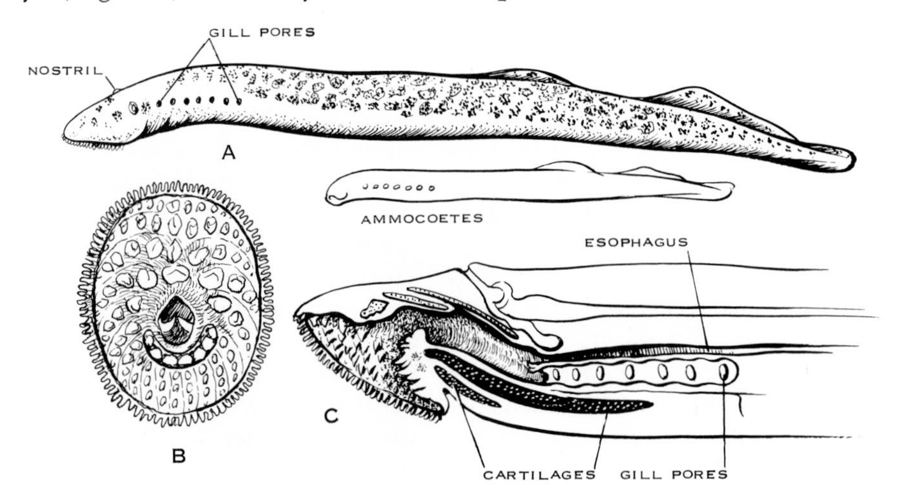

Fig. 2–3. Lamprey. A. Adult and larva. B. Mouth in front view. C. Head in sagittal section.

(A and B after Bigelow and Schroeder, Fishes of the Western North Atlantic, Part I, 1948, by permission of Sears Foundation for Marine Research.)

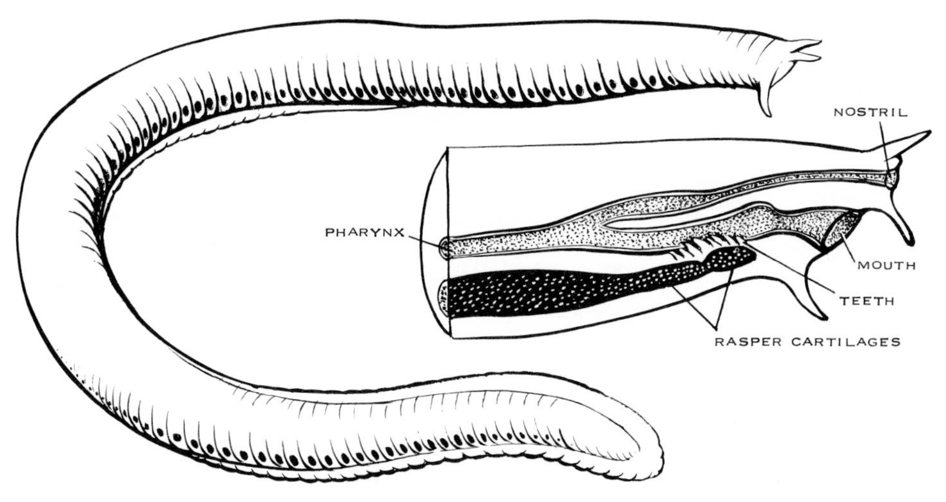

Fig. 2–4. Hagfish.

though it has a head, brain, major sense organs and other structures that the amphioxus lacks.

Various hypotheses have been advanced, for instance that the amphioxus is a permanent larva comparable to the ammocoete but has lost its adult stage; or that the ammocoete arose from an amphioxus-like stock and evolved its adult lamprey stage secondarily, etc. But as is the case with the origin of the phylum, there is practically no fossil record of differentiation of the subphyla and the superclasses of the Chordata, and there are not enough facts available to do more than state some of the possibilities.

The hagfishes (Fig. 2–4) are marine, and like the lampreys they lack jaws. They have a somewhat similar but more highly developed rasping device which works through a little soft anterior hole in the mouth. They are scavengers but they also attack living fish, gaining entrance through their gill openings and literally devouring the prey from the inside out. Hagfishes are excessively slimy.

The list of comparable organs shared by both lampreys and hags does not quite end with the rasper mechanism, but each of these animals has many features very different from anything known in any other living vertebrates. Both possess some characteristics which have been considered to be primitive, but each is also highly specialized in its own way. The hagfishes have a peculiar direct development without any larva comparable to the ammocoete.

While practically nothing can be gleaned from the fossil record about the past history of lampreys and hagfishes, it is an easy assumption that they are lone survivors of extremely ancient groups. This seems the more likely since the oldest fossil fishes yet discovered were also jawless. There are perhaps 15 orders of these clumsy armored creatures from the Ordovician, Silurian and Devonian ages, grouped variously by different authorities in several classes.

Significant resemblances have been pointed out between one of these agnathous classes, the Osteostraci or Cephalaspides (Fig. 2–5), and the modern lampreys. A quite different set of resemblances is seen between another of them, called Heterostraci or Pteraspides, and the modern hagfishes. This suggests that the lines which led down to today's jawless fishes separated from each other at least 300 million years ago.

The three (or more) ancient extinct classes of jawless vertebrates and the two modern ones (the lampreys of Class Petromyzones or Hyperoartii and the hagfishes of Class Myxini or Hyperotreti) are segregated in the **Superclass Agnatha.** All other vertebrate fishes have jaws. In view of the fundamental and undoubtedly ancient differences between the lampreys and hagfishes, the older device of listing them as two

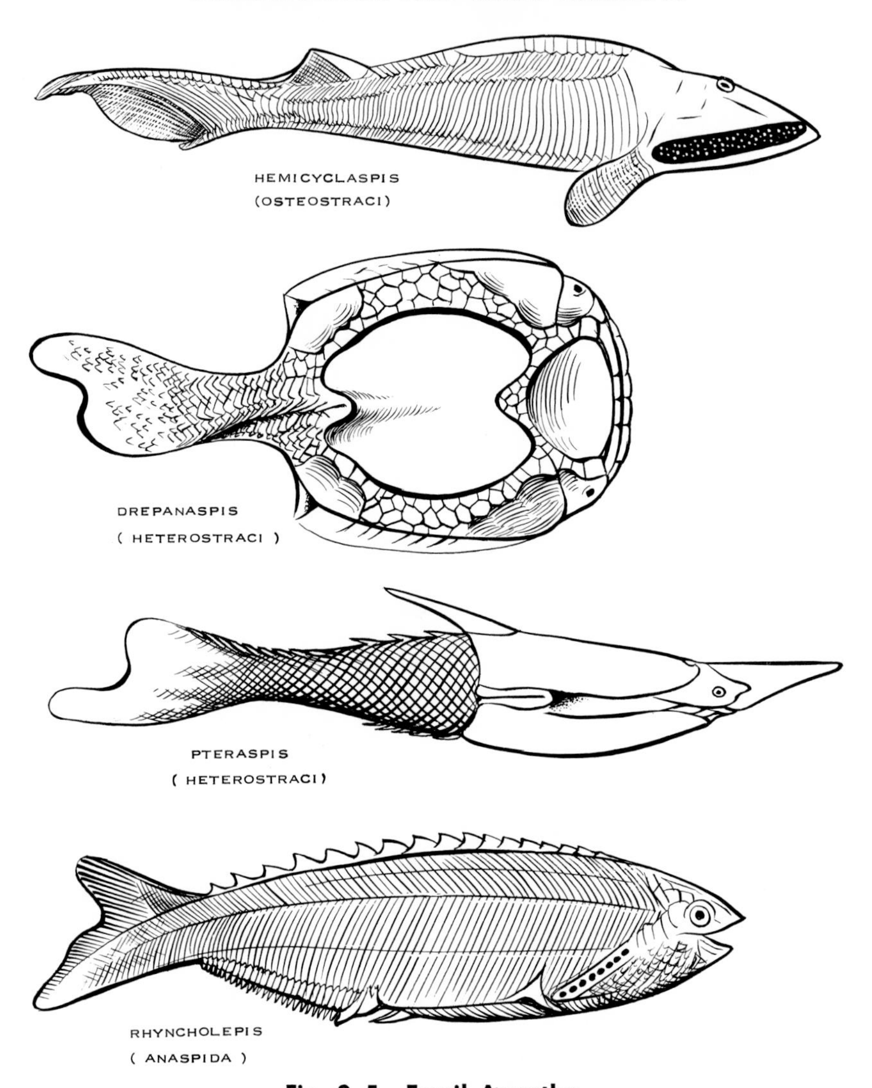

Fig. 2–5. Fossil Agnatha.
(Hemicyclaspis after Stensiö, 1939. Drepanaspis after Orbutschev, 1943. Pteraspis after White, 1935. Rhyncholepis after Kiaer, 1924.)

subclasses of a single class, Cyclostomata, is currently being challenged.

The differences between lampreys and hagfishes on the one hand and the fishes with jaws on the other are greater than the differences between the most primitive modern jawed fishes and man. Since the lampreys and hags are so aberrant, only brief mention of a few aspects of their morphology can be crowded into this introductory textbook. We will consider chiefly the modern vertebrates.

B. Superclass Gnathostomata

All the other fishes, and all the land vertebrates, have mouths that open between upper and lower jaws of cartilage or bone. These animals have anatomical patterns which can be compared in far more detail. They are united in the **Superclass Gnathostomata** (*stoma* means mouth). This is divisible into the predominantly aquatic **Series Pisces** and the predominantly terrestrial **Series Tetrapoda.** Although the fossil record contains broad hints as to how and when the tetrapods were derived from one sector of the Pisces, and this itself implies that the two groups are not completely separable, it is approximately true that Series Pisces includes jawed fishes with fins and gills, and Series Tetrapoda includes animals with legs or lungs, usually both.

1. **Series Pisces.** The jawed fishes underwent their most rapid evolution in the Early Paleozoic era, at the dawning of the recorded history of vertebrates. Already in Devonian times all the main classes of them were in existence together, each with many specialized types. Knowledge of their fossils has progressed very rapidly in recent decades, but has not yet reached a stage of stabilized nomenclature or agreement on lines of descent. Four of the classes of the Pisces have persisted more or less successfully into the present era and will be remarked on below: the **Elasmobranchii,** the **Holocephali,** the **Dipnoi** and the **Teleostomi.** Others, which flourished mightily and developed some species of large size and

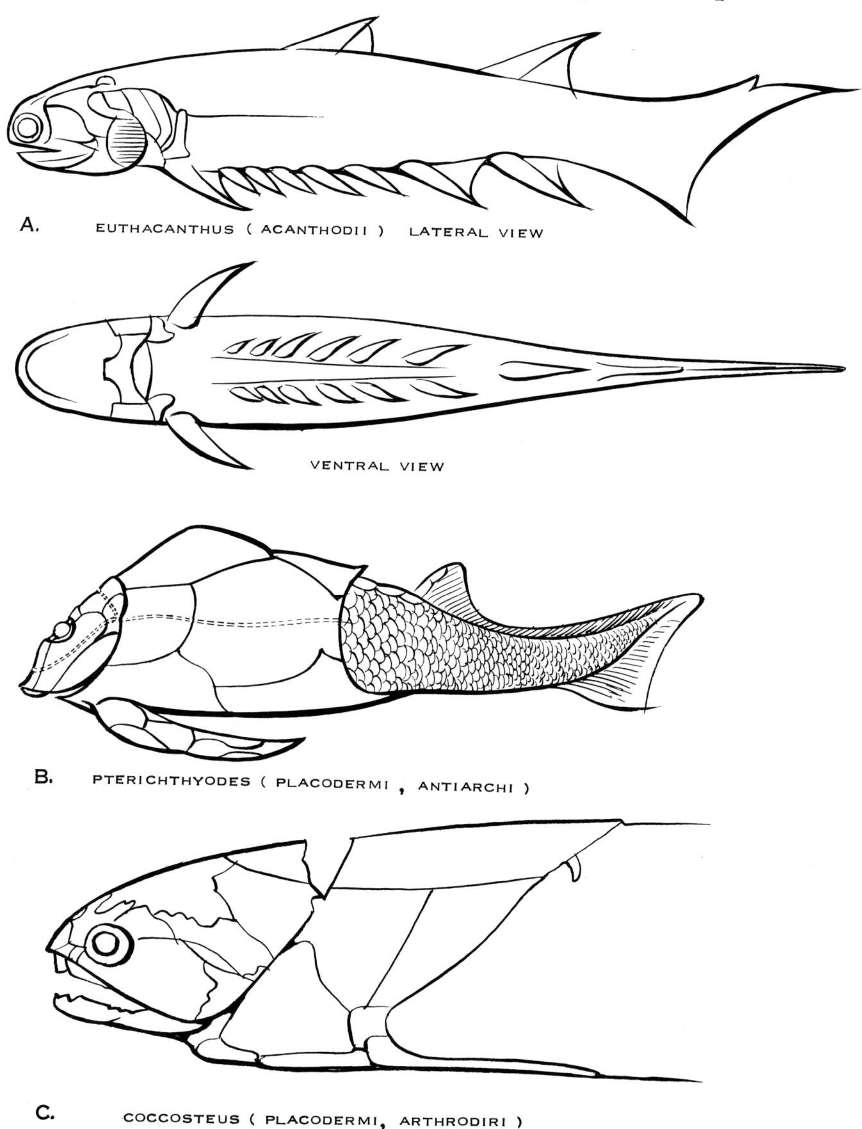

Fig. 2–6. Extinct groups of jawed fishes.
(Euthacanthus after Watson, 1937. Pterichthyodes after Stensiö, 1939. Coccosteus after Heintz, 1931.)

bizarre shape in the Paleozoic era, mostly died out in the Upper Devonian, a few persisting to the Lower Permian (Fig. 2–6). The **Antiarchi** (Pterichthyes) and huge **Arthrodiri** (Coccostei) have been described as experimental models in which a number of interesting anatomical devices were put to the test but were forced out of business by the competition. **Class Acanthodii,** the oldest known group of jawed fishes, maintained itself for a considerably longer period, and shows many more resemblances to the still successful elasmobranchs.

All these extinct groups are sometimes ranked as orders in Class Placodermi, but increasing knowledge of their anatomical diversity favors the subjective decision that they deserve to be kept in separate classes.

It is also a matter of opinion whether the two persisting groups of fishes with cartilaginous skeleton should be ranked as subclasses of a single Class Chondrichthyes (*chondros* means cartilage, *ichthys* means fish), or kept separately in **Class Elasmobranchii** and **Class Holocephali,** as in this book.

The elasmobranchs include a considerable variety of modern forms and a few notably primitive fossil ones. Two principal orders are the **Selachii** or sharks and the **Batoidei** or skates and rays (Fig. 16–1). In general the sharks are fast-roving fish-hunters and the rays are bottom-hugging mollusc-eaters; their bodies are adapted accordingly. There are a few sharks shaped like rays, and there are rays shaped like sharks, but the minor skeletal differences between the two groups remain constant so that each species can easily be allocated to its proper order by evidence from dissection.

The **Holocephali** (Fig. 2–7) show a number of constant minor differences from the elasmobranchs, and at least one fundamental one: their upper jaws, instead of remaining free and movable below the skull, fuse solidly with it at a very early stage of development. These fishes have never been a dominant group, and now lurk in small numbers at moderate ocean depths, living off molluscs.

The **Dipnoi** or lungfishes (Fig. 2–8) have always been a problematical group. There are only three surviving genera, locally distributed respectively in tropical rivers of Africa, Australia, and

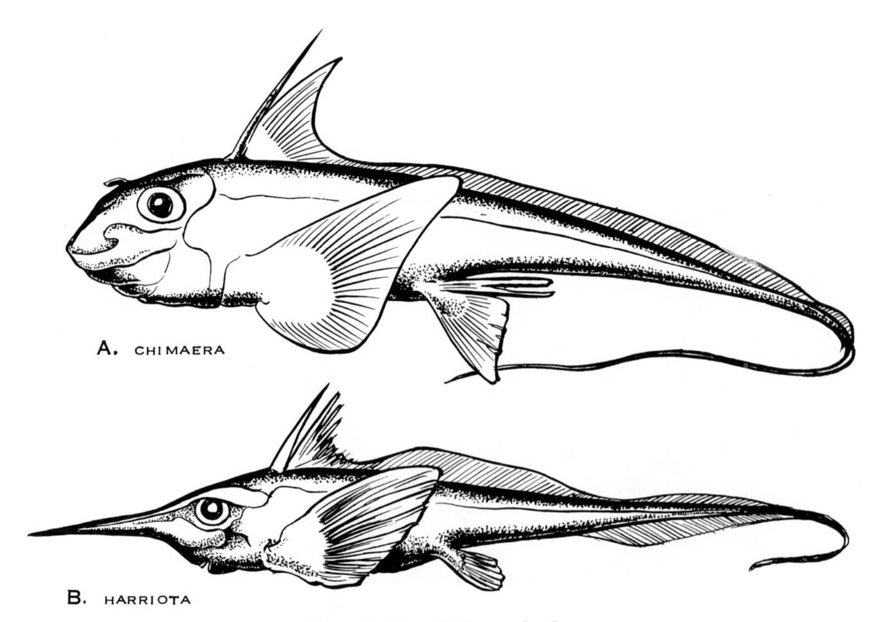

Fig. 2–7. Holocephals.

(After Bigelow and Schroeder, Fishes of the Western North Atlantic, Part II, 1953, by permission of Sears Foundation for Marine Research.)

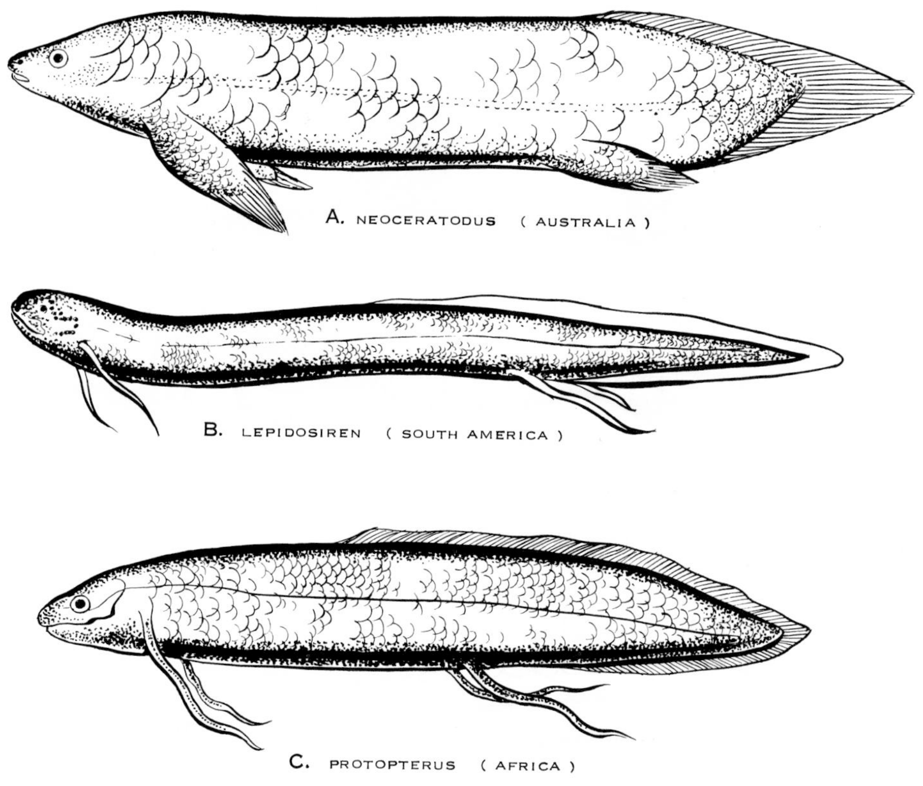

Fig. 2–8. Lungfishes.

South America. Thoroughly fishlike in most particulars, they nevertheless have true but somewhat peculiar lungs, and they periodically or preferentially breathe air. Dipnoan embryos are strikingly like those of Amphibia. The idea that they gave rise to land vertebrates was once strongly favored, but is no longer tenable. Even the most ancient extinct members of Class Dipnoi had important skeletal characteristics not found in any other vertebrate groups.

Recently there has been a tendency to include the Dipnoi with the crossopterygian fishes (see below)—from which land vertebrates undoubtedly did arise—in a class named Choanichthyes on the ground that these are the only fishes that have choanae, i.e. passages connecting the nasal cavities with the mouth. This grouping has been objected to on various counts [4]. In the first place, many true crossopterygian fishes do not possess such choanae. Secondly, the choanae found in the dipnoan fishes develop in the embryo in a different way from those found in true land vertebrates, and therefore can hardly be related to them. The origin of the Dipnoi and the closeness of their relations with the other vertebrate classes are subjects still in active discussion.

The **Teleostomi** are an enormous class, including more than a third of the living species of vertebrates. They have dominated both the fresh and salt waters of the earth since Devonian times, and within the limits of their class have achieved a maximum degree of specialization and adaptation. Two subclasses are distinguished, the **Crossopterygii** and the **Actinopterygii.**

Subclass Crossopterygii came into full flower in the Devonian period and had practically vanished by Permian times after segregating along two lines, the **Rhipidistia** and the **Coelacanthini.** The Rhipidistia undoubtedly became the ancestors of the first land animals, the amphibians, and then these parent groups were all wiped out. The fossil record of the coelacanths ends with

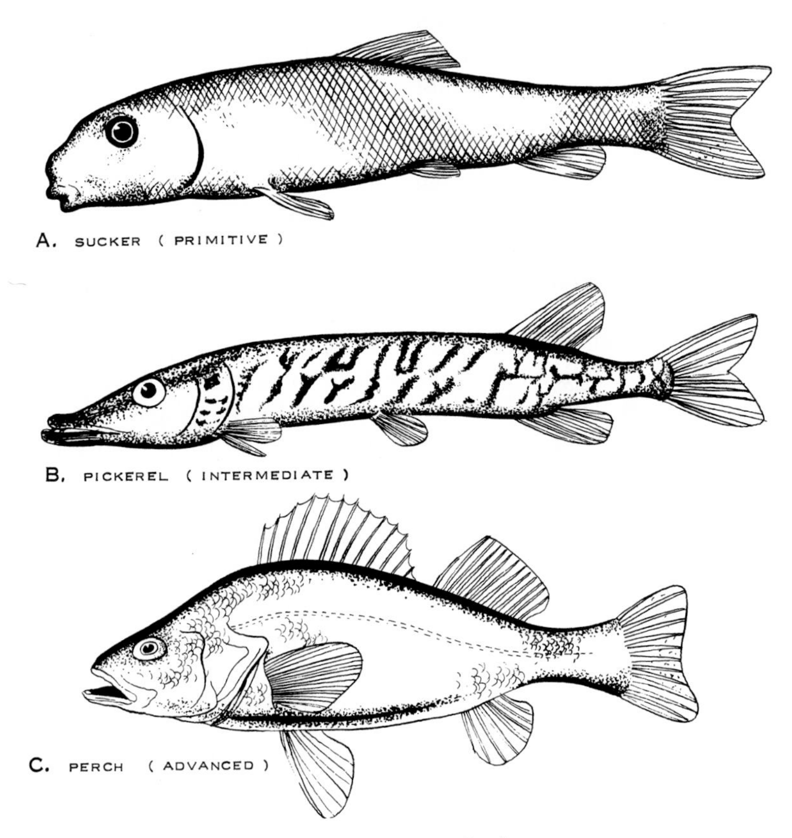

Fig. 2–12. Types of teleosts.

The very magnitude and diversity of the actinopterygian group results in its virtual exclusion from most introductory texts of vertebrate morphology. Water covers seven-tenths of the globe, and the habitats that have been developed in it equal or exceed in variety those bathed by air. The teleosts have mastered this entire realm. In numbers of individuals they vastly exceed the land animals. If teleosts were aided by something like human intellect and could study earth history with their own sense of values they would have no difficulty proving that their own group displays the most highly specialized and most intricate anatomý achieved by any living things, and that they are the pinnacle toward which all other efforts were directed. In their thinking, the land animals would probably be dismissed as unimportant aberrations or refugee groups.

2. **Series Tetrapoda.** The appropriateness of the name chosen for this gnathostome subdivision (*tetra* means four, *pous* means foot) is questionable, for there are some species which have lost one pair of feet (whales) and some that have lost all (snakes). Still, it is a fundamental feature of almost the entire assemblage that the paired appendages have become *legs,* which have a relatively stabilized pattern, quite different from that of most fish fins. Another feature is that practically all of them have and use *lungs,* which are quite different organs from the gas bladders found in most fishes. The snakes, which lack legs, do have well developed lungs. There are a few salamanders which have lost their lungs and respire through their moist skin instead; however these still have two pairs of well developed legs. The tetrapods are not defined in terms of any one character, but by a combination of a number of them.

For over a hundred years the tetrapods have been divided into four classes, the amphibia, repitiles, mammals, and birds. In a boxes-within-

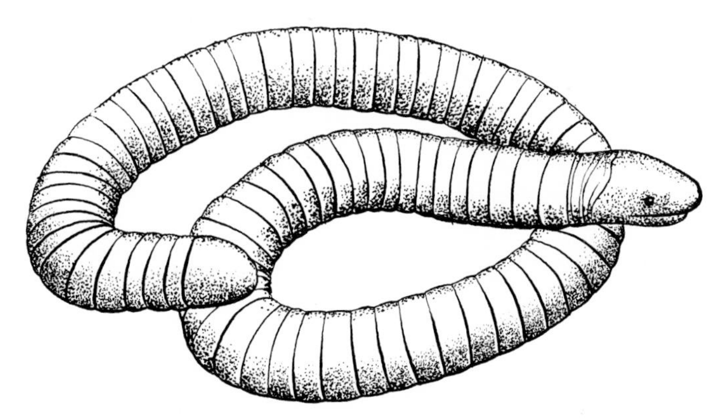

Fig. 2–13. ***Siphonops,*** **Order Gymnophiona.**

boxes classification of modern species this cannot be improved upon, but evidence is beginning to be presented that some if not all of these groups have multiple origins, which may lead to complications or sharp revision of our present genealogic-tree schemes.

Class Amphibia. The amphibians are sharply set apart from the other three orders in one striking developmental feature. The embryos of reptiles, birds and mammals are wrapped in three folded fetal membranes. These structures, called the **amnion,** the **chorion** and the **allantois,** are concerned with the protection, respiration, excretion, and nourishment of the embryo and fetus until it is borne or hatched. None of the modern amphibia produce any such fetal membranes.

Since there were amphibia in the Devonian era which intergraded anatomically with the most ancient reptiles, it is an interesting question what membrane-forming properties the embryonic skin of these creatures may have had. There is no way of knowing. But since the distinction holds for all surviving tetrapods, the reptiles, birds and mammals are put into a division of the vertebrates called the **Amniota** (the amnion is usually the first of the fetal membranes to be completed), and the amphibia fall loosely with all the fish groups into a contrasting division of **Anamniota.**

The members of Class Amphibia, besides being the only anamniote tetrapods, are distinguished by many other attributes. The modern species all have a soft, unscaled and glandular skin, which is relatively unprotected from drying. Most of them pass through a larval tadpole stage in which they breathe by means of special external gills. By remarkable good luck a few such tadpoles are preserved as fossils from the Devonian.

There are three living groups of amphibia, and one heterogeneous assemblage of extinct ones. The **Order Gymnophiona** (or Apoda) is seldom met with, its few members burrowing like worms in tropical forests (Fig. 2–13). It is a quite aberrant group and only inferences can be made as to its history. The **Order Urodela** (or Caudata) includes the familiar salamanders. All of these maintain a long tail throughout life, in contrast to the frogs and toads of the **Order Anura** whose tails are withered and resorbed as they emerge from the tadpole stage.

Recent evidence has been put forward [4] that the urodeles and the anura arose separately from two divergent lines of rhipidistian fishes which became extinct during Devonian times, but long gaps in the fossil record remain to be filled in before this can be cited as more than a strong probability. If it is true, Class Amphibia is not a "natural" classification group. The question is, however, still under discussion [7].

The fourth amphibian group, **Stegocephalia,** was created to contain a number of species of heavy-skulled clumsy land- or swamp-dwellers known from the Paleozoic and early Mesozoic times (Fig. 2–14). It too is now known to have had multiple origins and the grouping therefore loses some of its usefulness. Various of its members were the intermediate ancestors of the modern urodeles and anurans, and also of the rep-

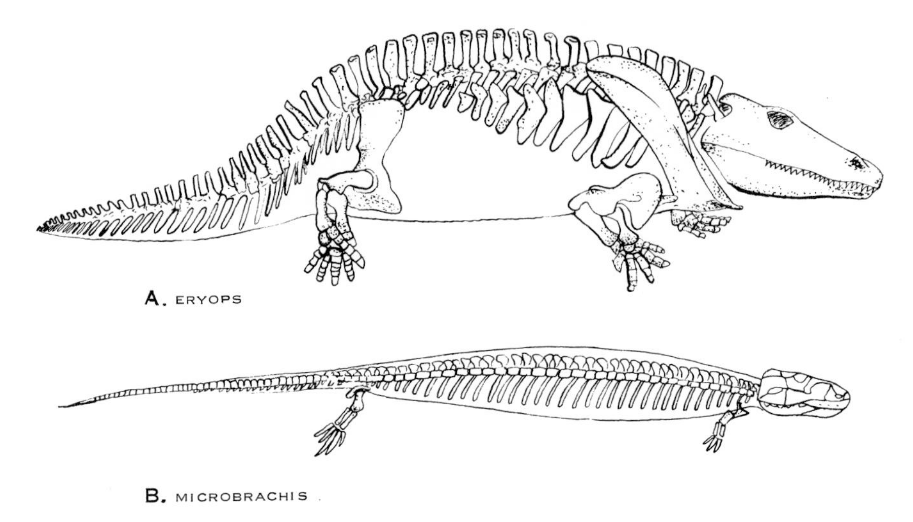

Fig. 2–14. Stegocephals.

(Eryops from W. K. Gregory, Evolution Emerging, 1951, by permission of The Macmillan Co. Microbrachis after Steen, 1938.)

tiles. Other lines specialized in quite different and less successful ways, and were mostly extinct at the end of the Paleozoic era.

Class Reptilia. The reptiles presumably had their origins from one or more of the stegocephalian groups in late Paleozoic times. The lines of descent are indicated in black in Figure 2–15 where they are known from fossils, and projected backward in time as white stripes where only guesses as to relations are possible. Reptiles completely dominated the land during the Mesozoic era, when they separated into a half dozen distinct subclasses and many orders, including an astonishing array of big and highly specialized species, such as plesiosaurs, ichthyosaurs, and many kinds of dinosaurs. Several orders returned to an aquatic life, and more than one took to the air. There were also many less flashy groups, including two orders which have left a fossil record of some of the principal developments that led to mammals Since the definition of the various extinct orders depends on technical aspects of skeletal structure, only the four which still live will be mentioned specifically.

The **Order Chelonia** contains the turtles. Their primitive skull structure suggests that they are close to the earliest reptiles known, but the curious specializations of ribs and carapace which are found in all the modern forms were already well established in the oldest specimens yet discovered. Since its appearance in the fossil record, it has been a very conservative group, but with minor adaptations it has managed to establish itself over the whole world, in swamps, forests, deserts and the open ocean.

The **Order Rhynchocephalia** has had a long history as determined by fossils, but persists only in a single lizard-like creature, the tuatara or sphenodon of New Zealand. Until recent historical times, its survival depended on the lack of aggressive carnivores in its habitats. Since the arrival of white men, its survival has depended on carefully maintained government preserves.

The **Order Squamata** includes two prosperous suborders, the **Lacertilia** or scaly lizards, and the **Ophidia** or snakes. Their stock seems to have been segregated from the mainstream of reptilian progress while still in a primitive condition, before the great explosive development of the dinosaur groups. There is indirect evidence that the specializations that set the snakes apart from the lizards took place during an epoch when their predecessors were living underground, and that the emergence of modern snakes into

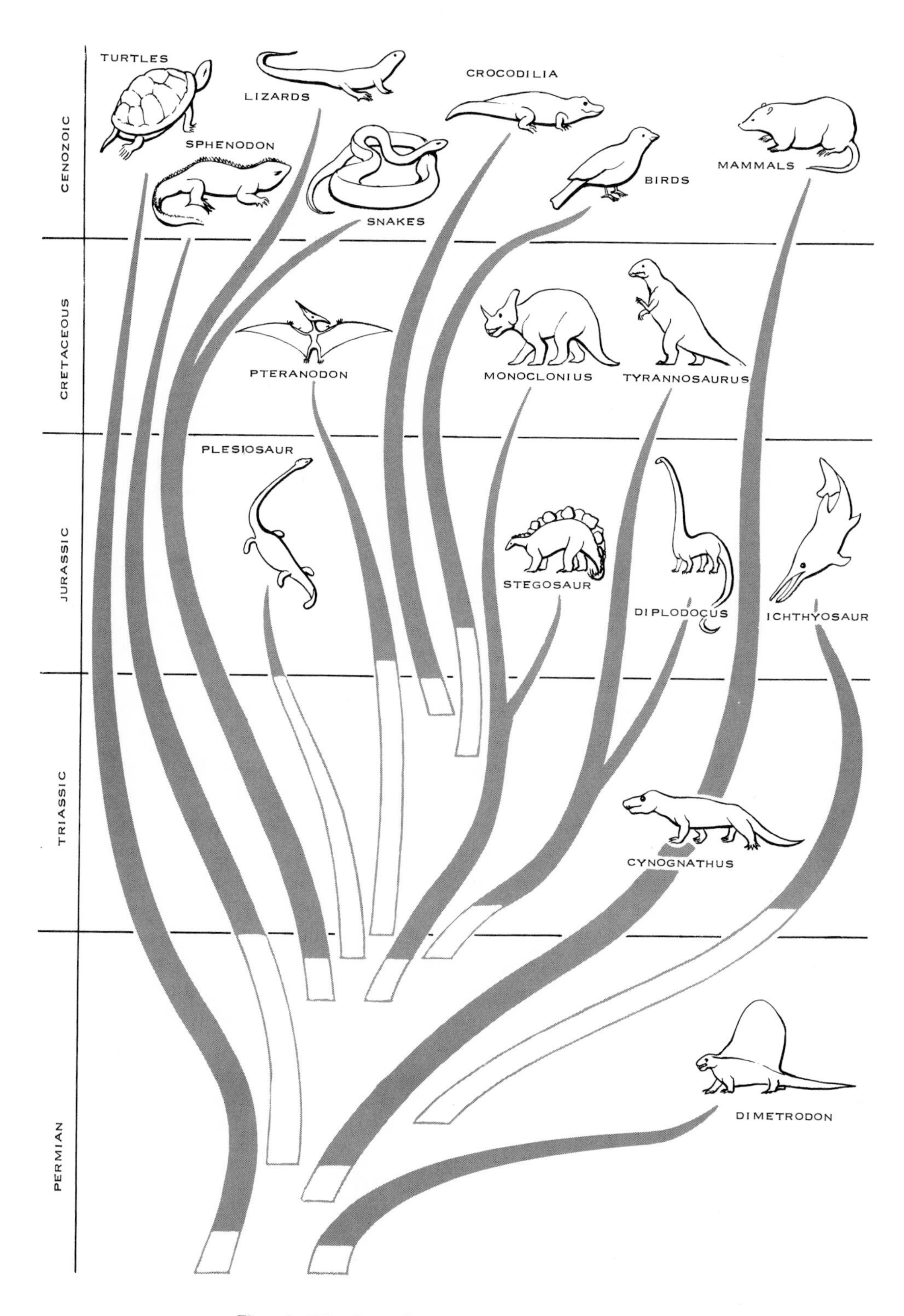

Fig. 2–15. Reptiles and their descendants.

the daylight has been relatively recent. Some lizards which live underground today are found to show various degrees of reduction or actual loss of limbs. A few modern snakes are entirely aquatic, and some are amphibious.

The **Order Crocodilia** is likewise relatively ancient. Apparently this group must have sprung out of the same stock as the unknown earliest reptilian ancestors of birds, together with the great group of birdlike dinosaurs or Ornithischia, such as the formidable *Tyrannosaurus* and *Diplodocus*. The members of all these heterogeneous groups are alike in various odd skeletal features suggestive of a common heritage. The earliest known Crocodilia and the most recent ones are rather similar. Even the modern crocodiles and alligators have anatomical features that could only have been inherited from ancestors that were adapted to walking on their hind legs.

Class Mammalia. Several Mesozoic subclasses of tiny generalized mammals are known from fossilized fragments of skulls and teeth, but their lines of descent are matters of conjecture. The oldest of them come from the Jurassic period, but there were mammal-like reptiles of rather primitive structure as early as the Permian, and rich collections of fossils show that during both Permian and Triassic times at least two orders of reptiles were trying out various structural modifications that later appear in the primitive mammalian skeleton. For all the record shows, it may be that the Mesozoic subclasses of mammals had a multiple origin from several reptilian stocks or at several times. All of these earliest subclasses are extinct with one known exception (Marsupials) and it was not until the dawn of the Cenozoic era that large and successful mammalian orders appeared in profusion In Figure 2–16, known lines of fossils are indicated in solid black lines. Dotted lines are guesses as to relations and times of origin.

At that time the mammals accomplished a regular explosion of progress, as the reptiles and the teleostomes had done before them. It is as though their pent-up inventiveness was released from some severe restraint. Possibly it was the complete disappearance of their principal reptilian rivals and predators. Most of the score or more of modern mammalian orders have a known history which begins with the fossils of that explosive Paleocene period, and they have dominated the land ever since.

There are two modern orders of mammals, the monotremes and the marsupials, which stand well apart from the rest in their morphology. The **Order Monotremata** consists only of the duckbill platypus of Australia and the spiny anteaters of Australia and New Guinea. The past history of the group is completely unknown. These animals have hair, rudimentary mammary glands and other structures found only in mammals, but in addition they show many reptilian attributes which appear nowhere else in the Class Mammalia. For instance, they lay eggs. Therefore in the classification scheme they are segregated as the only known order of a special **Subclass Prototheria.**

The **Order Marsupialia** is usually segreated in a **Subclass Metatheria** because of sharply individual characters. This leaves the rest of the modern mammals to be assembled in the large **Subclass Eutheria.**

So far as the fossil record shows—and this evidence may be misleading—the marsupials are the oldest of the surviving orders of mammals, specimens being reported from the Cretaceous. They once had a world-wide distribution, but are now much restricted, probably because of the rise of aggressive modern carnivores. They include the Virginia opossum and a few similar animals of Central and South America, but they dominate the Australian scene with a great variety of species, among them kangaroos, wallabies, koalas, and wombats. Each of many habitats, including plains, forests, bush, swamps, rivers, and treetops, has its own specially adapted group of marsupial species. There are even marsupials which live the lives of carnivores, fish-eaters, rodents and moles. The great progress of the Australian marsupials took place in singularly fortunate circumstances, for the continent became geologically and biologically isolated from the rest of the world after they colonized it, and before the rise of their really formidable modern enemies, such as the true carnivores of the cat,

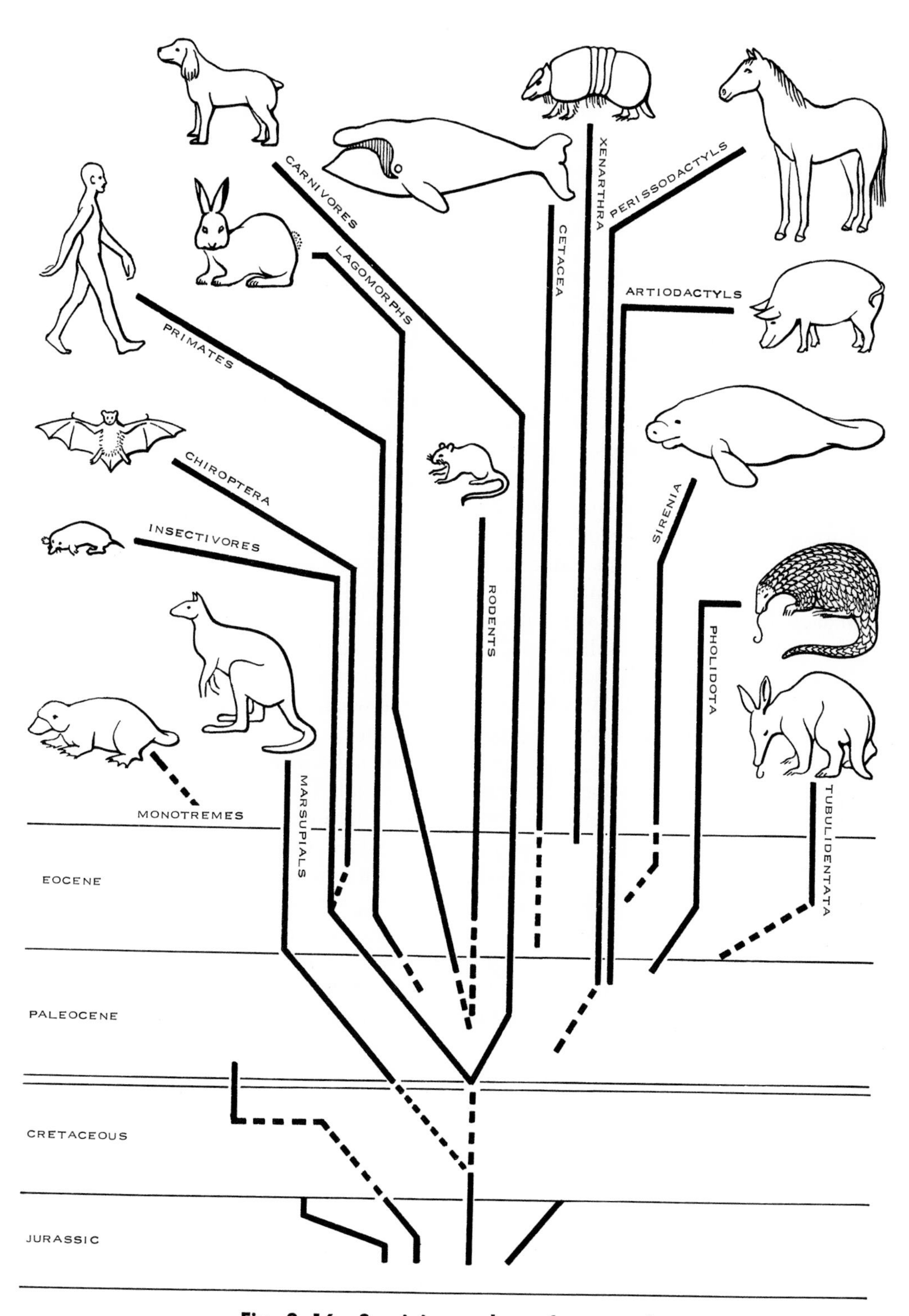

Fig. 2–16. Surviving orders of mammals.

dog, and weasel families, and that most destructive of all species, man.

The placenta, the embryonic nutritive device which is so successful and so characteristic of eutherian mammals, is present in marsupials only in a feeble state of development, or in some species not at all. The young of this order are brought forth from the uterus in a still fetal or larval condition, and for a long time continue their development attached to their mother's nipples inside a skin pouch on her belly. The pouch or marsupium gives the name to the order.

Subclass Eutheria. Some of the eutherian mammals should be mentioned. Modern representatives of the **Order Insectivora** include moles, shrews, and the European hedgehog. The earliest fossil representatives are so simple and generalized that they are thought to represent the stock from which several of the other orders might have arisen directly. The bats of the **Order Chiroptera** are primitive in most anatomical respects, and their remarkable achievement of flight is a triumph of adaptive detail, made without any profound alteration of the mammalian ground plan. The **Order Primates** is also a primitive one, including lemurs, a group of Old World monkeys, a group of New World monkeys, the great apes, and man.

The inclusion of man in a zoological group anywhere below the top calls for comment, because of widely prevalent views that the history of vertebrates has culminated in us if, indeed, the whole progressive sequence did not exist for the sole purpose of bringing us forth. Human thought on such questions is likely to contain a human bias. Unquestionably if the criteria of an animal's supremacy are the ability to think in abstractions, to reason, to remember, to communicate with his fellows and love and hate them, and to control and to wreck his own environment, man *is* supreme, and immeasurably in advance of his closest relatives. Zoological classifications and phylogenetic trees are constructed on morphologic grounds however, and human beings, along with other primates, are in most repects anatomically primitive and generalized in comparison with many other animals, such as horses and whales, and snakes and birds.

There are two orders of gnawing mammals. **Order Lagomorpha** includes the rabbits and hares. **Order Rodentia** includes the rest, such as rats and mice, the guinea pigs, the porcupines, squirrels, beavers, woodchucks, etc. This latter order probably exceeds any other among the mammals in number of species and certainly does in the number of its individuals. It furnishes the food on which most of the carnivorous forms ultimately depend.

The special **Order Carnivora** enrolls one suborder of modern terrestrial types with clawed feet (dogs, cats, weasels, bears, etc.), and one suborder of modern aquatic types with clawed flippers (seals, walrus). The **Order Cetacea** comprises whales, which are so thoroughly aquatic that they can no longer live on land. These animals were already well established as early as Eocene times, and it is supposed they may have shared a common ancestry with carnivores and some of the hoofed mammals, but firm evidence is still lacking. Whales have reached a size and a degree of specialization incomparably beyond any of the other orders of Eutheria. One suborder of them has teeth, the other has the mouth full of whalebone strainers and feeds on small plankton.

Mammals with hoofs are called ungulates. Nearly half the known orders of mammals are subungulate or ungulate in structure, including some which flourished mightily for a time and then, for unknown reasons, vanished. The two largest groupings are easily separable, because one has an odd number of toes and the other an even number.

The **Order Perissodactyla** includes the odd-toed horses, tapirs and rhinoceroses and a couple of extinct groups of clumsy animals of even larger size. The **Order Artiodactyla** is even-toed, and contains the swinelike forms such as true pigs, peccaries, and hippopotami, and a wide variety of ruminant animals such as camels, deer, antelope, sheep, cattle, and giraffes.

These two ungulate orders have in many cases moved into similar habitats and become superficially similar, but their common ancestry is extremely remote, and they differ in numerous minor morphological respects. The perissodactyls achieved a dominant position among herbivores early in the Cenozoic era and have long passed their peak, whereas the artiodactyls got a slower start and are dominant today.

There are several so-called subungulate orders which quite possibly had a common ancestry with the perissodactyls and artiodactyls, though they came into their specialized condition almost before their fossil record started. They include the **Order Proboscidea,** the elephants, mammoths, and mastodons, and the **Order Sirenia,** the sea cows. Both these groups once included a considerable range of species with nearly world-wide distribution, and both have dwindled close to extinction. The largest of the remaining species of sirenians was wiped out by sailors only a few generations ago, and it is altogether possible that the mammoths of Europe and North America were finished off by primitive men. Hunting scenes painted in caves in France and Spain only a few thousand years ago show mammoths among the other game, and well-preserved whole specimens have been recovered from Siberian permafrost.

The roster of modern mammalian orders may be concluded with three groups of animals which are familiar inhabitants of zoos, and are natives of warm countries, but have nothing else in common except that most of them are specialized for a diet of termites. **Order Xenarthra** includes the slow-moving leaf-eating sloths, the South American ant-eaters, and the armadillos. Since not all these animals are toothless, and some members of other orders do lack teeth, it is inappropriate to apply the older name Edentates to this group. **Order Pholidota** exists for only one type of mammal, the pangolin of the Old World, which is covered with scales like a reptile and at first sight seems to lack the hair that a mammal is expected to have. Actually the hairs are inconspicuously disposed in patterns among the scales. **Order Tubulidentata** contains only the African aardvark, another anteater.

In all three of these orders, and among certain monotremes and marsupials as well, similar adaptations have been independently achieved for a diet of termites: heavy forearms and foreclaws for tearing the nests apart, and long snouts, sticky tongues and blunt or reduced teeth for catching and eating the insects. Commonly also the wrists of the forefeet are turned inward in a posture which is better for digging and keeps the long claws out of the way in walking. This *convergent evolution* toward an anteater anatomy, and the adaptive radiation of the Australian marsupial stock, are examples of evolutionary phenomena which indicate the full power of the processes of natural selection.

Fig. 2–17. ***Archeopteryx.***
(After E. H. Colbert, Evolution of the Vertebrates, 1955, by permission of John Wiley & Sons, Inc.)

Class Aves. The class of birds has been postponed to the last in this chapter because, so far as the fossil record allows us to know, it was the latest in origin. There were archaic birds in the late Cretaceous, and good luck has brought us just two fairly complete specimens (*Archaeopteryx* (Fig. 2–17), *Archaeornis*) and a few scraps of more ancient Jurassic creatures which had acquired feathers and a few other birdlike features but were otherwise classifiable as long-tailed gliding reptiles. All present ideas about the origin of birds may at any moment be completely revised by the discovery of other such fossils.

Because of persistent resemblances in development and anatomy between birds and reptiles it is often convenient to speak of these two classes together as the group of **Sauropsida.**

Not only have the birds been the last vertebrate group to come to their peak, they have reached a state of anatomic intricacy and adaptedness beyond anything previously known. Picked examples of the mammals may excel them in intelligence, or in size or strength, or in the design and performance of some particular organ or physiologic system. But considering all the species of a class together, and reviewing all parts of the whole animals together in comparative dissections, the birds win easily in the matter of anatomic specialization. As a result, the class has had a great success.

The classification of birds must be slighted here, since it is based on quite minor points of structure. Disregarding several groups of extinct toothed birds, the major anatomical characteristics of the class are found in a very uniform state throughout. In fact, applying to birds the criteria of the importance of variations that are used in fishes or reptiles, most of the dozens of "orders" of birds in the usual classifications would be reduced to families.

There is only one major break in the relative uniformity of structure in the modern birds, and that separates a group of flightless species, the **Ratites**—ostriches, emus, cassowaries, rheas, and a few more—from the vast majority that fly and are called **Carinates.** It is no longer supposed that this is a natural subdivision. The belief grows that the ratites are a group into which various stocks of birds have drifted after living long enough in a safe enough environment to throw off the burdensome and unnecessary apparatus of flying. In fact, on the basis of skull structure there are some flying birds (South American tinamous) that show a kinship to ratites.

The orders of birds in most cases illustrate brilliantly the adaptation of structure for life in particular habitats or for obtaining particular kinds of food. Very instructive examples of the adaptations of feet, wings and bills may be seen in such ordinal groups as the loons, the ducks, the hawks, the gulls, the owls, the herons, the hummingbirds, and the woodpeckers. It is a difficult matter to construct a classification scheme for birds without reference to these impressive but superficial features. In this respect, the birds recall the teleostomes, which have likewise mastered a huge province and filled every habitat in it with specially adapted species.

REFERENCES

1. For instance, the Silurian fossils *Ainiktozoon* (Scourfield, 1937, *Proc. Roy. Soc.* London 121B: 533) and *Jamoytius* (White, 1946, Geol. Mag. 83: 89).

2. Gregory, W. K., 1951. Evolution emerging. Macmillan Co., New York. Eight different theories are reviewed. A newer one is presented by N. J. Berrill in *The Origin of the Vertebrates,* Oxford University Press, London, 1955.

3. Mayr, E., 1942. *Systematics and the Origin of Species.* Columbia University Press, New York.

4. Jarvik, E., 1960. *Théories de l'évolution des vertébrés.* Masson, Paris.

5. Millot, J., and J. Anthony, 1958. Anatomie de *Latimeria chalumnae.* Centre National de la Recherche Scientifique, Paris.

6. Berg, L. S., 1940. *Classification of fishes, both recent and fossil.* Russian edition republished, 1947, with English translation included. J. W. Edwards Publisher, Inc., Ann Arbor, Michigan.

7. Szarski, H., 1962. *Quart. Rev. Biol.* 37: 189.

3

Three Key Concepts in Morphology

Familiarity with observable fact does not create a science; that much is achieved by fish and monkeys. The unique and priceless part of science is what comes out of the mind and has no material existence at all. Facts there become linked in significant relationships, and these are expressed in generalizations and abstract concepts. An edifice of internally consistent theory is constructed out of the abstractions, which makes a new sort of sense out of all the observed facts At this stage there may finally emerge, almost miraculously, the power of prediction and control, which justifies the whole mental effort.

The history of science illustrates many times over the twin facts that great leaps of progress are made when new unifying concepts are dreamed up, and that progress slows and dies when outmoded concepts are retained too long. The most valuable, and also the most vulnerable parts of any science are its broad theoretical concepts.

Already the discussion of vertebrates has made free use of two important biological concepts, *development* and *evolution*. Both of these prepare the way for a third, which is *homology*. All three concepts must now be examined in turn, before the theoretical edifice of morphology is built upon them.

I. DEVELOPMENT

In many descriptions, adult anatomy seems as static as the contours of a marble statue, but it is nothing of the sort. Important changes are wrought by each decade in the structure of an individual man, as his family album shows on the surface, and as his surgeon can testify in depth. The embryonic and juvenile stages which are often thought of as merely preparatory are as typical of the species as its final form. In the sequence of changes from fertilization of the egg until death and dissolution, adult anatomy is only a condition of *relative* stability. The individual's whole life is a progression of developmental changes, the wrinkling and shriveling of old age no less than the dramatic events of birth and puberty.

A. A Case History

The life history of the common American spotted amblystoma * may be cited as an ex-

* The name of the spotted amblystoma is generally given as *Ambystoma maculatum* (Shaw). The spelling *amblystoma,* which has the virtue of a recognizable and appropriate meaning, i.e., "wide-mouth," has long been preferred by most experimental biologists, but has no justification in the formal rules of taxonomy. It is a nice question whether *Ambystoma* does either, since the name *Siredon* was applied to a Mexican species of this genus in

ample. It is a sequence which repeats itself predictably with the seasons. When the spring rains loose the grip of winter, the adults of this species come out of their tunnels in the forest floor and congregate in small vernal pools. The females pick up the small packets of sperm which the males had recently deposited on leaves and sticks in the water, and without further ado they lay bunches of fertilized eggs. Then the adults disappear, leaving the eggs to continue their history there in the water.

Let us follow the history of such an egg cluster, laid shortly after midnight in a shallow pool in a hemlock swamp, on the night of April 20. (See illustration inside back cover.) The partly matured eggs, coated with jelly from the oviduct walls, are fertilized as they pass through the cloaca. Before daybreak, a fertilization membrane has lifted off from each egg, second polar bodies have been formed, and the surrounding jelly mass has swollen to four or five times the volume of the departed parent female. New chemical activities and a complex flow of materials are set in motion in each egg (Chapter 6).

If the water had been warm, all the eggs in the cluster might have cleaved by sunup, but the swamp is still full of ice, so they remain uncleaved until midafternoon. Unable to control the rate, each egg nevertheless follows its own instructions in proper order, and passes through predictable 2-cell, 4-cell, 8-cell, 16-cell stages and so on, until its cytoplasm is carved into hundreds of tiny cells, adherent to each other and enclosing a central cavity. This **blastula stage** might be reached by the amblystoma individual at any time from 12 to 100 hours after fertilization, the rate being exactly predictable if the temperature is known. In the example being followed, the temperature of the water remains below 10° C, and it takes 3 days.

Until April 23, then, describable structure is at a minimum. The little embryos have no tissues or organs, and it requires technical methods to demonstrate that they have bilateral symmetry. One can only distinguish upper cells with less yolk, grading into larger and more yolky cells below. Or, one can find that the cells of the exterior are tightly joined and pigmented, while those of the interior are loose and light colored.

But on the afternoon of April 23, and continuing all the next day, there occurs a period of great activity, in which cells are deformed and caused to flow in patterned currents. Almost half the cellular sheet that formed the surface of the blastula moves to the interior through an indented spot, the **blastopore.** The original blastula cavity is obliterated by this invasion, and a new one is substituted, called the primitive gut cavity or **archenteron.** The cells that remain on the outside stretch to occupy the areas vacated by the immigrating ones.

With these movements in full flow, the embryo of April 24 must now be called a **gastrula.** The conversion of the blastula to a gastrula can be referred to as **gastrulation,** or the cellular maneuvers themselves can be described as **morphogenetic movements** (Chapter 7), since they are crucial in setting up the patterned anatomy of the next few days. The gastrula still has no segregated organs or tissues, but its cells are arranging themselves in **three germ layers.**

During and after gastrulation, two aspects of development become visible for the first time: **growth,** and **differentiation.** These two processes are continuous and overlapping, but with much local variation in intensity. In some instances they may seem to alternate cyclically. Until April 24, the volume of the nearly spherical embryos has not changed much, and the gain of new living material (which is the essential quality of growth) is chiefly at the expense of inert yolk materials stored in the original eggs. But from this date on there is to be a considerable inflow of oxygen and water from the environment, new localized differences will appear in the cells, and the embryos will heave and bulge and elongate with new patterns of growth. Each day of the final week of April will see a profound change in the shape and size of each individual.

For the purpose of analysis, the differentiation

1830, giving it a priority of nine years over Tschudi's misspelled *Ambystoma* 1. Like other famous but displaced scientific names that have gone into common parlance (the amphioxus, the sphenodon, the rhesus monkey), the name "amblystoma" is here retained without the capital letter, for want of any other common name.

may be described in three sequential phases. Actually, the phases progress at different rates in different parts of the embryo and thus overlap in time, but the totality of events is too complex to approach without the convenience of subheadings.

1. In the *first phase,* the event of prime importance is the emergence of the **basic vertebrate pattern,** in what we may call the **primordial embryo** An alternate term, the **neurula,** refers to the most conspicuous organ rudiment to appear at this stage. Our amblystoma eggs, at the end of their fifth day, have completed their gastrulation and show a definite elongation. On April 26, each suddenly acquires neural folds, and during the day these heave up in spectacular fashion and close over to form a central nervous system, lengthwise of the dorsal surface. This **neural plate,** or toward evening this **neural tube,** is underlaid by a midsagittal streak of **notochord** tissue, and flanked by the first of the right and left series of primitive body segments or **somites,** the number of which will double on April 27 and double again on the 28th. All these structures constitute the embryonic axis, below which lies the rudiment of the gut tube. The **three germ layers,** ectoderm, endoderm and mesoderm, are now in place (Chapters 8, 9), and in them the rudiments of the first organs are appearing. (The German word *anlagen* (singular, *anlage*) is now commonly used to denote such early embryonic structures, though the English word *rudiment* would do as well.)

2. The *second phase* continues the segregation and development of anlagen until practically all the organs of the individual's later life are recognizable in dissection, in rudimentary form. In the process, the more general arrangement of the cells in germ layers, earlier seen in the primordial embryo, is obliterated. By analogy with the terms gastrula and neurula, the name **pharyngula** has been adopted here for the embryo at the culmination of the second phase, since its most conspicuous new structural trait is the carving up of the lateral walls of the pharynx section of the primitive gut into columns or segments of solid tissue, separated from each other by incipient or actual pharyngeal clefts (Figs. 5–9, 5–10). Our little amblystomas from April 20 have become pharyngulas by May 3, the weather remaining cold and blustery. They still hang motionless in their protective capsules within the jelly mass, but if one releases them they will coil, flip and thrash in response to the lightest touch.

Vastly complex processes have newly become evident in their interiors (Chapters 8, 9). Mesoderm cells have begun to coat and penetrate the anlagen formed by the ectodermal and endodermal layers, and are also producing cavities and anlage concentrations of their own. The mesodermal heart was already beating on April 30. By now there are not only nerves and muscles, there are functioning kidneys and urine ducts, there are arteries and veins with blood flowing in them, and gills and limb buds, nose, eyes, ears, tail, liver and many other structures. In sum, the second phase is a period of active cellular differentiation (**histogenesis**), and of the emergence of organs (**organogenesis**).

Urged on by warmer weather, the little amblystomas reach a length of 15 millimeters and hatch from their partially digested membranes and wriggle through the softening jelly during several days after May 15. They scatter and cruise about, or hide in the trash at the bottom of the pool, but continue to live on the yolk provided by their mother for perhaps a week more. The processes of organogenesis and histogenesis continue for weeks and months, with the addition of finer details at slower rates. In some respects this continues throughout their life. However, experiments have shown that a third phase of differentiation sets in some time after the pharyngula stage.

3. This *third phase* could be characterized as the **functional period.** It has been very incompletely studied, but quite new sorts of influences are known to arise. The limbs, for instance, are established independently of the nervous system during the second phase of differentiation, but in the third phase they are unable to continue their development without it. The heart, which can achieve its fundamental pattern of chambers in the complete absence of blood, fails to make further progress if it cannot have blood to pump along. Form and function, or anatomy and physiology, are showing their inseparability in a new sense.

When its yolk is almost all gone, the little amblystoma starts to snap at moving objects in the water about it. Food is caught by violently inhaling it with a great gulp of water into the mouth, whereupon the water is squeezed out through the pharyngeal clefts. Tiny worms can force their escape through these same clefts at first, but the less powerful daphnid and ostracod crustacea are continually packed into the gut, providing a new source of nourishment. The late phases of differentiation are carried along on a rapid tide of growth during a completely aquatic **larval stage.** During this period of some months, the individual's length doubles two or three times without a great deal of change in its anatomy.

The little larva or tadpole swims actively in the water by means of its broad tailfin, using its slowly perfected and delicate limbs only for brakes, or as outriggers to keep it from rolling sideways when resting on the bottom. Its blood is aerated in beautifully tufted external gills, and the air-filled lungs are used only for buoyancy as long as the water is fresh. If the water is stagnant and poor in oxygen, the gills grow more luxuriantly and the larva makes occasional swift dashes to the top to fill its lungs with a gulp of fresh air.

There are a few species and local races of the genus *Ambystoma* in which the individuals remain tadpoles throughout life, acquiring full size and sexual maturity under water. In these, aside from the maturation of the sex organs, further development is chiefly a matter of growth rather than of new patterns of differentiation. In the spotted amblystomas however, as in most urodeles, the larval period is abruptly terminated after a few months, by a **metamorphosis** Our larvae from April 20 will probably reach this crisis suddenly in some week of August or September, depending on the benevolence of the season, but if the call does not come through before cold weather they may pass the first winter as larvae, under the litter in the deepest part of the pool.

When the metamorphosis comes, it is sudden and drastic. Every organ in the body gets a new spurt of differentiation, excepting certain ones which are destroyed. The skin becomes greatly thickened and heavily pigmented, in a wholly new pattern. It turns from a light mottled brown to dark glittering chocolate color, with two dorsal rows of bold yellow spots. The tailfin disappears entirely, and so do the fern-like gills and the pharyngeal clefts. The limbs are much strengthened, and the animal crawls out of water, breathing air. After some days of rest it begins to catch food in a wholly new way, by throwing at it and then retracting a sticky tongue, which has been recently developed in a remodeled mouth. It commences to live in a new world, with a new diet, new hazards, and a new and suitable behavior for them.

The transformation is consolidated in a couple of weeks or a month. Thereafter, the growth aspect of development becomes dominant again. For several years the individual increases in size and heaviness while retaining the same general appearance and proportions. The maturation of sexuality sets up a new cyclic fluctuation in the activity of various endocrine glands, under the influence of which the anatomy of both male and female, each in its own way, is annually altered toward a "nuptial state" before the breeding season, and then regresses to a more nearly neuter state afterward.

Apart from these sexual variations (which, however, affect most parts of the body), the adult life of the amblystoma is a second period of relative anatomical stability, in which only minor functional and nutritional changes occur. Then follows a period of old age and slight regression, which in a state of nature is promptly cut off by death and dissolution. Amblystomas are hoary with age at ten years.

B. Theme and Variations

This sequence of developmental events in the life of the individual is called **ontogeny.** The word was originally restricted to the events of embryonic development, but the effort to draw a line between the developing and the finished individual is fruitless and misleading. Nor can a sharp line be drawn between ontogenetic developments which are normal and those that are abnormal. Individuals of a given amblystoma species collected in one watershed may differ from those of another in such qualities as size or pigment pattern or growth rate, and are described as local races or subspecies, but they seem equally successful. Variations also occur within the individuals from a single clutch of eggs. It is not unusual to find specimens which have too many gills, or are albinos, or have two heads, or are cyclopian, or are twisted so that they can only swim in circles. Such aberrant forms are quickly eliminated by their enemies, but they are a product of the species and cannot be considered unnatural. They add to the known range of the developmental potential of the species. Tumors and cancers also show developmental powers which reside in the species but are not normally called forth.

Like the amblystoma, every other species of vertebrate has its own course of development through a predictable sequence of forms from fertilization to death. The phenomenon of a larval stage followed by *metamorphosis* is rather rare, but tadpoles like those of the amblystoma are found in the majority of amphibians. In some groups of teleostomes and in the lampreys, other kinds of larval forms and metamorphoses are found.

No one vertebrate life history can stand as a perfect example of what the rest are like. The amniotes, and most spectacularly the mammals, have altered their early development in ways unknown to amphibia and fishes though similar experiments have been tried independently in other phyla. The fertilized egg produces on the one hand a persisting individual, by processes comparable to those undertaken by the whole amblystoma egg. But on the other hand it produces an elaborate scaffolding of specialized tissues, the **fetal membranes,** and all these parts of the individual normally die and are discarded at the time of birth or hatching (Chapter 11).

In most vertebrates, the rate of growth dwindles until at last it merely equals the rate of needed replacement and repair of tissues, and the individual reaches a final adult size within a certain range of variation characteristic of the species. However it is possible that some fishes, like lobsters and trees, continue to grow bigger at diminishing rates until violence or disease makes an end of them. In such species, the maximum possible size is unknown.

The tissues of domesticated animals and man continue to develop new characteristics to the last, while the physical and mental powers wane and the body actually shrinks. This is called a **post-mature stage.** It is likely that many if not all other species would show such a stage if protected from the constant perils of their natural state.

A few generalizations and elements of constancy can be discovered in all the countless flowing streams of development that contribute to the morphology of living vertebrates:

1. The development of each species consists of a normal and predictable course of events, repeated in every individual much as in his relatives. Non-viable developments occur, but the permitted range of variation within one species at any given stage is small. The potentialities of the individual are rather exactly inherited from its parents and usually cannot be successfully manipulated by external forces to any significant but viable morphological deviation.

2. In every species of vertebrate, the egg first cleaves into a large number of cells, and these cells are then suddenly rearranged by a pattern of morphogenetic movements into three germ layers, the ectoderm, mesoderm and endoderm, before any tissues or organs appear.

3. In every species, certain basic attributes of the *phylum* appear before any of the special qualities characteristic of the adults of the *class* are seen. These basic features (surveyed in Chapter 5) include: bilateral symmetry about a longitudinal axis, segmented right and left series of somites, a notochord, a dorsal tubular nervous system, the three pairs of major sense organs, paired pharyngeal pouches or clefts, a chambered heart and a liver lying ventral to the intestine, paired kidneys with longitudinal ducts, paired pectoral and pelvic appendage buds, etc.

4. At later stages, the individual acquires the special organs and gross anatomy of his *class* (gills, fins, toes, hair, feathers, etc.), then of his *order* and *family*, and finally of his own species. Development, in other words, is from the general to the special, so far as the gross features are concerned. This long-established law does not refer to the little characters, which can be species-specific from the start. For instance, the embryos of two species of *Ambystoma* can be distinguished from each other at any stage by trivial characters of size, pigmentation, etc., which have nothing to do with the unfolding of the gross anatomical pattern. Nor does one forget that all the specific, and indeed the individual, potentialities are coded into the cells from the start, even in the uncleaved egg. It is the gradual expression of this molecular specificity that progresses from general structures to finer details.

Development, in the ontogenetic sense described above, is one of the principal phenomena of life, and the outstanding problem for the experimental morphologist. Research so far has merely nibbled at the edges of the great questions of morphology: What agent or what force drives the living substance of the fertilized egg to differentiate? What holds this development within, and guides it through, the course which is characteristic of the species? And what brings it to its natural terminus in adult anatomy and holds it there in a relatively stabilized condition? We know enough to predict the events of development, but do not know enough to control them. These are great frontiers.

II. EVOLUTION

All modern systems of classification of vertebrates incorporate the conclusion that biological evolution has taken place; i.e., that old forms of life have been replaced over long periods of time by new ones arising out of them. The ontogeny of individuals has an observable and impressive degree of uniformity down through a succession of generations; but new features do slowly creep into these ontogenies so that the species, the collection of interrelated individuals, is itself variously modified. Out of this irregularity emerges a sort of progress.

Life thus exhibits two kinds of development. **Ontogeny,** or the development of individuals, is to a very high degree repetitive and predictable. The development of species, unaffected by the periodic blooming and withering away of individuals, rolls on through centuries and millennia and is *non-repetitive* and *unpredictable.* Any student can watch the swift progress of ontogeny in the laboratory or in his own family, but this second kind of development, called **phylogeny,** runs slower than glaciers.

Practically no one familiar with the evidence available in this generation now challenges the assumption that evolution occurs. This widespread acceptance of what was once a radical idea should not relieve the student of his obligation to know why he is willing to believe what he does. Therefore the following brief summary is submitted as a framework for review.

A. Earth History

Analysis of known geologic structures, interpreted in terms of known and visibly operating geologic processes, has produced a rough timetable and a sequence for the establishment of the major strata of rocks in the outer crust of the earth. This history embraces a period now commonly estimated at four or five billion years. It is not known when life arose on the earth, but it must have been a billion or more years before the Cambrian period, for Cambrian rocks, which contain all but a handful of the earliest known unmistakeable animal fossils, show that numerous phyla had already then reached an elaborate state of development.

Fossil-bearing strata are classified as Paleozoic, Mesozoic, or Cenozoic, from the more ancient to the more recent. The Paleozoic era started about 600 million year ago and is divided into the Cambrian, Ordovician, Silurian, Devonian, Carboniferous and Permian periods. The Mesozoic era started about 230 millions years ago, and included the Triassic, Jurassic, and Cretaceous periods. The Cenozoic era started about 70 million years ago, and is divided into the Paleocene, Eocene, Oligocene, Miocene, Pliocene and Pleistocene periods.

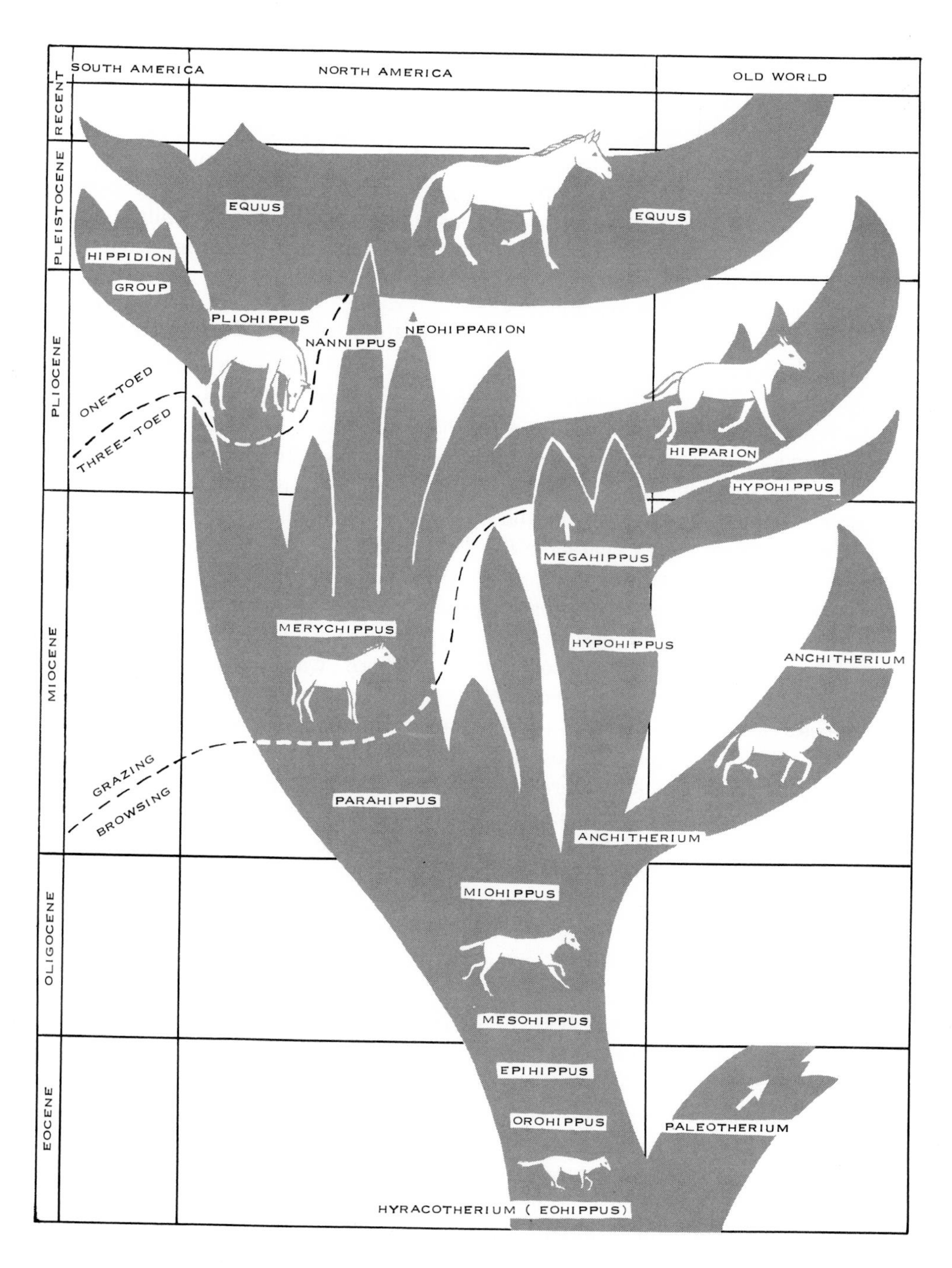

Fig. 3–1. Evolution of horses.
(After G. G. Simpson, Horses, 1951, by permission of Oxford University Press, Inc.)

B. Fossil Evidence

Analysis of the fossils which occur in the strata that were laid down in the successive eras and periods has produced the following generalizations: Species appear, flourish and disappear again, their life span being only a very small fraction of geologic time. There has been a continual transformation of the fauna and flora of the earth since the Cambrian, even families and orders having only a limited life span, old ones being replaced by newer ones. There are hosts of gaps in the fossil sequences, but in some of the kinds of animals which leave abundant fossils, for instance big-boned vertebrates (Fig. 3–1) or heavy-shelled molluscs, it is clear that the transformations were gradual and smoothly intergrading. It is usually assumed that all the fossil sequences would take on this character if they had been preserved as a complete record.

There were no land vertebrates in the early Paleozoic. The late Paleozoic land vertebrates were relatively clumsy types. In the Mesozoic they were succeeded by many lines of more complex reptilian species which conquered a great variety of habitats. By the Cenozoic, most of these had been replaced by quicker, more intelligent and more cleverly adapted mammals and birds. The general picture is one of continual progression from the archaic to the modern, from simple to complex types.

C. Evidence from Living Forms

Modern genetics has developed a huge body of information consistent with the theory that evolution of species is initiated by new hereditary variations produced by several sorts of mutation and recombination of genes; that it is shaped and guided by many special selective forces in changing environments; and that new species can arise by accumulation of such differences and their segregation by a variety of isolating mechanisms. Modern systematics, studying animals and plants in the field, shows clearly that species are not the fixed entities they were once thought to be, but are in a state of genetic instability. Many clear examples are now available to show that species evolution is going on today all around us [2].

It must not be thought that the theory of the *mechanisms* of evolution is adequate today to explain what the fossil record shows has happened. Many lively arguments are still in progress in that field of inquiry. Nevertheless the *fact* of evolution seems firmly established on evidence from the past and from the present.

D. History of the Vertebrates

1. The only major phylum which seems not to have left its record in Cambrian rocks is the Chordata. The earliest evidence of vertebrates consists of skeletal fragments from the Ordovician and Silurian periods (Fig. 3–2). Perhaps the ancestors of these left no fossils because they lacked hard skeletons. The most ancient vertebrates known from adequate remains were archaic agnathous fishes belonging to groups that became extinct before the end of the Paleozoic.

2. There was great evolutionary progress among the fishes during the Paleozoic. All their known classes and most if not all of their known subclasses arose then, including many orders that became extinct before the end of the era. In the particularly fertile Devonian times they gave rise to a large variety of animals which are for convenience classed as amphibia. Most of these died out before the Mesozoic era. Archaic reptiles began to be distinguishable from amphibian stocks toward the end of the Paleozoic.

3. The Mesozoic era was distinguished by continued spread and specialization of surviving teleostome stocks in fresh and salt waters, and by an enormous development of new reptilian orders, few of which survived into the Cenozoic. Mesozoic rocks of the Jurassic sequence also contain the first indications of the establishment of the class of mammals, and the preparations for the class of birds.

4. The Cenozoic seems to have started with almost a complete new deal of land vertebrates. The great dinosaurs, the gliding pterosaurs and the mammal-like reptiles had disappeared, and the skulking little Mesozoic mammals had apparently come out of hiding, inherited the whole

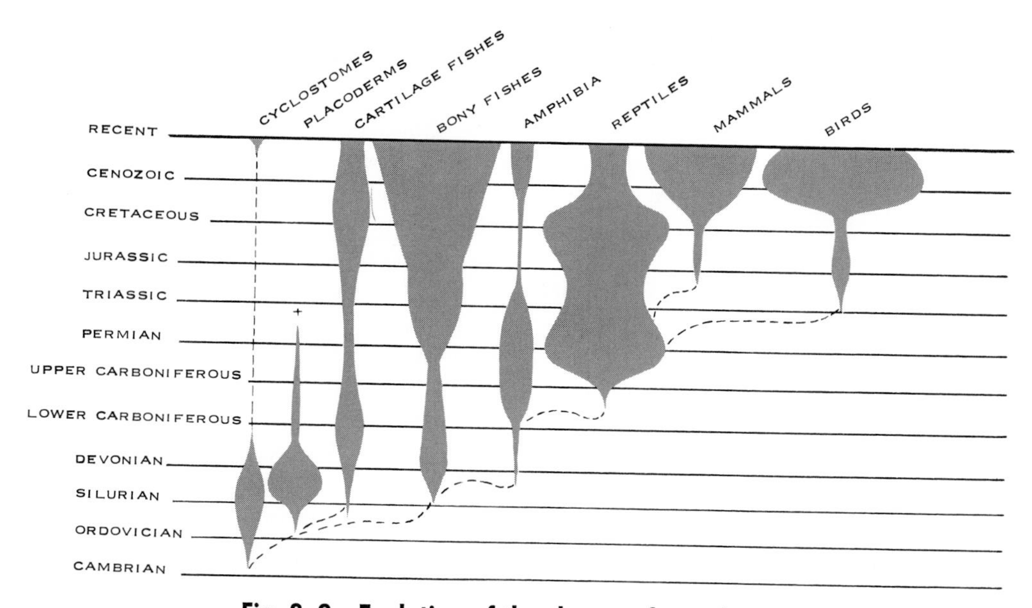

Fig. 3–2. Evolution of the classes of vertebrates.
(After G. G. Simpson, The Meaning of Evolution, 1949, by permission of Yale University Press.)

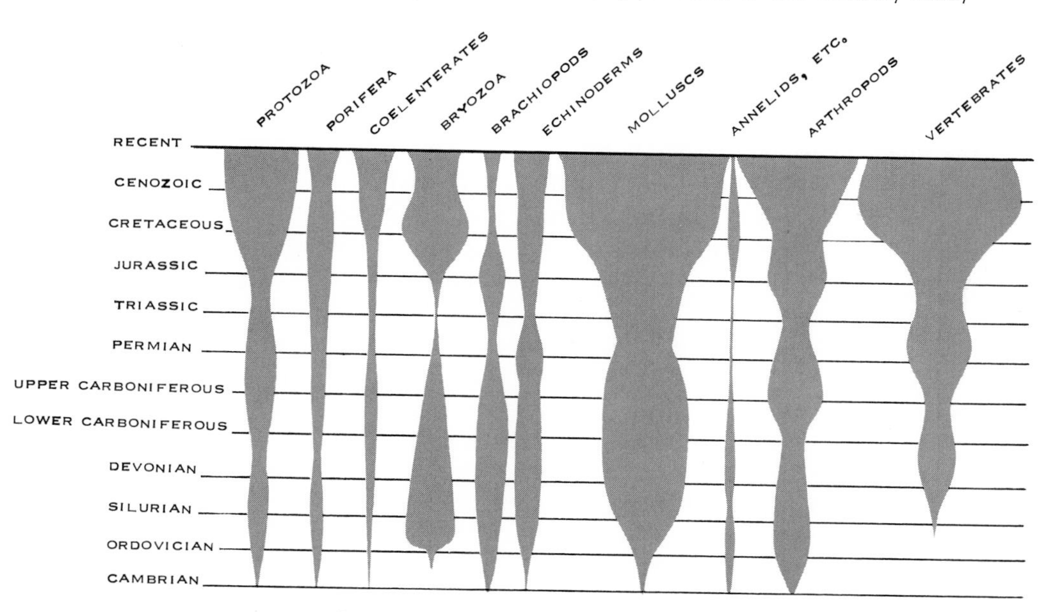

Fig. 3–3. Persistence of phyla.
(After G. G. Simpson, The Meaning of Evolution, 1949, by permission of Yale University Press.)

earth and become swiftly remodeled to take advantage of it. Hosts of new grazing forms suddenly appeared, to exploit the lands covered by the recently evolved grasses. And the birds, having by quite unknown steps developed the ability to escape attack through the air, managed a parallel adaptation to many new terrestrial niches. Both mammals and birds seem to have arisen from reptiles, but out of quite different archaic types.

5. No known phylum of first rank has ever become extinct (Fig. 3–3). Whatever its vicissi-

tudes in successive eras, and however much it has had to adapt itself to changing conditions, each of the great phyla apparently possesses so successful a ground plan, capable of so many fruitful secondary modifications, that it is immortal. Only an atomic or astronomic catastrophe such as the earth has not yet seen can kill off a major phylum.

On the other hand, it is equally clear that within each phylum whole classes have arisen, flourished for a time, and then become entirely extinct. And each class that has been in existence for a hundred million years or more usually has given off various orders which made their effort and lost out. Families all disappear in a few score million years, and genera and species have even shorter spans of existence The phylum is faced with continually and drastically changing earth conditions, and survives only by continual and costly exploitation of new developmental potentialities.

III. HOMOLOGY

One of the functions of morphology is to develop a vocabulary by means of which all animals can be described, so that generalizations can be made about their similarities and differences.

In the mental operations of Euclidean geometry, it is possible to imagine two triangles with such a high degree of similarity that they are congruent, which is to say that if they are superimposed they coincide exactly in all their parts. It is impossible for two actual horses, or two actual trout, to be so similar, but there is more likeness between two horses than between a horse and a trout. On the other hand one can pick out both similarities and differences between the horse and the trout. Early anatomists set out to discover all such similarities in complete ignorance of evolution and completely ignoring ontogenetic development as well. They treated animals as a short of transcendental geometry, and their sterile speculations throttled biological progress for the better part of a century; yet they did invent the term and the concept of homology.

Homology was, and still is, the *study of morphological resemblances between animals.* Structures were, and are, considered homologous if they show convincing similarities. Each species, to the transcendental anatomists, was a special creation modeled after an abstract idea, a sort of blueprint in the mind of the Creator, but executed freely, with variations perhaps representing His temporary whim. It was considered worth the effort to study all such similar variations and synthesize from them a generalized model which might stand for the archetype or blueprint from which the basic pattern of all existing examples was taken. An archetypal vertebra—not identical with any living or fossil specimen—was drafted on paper so as to show parts homologous with all known existing vertebral parts. Treatises were published on the archetypal vertebrate skull, limbs, etc

While this formalistic work helped with the development of a standardized anatomical vocabulary, it led to remarkable excesses. The head of a man was compared in detail with his trunk and abdomen, the jaws being considered homologous with the pelvis. The skull was interpreted as a group of transformed vertebrae. The body plan of an insect was homologized in detail with that of a vertebrate, and the segments of a worm compared with a string of attached individuals. The whole animal kingdom was compared with a single organism, and the whole plant kingdom with a leaf. All this homology literature of the time from about 1750 to 1850 is now well forgotten.

A. Criteria of Homology

The difficulty was a lack of understanding of both ontogenetic development and phylogenetic evolution. Both of these forced new criteria into the definition of homology, and brought under better discipline the effort to find the most fundamental features of morphology. In general it is now insisted that if parts of animals are to be considered homologous they must (1) have similar anatomical structure and relations to other parts in the body, and (2) have their ontogenetic origin from similar embryonic sources and by similar developmental processes.

B. Types of Homology

Clarification of thought was also gained by the recognition of two main sorts of homology, those to be found within a single individual and those seen by comparing equivalent parts of two different individuals. For not very apt reasons these are called *general homology* and *special homology*, respectively.

There are various sorts of general homology: (1) *serial homology* or the resemblance between members of a longitudinal series such as the vertebrae or the ribs; (2) *bilateral homology* or the resemblance between antimeres such as the right and left arm; and (3) *homology of scattered elements* like hairs or scales.

As examples of special homology, the wing of a bird is considered homologous with the arm of a man, or the incisor teeth of a squirrel with those of a horse.

When a relation of special homology is established by the twin criteria of anatomical relationships and embryonic development, the contemporary zoologist is ready to suppose that the homology is a product of divergent evolutionary trends from a structure in a common ancestor, and in exceptional cases he may see a direct confirmation of this in a sequence of fossils. It is quite otherwise, however, with a general homology. It would be absurd to think of a common ancestral arm from which the right and the left arms are derived, or to look for the common ancestor of the third and the fifth neck vertebrae. These general homologies arise out of similar repeated conditions of local development in the segmented and bilaterally symmetrical embryo.

C. Homology Scrutinized

It is important to come closer to an understanding of homology than a sentence or two of definition and a list of its criteria, for this is the concept on which all the comparative aspects of anatomy and embryology have been built.

While in theory a pair of homologous organs must satisfy criteria of similarity in both structure and development, the fact has to be faced that the strictest insistence on either would destory most homologies, if not all. The question is one of similarities, not identities, and there are even cases in which it is profitable to accept homologies where either the one or the other criterion fails completely. A few examples may be cited.

Sometimes it happens that an obviously comparable organ may take origin in different animals from different germ layers or from different parts of the embryo. For instance, the thymus gland is said to be formed in some mammals from ectoderm, in some from endoderm, and in still others from both. Muscles grow down into the pectoral and pelvic limb buds of sharks from local myotomes, but in amphibia they arise there by condensation of local mesenchyme even when the myotomes have been removed. In the salmon the pectoral buds develop in one of these ways, the pelvics in the other.

The gut tube is completed in amniotes from a hypodermis layer, and in anamniotes from the roof of the archenteron, or from its floor, or from both. The muscles, vertebrae, and notochord of the amphibian tail are formed through maneuvers rather different from those that produce the equivalent structures of the trunk. The amnion is formed in several different ways in mammals, and usually not in the manner found in birds and reptiles. In certain salamanders the lens of the embryonic eye is budded in from the overlying skin, but if it is later removed an apparently identical replacement can be formed by regenerative processes from a different source and in a different way. In the tunicates, the individuals produced by development of the fertilized egg through the tadpole stage cannot be anatomically distinguished from those produced by asexual budding, yet their developmental processes are not comparable in any single detail.

Analytic embryology reveals that parts that are obviously alike normally come from comparable parts of the embryo but the stimulus which releases their development may be derived from different sources. There are species of both *Rana* (frogs) and *Ambystoma* in which the lens will not form unless its parent tissue is in contact with the eye cup, and there are other species of the same genera in which the lens can form without such contact. In the tunicates, the central nervous system can form itself almost completely without the presence of mesoderm, whereas in most amphibia no neural development ordinarily takes place at all if there has not been prior contact stimulus of the ectodermal source by the underlying chorda-mesoderm organizer.

Presumably a frog egg is homologous with a human egg, but at least two-thirds of the latter is used up in forming fetal membranes which are discarded at birth. Which third of the frog is homologous with the man? If the adult frog has eight vertebrae and the man has thirty-three, is the frog's fifth vertebra homologous with only one, or with four and a half of the man's and in either case which one(s)?

While this list of puzzles could be prolonged, the cases are exceptional. In general experience, similar embryonic development is regularly associated with similar anatomical structure and relationships. The point to be understood is that embryonic development can sometimes be markedly altered by mutations without greatly changing the end-product, and successful embryonic mutations can be passed on into the heritage of the phylum just like any others. There is a striking example of this in the phylum Mollusca, in which one whole class, the cephalopods, has achieved an ontogeny utterly different in every respect from that of all other modern molluscs. In such cases there is no profit in denying the similarities (i.e., homologies) in the end products.

Nor on the other hand should the criterion of similar development be lightly discarded. Conditions in adult anatomy have been so profoundly transformed in different stocks of vertebrates that some homologies that are now generally accepted would have been missed altogether except for a study of comparative development. A great many other homologies proposed on the basis of slight or fancied resemblances in adult anatomy have been unequivocally confirmed or rejected by appeal to embryology.

Unfortunately there do remain certain questions of homology for which no answer seems to exist. The facial nerve of teleosts may run either anterior or posterior to the hyomandibular bone, or through it. The gill skeleton of the lampreys is outside the blood vessels, that of gnathostome fishes is inside them. In certain constellations of skull bones, particularly in the nose and ear regions of fishes, homology problems arise, to which there are various possible solutions, but no morphologic criteria either of embryology or of adult anatomy seem to be available for choosing between them. In the development of the muscular system certain broad homologies can be established between muscle-forming masses at early stages, but then these break up in countless ways, complicated by drifting and recombining of parts, so that in the end it becomes impossible to establish strict homologies of individual muscles, even by appealing to a supposed (and dubious) constancy of nerve supply. During phylogeny the nerves likewise seem to have variously extended and retracted both their peripheral distributions and their connections in the central nervous system, so that their homologies extend only to certain features of their main trunks and not to the nerve fibers of which they are composed or to their functional relationships. As in the case of the criterion of developmental similarity, too rigid an interpretation of the requirements of similarity in adult structure and relationships destroys the concept of homology itself.

In this quandary, efforts have been made to develop some such genetic definition as this: Homologous structures are those whose development and final form are products of the action of homologous genes. Homologous genes are those which have been reproduced and multiplied, with or without mutation, from the same gene in some common ancestor.

This new interpretation of homology may very likely be justifiable in broad outlines, but the geneticists themselves have suggested some grave difficulties in applying it. In most cases it is quite impossible to identify the genes or factors which bring about the structures and relationships with which the anatomist deals. This is so even for living animals, let alone extinct ones. One cannot therefore establish the most obvious homologies, much less settle homological disputes, by appeal to genetics.

The principle that homologous genes produce homologous structures, far from settling the old questions, raises worse new ones. A single gene in a fowl can produce both cerebral hernia and certain feather defects. A single gene in Drosophila can control both eye or body color and the shape and size of spermathecae. It would produce chaos to call such combinations of structures homologous just because the same gene is responsible for them. Also, identical results can be achieved by quite different mimic genes, even by genes operating at different stages of development. In other words, the homology of phenotypes, which is what the anatomists and embryologists deal with, is not the same thing as homology of genotypes.

The same mutation has been known to occur many times over in different laboratory stocks of animals. Shall the results of these independent mutations be considered homologous? Horns apparently arose more than once in separate stocks of the Eocene mammals called titanotheres. The one-toed condition was reached by the horses of North America during the same time that it was being reached by the entirely isolated and very distantly related South American stock of Litopterna. The condition of streptostyly, in which the quadrate bones are movably jointed with the skull, has been independently developed in lizards, birds and mammals. The genes involved in such cases may or may not have been homologous, but the mutations were certainly independent. Even if the responsible genes were identifiable, insoluble problems would remain.

The entire science of vertebrate morphology rests on the concept of homology. It is an interesting situation therefore that this concept resists a strict definition in any known terms, and the detection of homologies involves some subjective elements of personal decision and some frankly insoluble problems. This is perhaps to be regretted, but philosophers are well acquainted with the fact that the foundations on which all sciences rest are a mixture of fog and faith. The value of science comes from its fruits, not its roots. There is not much point in insisting that two living things are either completely homologous or that they are not homologous at all. What is valuable is to ask: To what degree are these things homologous? The establishment of a degree of homology carries with it the likelihood that what is true of one of them is more or less true of the other. This fruitful assumption has suggested most of the investigations from which the science of morphology has grown, and has brought out all of its generalizations and created all of its unifying vocabulary. Using the ideal concept of homology as a yardstick, it has been possible to distinguish between generalized and specialized organs and relationships, and between the fundamental pattern of vertebrates and its major and minor variations.

One interesting outcome of such inquiry is the demonstration that in a sense the soft gray substance of living matter is more resistant to change than bedrock. In the last three hundred million years many ranges of mountains have been forced up from the earth's surface and been worn level again, but the fundamental pattern of the vertebrates has endured.

REFERENCES

1. The name *Siredon* comes from Wagler, 1830, *System der Amphibien.* The name *Ambystoma* comes from Tschudi, 1839, "Classification der Batrachier," in *Mem. soc. nat. Neuchatel.* The taxonomic situation is reviewed by W. Wolterstorff, 1930, in *Abhandl. Museum Naturk. Vorgesch. u. naturw. Ver. (Magdeburg)* 6: 129.
2. Leeper, G. W. (ed.), 1962. *The evolution of living organisms,* a symposium. Cambridge University Press, London.

Part II

UNIVERSAL ELEMENTS

The amount of variation introduced into the inherited morphology of the vertebrates in the last half billion years makes it a formidable task for the beginner, in comparing the structure of mammals, birds, teleosts, and sharks, for instance, to sort out what is general and what is special.

The next two chapters therefore concentrate on structural elements which recur in all vertebrates with a high degree of regularity. These, added to the discussion, in Chapter 3, of broad aspects of development which are common to all, will furnish a vocabulary and a frame of reference for consideration of the developmental and anatomical variations in the various classes of vertebrates, which starts in Chapter 6.

When vertebrate embryos finish the cleavage stage and start to differentiate their special tissues and organs, remarkably uniform types of cellular specialization and cellular arrangement occur in all members of the group. It can be assumed that they are all operating under the control of genes derived from a common ancestor. The resulting *histological homologies* are clear-cut and fundamental, and are the subject of Chapter 4.

It has previously been noted that the anatomical groundplan of vertebrates emerges in its least complex form at a midembryonic stage as the product of early organ differentiation. This *anatomy of the pharyngula stage* will be elaborated more fully in Chapter 5.

These universal elements having been presented, they will serve as a target in the chapters of Part III, in which are discussed the developmental processes out of which the tissues and organs arise. In Parts IV and V the universal elements become a starting point for discussion of how their elaboration has resulted in the principal variations of the fundamental vertebrate pattern, found in the different classes. The nervous and hormonal apparatus, by which the activities of the whole body are coordinated, are considered last, in Part VI.

4

Tissues and Organs

Some time in the long lost pre-Cambrian past, the ancestors of vertebrates developed and stabilized a repertoire of cellular differentiations which was different from that of the lower chordate stocks, and even more different from those of other phyla. This has been handed down to modern vertebrates with interesting minor variations, and expresses itself anew in the ontogeny of each individual. A modern shark egg, after undergoing a period of cell cleavages, proceeds to recreate a pattern of differentiated cells and tissues which is for a while, in all major respects, like that produced by the egg of a lizard, a pigeon, or a human. The elementary results of this process of **histogenesis** or tissue development will be outlined in this chapter.

I. ANALYTICAL CONSIDERATIONS

The cleavage stage which precedes histogenesis is a period of mitotic cell divisions. The most important event of mitosis is the duplication of the DNA molecules of the chromosomes and the separation of the originals and their copies into the nuclei of the daughter cells. So far as appearances are concerned, the cells of the blastula and the later embryo are identical in their nuclear contents. Genetic evidence is clear that developmental potentialities are guided and limited by these nuclear stores of information, i.e., the genes located in the chromosomes. It should apparently follow that all the cells from a single egg should continue in the same line of development and produce only a single type of tissue, but this is obviously not true. The successive cleavages of the fertilized egg cell produce gland cells, muscle fibers, brain cells, skeleton, and many other tissues which differ sharply from each other.

What initiates this differentiation, this histogenesis? What channels it along each of many lines? These problems are being actively investigated but the answers are not yet clear.

One possibility is that the uniformly replicated genic material produces different results in the different cells of the embryo because it is acting upon different kinds of cytoplasm. It is easy to see in some vertebrate eggs, and is probably true in all, that the cytoplasm is nonhomogeneous to start with. There is usually a conspicuous gradient of yolk concentration from the vegetal to the animal pole, and a difference between the cortex and the interior of the egg, and there may be other regional differences. Streaming movements may be observed in egg cytoplasm, but not of an intensity that would homogenize the cell contents, and the cleavages finally segregate different qualities of material into different cells. Even if each of these cells received an identical assortment of genes, it might be supposed that these might express themselves in different ways according to the reactions they can initiate in different cytoplasms.

Another possibility, made plausible by recent experiments with nuclear transplants in frog embryos, is that the nuclear equipment of the cells does not remain constant, but is altered in special ways in different regions of the differentiating embryo [1].

If the zygote nucleus is sucked out of an uncleaved frog egg, there is no further development, or even cleavage. On the other hand, if the zygote nucleus is replaced by a nucleus from a small cell of the developing blastula, cleavage proceeds, and in a high percentage of cases a normal embryo is produced. This is clear evidence that the nucleus has not lost any of its potentialities during the chromosome replications of the mitosis during early cleavages.

It is much more difficult to replace the nucleus of the undivided egg with a nucleus from a tiny gastrula cell, and in early experiments [2] only a small proportion of such host eggs became normal embryos. Improved technique greatly increased the percentage of cases which went through cleavage, but significantly did not increase the proportion of the blastulas which went on to form embryos with normal structure. Also the types of abnormal development, obtained from transplanting nuclei from *ventral* parts of the late gastrula or neurula to the uncleaved egg, were different from those gotten by transplantation of nuclei from *dorsal* cells. It seems to be a tenable hypothesis that the potentialities of the nuclei themselves are changing in different ways in different parts of the late gastrula. The changes may be reversible to a degree, and their rates need not be the same in different species [3].

These experiments do not permit conclusions as to what is cause and effect in normal histogenesis. The changed nuclei are propagated within cells that receive different cytoplasms during cleavage. Are the nuclei exclusively guiding the differentiations that ensue, or do the cytoplasms limit or help guide the results? One needs to assume that in the normal embryo certain nuclei retain their full and unaltered complement of genes and carry them intact into the germ cells that will form the eggs or spermatozoa of the next generation, but this does not eliminate the possibility that nuclei may be altered by interaction with less generalized cytoplasms. Evidence of such nuclear alterations is now being obtained. But the elusive explanation of cell differentiation and of the normal patterns of histogenesis continues to be sought. The recent results from nuclear transplantation demonstrate chiefly that *both* the principal elements, the nuclear and the cytoplasmic, may be changing. Since neither element is yet sufficiently defined, the frontier of discovery is still open here.

Whatever may be the causes and the controls of histodifferentiation, the process starts with the cleavage stages of the embryo, and during the second and third stages of differentiation (cf. page 35) produces many types of tissues. All vertebrates exhibit pretty much the same catalog of fundamental tissues, which will now be described.

II. TISSUES

Probably all cells have some polarity. After the blastula stage is reached in an amphibian embryo the cells which are lined up on the outside show a flattened, pigmented, non-adhesive outer surface, a rounded inner surface and side walls which become more and more firmly attached to those of their neighbors. This polarization is not lost when some of the outer cells turn inward to form the gastrula, for the lining of the gastrocoel, formed by this inpocketing, is still pigmented and non-adhesive. Some cells of the interior retain their regular side-to-side attachments to their neighbors, and others lose it. Those that continue to be attached in regular polarized sheets are described as epithelial. Those that are more loosely organized may clump together in solid masses or become wandering ameboid elements.

A. Epithelium

Epithelium is the simplest category of tissues in basic design (Fig. 4–1), but can become specialized in many forms and functions. Its cells are so closely packed together that they have practically no intercellular substance, and are usually arranged in sheets which are underlaid by a common **basement membrane,** composed of fine matted fibers. Their free outer borders are non-adhesive. Such epithelial layers of cells are formed by each of the primary germ layers, ectoderm, mesoderm, and endoderm. They cover the outside of the body, the inner cavities, and the linings of ducts and tubes, including the intestine. Since their arrangement tends to present an unbroken front, they serve as barriers to the loss of contained material or to the invasion of chemicals or foreign organisms from without.

Very commonly these layers are secretory, receiving food and other materials through the basement membrane and putting out special products at the free surface. Other functions commonly undertaken by epithelia are the respiratory transmission of gases, the elimination of wastes, and the absorption of digested food substances. The ultrastructure, the chemistry, and the energetics of these processes are great frontiers for current research [4].

1. **Simple epithelia** are those in which the sheet is only one cell thick (Fig. 4–1 A, B). The height of the cells may be altered for special functions. For instance, **pavement epithelium,** which is composed of very much flattened cells, forms the lining of many body cavities, whereas the glandular surfaces of the intestine are coated with a thick **columnar epithelium** of tall cells (Fig. 4–1 B). Where such surfaces cannot function properly unless they are kept clean of debris, or where movement of the fluid within a cavity is required, the free surface of the epithelium develops a downy covering of delicate cytoplasmic whips or cilia which keep up a rapid coordinated beating.

2. When the cells of the tissue are heaped upon each other in irregular layers, they compose what is called a **stratified epithelium** (Fig. 4–1 C). As new cells are formed at the basement membrane many of them are squeezed out-

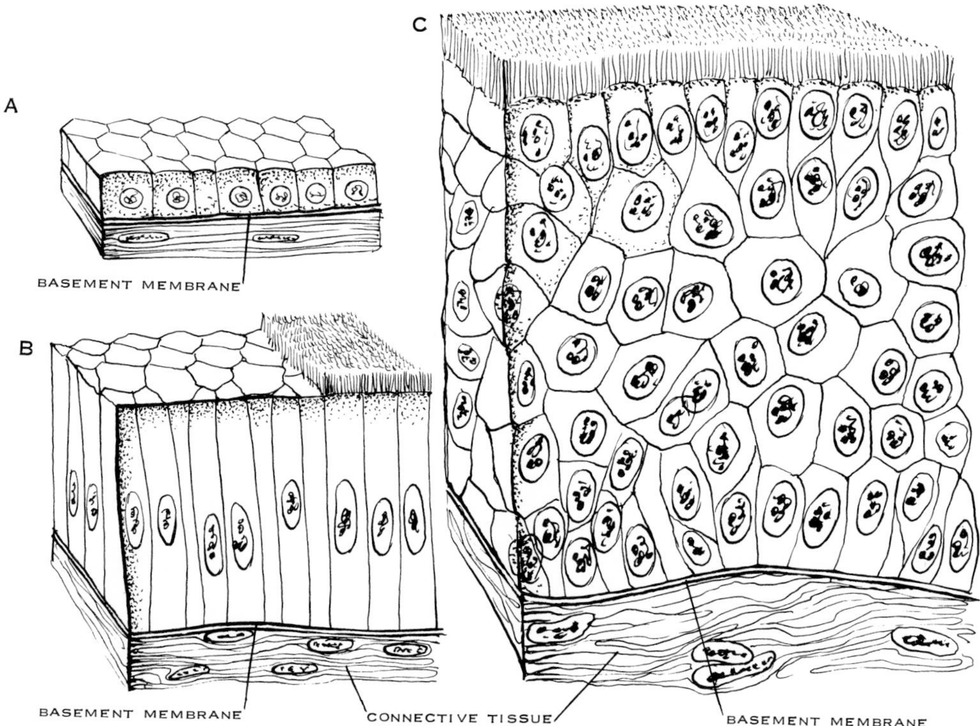

Fig. 4–1. Types of Epithelia. A. Cuboidal. B. Columnar. C. Stratified. Glandular

ward, gradually changing character as they grow older and become farther removed from their sources of supply. The epidermal part of the human skin is an example of stratified epithelium whose outermost layers thicken and toughen their cell borders at the expense of their actively living material.

It is not necessary for all the cells in an epithelium to be alike, for secretory and nonsecretory regions may be differentiated in close contact, or an area may consist of a close mosaic of secretory, ciliated, pigmented, and otherwise specialized cells. It is difficult to explain how two cells derived from the same source and developing side by side can differentiate into sharply contrasting types, but this accomplishment is illustrated in nearly every histologic preparation.

3. Groups of epithelial cells which are bound together and specialized for secretion are called **glands** (Fig. 4–2). In most cases the cells are organized in straight, coiled, or branching tubes, with a visible differentiation between the secreting part and the draining part or duct. The secreting cells tend to be columnar, the duct cells cuboidal or flat. Glands which have a duct system that carries the secretion away from the organ to the outside or to the intestine are characterized as **exocrine.** These are in sharp contrast to **endocrine glands** which lack ducts and pass their molecular secretion directly into adjacent blood capillaries for distribution through the whole body. The cells of endocrine glands are often epithelial in origin but their arrangement in sheets becomes very much obscured.

Exocrine glands exist in great variety, and secrete in different ways. **Serous glands** give off a watery fluid, **mucous glands** give off a thick mucilaginous substance. The **mammary** and **sebaceous glands** of the skin slough off parts of their own cells, which then disintegrate in the ducts to form the secretion. Ovary and testis cast out whole unbroken cells. The secretory cells of an exocrine gland may be arranged around a tubule or a bulb (alveolus); either **tubular** or **alveolar glands** may be either simple (unbranched) or compound (much branched), and **compound tubulo-alveolar glands** are not uncommon. Exocrine glands may have patches of endocrine glands scattered within them, as for instance the islands of cells in the pancreas which secrete insulin, and the interstitial cells of the testis which secrete sex hormones.

B. Tissues with Prominent Interstitial Substance

Blood, bone, tendons, and the fibrous matting under the skin do not at first suggest themselves as a logical category of related tissues. In fact, it has been difficult to find an appropriate name for the group, which some call the "connective tissues" and others "binding tissues." They have two things in common. First they develop from quite generalized embryonic cells that do not cling together but may even wander for a while before settling down and differentiating. Second, during the differentiation process they become further separated from each other by the formation of **intercellular substance.** Most of these tissues are derived from the embryonic mesoderm, but as will be described later a part of the ectoderm called "neural crest" also contributes to them. The tissues of this category are most easily distinguished from one another

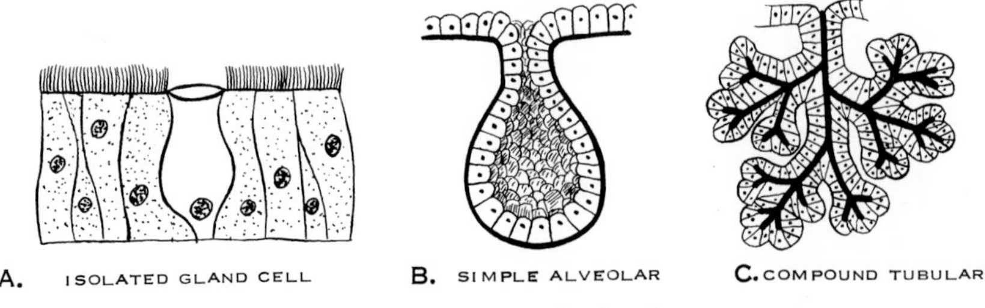

Fig. 4–2. Types of glands.

by the character of their intercellular substance, and by the patterns in which the cells group themselves.

1. **Mesenchyme** is primarily an embryonic tissue from which various other types are derived by processes of further differentiation. It consists of loosely arranged, irregularly shaped cells separated from each other by thin and relatively

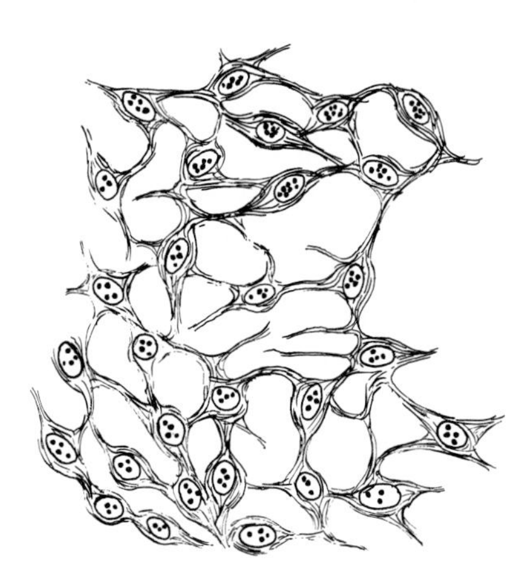

Fig. 4–3. Mesenchyme.

structureless intercellular substance (Fig. 4–3). The cells are slightly ameboid, and fill in the spaces not occupied by more condensed and individually identifiable anlagen.

2. There are a variety of **fibrous tissues,** all consisting of elongated cells scattered or straddled through a more or less abundant intercellular fluid matrix (Fig. 4–4). During their differentiation from mesenchyme, the intercellular substance of these true "binding tissues" has bundles and mats of slender non-living fibers deposited all through it. The cells themselves may become fixed or may continue to crawl about, and some of them develop the capacity to ingest foreign particles or dead cells. In some parts of the body the fibers are few and delicate, while in others—for instance the lower layer of mammalian skin from which leather is made—they form dense tough mats.

Fibrous tissues are incorporated into most of the organs of the body, supporting the blood vessels and nerves, furnishing a foundation for all the epithelial tissues, binding the muscle cells into groups and masses, fastening muscles to bones or cartilages, and creating the joints which tie the elements of the skeleton together. In addition they fill all the odd unused spaces between organs. Tendons, ligaments, fascias, and fatty tissues are all special variations on the pattern of fiibrous tissues.

3. **Cartilage** is one of the two principal rigid tissues of the skeleton. Its cells, originally mesenchymatous, form concentrated masses and become surrounded and separated by a solid intercellular matrix of considerable strength and rigidity (Fig. 4–5). In common language it is called gristle. The matrix may remain glassy bluish and apparently (though not actually) homogeneous, but it usually becomes visibly crisscrossed or heavily matted with fibers. Cartilage predominates in the embryonic skeleton, and though it may be almost entirely replaced by bone in adults of the more advanced vertebrate groups,

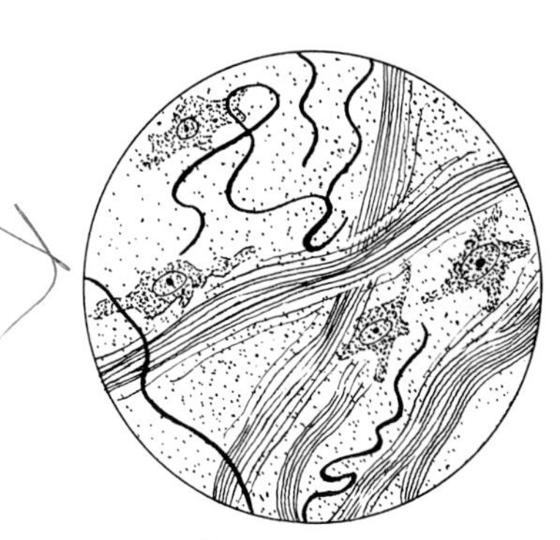

A. LOOSE, AREOLAR

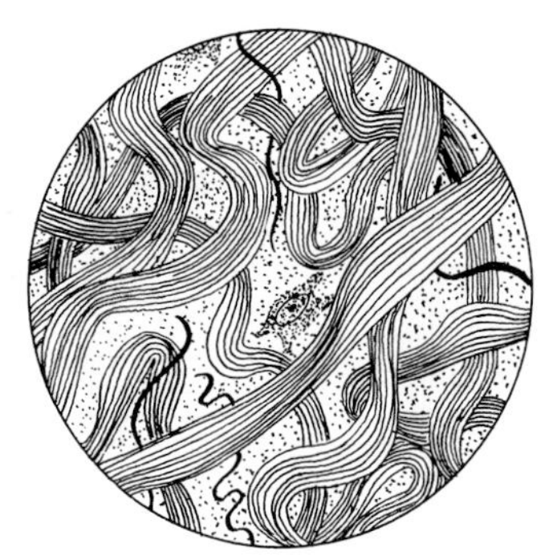

B. DENSE, DERMAL

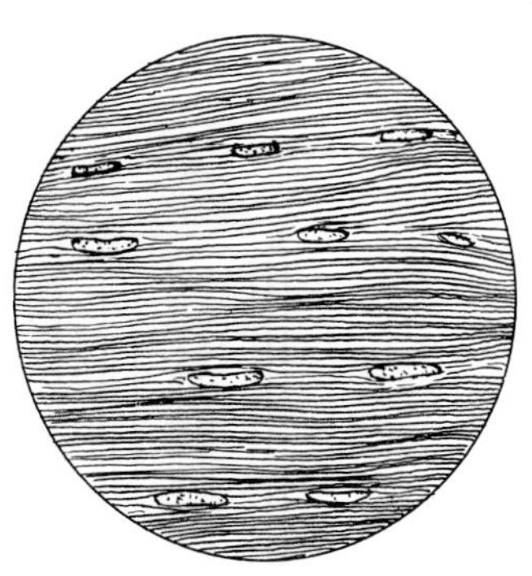

C. TENDON

Fig. 4–4. Fibrous tissues.

appendages), which tie them to the skeleton. These striated muscles are concerned with the intermittent and apparently purposeful reactions of the whole animal to the environment: pursuing, eating, fleeing, etc.; in contrast to the business of the smooth muscles in the unconscious and more nearly incessant maintenance activities of the viscera.

Skeletal muscles, unless they are bound up in myosepta, almost always have their two ends attached to different bones, either directly or indirectly. Usually one of the ends is more freely movable than the other, though often both can be moved. The relatively fixed end of the muscle is defined as its **origin,** the relatively movable end is its **insertion,** and one speaks of tendons of origin and of insertion. The **function** of the muscle is usually to bring the point of insertion closer to the point of origin by the shortening of the intervening myofibrils. Muscle function may bring about movements of the skeleton that can be described by words like extension, flexion, elevation, depression, rotation, etc.

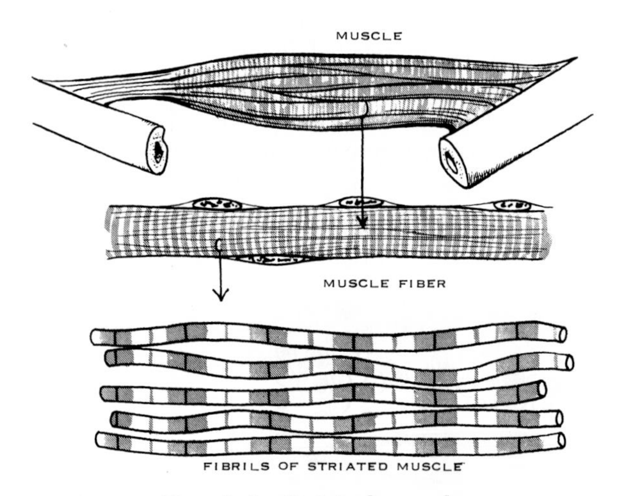

Fig. 4–8. Striated muscle.

3. **Cardiac muscle** has its own peculiarities. It is non-skeletal and involuntary like the non-striated muscle, but has cross-striations like the skeletal muscle (Fig 4–9). In contrast to both, it has an unresting spontaneous rhythmic activity, and its elongated cells are not spindle-shaped, but branch and fuse with one another in a continuous network. This intimate organization into a supracellular unit has the result that when contraction starts at any point in the mass it spreads throughout the entire heart. Normally the rhythmic beat starts at one end in a special "pacemaker" center, and spreads regularly along such paths that one heart chamber takes up the work of another in precisely the right sequence.

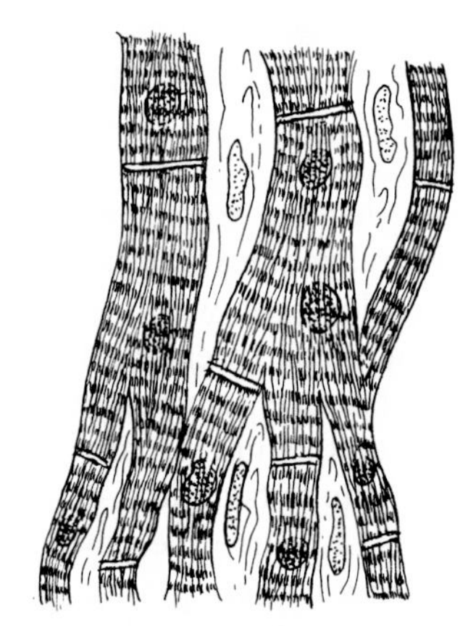

Fig. 4–9. Cardiac muscle.

D. Nervous Tissue

The cells of the central nervous system (brain and spinal cord), the peripheral nervous system (nerves and ganglia), and the special sense organs (nose, eyes, and ears) do not share any one distinguishing histological characteristic. They show many differences in size, shape, and pattern of tissue organization. Most of them spin out extremely long delicate branching processes, but some are more like epithelial cells, others more like mesenchyme. The most outstanding characteristic of the group is less anatomical than physiological: an extreme irritability expressed in fluctuations of the difference in electrical potential between the inner and outer surfaces of their cell membranes.

1. Neuron Structure. The commonest cellular unit in the nervous system is the nerve cell or **neuron.** There are two functionally distinct activities going on in a neuron: the synthesis of materials needed for fuel and repair, and the irritability reactions. The descriptive terms for the parts of neurons, which were invented before these functions were understood, are now inadequate [5]. Neural diagrams traditionally show a cell body or **soma,** with outgrowths on one side labeled **dentrites** and described as receiving stimuli; and a long outgrowth on the other side, labeled **axon** and described as a transmitter of impulses, an effector. But note that in Figure 4–10 the sensory neuron at the left has its soma in a ganglion on a side branch off the junction of what are called a single long dendrite and an axon; these two are not only actually continuous, they are structurally and functionally a unit, transmitting toward the central nervous system a nerve impulse which has arisen at a point where membrane potentials from a system of sensory branched terminals have become confluent. The motor neuron on the right has its soma embedded in the central nervous system between what are called dendrites and a single long axon; among such neurons only the axon is concerned in transmitting the nerve impulse, and the dendrites, in particular instances, may or may not be receptors.

Other patterns of neurons further confuse the effort to define axons and dendrites in terms of their relation to the soma. In fact the position of the soma in the neuron is apparently irrelevant to the regional specialization of the excitable surface membrane. Therefore the suggestion [5] is here adopted that the term **axon** be applied to that part of the neuron that propagates a nerve impulse, irrespective of its length, branching or relation to the soma. The term **dendritic zone** is given to the sum of all parts or processes of the neuron which can generate an electrochemical membrane response to an outside stimulus,

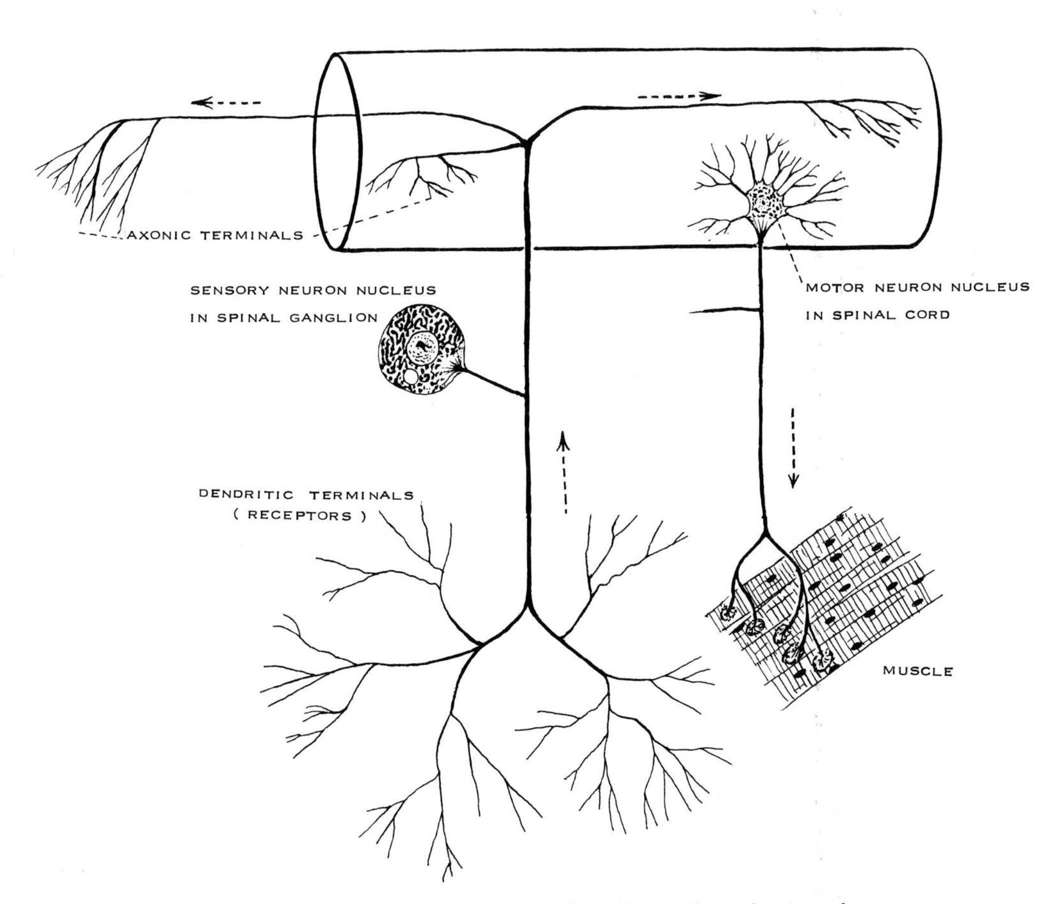

Fig. 4–10. Peripheral neurons. Arrows show lines of conduction along axons.

whether this be sensory, synaptic, or other. A **dendrite** is then any branching process that belongs to the dendritic zone. Thus, the entire sheathed part of the sensory neuron in Fig. 4–10 is an axon, and the soma is nowhere near the junction of dendrites with axon.

This terminology helps to distinguish the neuron's functionally distinct activities. The **soma** contains the nucleus and synthesizes the cytoplasmic materials which flow out from it to all the processes. The **cell membrane** clothes the soma and the processes, and flickers with the most extraordinary electrochemical activity. The excitable membrane is by no means uniform over the whole neuron. Some parts are excited in one direction or another in varying degrees by sensory or synaptic stimuli from outside, and others are specialized to propagate a nerve impulse (see below, page 60). Still others have rhythmic and integrating functions.

The neuron that brings you news that you have stubbed your toe has its dendritic zone under the skin, while its soma lies in a ganglion close to your lumbar spinal cord. If the soma were enlarged to the size of an orange, the axon might correspondingly be nearly a mile long and half an inch in diameter, and the dendrites would be in proportion to the electric wiring in a large house. But no two neurons are alike. One may have a small axon and a vast number of tiny branches in the dendritic system. Another may have an axon which divides and extends in many directions with different localized patterns of ramification (Fig 4–11). There are neurons with cell bodies about 20/1000 of a millimeter long, and axons fully a meter in length, and there are others whose whole distribution may be seen within a space only a few microns square on a slide. Structurally there is an intergradation from neurons through neuroglia cells (page 60) to connective tissue cells.

2. *Neuron Development.* Each of these neurons is developed from a generalized embryonic cell called a **neuroblast.** Figure 4–12 shows three stages in the outgrowth of axons from frog spinal ganglion cells grown for two days in tissue culture. All the processes of a single neuron are produced in this way from a single microscopic cell. Furthermore, the neuron maintains this unity throughout its life. Substances that are synthesized in its nucleated soma are transmitted by a sort of pumping action outward into its branches, and these branches will degenerate if cut off from the source of their nourishment. When mutilated, the neuron restores its axon by regeneration outward from the soma.

The first neurons to reach out among the muscles, viscera, and conective tissues of the em-

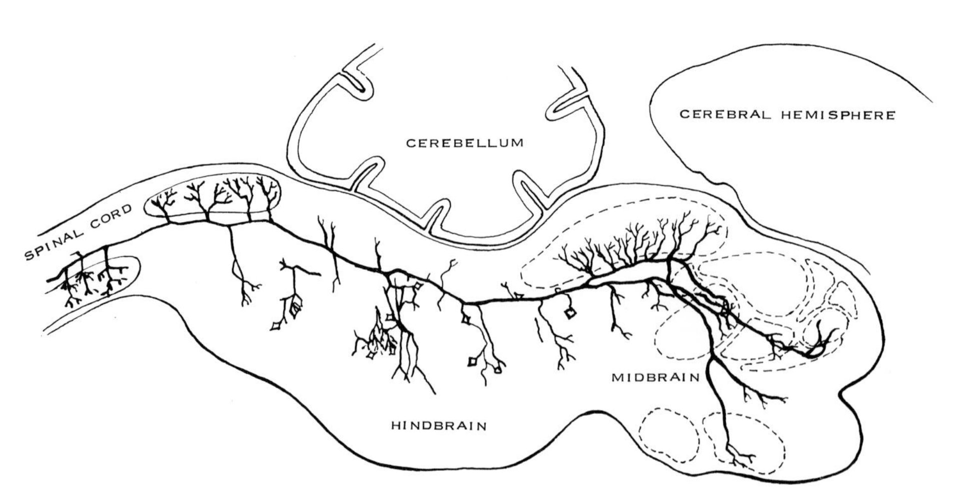

Fig. 4–11. A central neuron.
(After Scheibel and Scheibel, in Reticular Formation of the Brain, 1958, by permission of Little, Brown & Co.)

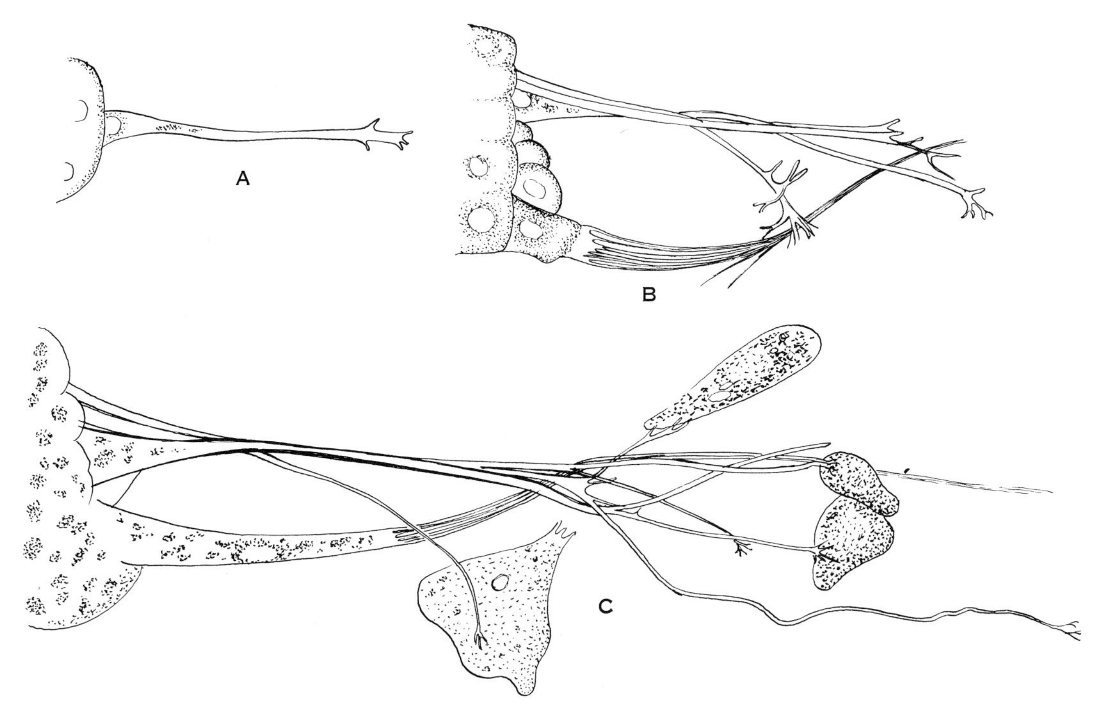

Fig. 4–12. Development of neurons in tissue culture. A. Cultured 24 hours. B. 34 hours. C. 46 hours.
(After R. G. Harrison, 1907.)

bryo act as pathfinders. The processes send out little temporary pseudopodia from their tips, as though feeling for contacts. Various observations fit with the idea that the direction of their outgrowth is determined by an oriented substrate of macromolecules or submicroscopic particles along which they glide. The neurons that differentiate later tend to follow the early exploratory pathfinders, so that bundles of axons build up, running in similar courses. Special connective tissues binds up and insulates such bundles, which are then identifiable as **nerves.**

A nerve found in dissection commonly contains thousands or tens of thousands of the axons of individual neurons. Those which are carrying nerve impulses outward from the central nervous system to the periphery are classed as motor fibers, those transmitting in the opposite direction are sensory. A peripheral nerve almost always includes both sensory and motor axons, as defined above.

Inside the brain and spinal cord, a similar tendency is seen for late-developing neurons to follow pathfinders, but here the bundles are not sharply segregated from one another by connective tissue envelopes, and only the very largest of them are detectable in dissection. They are called **tracts,** and their analysis requires special staining technique and the study of microscopically thin serial sections.

Long sensory or motor axons outside the central nervous system tend to attract **sheath cells** which line up along them at spaced intervals. These cells arise in mesenchyme from ectodermal sources. When one of them finds an unoccupied section of a nerve fiber, it proceeds to wind a doubled sheet around and around it, laying down a spiral wrapping of an insulating material called myelin (Fig. 4–13). In the intervals between successive sheath cells down the length of a single nerve fiber there develop **nodes** where the myelin sheath is incomplete. Not all axons and dendrites become conspicuously myelinated, and the proportion of fibers with a heavy coat to those with

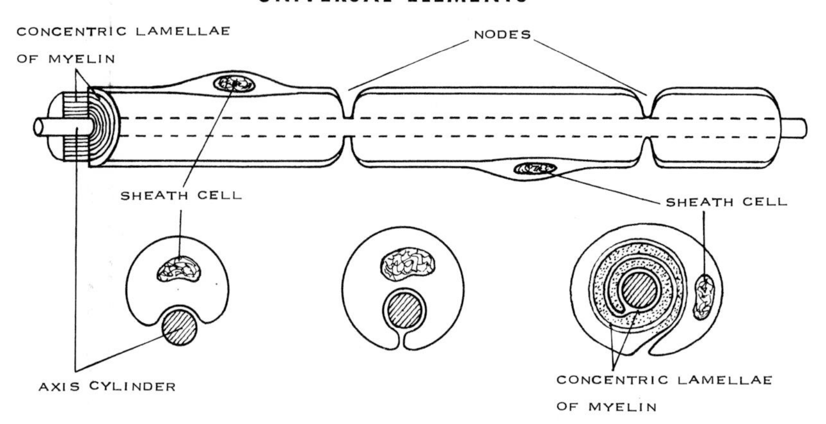

Fig. 4–13. Sheath cells on neuron. *Upper:* Dissection of a myelinated nerve fiber. *Lower:* Envelopment of axis cylinder by a sheath cell.

(After B. B. Geren, 1954.)

little or none varies from one nerve to another. Within a single nerve the proportion increases during the individual's lifetime.

Inside the central nervous system, many of the axons, but by no means all, acquire similar spiral wrappings of myelin, through the agency of **satellite cells** or oligodendrocytes. The whole central nervous system is held together, and the neurons further insulated from one another, by a rather soft weak kind of ectodermal connective tissue called **neuroglia.** The glia cells have branching processes reminiscent of axons and dendrites (Fig. 9–6). They develop from embryonic cells which are at first indistinguishable from those that form neurons.

3. *Nerve Impulse.* It was known from the time of Galvani (late 18th century) that peripheral nerves would respond to electric charges. In the 20th century, development of techniques for measuring minute currents allowed the demonstration of nerve impulses of an electrical nature in peripheral nerves. The dissection of these nerves into individual nerve fibers made it possible to show that a non-diminishing all-or-nothing spike discharge went the length of a sensory fiber toward the central nervous system when its skin area or its muscle was stimulated, or a similar discharge went in the opposite direction along a motor axon toward its muscle. If the discharge was initiated in the middle of the nerve fiber it went both ways.

This wave of electric disturbance, the *nerve impulse,* is now interpreted in terms of an upset ionic equilibrium at the surface of the neuron (Fig 4–14). In the resting state, a potential difference of something less than 100 millivolts exists between the inside and the outside of its surface membrane, presumably because the membrane is permeable to certain ions and not to others. The potential difference due to the polarization of this membrane may be reduced to zero and reversed, or made to fluctuate in other ways with extreme speed and sensitivity, by various sorts of chemical and physical stimuli. This response may break over into the swiftly propagated and self-sustaining chain reaction, the nerve impulse. Such changes are thought to be the byproduct of syntheses, hydrolyses, and temporary combination of acetylcholine, which may follow each other within the cell at intervals of a few milliseconds.

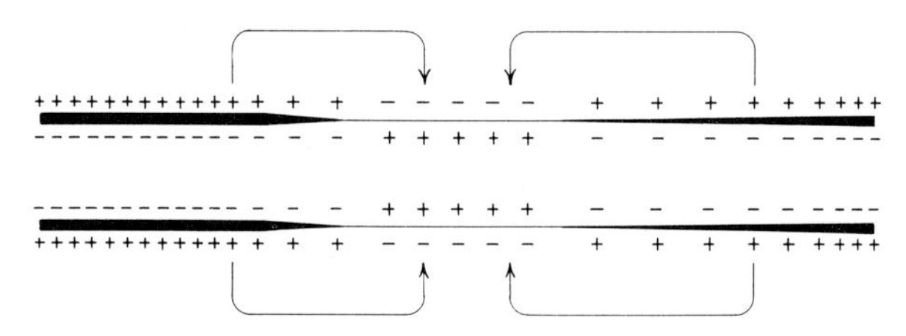

Fig. 4–14. Change in membrane polarization during passage of nerve impulse.

(From Fulton's Physiology, 17th edition, 1960, by permission of W. B. Saunders Co.)

The terminal finely branched twigs of axons, except those which end in specialized contacts on muscles, glands, etc., usually end in extremely small knobs (*boutons terminaux*) very close to the cell bodies or dendritic stems of other neurons. There is probably no cytoplasmic continuity between the cells at these points, and the space between the knobs of the first neuron and the parts of the second neuron is called a **synapse.** Most neurons form synapses with many other neurons. When a nerve impulse is initiated near or in a neuron's cell body and spreads down through an axon to its terminal knobs, there is always a slight delay, after which a similar impulse may be started up in the neuron on the other side of the synapse. The nature of the transfer mechanism itself is not completely understood, but it only works one way. The stimulation passes only from the axon to the second neuron's dendrites or soma.

Stimuli reaching a synapse are not necessarily able to cross the barrier. The second neuron may be able to react only when stimuli reach it in special rhythms, or when a certain number of them hit it from enough sources in a given time to build up past a threshold level. Many stimuli are inhibitory.

4. Reflex Arcs. **Sensory neurons** lie mostly outside the central nervous system. Their somata, with rare exceptions, lie in cellular masses called **ganglia** just outside the brain and spinal cord. They are stimulated at their peripheral endings, and only their transmitting fibers enter the central nervous system. The dendrite systems and somata of most **motor neurons** lie entirely within the brain or spinal cord and derive their excitation from synapses there. Only their axon fibers course through the peripheral nerves. Direct synapses between sensory and motor neurons are very rare within the central nervous system, except in early embryos. Usually several, or thousands, or millions, of neurons which lie entirely within the brain or spinal cord, act as intermediaries. These will be called **central neurons.**

When a peripheral area of the body has been stimulated and a behavioral reaction to it has taken place, nerve impulses must have gone up the sensory path, through central neurons and back down motor axons. If this pathway involves a few neurons and produces a stereotyped response in a predictable short interval of time, the behavior is called a **reflex,** and the pathway a **reflex arc** (Fig. 4–15).

Physiology texts list large numbers of special reflexes which can be elicited in laboratory animals and in man. They are not at all typical of the whole behavior of real individuals, which is conspicuously non-predictable, broadly integrated, and usually appropriate to the circumstances. Reflexes have somewhat the same relation to total behavior that a doorbell circuit has to a servo-mechanism. The earliest fruitful efforts to study nervous activity naturally focused on the reflexes because of their relative simplicity,

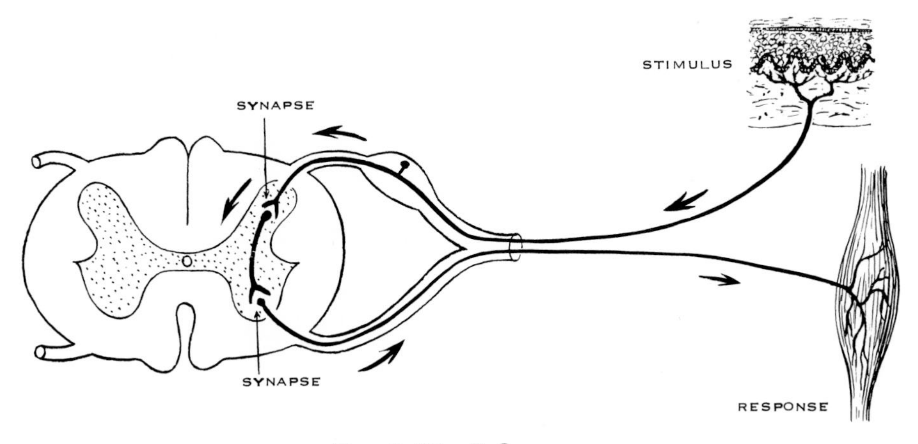

Fig. 4–15. Reflex arc.

but it has become increasingly clear that it is impossible to interpret central nervous activity as an infinite collection of reflexes, or even to compare the brain to a telephone switchboard a million times compounded. It is a different kind of mechanism altogether: an extremely elaborate computer combined with information-gathering and executive devices.

5. *Types of Neuronal Activity.* When electrodes are placed upon the peripheral axon of a motor or sensory neuron and a stimulus is applied, it is found that the nerve impulse passes without diminution the full length of the fiber. It is an all-or-nothing reaction, whose velocity is constant for any given axon. After an extremely brief interval the altered membrane potential is restored to the resting state and the fiber is ready to be fired off again.

For lack of direct information it was formerly supposed that the parts of the neurons inside the central nervous system reacted in this same way. Phenomena which were detectable from the outside, such as the raising or lowering of thresholds for reflex response, the speed-up or delay or alteration in the nature of response, etc., were thought to be established in some way at synapses within the central nervous system.

All such theories are being currently re-examined on the basis of new types of information obtained by actually inserting extremely fine glass electrodes within the soma, the axon, or the larger dendritic stems of individual neurons both outside and inside the central nervous system. The new techniques indicate that the spike discharge of the propagated nerve impulse occurs on only part of the neuron, and that other parts of the same neuron may, either during the resting state or during an axonic spike discharge, have their membrane in quite different states [6]. It has long been understood that every central neuron was anatomically different from all others, but it now appears that each one may at any given instant show a variety of membrane potentials in its different parts. From one millisecond to the next, each of these parts may be changing in its own way, depending on synaptic transmissions from the dozens or hundreds of axonic knobs sent toward it by many other neurons, as well as on feedback impulses from the discharge of its own axon. Phenomena of integra-

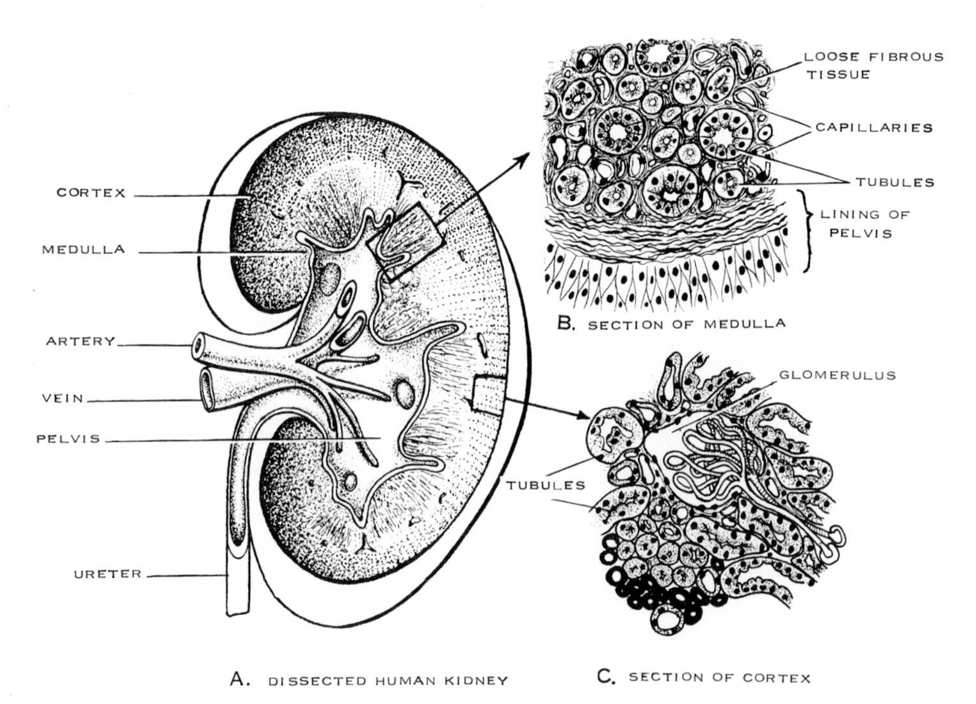

Fig. 4–16. Tissues in an organ: kidney.

tion, evaluation, selection, facilitation, inhibition, etc. apparently may occur within the single neuron before a spike discharge is initiated. This is a source of wry satisfaction to the new mechanists who hope to interpret the brain as a combination analog and digital computer, and who fully recognize the complexity of the wiring necessary to construct a machine which could do what the brain is known to do. The brain has enough circuits. The neurons do not fire each other off "like rows of falling dominoes." Each neuron is a computer in itself and the combinations of them serve as higher-level computation systems. The further exploration of these complexities is another of the great biological frontiers [3].

III. ORGANS

The term **organ** is very loosely defined: it is any part of the body which is anatomically distinct from others or has a special function. A good many organs contain within themselves smaller repeated tissue patterns or **organelles** such as the tubules or alveoli of glands, the liver lobules, the renal corpuscles and glomeruli of the kidney, the fibers of striated muscle, etc.

All organs, with trivial exceptions like the lens of the eye or the fingernails, are composed of more than one kind of tissue in a patterned mixture. For instance, the **kidney** (Fig. 4–16) is primarily composed of *epithelium* since it contains hundreds of branched and contorted urine-forming and urine-collecting tubules, but it also contains many *connective tissues.* It is full of blood carried in arteries and veins that have *muscular* as well as fibrous walls. Delicate fibrous tissue supports all these blood and urine vessels, and a tough capsule of similar tissue binds up the whole package, frequently including a good measure of fat or lymphoid tissue. Both sensory and motor *nerves* penetrate the capsule to supply the tubules and the blood vessels. Thus the kidney includes all four major types of tissue, and several minor types.

So does the **intestine** (Fig. 4–17). Its central cavity is lined by a richly developed *epithelium,* differentiated into a variety of kinds of cells and laid on in tiny fingerlike projections and macroscopic ridges and glandular infoldings. This is supported by a surrounding layer of loose soft *fibrous tissue* rich in blood and lymph vessels, and containing a web of delicate *nerve* fibers. Outside all this there are the circular and longitudinal layers of *smooth muscle,* each embedded in more *connective tissue* and supplied with its own characteristic pattern of blood vessels and nerves. Still farther outside comes a layer of tougher connective tissue which in turn is covered by the pavement-epithelium of the body cavity and mesenteries.

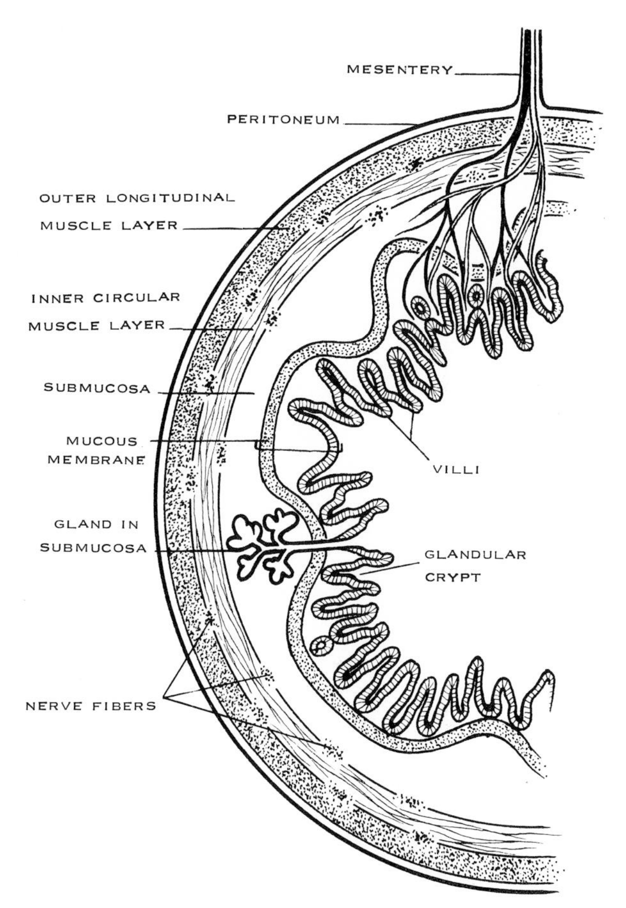

Fig. 4–17. Tissues in an organ: intestine.
(Adapted from Histology by Ham and Leeson, 4th edition, 1961, by permission of J. B. Lippincott Co.)

For another example, the **eye** is a special sense organ, but most of its parts are merely accessory

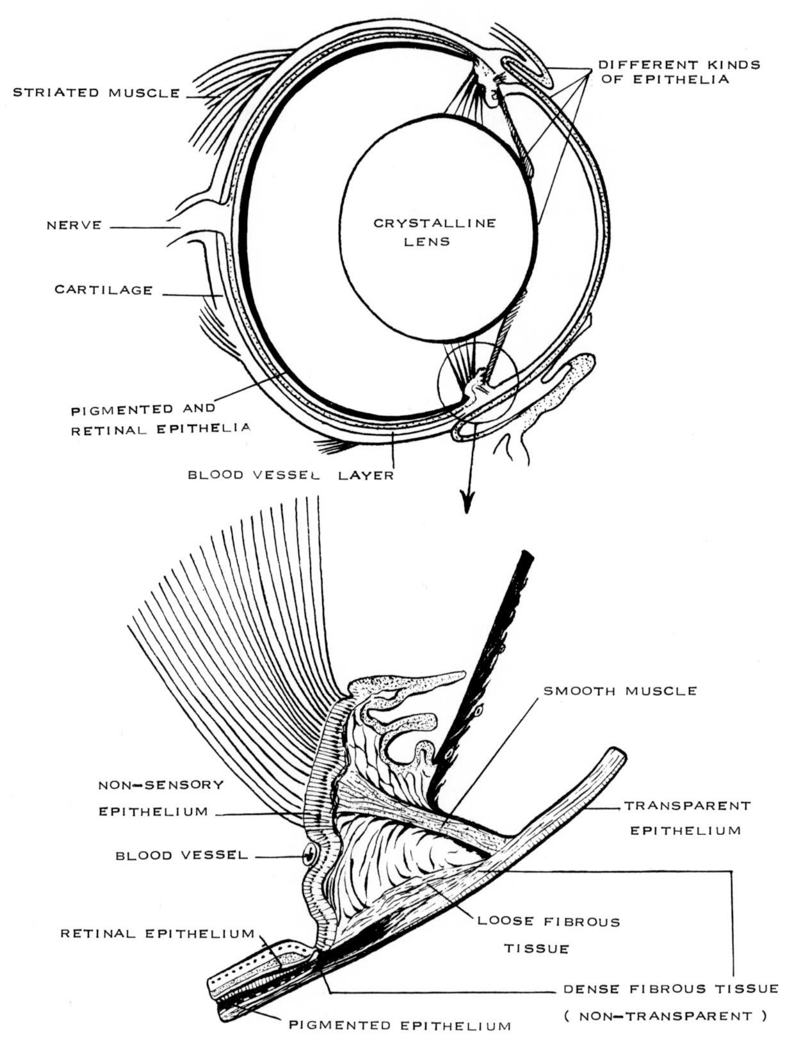

Fig. 4–18. Tissues in an organ: eye. *Upper:* Section of whole eye. *Lower:* Ciliary region, enlarged.
(After G. L. Walls, The Vertebrate Eye, 1942, by permission of Cranbrook Institute of Science.)

(cf. section of whole eye in Fig. 4–18 above, with details of ciliary region enlarged below). Its cornea contains epithelium, several layers of fibrous tissue, and nerves of ordinary skin sense. The inner and outer surfaces of the iris are lined by different kinds of epithelium, and between these lie fibrous connective tissue, blood vessels, blood, and smooth muscle. The retina contains a pigmented epithelium, two layers of neurons, a collection of supporting cells and a spray of blood vessels in addition to the special epithelium of sensory visual cells. The rest of the wall of the eyeball contains a variety of connective tissues including usually cartilage or bone or both, as well as blood vessels.

The **gonad** contains germinal epithelium, which is organized into follicles in the ovary (Fig. 4–19) and into seminiferous tubules or lobules in the testis (Fig. 4–20). These parts constitute the essential or functional elements characteristic of the organ and are distinguished as the **parenchyma** while the supporting framework

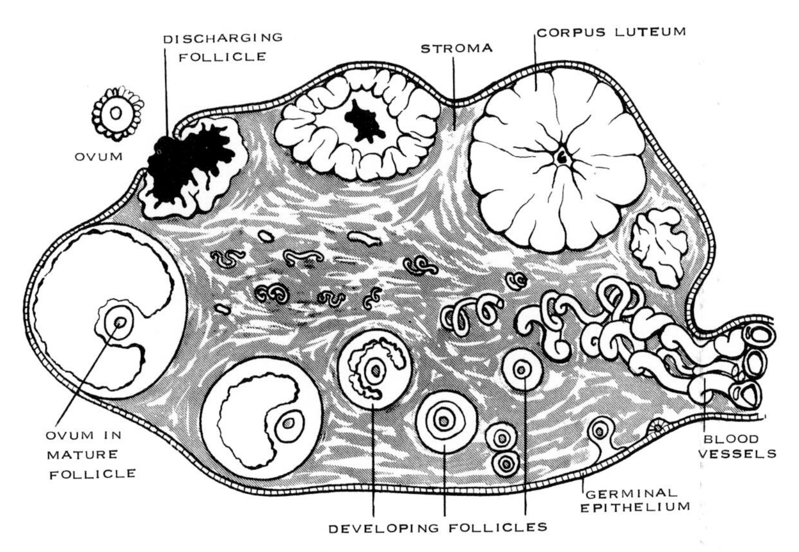

Fig. 4–19. Tissues in an organ: ovary.
(Redrawn from B. M. Patten, Foundations of Embryology, 1958, by permission of McGraw-Hill Book Co., Inc.)

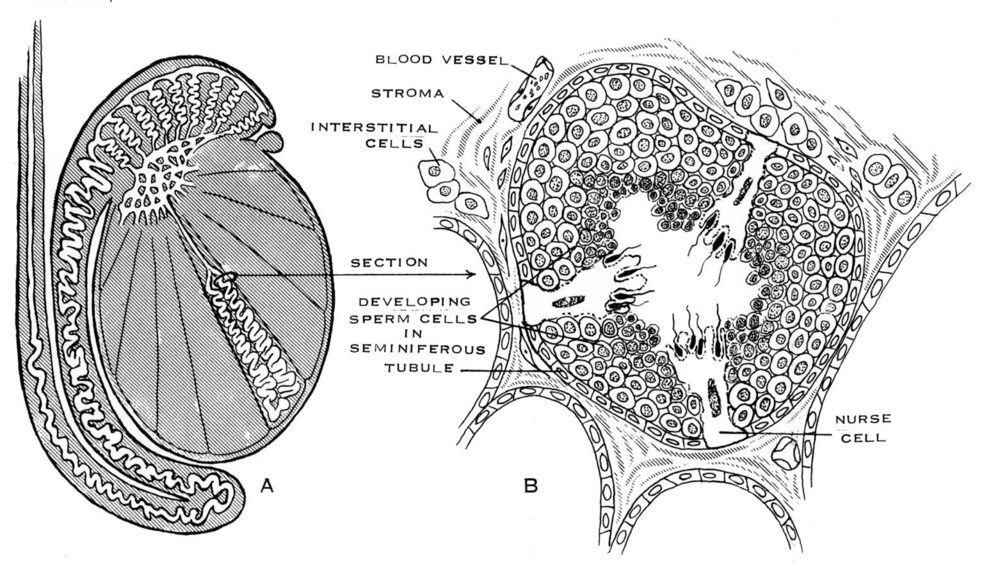

Fig. 4–20. Tissues in an organ: testis. A. Longitudinal section of whole testis and epididymis with one of the many seminiferous tubules indicated. B. Cross-section of one seminiferous tubule.

is known as the **stroma.** The latter consists of crisscrossing and interpenetrating fibrous tissues which embed not only the parenchyma but also arteries, veins, lymph vessels, nerves, and small patches of endocrine gland tissue. The whole organ is wrapped in a tough coat of connective tissue and an epithelium derived from the lining of the body cavity.

IV. MORE ANALYTICAL CONSIDERATIONS

It may be deduced from these few examples of the finer structure of organs that a part of the process of organogenesis is the approach and interpenetration of groups of cells from different sources, as well as the simultaneous differentiation of very different sorts of cells in close proximity to each other. Different combinations from the basic catalog of tissues produce a great many highly individualized local patterns, and homologies can be recognized in these groupings also. The research of past generations has built a library of knowledge as to *what* happens, but it is mostly a task for the future to determine *why* it happens, and under what guidance and restraint. This is the field of *analytical embryology*, some of whose problems and preliminary interpretations are presented in Part III, Chapter 10.

The differentiating cells, tissues and organs are clearly under a precise set of controls, otherwise there would be nothing predictable about ontogeny and there would be no such thing as a normal anatomy for each species. Abundant evidence comes from the field of genetics that the individual's inherited genes continually control development by acting within the cells. There are also local and temporary controls that come from outside the cells, as revealed by experimental manipulation of embryos.

The importance of these controls is illustrated by what happens when cells escape them, and begin, one might say, to live outside the law. Instead of remaining subordinated in the usual arrangements and numbers seen in normal anatomy, such cells multiply at excessive rates and pile up in disorderly masses called tumors. Worse, they may become actively migratory and aggressive, invading new regions, interrupting normal functions and bringing about a general breakdown. They are then defined as cancers. We know what happens when these cells escape from control. Unfortunately, we do not know what the controls are, and how they operate.

More evidence of supracellular controls that guide and limit normal development is seen in the phenomenon of **regeneration.** Certain small tunicates (for instance *Clavelina,* Fig. 2–1) may be cut into dozens or even hundreds of pieces, and the cells of each piece will reorganize themselves more or less successfully into a small individual which can then grow to normal size and complete anatomy. If the eye of a salamander is removed, a whole new one may grow back from the scrap that remains, and reach normal size and structure. Salamanders can also regenerate whole limbs.

In most vertebrates the power of regeneration is sharply limited, being seen only in a few tissues such as epithelium and bone, and otherwise restricted to its preliminary stages, i.e., to wound healing. Nevertheless, where regeneration occurs at all, it demonstrates the presence of certain reserve cells in the tissues, which can be mobilized and guided through an unprecedented development, the end result of which is the restoration of a missing part Since this regenerative development is faster than the growth and differentiation going on elsewhere in the body, cells have either recovered their embryonic vigor by unknown means, or else they have been released from some sort of normal restraint, the nature of which is unknown. Since regeneration stops at or before the time when the full size of the normal organ is reached, the embryonic vigor is only temporarily bestowed on, or released in, the cells in question. What starts or stops the process, or guides it, is completely unknown.

This chapter began with a description of types of tissues and structurally specialized cells, and the organ patterns in which they are found. It ends with the comment that we do not know why these cells become structurally different or why they group themselves as they do in the body. In fact, the general statement may be made that all the known and described aspects of morphology stand as a catalog of phenomena which still have to be analyzed in terms of the living processes that bring them into existence. For all that its descriptive phase is well advanced, the science of morphology is still very young.

REFERENCES

1. King, T. J., and R. Briggs, 1956. *Cold Spring Harbor Symposia Quant. Biol.* 21: 271.

2. Briggs, R., and T. J. King, 1960. *Develop. Biol.* 2: 252.

3. Gurdon, J. B. 1962. *Develop. Biol.* 5: 68. Also Moore, J., 1960. *Develop. Biol.* 2: 535.

4. Paley, S. L. (ed.), 1958. *Frontiers in cytology.* Yale University Press, New Haven, Conn. A series of lectures on the vistas opened by electron microscope work.

5. Bodian, D., 1962. *Science* 137: 323.

6. Bullock, T. H., 1962. *Am. Zoologist* 2: 97.

5

Anatomy of the Vertebrate Pharyngula

In the last chapter, certain cellular differentiations, the organization of cells into certain types of tissues, and the combinations of these in clearly homologous organs were described as "universal elements" in the morphology of vertebrates. To these elements we now add the characteristic *pattern of organs* which emerges in the members of the group when they reach the pharyngula stage of development. The **pharyngula** has been defined as a stage beyond the gastrula and the neurula, in which the walls of the pharynx have become carved up into a relatively simple series of paired segments alternating with pharyngeal clefts or grooves.

All vertebrate embryos at this stage have acquired a similar and nearly complete set of organs, similarly arranged, which constitutes the **basic pattern of vertebrate anatomy.** With minor exceptions these structures have not yet acquired the special anatomical characters by which species, families, or even orders of vertebrates may be told apart, and they represent the common anatomical heritage of the phylum in as simple a state as it is possible to find.

For the beginner in vertebrate morphology, the similar organs and similar arrangements of the pharyngula may conveniently serve as an introduction to the complexities of both comparative embryology and comparative anatomy. The prepharyngular development of the several classes of vertebrates is full of contrasts, difficult to analyze in terms of observable structures, and it makes sense only if the heterogeneous processes are understood as pointing toward the anatomy of the pharyngula as their goal. Beyond the pharyngula stage the basic set of similar organs differentiate along various lines of specialization in the different classes, new organs are added to the list within certain taxonomic groups and not in others, and some spectacular rearrangements of structure take place in the body. The resulting bold contrasts in adult anatomy can be most easily understood if they are seen to have developed from the relatively standardized arrangements of the pharyngula as a *point of departure.*

In the development of an individual, the pharyngula stage cannot be defined as a particular moment, it is rather a certain period during which structure is rapidly emerging and evolving. In comparing a series of vertebrates at this stage, one can recognize the "similar organs, similarly arranged," but no two specimens are exactly alike. In fact they present some quite obvious differences, and to abstract from them a basic pattern of vertebrate anatomy requires that certain integral parts of each must be left behind.

The vertebrate pharyngula, as an abstract concept, is no more real than *the typical vertebrate,* or *the gene* or *the atom* or any other concept invented by science for the purpose of communicating experience. One uses such terms because they are useful.

Some of these actual pharyngulas have a tailfin and some do not. Those which are tetrapods have lung buds, the fish pharyngulas lack them. They all have a liver, to mention an organ at random, but the livers of fishes, birds and mammals are interestingly different in detail even at the pharyngula stage. Arteries can be compared easily but there is little uniformity in the veins. Most conspicuously, the circumstances and needs for respiration, nutrition, and excretion at this stage have been met by a good many structures of a temporary nature, aptly referred to as scaffolding tissues, which are in bold contrast in the different classes of vertebrates.

Such differences will be mentioned briefly in this chapter and passed over lightly in the interest of bringing out what is relatively standardized. The difference between this abstracted basic anatomy and the biological wholeness of the embryo will be clear to the student as he examines pharyngulas in the laboratory. The fact is that evolution has taken place at the pharyngula stage just as it has at the early embryonic and the adult stage in the different stocks of vertebrates. The usefulness of an introductory examination of pharyngulas is that they show much more extensive structural similarities to each other than their precursor stages do, and if one disregards the temporary scaffolding, which leaves no mark on adult anatomy, they show far less difference from one another than later stages do.

I. ANATOMY OF THE PHARYNGULA

A. Central Nervous System

The **brain** and **spinal cord** occupy the dorsal midline of the pharyngula (Fig. 5–1). They are a continuous hollow tube, of which the anterior part is conspicuously enlarged in three masses, the **forebrain, midbrain,** and **hindbrain,** containing expansions of the central canal called ventricles. The forebrain and midbrain have thick roofs, but that of the hindbrain is extremely thin, ex-

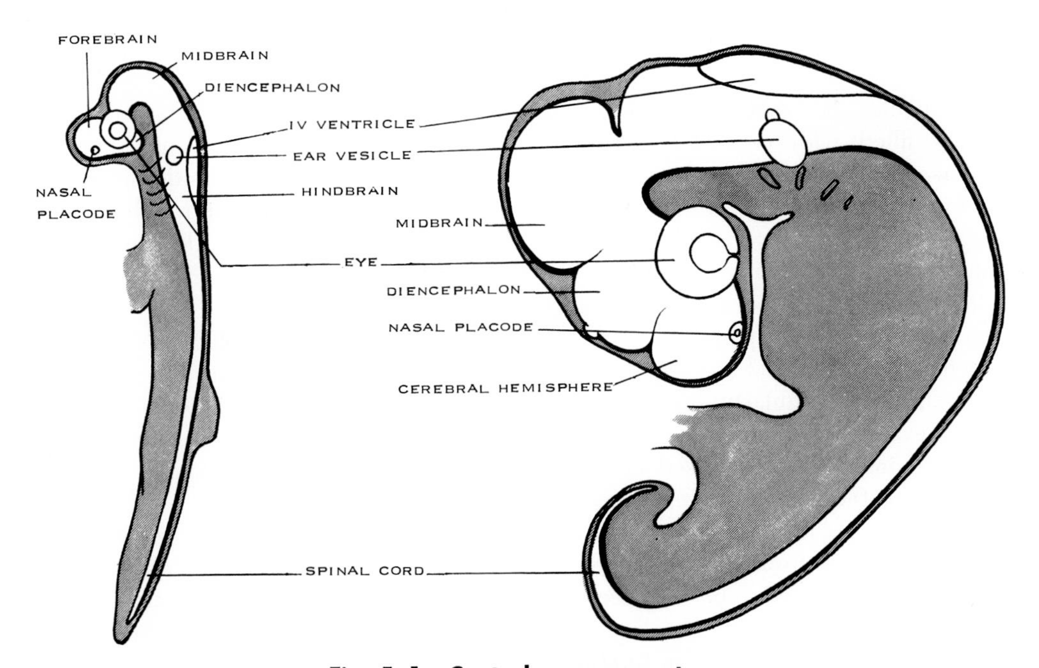

Fig. 5–1. Central nervous system.

(Chick modified from B. M. Patten, Early Embryology of the Chick, 3d edition, 1929, by permission of McGraw-Hill Book Co., Inc. Shark after R. E. Scammon, Keibel's Normentafeln, Vol. 12, 1911, by permission of Gustav Fischer Verlag.)

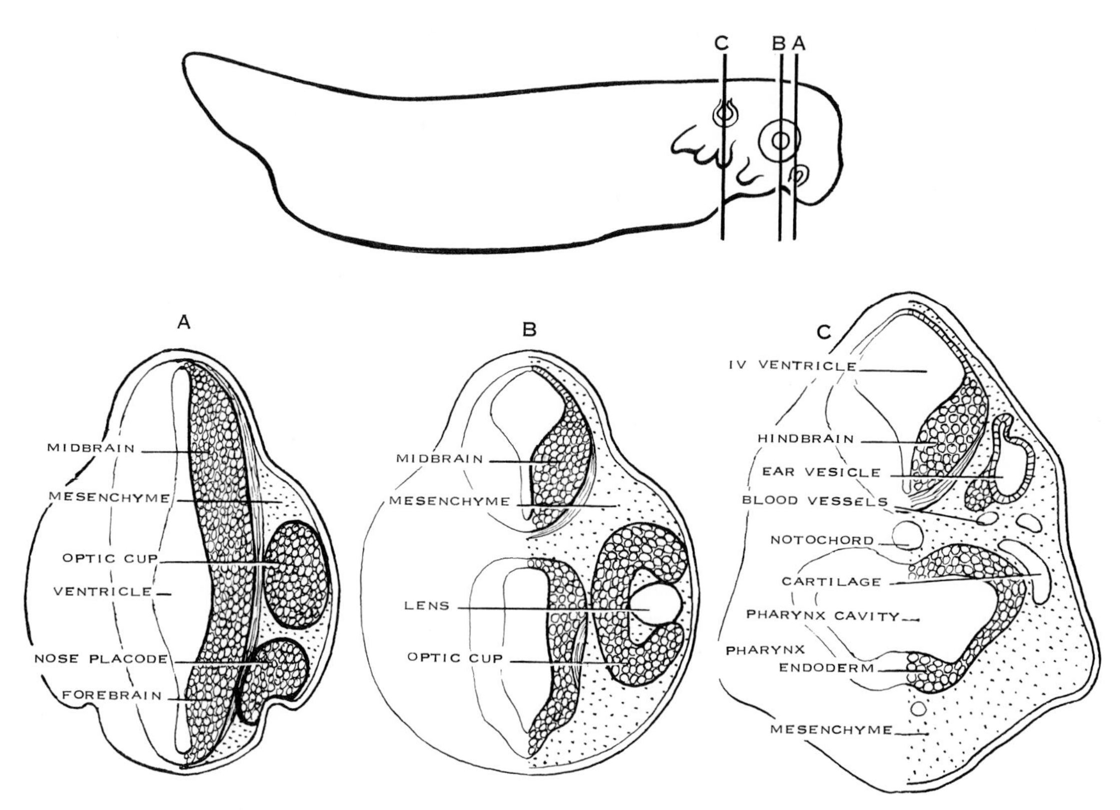

Fig. 5–2. Head anatomy of the amblystoma pharyngula.

posing a triangular **IV ventricle** within. The ventricles are filled with cerebro-spinal fluid.

There is a cephalic flexure of about 90° between the forebrain and the midbrain, the forebrain being bent ventrad so that the midbrain may actually appear at the front end of the animal. Other flexures may occur in the axis of the central nervous system, particularly in the amniotes, where it is C-shaped or even spiral.

The forebrain vesicle regularly shows a pair of stalked lateral expansions, the **optic vesicles,** into which the overlying skin has pressed epithelial spheres. These are the anlagen of the **eyes** and their **lenses** (Fig. 5–2). There may also be anterolateral expansions from the forebrain, especially in amniotes, destined to become **cerebral hemispheres.**

The midbrain, by contrast with the forebrain, is rounded and simple in appearance. The hindbrain has its thick walls laid open like the pages of an open book, enclosing the IV Ventricle.

Microscopic sections of the central nervous system show a central or ventricular accumulation of cell bodies (the **mantle layer**) and a peripheral layer of axonic outgrowths (the **marginal layer**), the thickness of the latter varying in different parts.

B. Notochord and Dorsal Aorta

Immediately ventral to the central nervous system in the sagittal plane, running from the level of the midbrain to the end of the tail, is a turgid elastic rod of peculiar vacuolated tissue, the **notochord** (Fig. 5–3). Posteriorly it dwindles to an indistinct end, just where the spinal cord does. Anteriorly it maintains its strength nearly to the forebrain, but generally shows a narrowing and buckling at its tip. In the anamniotes the notochord rivals the spinal cord in diameter. In amniotes it is tiny and buried in abundant mesenchyme tissue.

Immediately ventral to the trunk section of the

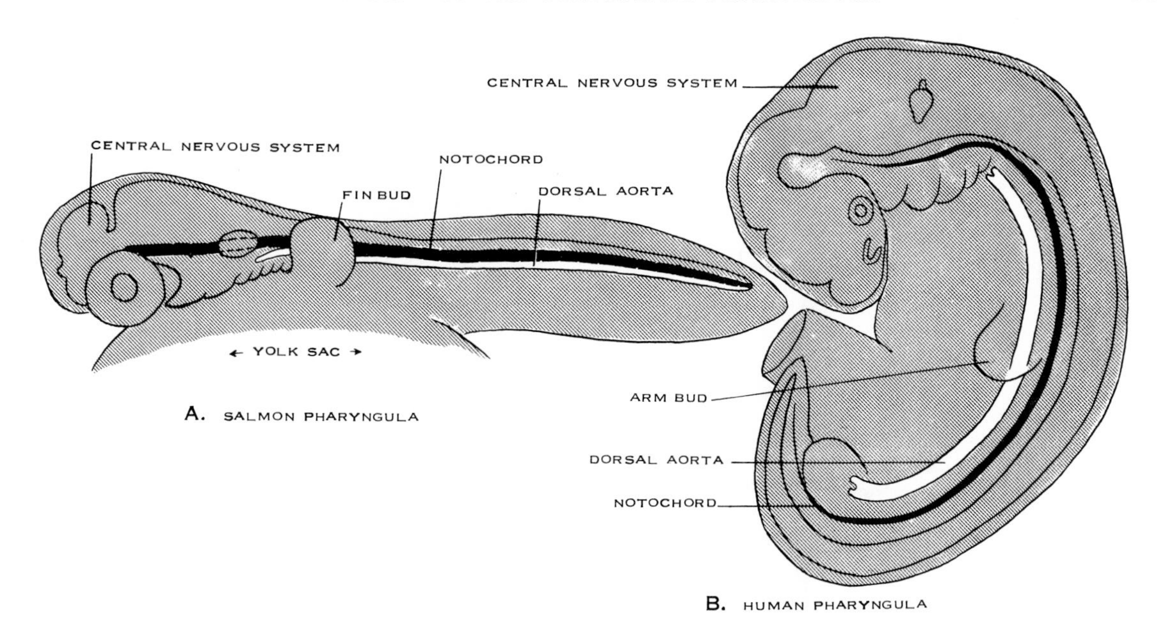

Fig. 5–3. Notochord and dorsal aorta.

notochord lies the **dorsal aorta,** which is created by the anterior confluence of some paired arteries dorsal to the pharynx (the aortic arches, described later), and carries blood toward the tail, distributing through many branches to all parts of the trunk.

C. Endodermal Tube and Associated Structures

Ventral to the central nervous system, notochord, and dorsal aorta, and like them in the midsagittal plane, lies the **alimentary canal** (Fig. 5–4). It is lined by endoderm on the inside and coated with mesodermal cells on the outside. Its bulk and disposition vary according to the amount and location of the embryonic yolk supply, the differences being referable to temporary scaffolding (details in Chapter 11).

Anteriorly, the alimentary canal is (or, in amphibian pharyngulas, is about to be) wide open to the outside through a subterminal **mouth.** In the head region it is considerably expanded

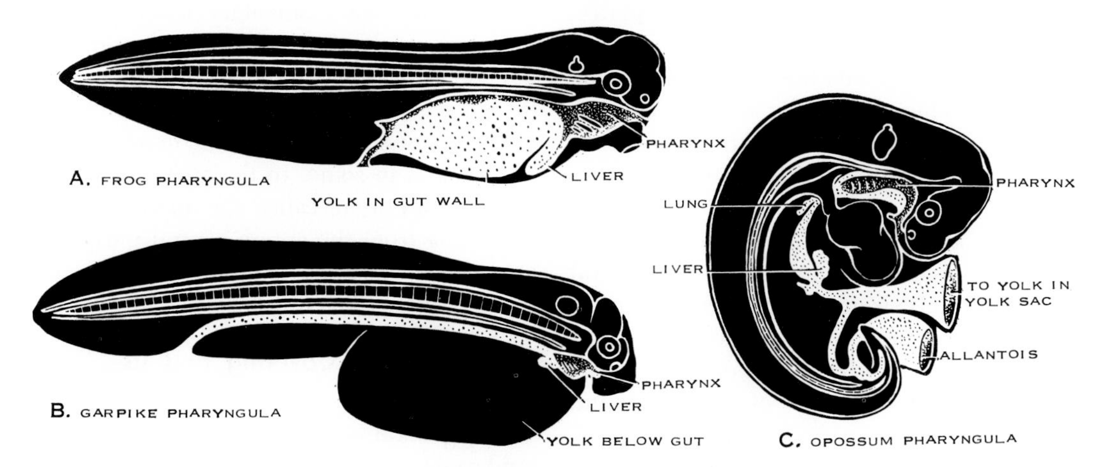

Fig. 5–4. Intestine.
(Opossum after E. McCrady, 1938.)

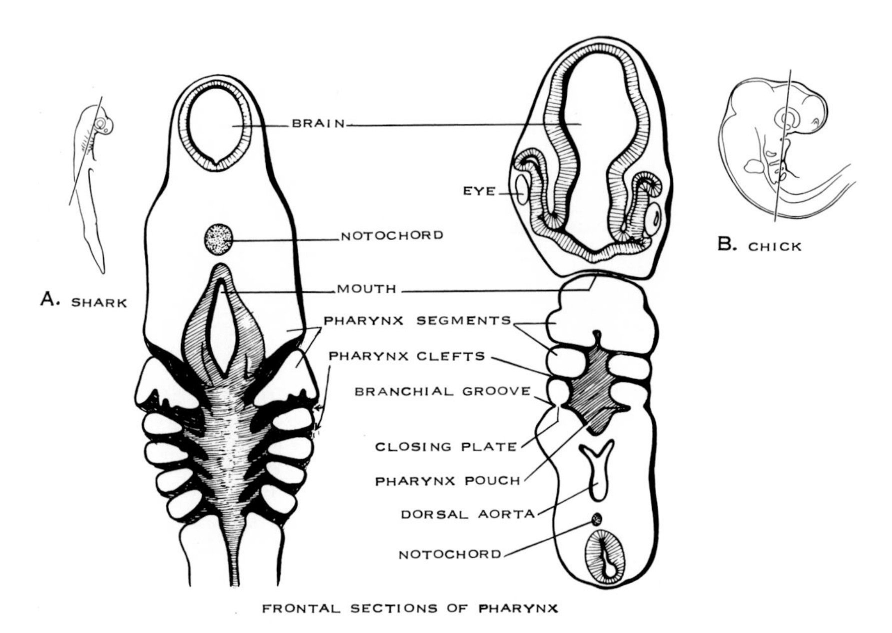

Fig. 5–5. Frontal sections of pharynx.
(Acanthias section after J. S. Kingsley, Comparative Anatomy of Vertebrates, 1912, by permission of McGraw-Hill Book Co., Inc.)

into a dorsoventrally flattened chamber, the **pharynx,** whose lateral walls are carved into a succession of thick pillars, the **pharynx segments,** by actual or virtual **pharyngeal pouches** (Fig. 5–5). These pouches are extensions of the endoderm-lined pharynx cavity outward toward the ectoderm, which may be grooved inward to meet them. Where the endoderm and ectoderm have met by such matching movements, they fuse together to form thin translucent **closing plates.** At the pharyngula stage some of the closing plates have usually broken through, forming **pharyngeal clefts.** These bilaterally symmetrical successions of simple pharynx segments and pouches or clefts have suggested the name for the pharyngula stage.

Posteriorly, the pharynx cavity narrows down sharply and passes over into that of the general intestine. In tetrapods and lungfishes, but not in other vertebrates, there is an area of midventral outgrowth from the posterior end of the pharynx which constitutes the anlage of the **lungs** and their accessories.

Somewhat farther back the rudiments of the **liver,** the **gallbladder** and the **pancreas** are clustered about the intestinal tube, from which they have sprouted (Fig. 5–6). The liver is an irregularly shaped collection of cords or plates of glandular cells interbraided with venous blood channels.

Beyond this level, the **intestine** is variously complicated by yolk relations in most vertebrates (see pages 190–192), but at its posterior end it bends suddenly ventrad. Here there regularly develop at least momentary junctions between the alimentary tube and a pair of primitive kidney ducts forming a common chamber called the **cloaca.** This relationship is promptly wiped out by new specializations in many vertebrates but persists in some. In the amniotes, a balloon-like scaffold organ called the **allantois** opens out by a tube from the antero-ventral portion of the cloaca and serves as a respiratory and excretory organ. Nothing like it is known in any anamniote.

D. Ectodermal Covering and Its Derivatives

The general ectoderm is differentiated into an **epidermis,** and inside this layer the mesenchyme is collecting in preparation for forming the **der-**

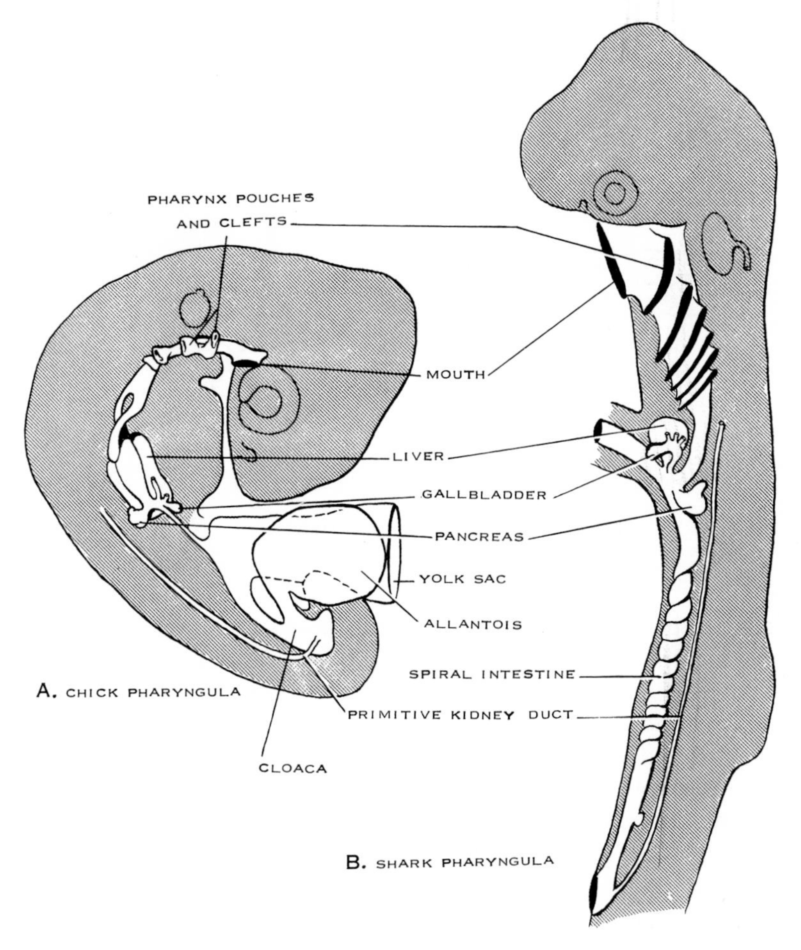

Fig. 5–6. Intestinal derivatives, kidney duct, and cloaca.
(Chick modified from B. M. Patten, Early Embryology of the Chick, 4th edition, 1951, by permission of McGraw-Hill Book Co., Inc. Shark after R. E. Scammon, Keibel's Normentafeln, Vol. 12, 1911, by permission of Gustav Fischer Verlag.)

mis layer of the definitive skin. Certain organs, for instance the lenses of the eyes (Fig. 5–2 B), are represented by anlagen in the form of thickenings or **placodes** in the ectoderm. The **olfactory organs** (Fig. 5–2 A) appear as thick placodes grouped about a pair of superficial pits, their inner surfaces pressed against the anterior walls of the forebrain. Between them in the midline, sandwiched between the roof of the mouth and the base of the forebrain, lies the **hypophysis** (Fig. 9–7), one of the principal components of the future pituitary gland. A pair of epithelial sacs, the **otic vesicles** (Fig. 5–2 C) fit against the sides of the hindbrain at its anterior end. They are derived from placodes, and are the anlagen of the **inner ears.** Smaller sets of placodes above the pharynx segments and alongside the hindbrain contribute to the cranial nerve ganglia.

E. Mesodermal Somites

Conspicuous mesodermal blocks, the **somites,** lie in a fairly uniform series on each side, lateral to the notochord and reaching up dorsally on either side of the spinal cord (Fig. 5–7). As seen in transverse sections the somites show thick central portions, the **myotomes** or principal muscle-forming structures; and medioventral portions with less well defined boundaries, the **sclerotomes,** which are primarily concerned with formation of parts of the skeleton. Mesenchyme

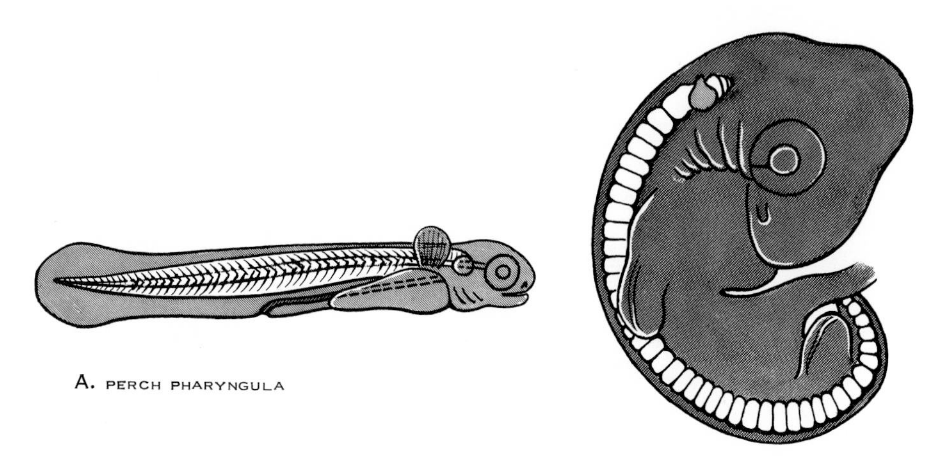

Fig. 5–7. Somites.
(Lizard after K. Peter, 1904.)

is dispersed in considerable quantities from the sclerotomes, enveloping the notochord and the central nervous system.

Trunk myotomes near the anterior end of the series are beginning to send thin sprouts called **muscle processes** ventrolaterally along the flanks, inside the dermal mesenchyme that lines the surface ectoderm. The somite series can be traced on each side almost to the tip of the tail in anamniotes, and at least into the tail in the amniotes. Anteriorly it can be traced forward to the ear vesicle.

F. Spinal Nerves

Wedged in between the spinal cord and the myotomes on each side of the trunk lie series of **spinal ganglia** (Fig. 5–8). They are embedded in mesenchyme and consist of groups of neuro-

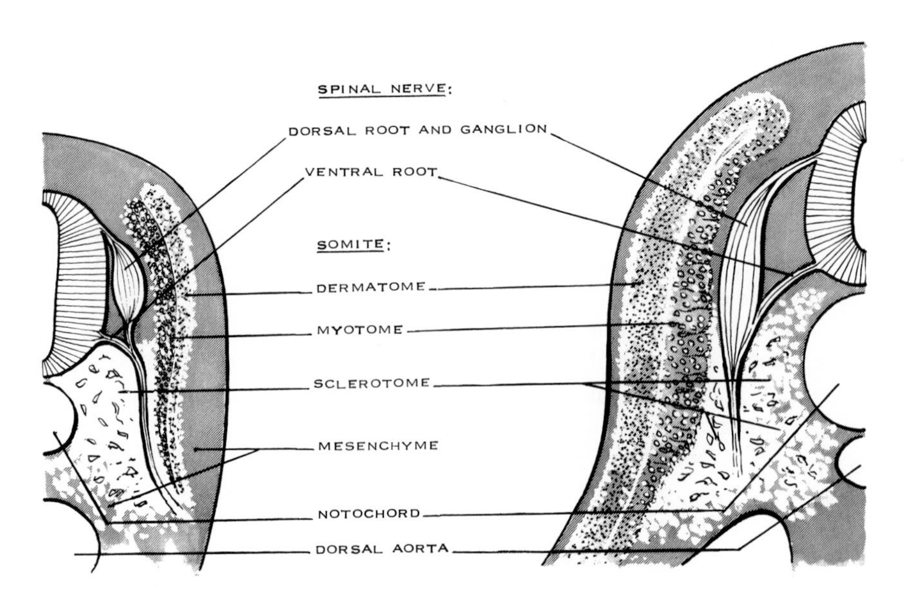

Fig 5–8. Somites and spinal nerves.
(Electric ray after F. Maurer, 1906.)

blasts that are differentiating into sensory neurons. The segmental series of ganglia fades out in the tail, and is broken off anteriorly at about the junction of head and trunk. Some of the more anterior ganglia have already sent nerve processes out toward the myotomes, and segmental groups of neurons are also growing out from the spinal cord in company with them, skirting the ventral borders of the ganglia. The neurons arising from the ganglia are *sensory*, the ones arising from the spinal cord are *motor*. The groups of sensory and motor neurons constitute a segmental series of spinal nerves on each side. The process of assembly of spinal nerves from these components is usually incomplete at posterior trunk and tail levels of the pharyngula stage.

G. The Pharynx Segments

Vertebrates always show the characteristic subdivision of the lateroventral pharynx walls into segments, but with variations in number and size. The usual number of pairs is six, but from seven to nine segments occur in various gnathostome fishes. The lampreys have nine pairs, and some species of hagfishes have as many as seventeen pairs.

There is also variation in the degree to which the endodermal pouches set them apart (Fig. 5–9). The pharyngulas of sharks and lampreys have such wide pharyngeal clefts * that one can look through the series of one side, across the pharynx cavity and out the series on the other side. At the other extreme, in amphibia and some teleosts, only closing plates are present and the clefts are opened up much later.

In amniotes the central nervous system undergoes a strong cervical flexure so that the more posterior pharynx segments are pinched into a small triangle between this and the precociously developed heart, and their endodermal pouches may not even be able to reach the ectoderm to form closing plates. However, clefts do open between several of the more anterior segments in the series.

Comparable elements enter into the structure of all the pharynx segments (Fig. 5–10). Each is covered on the inside by endoderm and on the outside by ectoderm, and is limited anteriorly

* Pharyngeal clefts are often called "gill slits," but if you use this term you should realize the full extent of its inappropriateness. In half the vertebrates none of the clefts ever bear gills, and in the other half only some of the posterior ones do. No true internal gills are present at the pharyngula stage in any vertebrate.

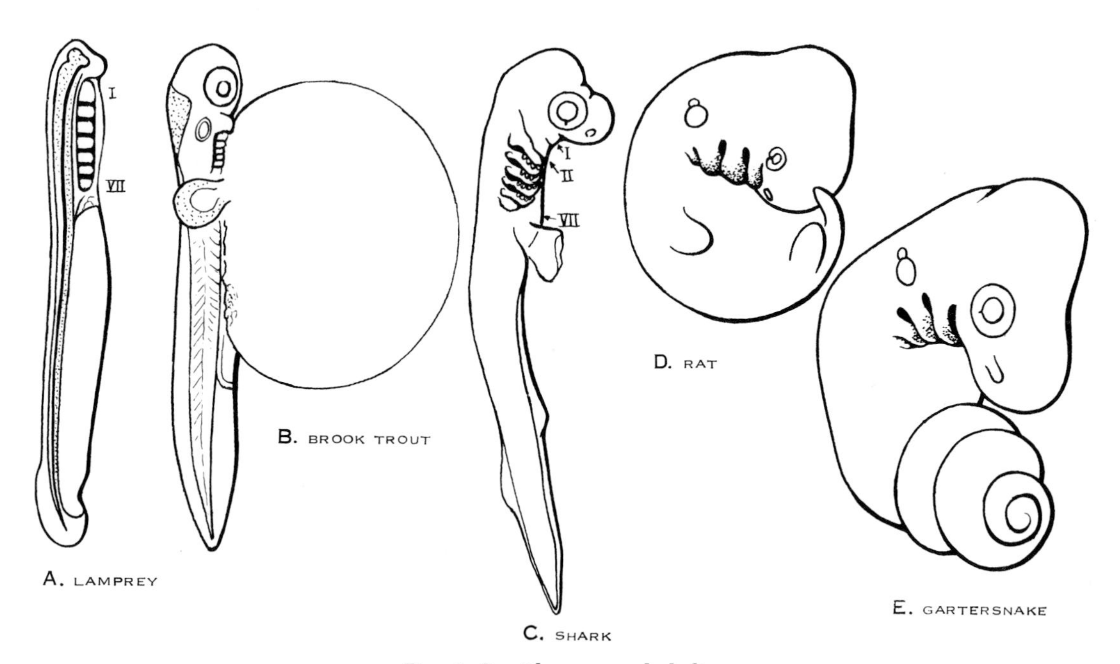

Fig. 5–9. Pharyngeal clefts.

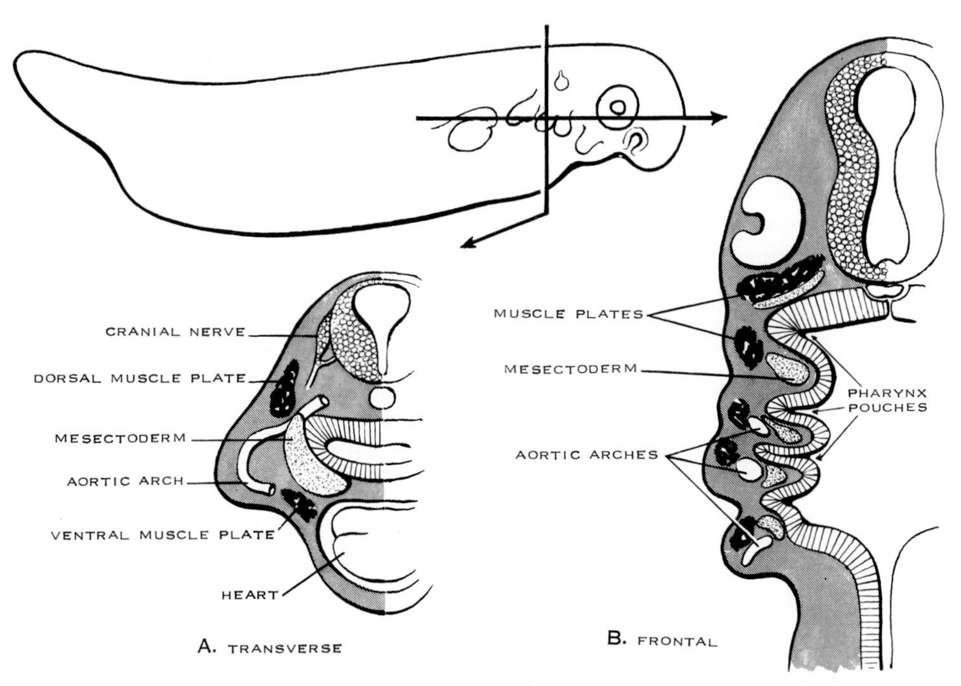

Fig. 5–10. Components of pharynx segments in the amblystoma.

and posteriorly by a closing plate or pharynx cleft, except that the anterior limit of the first one is the corner of the mouth, and the last one grades into mesenchyme posteriorly.

Inside these boundaries, each well-developed pharynx segment contains a **muscle plate,** a band of mesoderm which will form jaw, face, or gill muscles, and inside this lies an **aortic arch,** designed to carry blood dorsad from the heart to the dorsal aorta. Alongside the aortic arch a **nerve** descends from the hindbrain. A strip of **mesectoderm** lies internal to all these, between them and the endoderm. It is ectoderm-derived mesenchyme, much of which will form skeletal parts.

Differences in the timing of the development of parts of the head introduce some variations into the pattern just described. Some fish pharyngulas show the pharynx-segment skeleton already well differentiated, whereas this process has hardly begun in some amniote pharyngulas. Also, not uncommonly, the aortic arches at the anterior end of the series may disappear before those at the posterior end begin to carry blood. These variations exist but are discounted for present purposes.

The first pharynx segment on each side is called the **mandibular segment** since the skeleton which will be formed in it is the mandibular cartilage or primordial lower jaw. Except in the agnathous fishes, part of the mandibular segment overflows dorsoanteriorly below the eye region as a bulge called the **maxillary process.** (Most vertebrates later develop maxillary bones as part of the upper jaw apparatus.)

The second pharynx segment is called the **hyoid segment** since its skeleton-forming tissue will produce the tongue-supporting **hyoid arch,** again excepting the agnatha. The third pharynx segment, and the others posterior to it, are often called **branchial segments,** since these are the ones out of which gills may later be produced in fishes.

Four **cranial nerves** arise on each side of the hindbrain to supply the six or more pharynx segments (Fig. 5-11). They will later be analyzed as the **mixed** cranial nerves (i.e., both sensory and motor in function) of the **visceral**

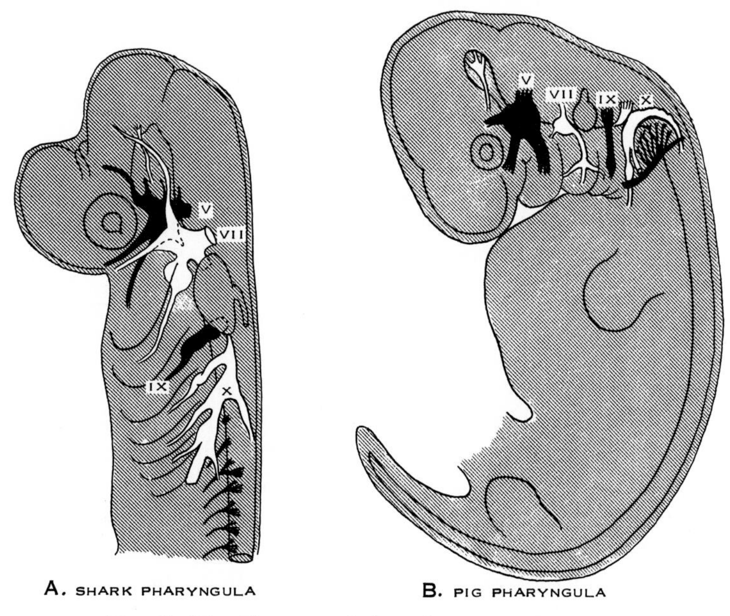

Fig. 5–11. Nerves of the pharynx segments.
(Shark after R. E. Scammon, Keibel's Normentafeln, Vol. 12, 1911, by permission of Gustav Fischer Verlag.)

series. (The pharynx, as part of the alimentary canal, may be considered as a visceral structure.)

The mandibular segment is served by the **trigeminal** or V cranial nerve.

The hyoid segment is served by the **facial** or VII cranial nerve.

The first branchial segment is served by the **glossopharyngeal** or IX cranial nerve.

The remaining segments are all served by the compound **vagus** or X cranial nerve, which sends an individual branch down into each of them, at least in the anamniotes.

The topographical relations of these structures at the pharyngula stage are the key to innumerable puzzling arrangements that develop later. It should be noted that all the pharynx segments lie below the brain level, and that the otic vesicle lies at the anterior limit of the outer wall of the hindbrain.

The V and VII cranial nerves pass outward to their respective segments anterior to the otic vesicle, and may therefore be called the **pre-otic visceral nerves,** while the IX and X nerves are **post-otic** in position But while the hyoid segment receives a pre-otic nerve, its own position is almost exactly ventral to the otic vesicle. In fact, the skeleton that is developed in the hyoid segment comes regularly into relationship with the capsule of skeleton that later forms around the otic vesicle, and this contact is exploited in several different ways in different classes of vertebrates. Thus the anatomy of the fairly standardized pharyngula provides a clue to the homology of some highly divergent specializations in comparative anatomy.

The branchial segments are supplied by post-otic nerves and are clearly post-otic in position at the pharyngula stage.

The pharyngeal cleft which divides the mandibular from the hyoid segment (or the endodermal pharyngeal pouch if it does not open through) is given the name **hyomandibular.** The cleft or pouch between the second and third segments is the **hyobranchial.** More posterior ones are called **branchial** clefts or pouches.

H. Circulatory System

The **heart** is a head organ, lying below and between the more posterior pharynx segments. It is actively beating at the pharyngula stage, and **red blood** is coursing out to the arterial system from it, thence to pass through capillaries into the veins and so back to the heart. The pulsating of the heart is facilitated by its location in a **pericardial cavity.**

The heart is essentially a muscular tube, thrown into an asymmetrical sigmoid coil, with four unequal-sized chambers bulging from it (Fig. 5–12). These are named, in order from the receiving to the discharging end, the **sinus venosus,** the **atrium,** the **ventricle,** and the **bulbus cordis.** The bulbus cordis of amniote pharyngulas, tapering down as it approaches the anterior limit of the pericardial cavity, divides immediately outside the cavity into the roots of the **aortic arches,** which fan out like the legs of a spider, each toward its own pharynx segment. In the anamniotes, the division of the aortic arches is ofen not so abrupt, so that an arterial trunk intervenes between them and the bulbus cordis, called the **truncus arteriosus** or **ventral aorta.**

Directly or indirectly, the blood stream is divided into six pairs of aortic arches in most vertebrates, one arch entering each of the first six pharynx segments on each side (Fig. 5–13). The bony fishes, which generally have a seventh pair of segments (5th branchial), only have aortic arches in the first six. Sharks and cyclostomes have more.

The successive pairs of aortic arches are not brought into function simultaneously but in an anteroposterior succession during development. This establishment wave is followed by a wave of modifications and specializations which will be described in Chapter 17 of Part IV. In the pharyngulas of birds and mammals, aortic arches I and II (in the mandibular and hyoid segments)

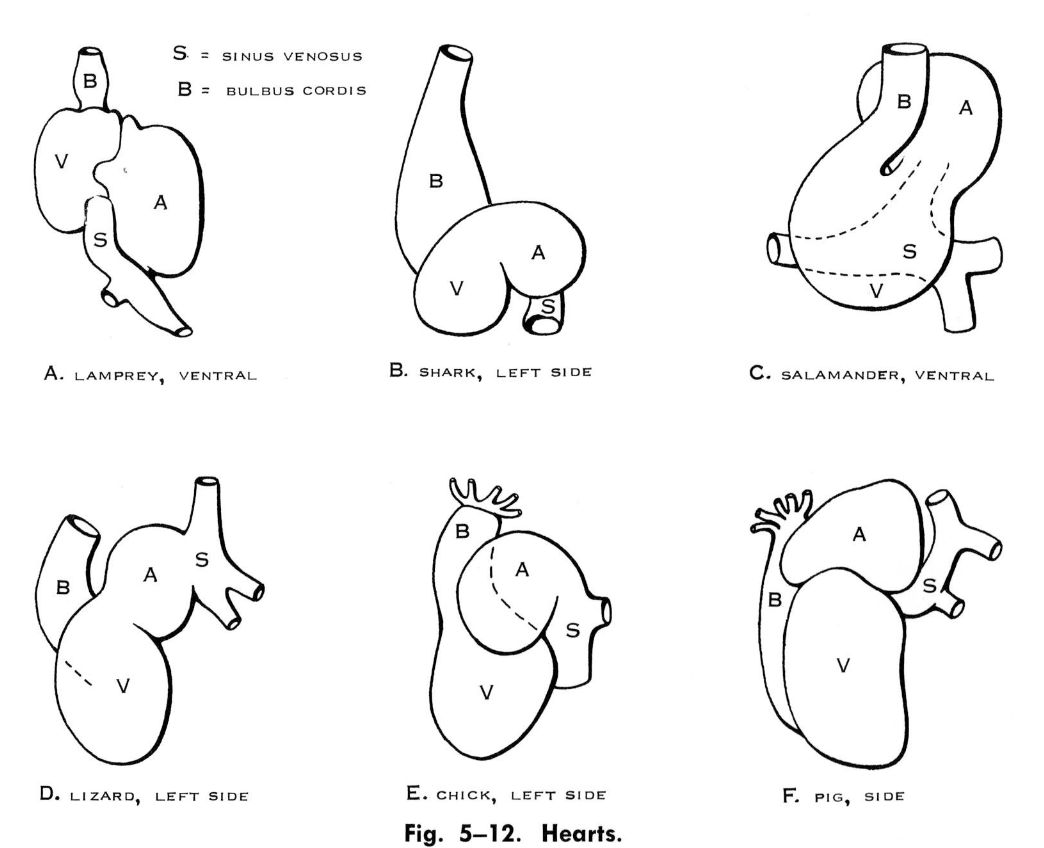

Fig. 5–12. Hearts.

(Lamprey after J. F. Daniels, 1935. Shark, salamander, and lizard after Hochstetter, 1906. Pig after B. M. Patten, Embryology of the Pig, 3d edition, 1948, by permission of McGraw-Hill Book Co., Inc.)

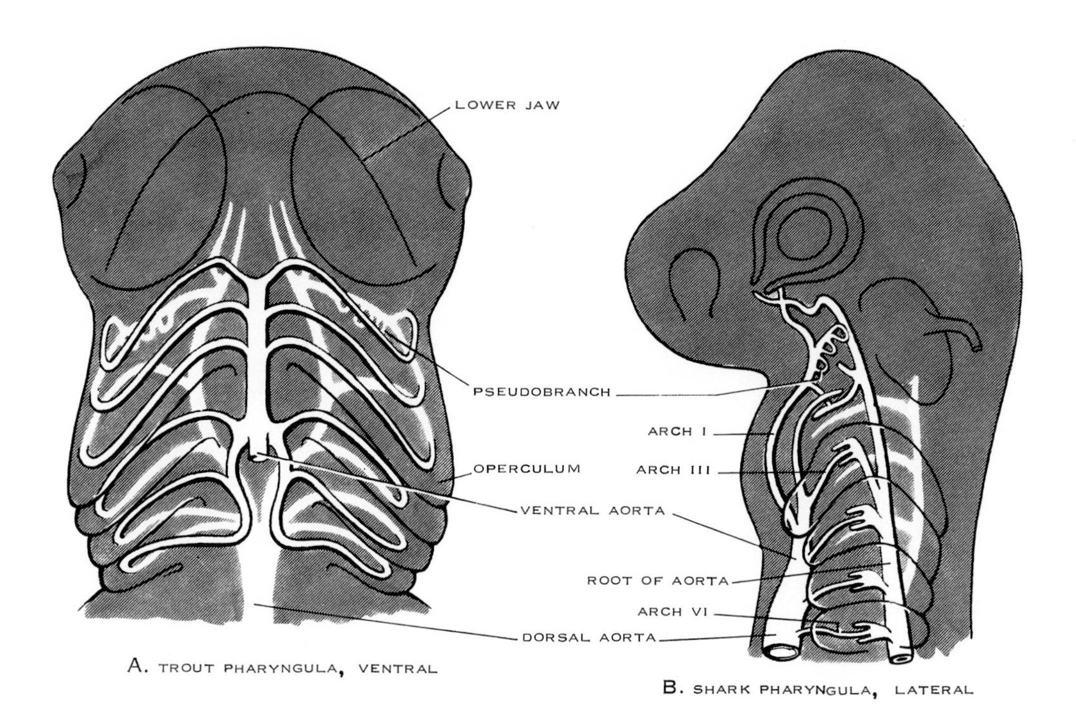

A. TROUT PHARYNGULA, VENTRAL

B. SHARK PHARYNGULA, LATERAL

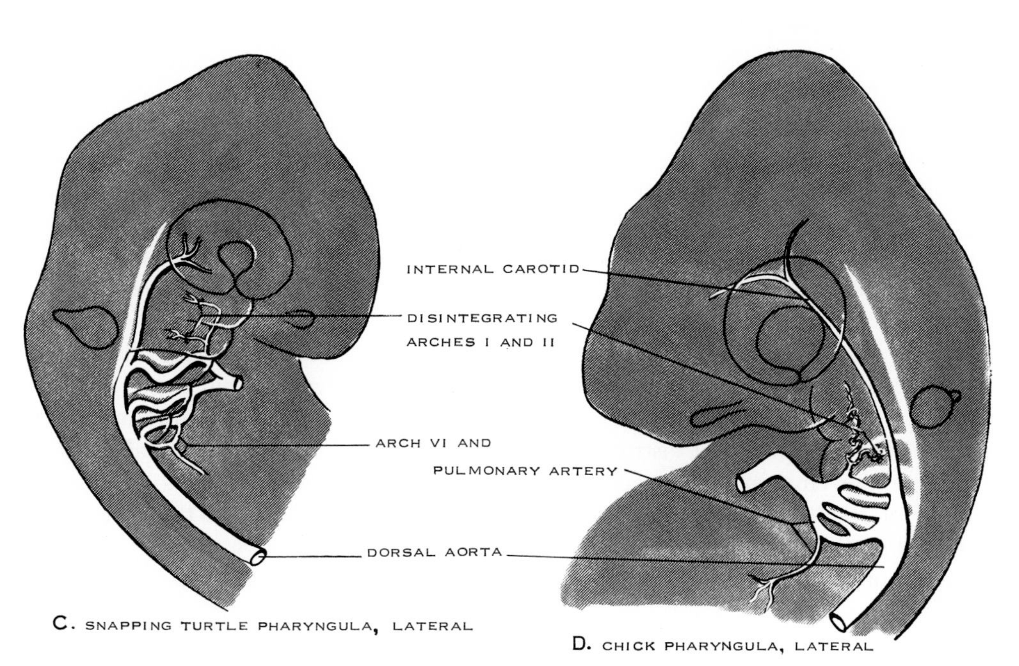

C. SNAPPING TURTLE PHARYNGULA, LATERAL

D. CHICK PHARYNGULA, LATERAL

Fig. 5–13. Aortic arches.
(Shark and trout after A. Dohrn, 1886. Chick after A. F. W. Hughes, 1934.)

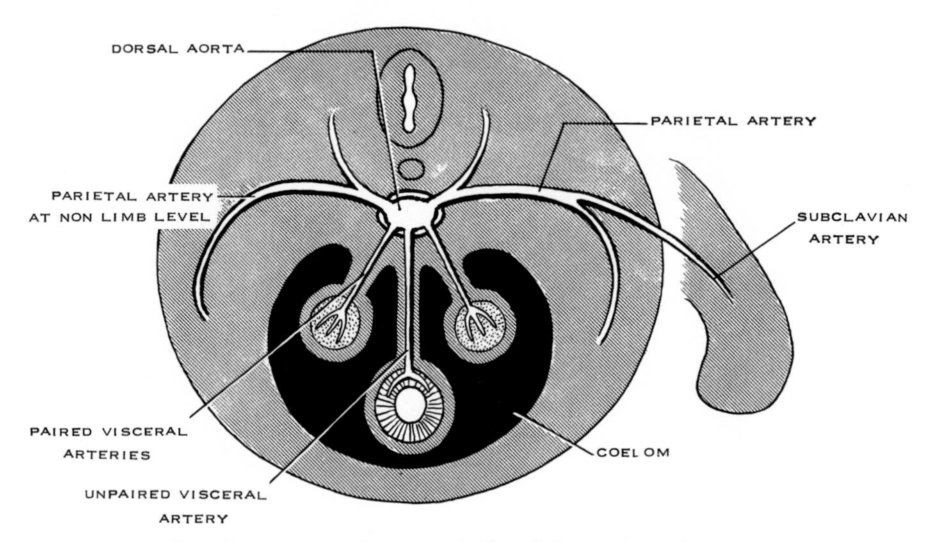

Fig. 5–14. Distribution of blood from dorsal aorta.

have passed their prime and become obliterated before the VI arch of the fourth branchial segment is well formed. In shark pharyngulas on the other hand, all the aortic arches from I through VII form quickly and remain in simultaneous function for a while before the anterior ones regress. In the bony fishes, usually the I aortic arches have been lost prior to the pharyngula stage.

Each functional aortic arch passes dorsad through its own pharynx segment, and all of them then converge in posteromedial directions over the roof of the pharynx, joining and combining their blood streams in the **dorsal aorta** in the midline. This, as previously noted, proceeds caudad just ventral to the notochord and dorsal to the intestine.

The dorsal aorta is the principal distributor of arterial blood to the embryo, giving off many **paired parietal** or **somatic arteries** that parallel the spinal nerves in distribution to the periphery, and **unpaired,** non-segmental **visceral arteries** that supply the alimentary tract (Fig 5–14). It also gives off varying numbers of renal arteries to the kidneys, according to the needs of these organs. They belong to a category of **paired visceral arteries.**

The dorsal aorta also gives off paired **subclavian arteries** to the forelimb buds and paired **iliac arteries** to the hindlimb buds. These are both actually members of the paired parietal series, enlarged sufficiently to take care of their locally expanding territory.

In amniotes, a pair of huge **allantoic** or **umbilical arteries** arise in common with the iliac arteries, and supply fetal membranes. In vertebrates with large yolk sacs, a visceral pair is commonly enlarged to serve as **vitelline arteries.** These temporary scaffold structures leave no significant mark on adult anatomy.

An artery called the **internal carotid** arises from the dorsal end of the most anterior functioning aortic arch of each side It runs forward in the skull-forming mesenchyme, passing ventral to the ear vesicle and dorsal to the eyeball, supplying blood to these parts and to the brain. It could be classed as a dorsal branch of the aortic arch, or classed with equal justification as a forward continuation of the root of the dorsal aorta.

In all vertebrate pharyngulas, the venous blood is returned to the sinus venosus of the heart from the head, trunk and tail in three streams (Fig. 5–15). Two of these are the right and left **common cardinal veins,** and the third comes directly or indirectly from the liver. Each common cardinal vein is formed by the joining, just lateral to the sinus venosus, of an **anterior cardinal vein** which drains the head, and a **posterior cardinal vein** which drains the trunk and tail. The former runs dorsal to the pharynx segments outside the ganglia of the post-otic visceral cranial nerves, and outside the ear vesicle. The latter may be traced posteriorly just lateral to the dorsal aorta on each side, receiving intersegmental tributaries that drain the somites.

The third stream of venous blood is highly variable at the pharyngula stage, being involved with various scaffolding structures, but much of it is always intercepted by the liver, in the substance of which it divides into a braided system of capillaries. This enables the liver cells to perform crucial biochemical functions relative to the blood. In all vertebrates except the teleosts (in which the yolk mass temporarily intervenes), the blood from the liver flows directly to the sinus venosus through one or two short **hepatic veins.**

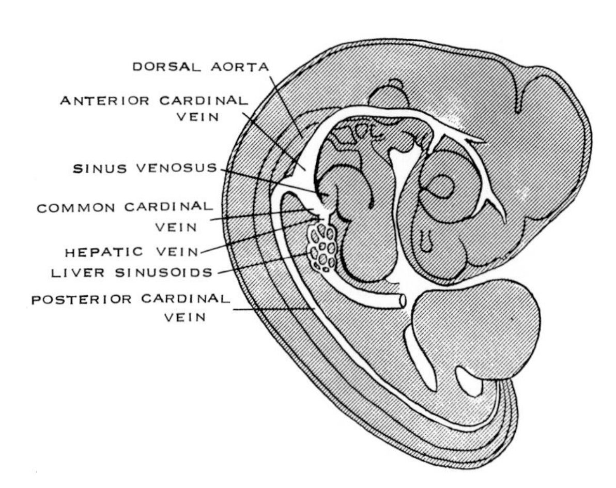

Fig. 5–15. Principal veins of chick pharyngula.
(Modified from B. M. Patten, Early Embryology of the Chick, 4th edition, 1951, by permission of McGraw-Hill Book Co., Inc.)

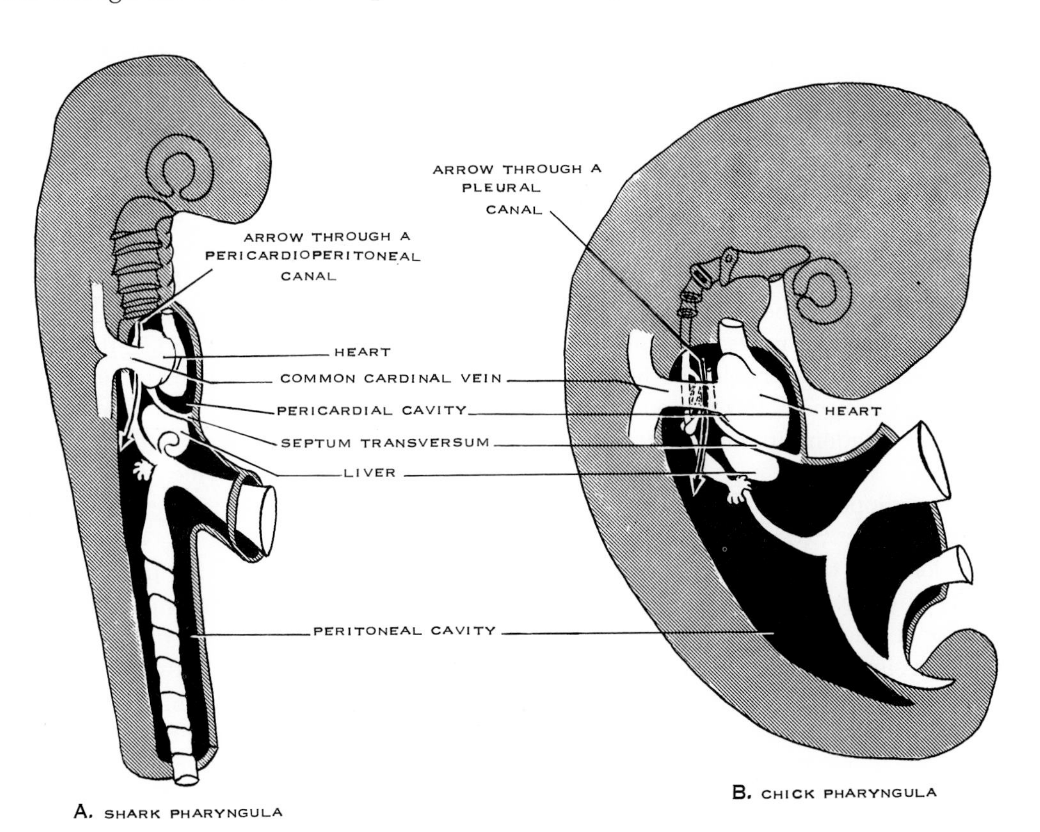

Fig. 5–16. Coelom and septum transversum.
(Shark after R. E. Scammon, Keibel's Normentafeln, Vol. 12, 1911, by permission of Gustav Fischer Verlag. Chick modified from B. M. Patten, Early Embryology of the Chick, 4th edition, 1951, by permission of McGraw-Hill Book Co., Inc.)

I. The Coelom and Mesenteries

At the pharyngula stage there is a single continuous body cavity, the **coelom,** which contains the heart and the developing digestive viscera (Fig. 5–16). The heart lies in a section of the coelom called the pericardial cavity. It is attached at the anterior wall where the bulbus cordis enters solid tissue below the pharynx segments, and also at the posterior wall where the great common cardinal veins and the hepatic veins enter the sinus venosus. The rest of the heart swings free.

In most vertebrate pharyngulas the great veins pass across the **septum transversum** to reach the sinus venosus. (Some bony fishes are exceptions because of the temporary location of yolk masses.) The septum transversum is a sheet of mesoderm cells attached to the body wall ventrally and laterally, all but constricting the coelom in two. The part of the coelom anterior to the septum transversum is the **pericardial cavity** that contains the heart, and the part posterior to it is the **peritoneal cavity.**

In all vertebrates except some bony fishes the liver has planted itself firmly against the posterior wall of the septum transversum, being thus in a characteristically close relation to the heart in the midventral line, below the alimentary canal. In the exceptional fishes it is yolk which intervenes between the liver and the heart, and with the disappearance of this temporary food store the same relationship makes its delayed appearance.

Paired pericardioperitoneal canals may still be found connecting the two major subdivisions of the coelom dorsal to the septum transversum at the pharyngula stage, one on either side of the alimentary canal, each lying medial to the common cardinal vein. The lung buds of amniotes bulge into these tunnels, which may therefore be called **pleural canals.**

The intestine is suspended from the dorsal wall of the peritoneal cavity by an unbroken **dorsal mesentery** (Figs. 5–14, 5–17), which at this stage is composed of a variable amount of mesenchyme between two epithelial layers of mesoderm The unpaired visceral arteries from the dorsal aorta reach the intestine through this mesentery. The peritoneal cavity has an outer lining which is applied to the body wall, and an inner lining wrapped over the intestine and the liver. The outer part is called the **parietal peritoneum;** the inner, **visceral peritoneum.** The lining of the pericardial cavity also has its parietal and visceral parts, the latter applied to the heart. In the case of the peritoneum, the dorsal mesentery connects the two parts.

The entire outer wall of the coelom may be defined as the **somatopleure** (Fig. 5–17). It consists of the lining of the cavity itself—the parietal pericardium or parietal peritoneum—and the outer ectodermal epithelium, and all intervening layers of tissue together with their blood vessels and nerves. The **splanchnopleure** is the tissue between the peritoneal cavity and the internal cavity of the intestine. It consists of the visceral peritoneum, the endodermal gut epithelium, and all intervening tissues such as mesenchyme, developing layers of smooth muscle, blood vessels, and nerves.

J. Epimere, Hypomere, and Intermediate Mesoderm

The mesodermal parts heretofore described fall under two headings, epimere and hypomere. The **epimere** lies mostly dorsal to the notochordal axis of the pharyngula, and includes the somites and their derivatives; i.e., the myotomes, the sclerotomes, and associated mesenchyme. The **hypomere** lies ventral to the notochordal axis and includes the coelomic cavities, their linings and associated mesenchyme, the gut muscle, heart muscle, and the mesodermal constituents of the pharynx segments.

If the entire coelom of the pharyngula is dissected open, a strip of **intermediate mesoderm** may be found on each side of the notochordal axis, sometimes wedged between epimere and hypomere, sometimes bulging into the coelom from its dorsolateral roof (Fig. 5–17). It runs approximately the full length of the trunk, from heart level to cloaca. Intermediate mesoderm has to do with the formation of kidneys and gonads, and their ducts. At the pharyngula stage the gonads and gonoducts have not differentiated, though their cellular constituents have been marshalled in readiness. On the other hand, differen-

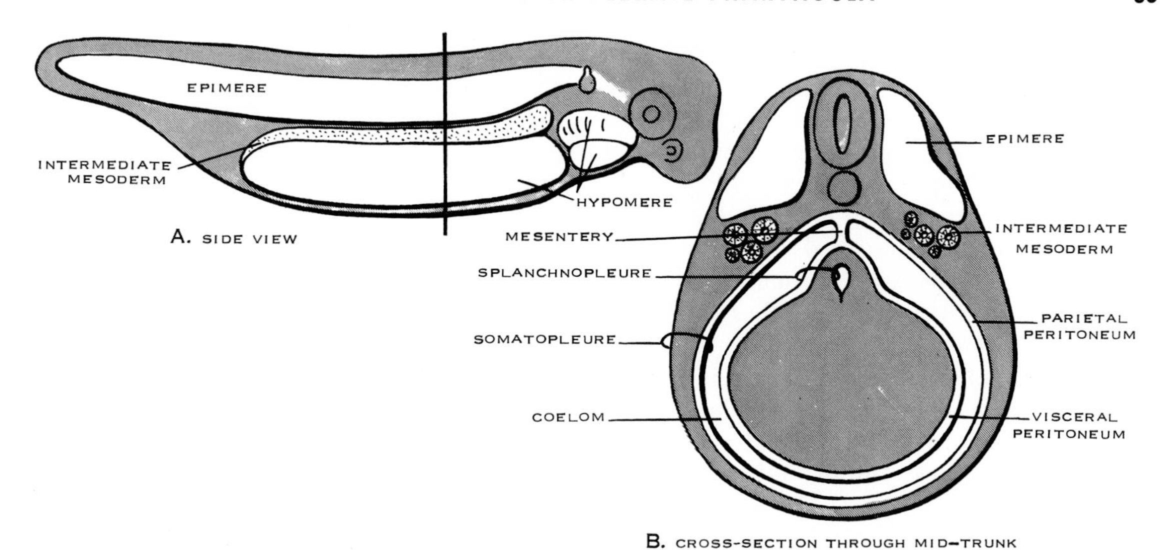

Fig. 5–17. Subdivisions of the mesoderm.

tiation of kidney tubules and urine ducts has taken place, though not to a uniform degree in different classes of vertebrates (Fig. 5–18).

A longitudinal **primitive kidney duct** has been differentiated on each side in every vertebrate pharyngula, running the entire length of the strip of intermediate mesoderm on its lateral border. Much of the intermediate mesoderm on each side has differentiated—or will be differentiating—into a large number of **kidney tubules** which are highly contorted, but in general wend their way mediolaterally to the primitive kidney duct, into which they empty.

Various close contacts are established between the kidney tubules and nearby arteries and veins, which permit wastes and fluid to be extracted by

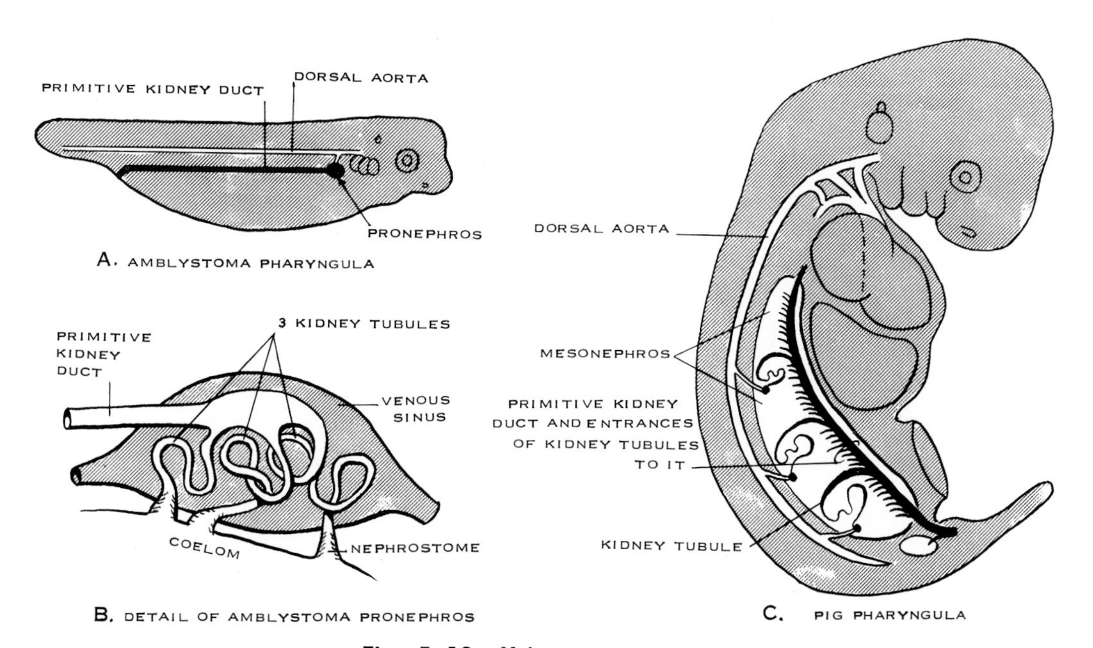

Fig. 5–18. Urinary apparatus.
(Pig after McCallum, 1902, and Lewis, 1920.)

the tubules from the blood, secreted as urine, and passed in this form into the primitive kidney ducts. These two ducts, whose function is the transport rather than the secretion of urine, both end at least temporarily in the cloaca.

The extent of variation in the timing of kidney tubule formation is measured by the contrast between the pharyngulas of the amblystoma and the pig (Fig. 5–18). The former has completed the differentiation of only three tubules at the anterior end of each intermediate mesoderm strip. Each coiled mass of three tubules lies just inside the pectoral limb bud of that side, and is called a **pronephros.** On the other hand the pig has already formed and obliterated its two pronephroi and has completed another 40 or 50 highly differentiated tubules on each side, which are massed as far back as the pelvic region at the pharyngula stage. Since more tubule differentiation is still to come within the pelvis, these middle kidneys of the pig are called **mesonephroi.** The difference between the two species is partly a matter of timing. In most of the vertebrates a wave of tubule differentiation sweeps down the intermediate mesoderm strip from anterior to posterior, followed in part by a second wave of destruction or alteration of tubules (see Chapter 27).

K. Appendages

In the anamniotes, a median **ventral tailfin** and a median **dorsal fin** extending through both tail and trunk, are being established at the pharyngula stage (Figs. 5–3, 5–4). They consist chiefly of an ectodermal covering and a filling of mesenchyme.

In all vertebrates except the lampreys, hagfishes, snakes, and a few lizards, a pair of **pectoral limb buds** have also appeared. With the same exceptions and a few additional cases in which there is an unusual relay in appearance, a pair of **pelvic limb buds** are also pushing out. In their primordial condition these limb buds consist of an ectodermal covering, a central core of mesenchyme which will presently form skeleton, and dorsal and ventral masses which will pres-

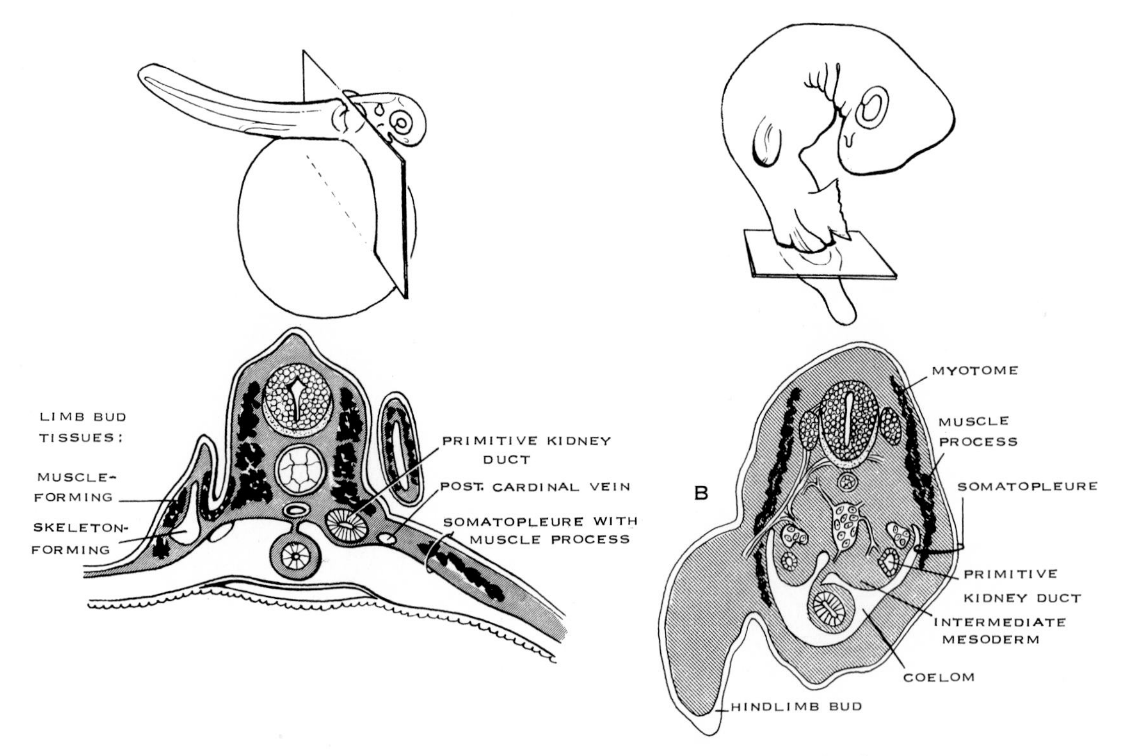

Fig. 5–19. Relations of salmon and turtle limb buds.

ently form muscles (Fig. 5–19). The special qualities of paired fins and jointed legs differentiate a little later, from these primordial limb buds.

The relations of the limb buds to other parts of the pharyngula should be noted, since they are the keys to various structural modifications in the adult body. They lie in the somatopleure at the dorsal limits of the body cavity, immediately external to the ventral borders of the somites. The muscle processes of the somites, accompanied by the spinal nerve branches and segmental arteries and veins, are spreading ventrally into the somatopleure inside of, and anterior and posterior to, the limb buds. The pectoral limb buds lie far forward near the head, directly behind the last pharynx segments.

II. PREVIEW OF POST-PHARYNGULAR DEVELOPMENTS

The anatomical differences characteristic of the separate classes and orders of vertebrates are dealt with in Parts IV and V of this book. They practically all appear after the pharyngula stage, and by several different methods:

1. The "similar organs" of the pharyngula may take divergent paths of specialization. For instance, the skin of pharyngulas consists of a simple epithelial epidermis underlaid by primitive connective tissue. Comparable developments appear in it in reptiles, mammals, and birds, but with characteristic variations which lead respectively to scales, hair, and feathers. The very different patterns of flank muscles in fishes and mammals emerge rather late in development, but have a common origin in the similar myotomes with similar segmental nerve supply at the pharyngula stage.

2. Unique organs may arise in certain groups, which cannot be homologized with anything in the others because the tissues and regions that give rise to them in the one case fail to produce anything comparable in the others. For instance, the cerebral cortex of mammals arises in parts of the brain which are identifiable but never show any such development in fishes. And the internal gills of fishes develop after the pharyngula stage out of the lining of the pharynx segments, whereas the similar parts of mammals never show any such activity.

3. Trends in differentiation may be carried to different lengths though along similar lines. For instance, the vertebral column of fishes, which is formed in cartilage, may remain cartilaginous throughout life, or may be partly, or completely, replaced by bone in later development. The surface of the skull, which is laid down in all higher fishes and land vertebrates as a mosaic of separate bones, may remain so, or in various fishes, amphibia, reptiles, mammals, or birds may achieve any degree of consolidation by fusion of elements.

4. Growth of parts may proceed at very different rates relative to each other. Thus, without fundamental alteration of anatomical pattern, arise the differences between the pectoral fins of sharks and skates, or the necks and legs of sheep and giraffes.

At the pharyngula stage, before the picture is complicated by these later divergent trends and novel developments, the basic heritage of the phylum stands visible in its simplest anatomical form.

Part III

DEVELOPMENT TO THE PHARYNGULA STAGE

In Chapter 3 it was told how the fertilized egg of the amblystoma proceeds through cleavage, blastula, gastrula, and neurula stages to the emergence of the basic vertebrate pattern in the pharyngula. In the next few chapters we turn to comparative studies of these developments in other vertebrates. It will soon be clear that the last few hundred million years have produced so many adaptive specializations in the early embryonic stages of different classes of vertebrates that it is impossible to describe them all in the same *anatomical* terms. Only when each is considered in terms of *dynamic processes* can it be seen that they are all travelling the same path toward the pharyngula pattern, using different structural devices to marshall their cells through comparable maneuvers toward comparable arrangements.

Part II of the text, just ended, was primarily descriptive. Its purpose was to lay down concepts and vocabulary, explaining the goal toward which all the processes of early embryology are reaching. Part III will now change in tone, for these dynamic processes can only be explored and understood by experiment. This is the great province of modern analytical embryology. One must learn sequences of structures, but the most challenging questions are those of causal relationships, interactions, and the play of special biological mechanisms.

6

Germ Cells, Fertilization and Cleavage

From its very beginning, the development of the individual is conditioned by structures and arrangements carried into it by the egg and the sperm cell. One must therefore start an account of early embryonic life as far back as the ovary and the testis of the two parents. The salamander amblystoma (see end paper, back cover) will be used as a specific example before considering the related variations in other vertebrates.

I. SPERMATOGENESIS AND SPERM DEPOSIT

A. Salamander

The amblystoma testis is a firm ovoid abdominal organ which consists of a large number of epithelial tubules which are so short and wide that they can also be called lobules. These radiate from a central collecting duct system and are bound up in fibrous tissue. Spermatozoa are produced in the lobules and make their way toward the cloaca through a complex set of ducts derived from the embryonic kidney apparatus (Chapter 29).

Just before the short breeding season the seminiferous lobules of the male amblystoma are all tightly distended with clumps of mature spermatozoa. Just afterward, the collapsed tubules degenerate and are replaced by new ones, the regeneration starting at one part of the testis and spreading to the rest. Within each tubule at a given time all the germ cells or sperm-forming cells are at the same stage of development, but in the months just after the breeding season spermatogenesis is resumed in the different tubules at various times. Therefore, a section cut across a number of them will show various stages in sperm formation. The process occurs in four distinct phases (Fig. 6–1):

1. In **multiplication**, two types of cells move inward together from the covering epithelium of the testis to organize a tubule: large clear **spermatogonia** and small densely packed **follicle cells.** The former, the predecessors of the sperm cells, are at first individually surrounded by the latter. Their descendants develop within a tubular epithelium of follicle cells, undergoing an intensive multiplication by regular mitoses over several months. The tubule makes a connection with the collecting duct system. The differentiating spermatozoa later become attached to certain follicle cells which are differentiated as **nurse cells.***

* Many zoologists have been trained to call the nurse cells *Sertoli cells.* It is debatable whether to forget a dead scientist, who surely had his best reward in the joy of his work, or to memorialize him by forcing all students to remember a meaningless name for something he noticed rather than one that carries pertinent information. The general policy on eponyms followed by this text is stated

2. The second phase is a **growth period.** The numbers of spermatogonia reach a maximum, and mitotic figures become uncommon. When they have increased markedly in size, the germinal cells are recognized as **primary spermatocytes.**

3. The third phase, or **maturation,** occurs quite suddenly in two cell divisions which are fundamentally different from ordinary mitosis and are therefore distinguished as **meiotic** or **reductional**

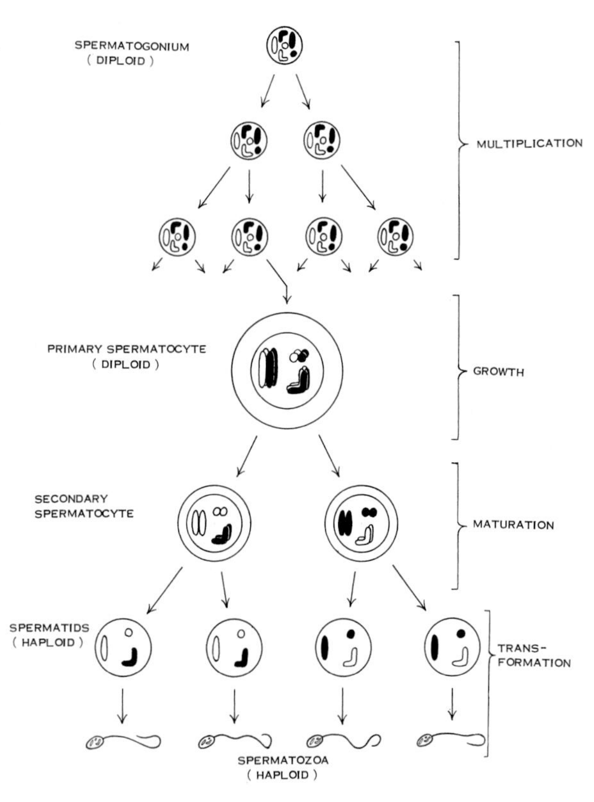

Fig. 6–1. Spermatogenesis.

divisions. The first meiotic division of one of these cells produces a pair of small **secondary spermatocytes,** and the second produces from each of these a pair of **spermatids.**

The number of chromosomes in a representative somatic cell in the amblystoma is 28, occurring in 14 homologous pairs[1]. When one of these cells undergoes ordinary mitosis, every chromosome has reproduced itself in preparation, and each of the daughter cells acquires the same set of 28 chromosomes. But during the two meiotic divisions this duplication of chromosomes only takes place once, and the end result is to distribute the 56 chromosomes (14 homologous pairs doubled to form 14 homologous quadruplets) among the four spermatids derived from each primary spermatocyte. In other words, each spermatid receives one complete haploid set of 14 chromosomes.

on page 6. Preferred synonyms are listed after some of the most commonly used of these verbal gravestones in the index.

Another special feature of meiosis is that during the rather long period of preparation for the first reduction division the homologous pairs of chromosomes line up with each other in close contact, and may swap pieces with each other. This **conjugation** or synapsis increases the amount of random shuffling of genes to be transmitted to the next generation, and compounds the variability and the evolutionary potential of the species.

4. At the fourth stage, after the maturation divisions have been completed, all the spermatids begin a slow **transformation** to the special structure of the **spermatozoon** (Fig. 6–2). When this is finished, the sperm cell has a thin curved thread-like head containing the chromosome material, a short middle piece, and a much longer and very slender tail with an undulating membrane. The sperm cells rest quietly in tight bundles in the testis lobules, attached to nurse cells, until the breeding season. They are then discharged toward the cloaca by the contraction of smooth muscle in the testis wall and in the urogenital ducts. On their way through the cloaca they are assembled into packets and encased in jelly secreted by cloacal glands. These so-called **spermatophores** are stuck to submerged leaves, grass, etc., by the males as they wander about in the breeding pool, and are later picked up by the females. Male and female amblystomas do not copulate or embrace, and it is a curious feature of the breeding habits of this genus that the parents of a clutch of eggs may never even have met.

B. Other Vertebrates

The testes of other vertebrates may contain very loosely arranged lobules or long coiled and

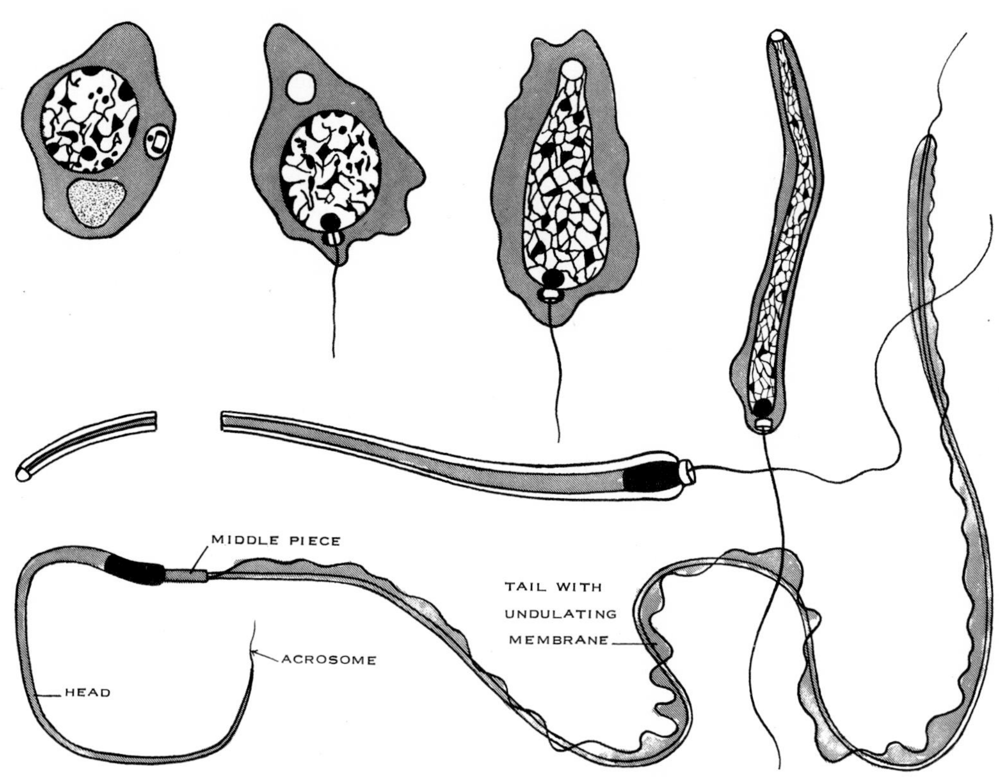

Fig. 6–2. Transformation of the amblystoma spermatid.
(After Branca, 1904, and Fick, 1893.)

ramifying tubules (Fig. 4–20). These may be perennial structures, or they may be collapsed and replaced seasonally as in salamanders. Most species have an annual breeding season and a long resting season and it is rather unusual to find a frequently recurrent or even continuous sexual activity, though this is known in some teleosts, birds, and mammals. The seasonal activity is brought about by action of pituitary hormones directly on the testes, and may be induced out of season by the administration of the specific hormones or their chemical relatives. A more complex chain of reactions is known in some fishes, birds and mammals. The seasonally increased daily light/dark ratios, or similar experimentally arranged light rhythms, act through the central nervous system to reactivate the pituitary, and through it the gonads.

As will be detailed in Chapter 29, vertebrates have many different ways of delivering their spermatozoa to the outside. Some, including the majority of fishes and amphibia—with exceptions in each class—shed their sperm in the same vicinity where eggs are being shed, so that fertilization is external, in the water. This may happen with the male clasping the female in an amplexus, as is the practice with frogs, or with the sexes in a close huddle or dance, as with trout or perch. A true copulation, involving the deposit of sperm inside the female, occurs in most cartilaginous and a few teleostome fishes, and in a few amphibia and all amniotes, either with or without special male organs for intromission.

In spite of the great differences in male anatomy and sexual behavior implied in these breeding methods, the process of spermatogenesis itself is constant among vertebrates. There is always a *proliferation* of spermatogonia and follicle cells from the lining of the gonad, followed by a period of *growth* of the spermatogonia and then a *maturation* through primary and secondary spermatocytes to spermatids and a *transformation* to spermatozoa. During the maturation divisions the chromosome number is reduced to half that of the somatic cells by a separation of the homologous pairs. Variations on this process are remarkable for their rareness.

II. OOGENESIS AND OVULATION

A. Salamander

The amblystoma ovary is an elongated abdominal organ consisting of a host of developing egg cells of all sizes arranged as a bag around a central cavity, loosely tied together by fibrous tissue and lined externally by epithelium continuous with the lining of the general abdominal cavity. As in the testis, the **germ cells** bud in from the surface epithelium of the ovary, each wrapped in a covering of **follicle cells.**

1. **Multiplication.** During youth, comparable with the annual period of multiplication in spermatogenesis, there occurs a great increase in the number of these germ cells or **oogonia,** vastly in excess of the number of eggs that will ever be released in finished form.

2. **Growth.** In preparation for each new breeding season, several hundred of the oogonia go through an exaggerated period of growth, in which their diameter increases tenfold. The enlarged eggs, called **primary oocytes,** become visible to the naked eye, and when they approach their full size they develop a heavy content of yolk granules and conspicuous brown surface pigment. Most of the pigment lies in one hemisphere, and the heaviest yolk in the other. Microscopic sections reveal that each oocyte is coated with a thin epithelium of follicle cells, which secrete upon it a thin transparent membrane, the **chorion.** Meanwhile the follicle cells have increased in number but not in size.

3. **Maturation.** The oocytes, like the spermatocytes, go through the same two special meiotic divisions. As before, the chromosomes are only duplicated once for these two divisions, and the four cells derived from a single primary oocyte receive each one haploid set of 14 chromosomes (Fig. 6–3). As before, a conjugation of the homologous chromosomes prior to their separation allows some swapping of sequences of genes received from the two parents of the previous generation.

In spite of the similarity of these events in oogenesis and spermatogenesis, important differences should be noted:

(a) The primary oocytes of one season's crop all undergo their first meiotic division simultaneously, during the process of ovulation, i.e., in the few hours during which they are being released from the ovary and marshalled into the oviducts. In the testis, each lobule's crop of spermatozoa matures in its own time and the process is spread over a period of months in the organ as a whole.

(b) The second meiotic division does not normally follow the first one automatically as in spermatogenesis; in fact it does not occur at all in the developing egg unless fertilization occurs. In some way which is still not understood, the entrance of the spermatozoon into the secondary oocyte *releases it from an arrested state,* and the second meiotic division occurs promptly thereafter.

(c) The product of the two maturation divisions in spermatogenesis is four unfinished spermatids from each spermatogonium; in oogenesis the product is one finished **egg** which has already been fertilized, and three tiny useless cells, the **polar bodies.** The nuclear divisions of oogenesis and spermatogenesis are comparable, but the cytoplasm of the male cells is divided equally, and in the female cells the division is grossly unequal, with 75-per cent wastage of the nuclear materials of heredity.

The nature of maturation having been described, the history of the egg during and immediately after this process may be followed, as it occurs in the amblystoma. **Ovulation,** the squeezing of the egg cell through the surface epithelium of the ovary and into the general coelomic cavity, is initiated by hormones from the pituitary gland. During this process, the coating of follicle cells is brushed off, leaving the egg still protected by the loosely adherent chorionic membrane. The first polar body, product of the first meiotic division, pinches off from its upper pole

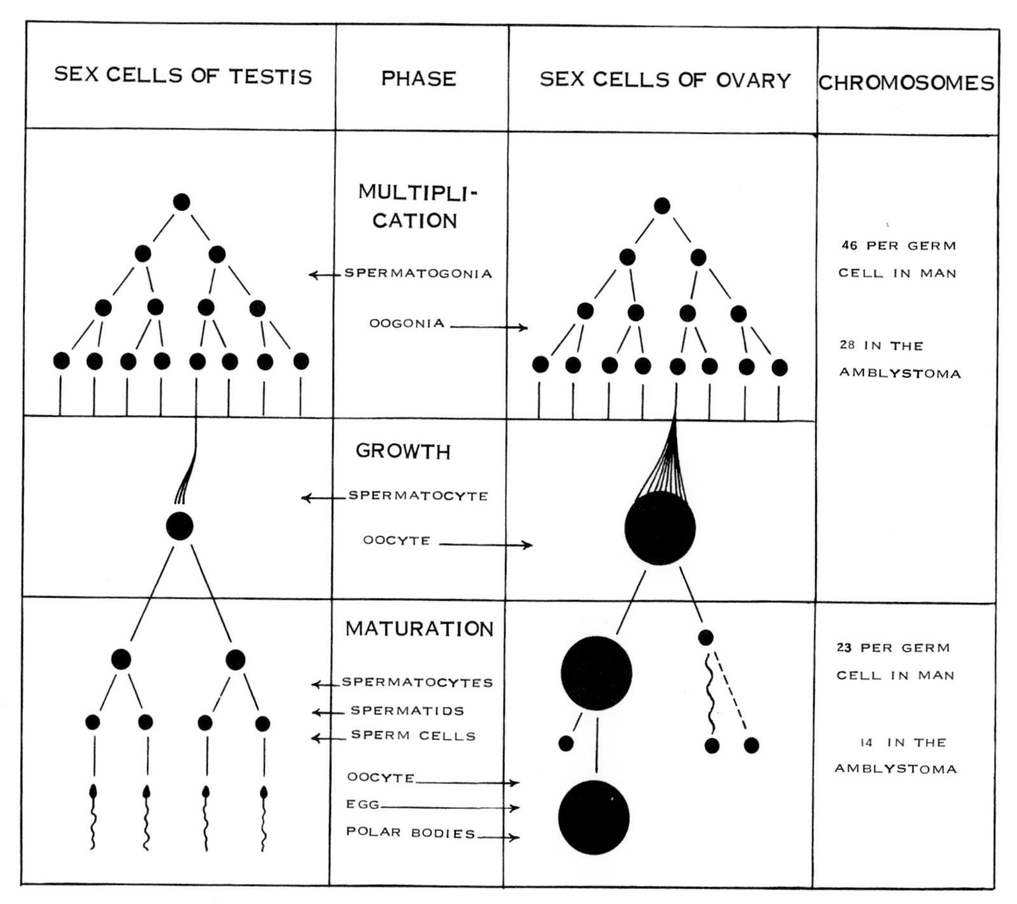

Fig. 6–3. Spermatogenesis and oogenesis contrasted.

at this time, as evidence that it has become a secondary oocyte.

During the breeding season only, and only in the females, the cells that line the coelom develop strong cilia which beat in the direction of the openings at the anterior ends of the oviducts. The eggs that drop away from the ovary into the coelom are thus shepherded toward and into the oviducts, which then pass them along toward the cloaca. During the slow passage down the oviducts all the eggs in their chorionic envelopes become coated with a very gummy material secreted by the inner oviducal epithelium. Perhaps fifty or a hundred such coated eggs accumulate in each oviduct during the hours occupied by the ovulation process.

In the meantime the female amblystoma has come above ground and scrambled down to the breeding pool. There she finds spermatophores which have been previously deposited by males, and one of these packets she manages to take into her cloaca, where it disintegrates and releases the active spermatozoa. The eggs from both oviducts are thus met by swarms of spermatozoa as they are later being squeezed through the cloaca to the outside. Since the spermatozoa are physically and chemically equipped to drive and digest their way through the oviducal gum and the chorionic envelopes, each egg is fertilized while it is being laid.

Contact with the water causes the gum that holds all the eggs together to swell enormously and lose its stickiness A few hours after being laid, the eggs are found neatly spaced in the interior of a tough slippery mass of clear jelly which has become many times the size of the female that laid it. The jelly has no nutrient value but does protect the embryos from leeches, beetles, fish, newts and other predators that abound in the pool. By the time the developing embryos are ready to hatch, the jelly has started to disintegrate and they wriggle out of it with no difficulty.

While the jelly is beginning to swell, the act of fertilization has released the block to the second meiotic division, and a second polar body is given off, appearing like the first one at the upper pigmented pole of the egg. Meanwhile, the first polar body has also probably divided, so that the finished egg, practicaly undiminished in size, has three little nucleated bodies, almost devoid of cytoplasm and therefore completely lacking in developmental potentials, perched upon it.

The chorionic membrane increases considerably in diameter and lifts away from the surface of the egg because of the passage of water to its interior. A thin transparent vitelline membrane, theretofore present but undetected, separates from the cortex of the egg outside the polar bodies. Since nothing then remains to hold the latter in place, they soon roll off into the fluid-filled space between the vitelline membrane and the egg, and are lost.

B. Other Vertebrates

The architecture of the ovaries and their ducts, and the procedures leading up to the establishing of a growing embryo in a suitable environment, have been modified in many ways in different evolutionary lines of vertebrates. The number of eggs produced at a time varies from one (man, flamingo) to more than two million (cod, sturgeon). The fertilized egg may carry with it enough stored food for a development of nearly two years (spiny dogfish) or barely enough to last it a week (placental mammals). There may be annual breeding seasons, or rhythms of breeding activity which are not determined by particular times of the year. The eggs may be fertilized inside the mother or outside. If inside, they may be retained throughout embryonic development, or during only part of it, or discharged at once.

Vertebrate ovaries occur in all sorts of sizes and shapes, and they may be paired or fused into a single mass. They may be solid, or have many or a few central cavities, or only one. In general, at the time of ovulation, the eggs break away from the outside of the ovary and enter the coelom, but in some teleosts they may be shed into a central ovarian cavity and never enter the coelom at all. The trigger that sets off the ovulation process may be external and seasonal, or intrinsic and either nervous or hormonal, or both, or it may (in certain kinds of mammals) be a specific event like copulation (cf. Chapter 30).

Some of the bony fishes have oviducts quite different from those of the amblystoma, and some have none at all. The eggs are usually provided with a variety of membranes, and often with tough shells and nutrient albumen, according to special arrangements evolved along quite different lines in different vertebrates.

Unaffected by these countless adaptations, some of which are detailed in Chapter 28, the actual process of oogenesis stands unchanged in the phylum. Oogonia and follicle cells always arise from the surface epithelium of the ovary and proliferate and mature in its depths. As the season progresses, certain oogonia undergo rapid growth. The first meiotic division and the release of the first polar body occur at the time of ovulation, and the second just after fertilization. This characteristic delay in the second meiotic division is by no means universal among animals of other phyla, but is characteristic of vertebrates with the possible exception of a few mammals [2]. The finished egg and each of the polar bodies contain unpaired chromosomes, the number in each case being half of that which is characteristic of the somatic cells of the species.

III. FERTILIZATION

A. Activation

The unfertilized freshly ovulated egg is a remarkably unstable system. If sperm cells do not reach it promptly, fertilizability is lost, and in spite of the fact that its cytoplasm is still crowded with unused food resources it rapidly deteriorates and dies. In certain frogs, increased delay of fertilization results first in an increase in the percentage of eggs that develop into males in the population of the experiment, then in an increase in percentage and degree of abnormal development, and still later in the appearance of tumors and malignancies in the developing embryos. At last, no fertilization is possible. Similar results are recorded in guinea pigs which have been allowed to copulate after increasing delays from the time of ovulation. Fertilizability itself is lost in a matter of minutes in some species, ten or twenty hours in others. Deterioration is somehow arrested by the prompt application of sperm.

Much still remains to be learned about the physiology of fertilization, though the visible events are known. The sperm tip carries enzymes for digesting its way through jelly or membranes that surround the egg. A protein secretion of the egg, called fertilizin, and a corresponding antifertilizin from the sperm, seem to react together like an antigen and its antibody and are involved in the attachment of the sperm to the egg cortex [3].

In the darkly pigmented amphibian egg it may be seen that the spermatozoon which first reaches the cell membrane makes a penetration, carrying with it a trail of the fine-grained pigment from the cortical layer. Its point of entrance is marked by the raising of a plug of clear cytoplasm, and a wave of physiologic reaction is set in motion which may result in measurable changes in viscosity and gaseous metabolism of the egg. Streaming of particles may be seen in the egg cortex, and the primary egg membrane (called vitelline membrane in amphibia) is lifted off. The search for the essential nature of fertilization is impeded by the demonstration that none of these features occurs in all species [2].

Resistance to the entry of more spermatozoa very quickly develops, though in the relatively large eggs of elasmobranchs, reptiles, and birds this reaction does not spread completely over the surface before a few extra have gotten in. Even in amphibian eggs it often appears that more than one sperm has entered, but in none of these have the excess gametes been proved to enter into the mitotic events of the cleavage stage. Finally the block to the second meiotic division of the egg nucleus is removed and the second polar body is given off.

All the events and changes listed above constitute the **activation phase** of fertilization. All of them—except of course the formation of the pigment trail—can be reproduced experimentally in the freshly ovulated egg by other means than sperm-cell entry. In fact various phenomena of activation are often observed in the eggs of fishes, amphibia and birds which fail to be fertilized after being deposited. The experimenter finds that almost any chemical or physical shock will produce an activation. On the other hand, a second or **regulatory phase** of fertilization is a prerequisite for further development.

B. Regulation

The phase of regulation normally includes the union of the nuclei of the egg and sperm. It will be recalled that in the maturation of both gametes, the complete equipment of chromosomes seen in ordinary mitosis, i.e., the number of chromosomes characteristic of the species, was reduced from the paired or diploid to the unpaired or haploid condition by the separation of each pair during the reduction divisions and the assignment of one partner from each pair to each of the daughter cells. When the spermatozoon enters the egg, its chromatin-containing part condenses into a **male pronucleus** close to the cortex where it entered; and the egg nucleus, quickly concluding its maturation by the formation of the second polar body, condenses into a similar **female pronucleus** close to the cortex at the upper pole of the egg.

Now, under the influence of quite unknown forces, the haploid male and female pronuclei drift toward the center of the egg, where they meet. Henceforth they act as one, the **zygote nucleus.** During the preparations for the first cleavage of the fertilized egg, the chromosomes become separately distinguishable again, and it may then be seen that they are once more arranged in pairs, their total number restored to the diploid. One member of each pair has been derived from the male parent, one from the female parent.

In general, any other spermatozoa that may have entered the egg now rather promptly disappear; as an exception, in the eggs of elasmobranchs, reptiles, and birds, they possibly may help to form a syncytium or non-cellular layer over the surface which serves to contain the huge yolk mass, but they do not take any part in the formation of the embryo itself.

Development of the egg independently of fertilization by sperm is called **parthenogenesis.** It is certainly very rare in vertebrates, but does occur sometimes in turkeys. It is a normal event in many species of other phyla. On the other hand, **artificial parthenogenesis** has been accomplished in various fishes, amphibia, birds, and mammals, with many different experimental techniques. It is not difficult to produce an activation, but further development occurs only in a very small percentage of cases.

When artificial parthenogenesis is completely successful, however, it not only shows that the spermatozoon is not necessary for activation, it reveals that the union of male and female pronuclei is not the essential feature of the regulative phase. This can also be shown by allowing the normal entrance of a spermatozoon into an egg and then sucking out either the male or the female pronucleus with a fine pipette, after the activation phase is under way. In any of these experiments, it is possible for development to proceed in a small percentage of cases.

Regulation is essentially the *restoration of normal nuclear and mitotic function.* It can be produced by sperm of the same or sometimes of different species, by the introduction of a tiny bit of blood, or by many other agents. Often it is found that the individuals reared from artificial parthenogenesis have restored the diploid condition of their chromosomes by an extra division of the pronucleus before the regular cleavage mitoses begin. On the other hand it is sometimes possible to rear fairly healthy haploid individuals. Much still remains to be learned about the physiologic significance of normal fertilization.

There is far less question, however, as to the great genetic and evolutionary importance of both meiosis and fertilization. Through these two devices, the mutant genes which a species is continually producing are being shuffled about into new combinations among new individuals in the population. As these come under the operation of luck and the selective action of many natural agencies, the species is being directed through time toward a state of more successful adaptation to changing environmental conditions —or else toward extinction. Biparental inheritance through these mechanisms has marked evolutionary advantages over parthenogenesis or asexual reproduction.

IV. CLEAVAGE AND BLASTULA STAGES IN AMBLYSTOMA

The eggs of the amblystoma are generally fertilized and laid in the early morning. Inside of a few hours, even before they have completed their first cleavage, they already show **bilateral symmetry** as well as **polarity.** These are two very fundamental attributes, without which the further development of vertebrate anatomy would be impossible. Where do they come from?

A. Establishment of Polarity

Polarity can readily be seen in the eggs of most amphibia long before they leave the ovary, because of the dark pigment that is massed in one hemisphere and the coarseness of the yolk in the other. Also, before maturation the diploid oocyte nucleus or germinal vesicle can be seen as a pale gray spot at the center of the surface of the pigmented hemisphere marking the **animal pole.** The unmarked spot diametrically opposite to the germinal vesicle is called the **vegetal pole.** One can guess that the pre-fertilization polarity of the egg is determined by its orientation to the blood vessels and the surface epithelium of the ovary itself.

B. Problems of Symmetry

A pattern of regional variations in the cytoplasm of the amblystoma egg has been cited as evidence that a **bilateral symmetry** also exists before fertilization. Similar evidence has been found in a few other amphibian eggs and may well be of general occurrence. It is not clear at present how important this obscure symmetry of the unfertilized egg may be, for there are other factors which operate later, helping to determine the symmetry of the grown tadpole.

When viewed by strong reflected light under the microscope just after activation, the pigmented surface of the amblystoma egg shimmers with cytoplasmic movement. Two distinct rearrangements shortly occur, the first of which (1) involves the whole egg, while the second (2) chiefly involves its cortex.

1. As the freshly fertilized eggs ooze out of the female's cloaca they are held quite firmly by their own membranes and the surrounding oviducal gum, and in spite of the fact that they come to lie in all possible relations to the force of gravity they find it at first impossible to rotate their heavy vegetal hemispheres downward. In a few minutes, however, as a response of the membranes to both the action of the water and the activating effect of the sperm, the grip on the eggs is relaxed and they all turn dark side uppermost. This rotation is merely a response to gravity (Fig. 6–4).

2. If at this moment the marginal zone between the animal and vegetal hemispheres is marked with dyes or tiny burns, one shortly sees that the center of the pigmented cap shifts 15 degrees or so down one side, and the marginal zone runs lower on that side of the egg than on the other. This second rearrangement has been best studied in frog eggs. It is considered by some to be a specifically cortical movement, leaving the main interior of the egg undisturbed. As one of its results, in a good many anura and urodeles, a **gray crescent** appears between the dark upper pigment and the lower yolk on one side of the egg's equator, as though deeper material had been unmasked by the shifting of the pigmented cap toward the other side [4]. Whether or not a bilateral symmetry could be detected earlier by cytologic means, the amphibian egg has acquired an externally visible symmetry as soon as it develops a gray crescent.

The plane which is determined by the three points, the animal pole, the vegetal pole, and the center of the gray crescent, now divides the egg into halves which are mirror images. Marking experiments show that this normally remains the plane of bilateral symmetry of the grown animal. Usually also it is the plane of the first cleavage, which thereby cuts the egg into right and left halves; but exceptions to this frequently occur spontaneously and can easily be produced experimentally. In sharp contrast to rather rigidly predetermined conditions in many invertebrate eggs, it seems to be of no consequence what the

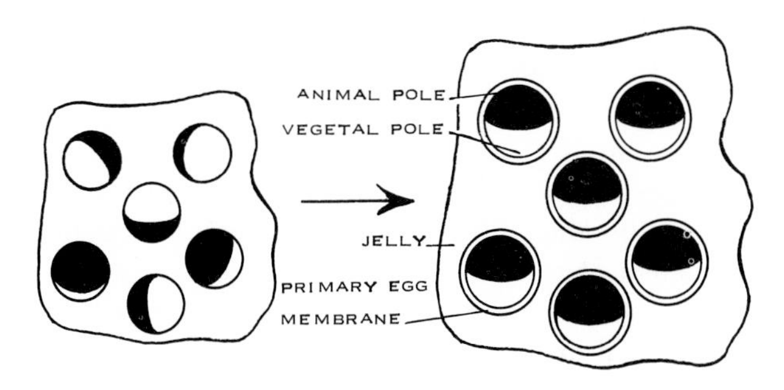

GRAVITY ROTATION

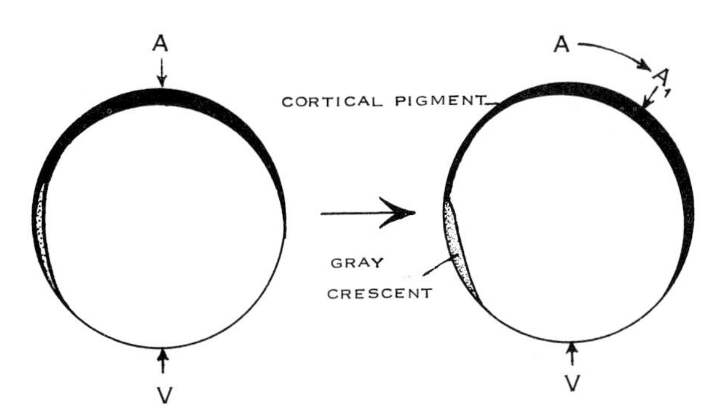

FORMATION OF GRAY CRESCENT

Fig. 6–4. Pigment changes at fertilization in the frog egg.

pattern of cleavage planes may be in the eggs of vertebrates. Their bilateral symmetry certainly is not determined by the preparations for the first cleavage; the reverse is more likely.

Could this plane then be determined by the point of entrance of the spermatozoon? It was known over a hundred years ago that the plane of first cleavage in the frog usually coincides with the eventual plane of bilateral symmetry. By introducing sperm with a fine pipette, it was demonstrated not long afterward that the first cleavage plane usually cuts through or close to the sperm entrance point. However, careful mass experiments always show exceptions to this rule, running to high percentages in some species. And one has to take into account that bilaterality is regularly established in polyspermic eggs, and in eggs forced to develop parthenogenetically.

More recently it has been determined in a study of parthenogenetic frog eggs that the plane in which the egg rotates in relation to gravity, which can be controlled at will by prearranging the freshly laid egg, coincides with the plane of the movement that unmasks the gray crescent. This implies that gravity can determine symmetry when the sperm entrance does not. Or it may be that an earlier cytoplasmic symmetry, such as has been claimed for the unfertilized egg, can continue to exist and to determine the eventual symmetry of the embryo, if not overridden by one or the other of these external factors, gravity and the spermatozoon.

It seems safe to say that pre-fertilization conditions of symmetry in the egg are in a labile form, and can be strengthened or altered by external factors. There are simple experiments which show that symmetry can be shifted even at the two-cell stage. Some urodele eggs can be constricted so as to separate the two first blastomeres from each other, and rarely both of these can develop into half-sized tadpoles of quite normal anatomy. It has even been possible to join two such constricted embryos into a single giant individual and even this sometimes produces a tadpole with normal anatomy instead of fused unmatching quadrants. Such results cannot be obtained without some alteration of previously established conditions of symmetry.

C. The Surface Coat

The loss of follicle cells, and the succession of new environments experienced by the maturing amphibian egg as it passes down the oviduct and to the water outside the mother, all coincide with the development of a tough cytoplasmic cortical layer on its surface. This **surface coat** turns out to be an important controlling agent in the behavior of the surface cells of the blastula and gastrula, as will be seen in the next chapter. It contains fine pigment granules and has marked properties of elasticity, low surface tension, complete lack of adhesiveness, and an ability for self-repair. Under certain conditions it can be stripped off the egg as an entity. When a very small hole is punctured in it, the edges first retract, and then advance toward each other so as to close the wound. The coat is thought to be the result of surface forces which attract large molecular constituents of the cytoplasm—proteins, lipids, etc.—which organize themselves into a cortical membrane. Structures similar to the amphibian surface coat have been studied in embryos of teleosts and may be of general occurrence.

D. Cleavage

The first cleavage of the amblystoma egg, and the second which follows an hour or two later, both start at the animal pole. They pass down to the vegetal pole roughly at right angles to each other. The internal yolky cytoplasm is so resistant that the second cleavage has started by the time the first is beginning to crease the vegetal pole. The third cleavage, by which the embryo passes from a 4-cell to an 8-cell stage, is more or less at right angles to the other two, indenting the surface along a line of latitude above the equator. The new cells are called **blastomeres,** the smaller upper ones being **micromeres,** the larger yolky ones below being **macromeres.**

The surface coat is never actually interrupted by the cleavage process but continues to bind the blastomeres together. If colored spots are printed on the egg surface with vital dyes in the paths of the cleavage furrows, the spots are deformed and partly carried inward, showing that there is an actual movement of cortical materials from the egg surface to the new interior surfaces of the dividing cells. At first the blastomeres are not completely separated from each other internally, so that if one of them is widely opened the whole organism empties itself through the wound and collapses. Later however the internal cell membranes become more firmly knit, and under certain conditions which weaken the surface coat—weak alkaline solutions, calcium-free water, etc.—the blastomeres can be separated from one another and cultured individually.

E. Blastula

In the amblystoma, the lines of cell division begin to be irregular at the fourth cleavage, and the micromeres divide increasingly faster than the more stodgy macromeres. A cavity appears in the center of the embryo, defining it as a **blastula** stage.

When this cavity or **blastocoel** first appears, its wall is everywhere 1 cell thick, but in a few more hours the blastomeres undergo tangential cleavages so that small internal cells become separated from the parent cells that still line the exterior. At about this time, ingression of cortical materials into the cleavage furrows practically ceases, and the furrows themselves become shallower, eventually disappearing. The contour of the blastula, at first strongly incised by the cleavage furrows, becomes merely pebbled and then smooth, the external cells forming a tightly joined mosaic (Fig. 6–5). This may be due to either or both of two factors, a contraction of the surface coat, or a tendency for the adjacent surface cells to "zipper together," thus developing a maximum of cell-membrane surfaces in common, at the expense of surfaces freely exposed in furrows.

In the meantime, the internal cells are always decreasing in size and increasing in number, faster at the blastocoel roof than at its floor. Not being held together by a surface coat, they are rounded and loose for a time. The bigger ones at the blastocoel floor look a bit like potatoes at the bottom of a bowl. In the late blastula stage they pull more tightly together, and the lining of the blastocoel eventually becomes smooth. The blastula arrangement persists for two or three days in the amblystoma at normal rates of development, but much longer if the water is chilled.

Although there is not yet any hint of specialization in the sense of histogenesis, the continual adjustments of the blastomeres described above show that maturing processes are taking place. Also, regional differences are beginning to show up in the blastomere population, in the form of gradients from one part to another, for instance in pigmentation, cell size, yolk content, adhesiveness, motility, viscosity, surface tension, relation to the surface coat, and so on. Some of these differences are no doubt the product of cytoplasmic reactions to two different cellular environments. The outer cells, bathed by the fluid of the vitelline space, have the greater oxygen supply. The inner cells are bathed by the slightly more acid blastocoel fluid. Other differences are no doubt derived directly from preexisting cytoplasmic differentiations in the undivided egg.

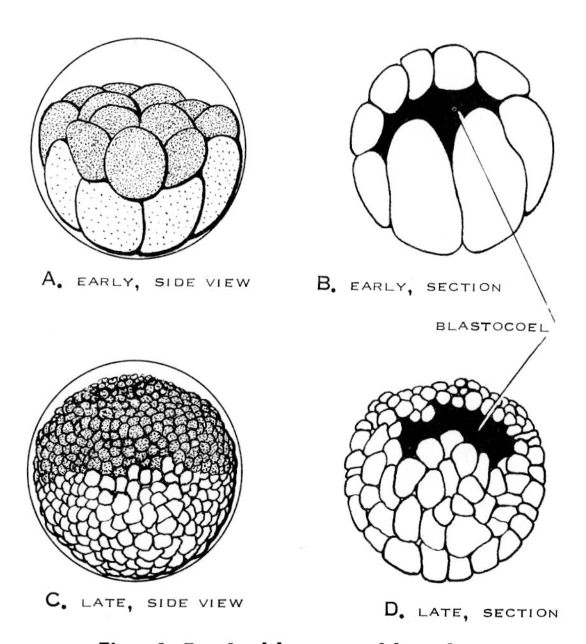

Fig. 6–5. Amblystoma blastulas.

There is little synthesis of new cytoplasm during the cleavage and blastula stages, but the genic components of the nuclear material are actively duplicated at each successive mitosis. The genic duplication occurs partly at the expense of the reserves accumulated in the large germinal vesicle of the egg before maturation and partly by exchange of materials with the cytoplasm, and this gradually shifts the nucleus/cytoplasm ratios toward those of adult somatic cells. With every mitosis, the nuclear membranes of the cells break down, renewing the interactions between nuclear and cytoplasmic materials. Even if one supposed that the genic material of the chromosomes has so far been transmitted unchanged throughout the cell lineage of the cleaving egg, the same genes are now beginning to find different cytoplasmic substrates to work on in the increasingly different parts of the embryo. Invisibly, the stage is being set for the dramatic burst of movements and differentiations of the next few days of development.

V. CLEAVAGE AND BLASTULA STAGES IN OTHER VERTEBRATES

The eggs of vertebrates vary in diameter from more than 200 millimeters (certain sharks, ostriches) down to half a millimeter (some teleosts), and even those of the same size vary enormously in their ratio of yolk to cytoplasm, clarity or pigmentation, rates of cleavage, and other visible characters. There are four intergrading types of cleavage.

A. Total Subequal Cleavage

Vertebrate eggs with relatively little yolk (described as **oligolecithal**), and that yolk fairly uniformly distributed throughout the cell (**isolecithal**), generally divide into two nearly equal blastomeres, and these again nearly equally, etc., until the embryo is made up of one or two dozen cells that hang together very loosely. This total subequal cleavage is very common and remarkably regular among many invertebrate phyla and is found also in the amphioxus and most of the tunicates, but among true vertebrates it is found only among the isolecithal marsupials and placental mammals (cf. monkey, Fig. 6–6). In these mammals, however, the regularity is lost; for instance, 3-cell and 7-cell stages may occur casually amongst the geometrical 2-4-8–cell stages.

It is strange to find a total cleavage in modern mammals, for all of their ancestors for many hundreds of millions of years past had no doubt had heavily yolky eggs with utterly different cleavage patterns. Probably the adaptation of mammalian eggs to development within a uterus and with nourishment through a placenta made possible a subsequent degeneration of the yolk-producing apparatus. The adjustment of the cleavage pattern could have followed from this. Nevertheless, none of the other similar experiments in viviparity among vertebrates, for instance in certain sharks, teleosts, and lizards, have affected yolk production in this way.

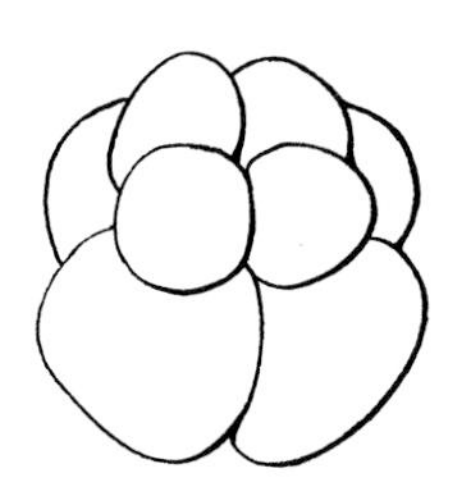

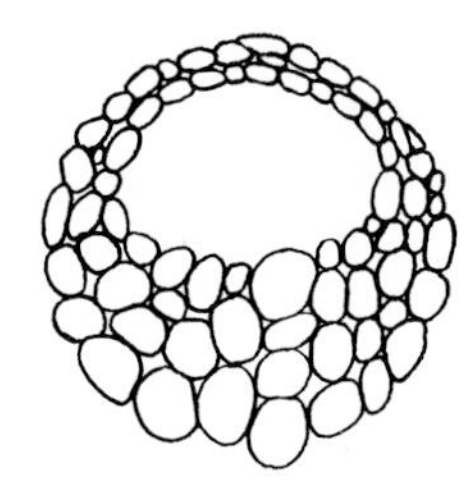

A. LAMPREY, 8-CELL STAGE AND BLASTULA

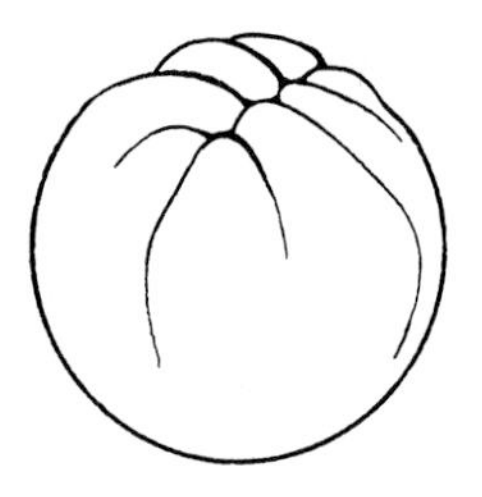

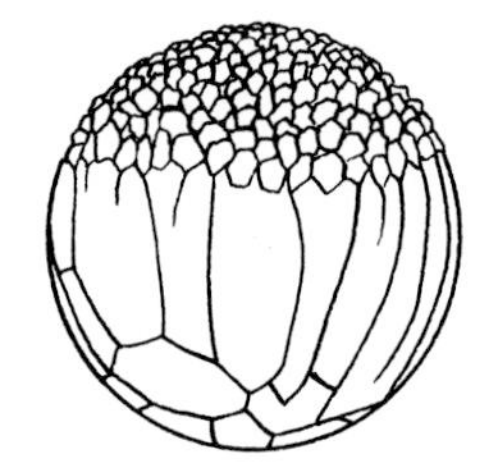

B. STURGEON, 8-CELL STAGE AND BLASTULA

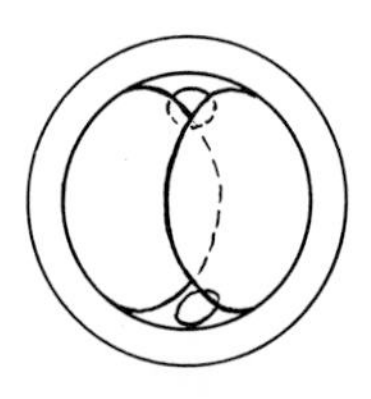

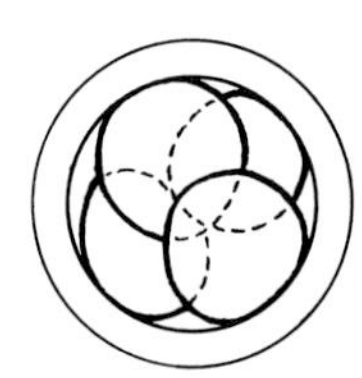

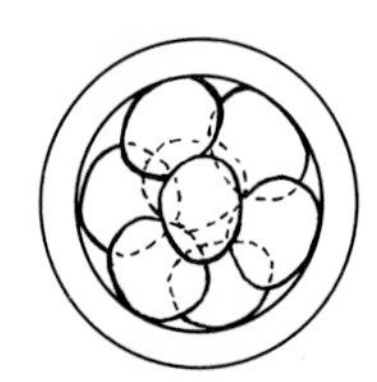

C. MONKEY

Fig. 6–6. Types of total cleavage.
(Lamprey after L. Glaesner, 1910. Sturgeon after B. Dean, 1895. Monkey after Lewis and Hartman, 1933.)

B. Total Unequal Cleavage

Eggs with somewhat more food, like those of the amblystoma, cleave so as to produce micromeres with less yolk and macromeres with more. This total unequal cleavage is found in practically all the modern amphibia, in the lampreys (but not in the hagfishes), and in sturgeons and lungfishes. In some mammals such as the bat, cleavage is unequal, producing a regular pattern of micromeres and macromeres at the 8-cell stage, little different from that of a frog except in transparency and size. Quite un-froglike, however, is the almost complete separation of the blastomeres from each other during the first several cleavages.

The lampreys (Fig. 6–6) have cleavage patterns which, in their geometric pattern, and in the small range in size between macromeres and micromeres, furnish a transition between subequal and unequal types. On the other hand, the holostean bowfin and garpike, and very-heavy-yolked amphibia of various species, have such difficulty cleaving their vegetal hemispheres that they furnish transitional intermediate cleavage patterns between the total and the partial types.

C. Intermediate Cleavage

If the yolk is packed very heavily into the lower part of the egg (a **telolecithal** condition) the cleavage planes which start at the animal pole may encounter such extreme resistance that they are unable for hours or days to carve up the vegetal hemisphere, during which time many generations of divisions are taking place above (cf. sturgeon, Fig. 6–6). If this delay exists but all the yolk is eventually marshalled into separate blastomeres, the cleavage is intermediate in temporary appearance but is nevertheless eventually a **holoblastic** or total type, like the first two described.

D. Partial Cleavage

In many other vertebrate eggs, no effort is made to carve up the yolk reserves, and cleavage is said to be **meroblastic** or partial. Before fertilization there is a very thin film of clear cytoplasm on the surface of the egg. In preparation for cleavage, the greater part of this material moves to the animal pole, where in the case of teleost eggs it accumulates temporarily in a pronounced hillock. Only this is cleaved, and it produces an expanding **blastodisc** or cap of embryonic tissue that gradually moves down over the yolk and covers it (cf. Fig. 6–7).

This so-called *discoidal cleavage* is rare in other phyla (though cephalopod molluscs and

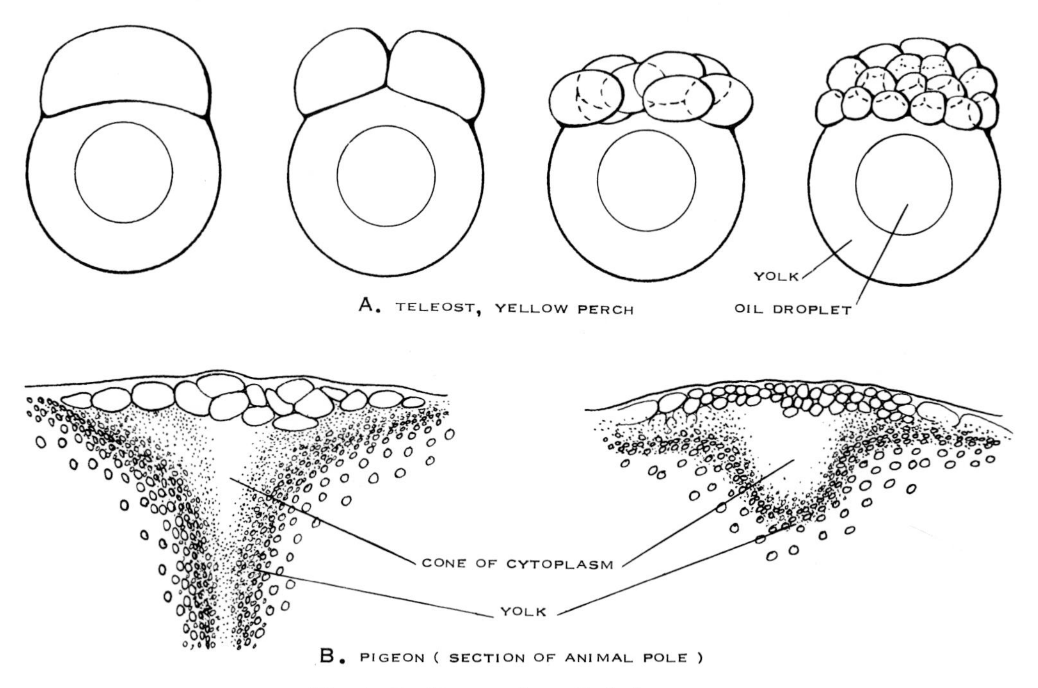

Fig. 6–7. Types of partial cleavage.
(Pigeon after M. Blount, 1907.)

the scorpions have it), but it is the main type in the vertebrates. It is found in the hagfishes (but not lampreys), in all the types of elasmobranchs, in the teleosts, and in reptiles, birds, and the egg-laying monotremes.

A special non-cellular yolk membrane lines the rest of the egg and holds in the fluid yolk. The expanding blastodisc finally encloses the yolk and its thin membrane, forming a strong yolk sac of extra-embryonic epithelia and connective tissue. This complete segregation of a pure yolk mass from the dividing cells of the embryo is what distinguishes true partial cleavage from the discoidal intermediate types previously mentioned.

The pattern of cleavage seen in any egg is certainly influenced by the distribution and amount of yolk, but probably not determined by this alone. Frog eggs, when centrifuged until their yolk granules are firmly packed into the vegetal hemisphere, are forced into a discoidal cleavage but do not thereby acquire either a yolk sac or a non-cellular yolk membrane. Many teleost eggs contain less yolk than frog eggs, yet they do not cleave holoblastically. Different species of teleosts have extremely different yolk/cytoplasm ratios, yet their pattern of cleavage is monotonously similar. When divested of their yolk and cultured, the embryonic cells may undergo what looks like complete subequal cleavage, but in most of the species tried the result is early stoppage or complete prevention of organogenesis, for the blastomeres do not carry sufficient reserves.

VI. BLASTOCOELS

Cavities like that of the amblystoma blastocoel arise in all of the vertebrates that have total-unequal and intermediate cleavages (types 2 and 3 above), and in the same manner. With greater yolk/cytoplasm ratios, these blastocoels are compressed and displaced toward the animal pole, but in such the floor of the blastocoel consists of yolky cells.

Cavities of another sort arise in the vertebrates with discoidal cleavages of type 4, and in two different ways (cf. Fig. 6–8). In the teleosts for instance, after the cells of the blastodisc have started to spread peripherally, the ones in the center simply lift off the yolk. The cavity may be large or very small according to the species, but its floor is composed of the yolk membrane, into which nuclei have moved. The floor, in other words, is a syncytium, not cells of the vegetal hemisphere. On the other hand, in reptiles and birds the blastodisc spreads smoothly over the yolk for a while, and then a cavity appears under it by the liquefaction of yolk. The floor is neither cells nor syncytial yolk membrane, it is naked yolk. There are thus three types of

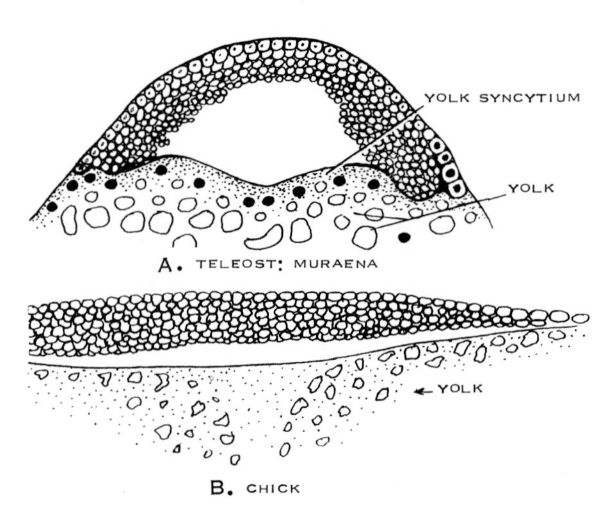

Fig. 6–8. Segmentation cavities.
(Muraena after J. Boeke, 1903.)

blastocoels, one intra-germinal, and the other two sub-germinal, but formed differently. It is perhaps not a fruitful question to ask if they are homologous; they may however present important environmental differences to the cells nearby, variously affecting their behavior.

The condition in the viviparous mammals is still more curious (Fig. 6–9). In the opossum at the 32-cell stage there is an appearance of a simple blastula not unlike that of the amphioxus or various invertebrates. Already at this stage in the placental mammals, and almost at once thereafter in the marsupials, however, the hollow ball of cells shows a thickening at one pole called the **inner cell mass,** from which the later embryo arises. It could perhaps be compared

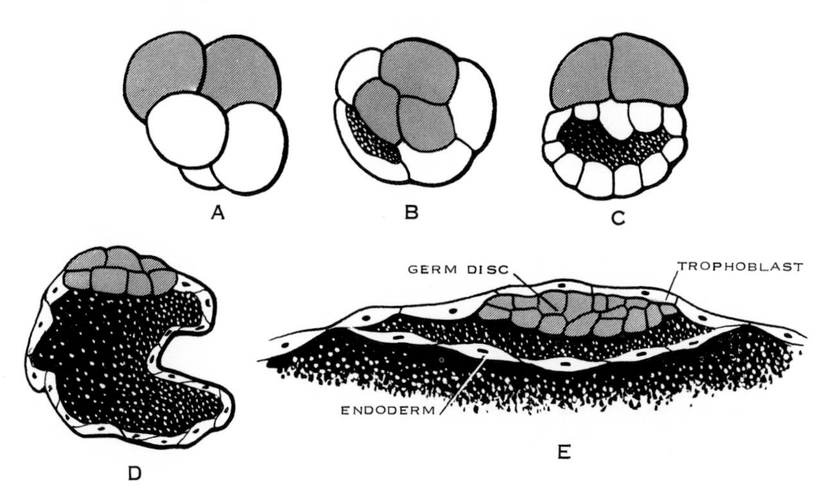

Fig. 6–9. Early development of the pig (1).
(After Heuser and Streeter, 1929.)

with the blastodisc of the early reptile or bird embryo. The rest of the sphere of cells is a thin layer called trophoblast (*trophe:* nutrition), which soon serves to attach the little embryo to the wall of the uterus and initiates the formation of a placenta.

This mammalian stage is not called a blastula but a **blastocyst,** in recognition of its unique features. Its cavity may be thought of as a vestige of a yolk sac, from which the yolk of the ancestral reptiles has been lost. This is a reasonable homology, but both the cavity and its walls are formed in a new and precocious way, and have acquired new functions. A little empty yolk sac is completed at a later stage in mammals by providing new endodermal and (usually) mesodermal walls, around either the same space or a more restricted inner one. Different mammals accomplish this in different ways.

One is concerned here with structures that have ben evolved in adaptation to conditions of embryonic existence. This evolution has been going on as long as has the evolution of adult structures, and unfortunately it has left no fossil record whatever. As a result there are actually more difficulties in reconstructing history and deciding questions of homology in relation to early embryonic structures than there are in clearing up such relationships in adult anatomy. It should have become clear already that diversity is the rule among vertebrates, not only in their adult stages but at the very beginnings of their embryonic development.

REFERENCES

1. Parmenter, C. L., 1919. *J. Morphol.* 33: 169.
2. Rothschild, N. M. V., 1956. *Fertilization.* Mentor, London.
3. Tyler, A., 1955. Gametogenesis, fertilization and parthenogenesis. In B. H. Willier, P. A. Weiss, and V. Hamburger (eds.), *Analysis of Development.* W. B. Saunders Co., Philadelphia.
4. Ancel, P., and P. Vintemberger, 1948. *Bull. biol. France et Belg. Suppl.* 31: 1.

7

The Morphogenetic Movements

Cellular migration is not a characteristic of the cleavage stage. The egg substance is passively carved up into smaller and smaller blastomeres, and streaming within the cytoplasm or over the cellular surfaces is thereby continually restricted to smaller and smaller districts. When cavities appear, the cells are passively lifted away from each other, or off the yolk mass. There is no drifting of cells or active deformation of the embryonic mass.

Then rather suddenly the whole cellular community is in motion. Radical rearrangements of its districts are brought about, interrupting the smooth gradients of previously detectable cytoplasmic differences within it and bringing cells of markedly different origins and compositions into close contact. The first phase of these movements results in the appearance of the **primordial embryo,** which has an elongated embryonic axis, three **germ layers** (ectoderm, mesoderm, and endoderm), and the earliest anlagen of organ systems.

The second phase sees the condensation in visible form of the main parts of practically all the organ systems, the first differentiation of the special tissues, and the establishment of the anatomy of the **pharyngula.**

The name **morphogenetic movements** is given to all these cellular rearrangements, since their result is the creation of a complicated visible anatomy out of the materials of a relatively structureless blastula.

The movements of the first phase, which will now be considered, are not the independent migrations of single cells, for they appear chiefly on the external surface of the egg where the cells are all tied together by the surface coat. Since most of the pigment of the animal hemisphere of the amphibian blastula is held within this coat and makes some of the movements plainly visible to the casual observer, the general aspects of the first phase have been known for a long time. Knowledge of details however, and the resolution of some disputed points, depended on the technique of local application of **vital stains,** first thoroughly exploited in the 1920's by W. Vogt [1].

Vital stains are colorations of living cytoplasm produced by relatively non-toxic dyes such as neutral red, Nile blue sulfate, and Bismarck brown. If small pieces of agar or cellophane are impregnated with these dyes and pressed lightly against the embryo, they print localized spots of color on it. The spots do not diffuse appreciably from cell to cell, at least in amphibia. If small spots of various shapes, sizes, and colors are printed in a precisely mapped pattern on the surface of an early blastula, careful records can be kept of their distortions or driftings in the ensuing hours and days until they fade from sight.

For instance, colored marks placed on the marginal or vegetal zones of the amphibian blastula not only can be watched as they elongate toward the blastopore and disappear through it (Figs. 7–6 to 7–8), they can also be followed to their destinations in the interior during the neurula and tailbud stages, by dissecting a number of similarly marked embryos at intervals during the next several days. Collecting information from hundreds of experiments, in the course of which spots are printed on every latitude and longitude of the blastula surface and followed to their individual destinations in the germ layers and organs of the formed embryo, it is possible to construct a **fate map** for the blastula of a given species (Figs. 1, 13, 16, 18, 22 and 23 of this chapter).

Chapter 9 will develop some of the reasons why such a map tells only what the particular parts of the blastula would normally develop into, and not necessarily what can happen in particular cases. The map does nevertheless symbolize certain regular aspects of early embryonic development.

The general pattern of morphogenetic movements is well known in amphibian embryos, from studies of more than a dozen species [2]. The unpigmented embryos of other kinds of vertebrates are less favorable for work of this sort, but preliminary surveys have been made on the embryos of representative species belonging to most of the other important classes. Whereas the *structures* of frog, trout, turtle, chick, and pig embryos at these stages are so different that there has been much dispute over their homology, the charting of the morphogenetic movements has revealed an underlying unity of *processes* throughout all the classes. The patterns of movements around and through the structures are comparable for all the vertebrates.

The experiments show that the structures themselves are unimportant. They have been aptly referred to as **formations of maneuver.** They are like photographs of the temporary arrangements of groups of soldiers in their disciplined movements from one part of a parade ground to another. The formations appear during the movements and disappear when they have been completed.

Special terms are given to various morphogenetic movements for the convenience of description:

1. **Epiboly** is movement outward and downward from the animal pole over the surface of a spherical embryo (Fig. 7–2), or movements outward from the center of the embryonic area when this appears as a flattened disc.

2. **Immigration** is the general term for the movement of cells from the surface to the interior (Fig. 7–3). There are several types of immigration. **Invagination** is the formation of a pocket of cells from the surface projecting into the interior, the cells still being held together by

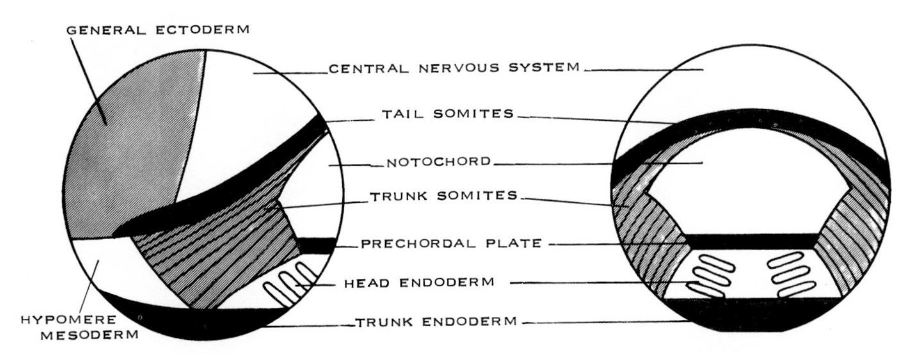

Fig. 7–1. Fate map of the amblystoma blastula.
(After Pasteels, 1942.)

the surface coat, as a sort of epithelium. **Ingression** is the separation of cells from the surface coat and their migration inward, singly or in a mass. They undergo a de-epithelization in the process, whereas cells that invaginate continue to retain their epithelial arrangement. **Delamination** is the formation of a zone of cleavage between superficial and deeper cells in a single sheet, converting it directly into two sheets. Much of the delamination described by earlier embryologists has been shown by better methods to be ingression or invagination.

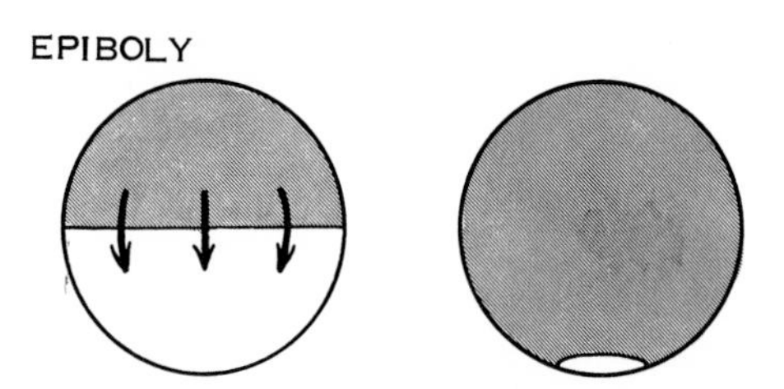

Fig. 7–2. Epiboly.

3. **Convergence** (Fig. 7–6) and **divergence** refer, respectively, to movements toward or away from the axis of bilateral symmetry. One does not see divergence on the surface at early stages except in the form of epiboly. In the interior it is not met with at early stages except in relation to the yolk sac, or the fetal membranes of amniotes. Convergence is usually combined with the movement of extension.

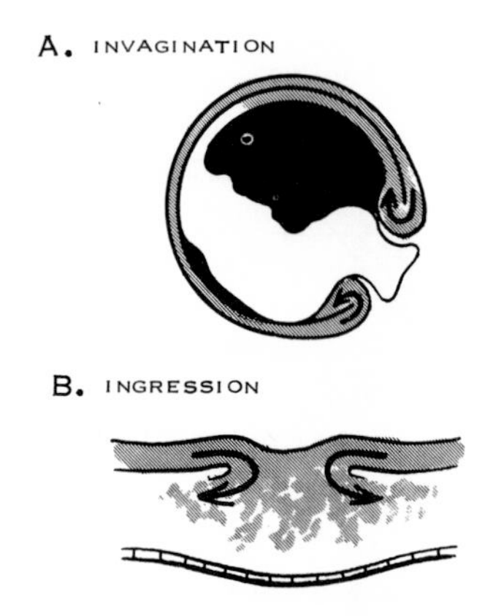

Fig. 7–3. Immigration.

4. **Extension** (Figs. 7–6, 7–8, 7–27) is cellular migration or the lengthening of cells (or both) parallel to the embryonic axis, whether external or internal, and in either direction. There are many special examples of this, producing swift changes in the shape of the embryo.

I. MORPHOGENETIC MOVEMENTS IN URODELES

Fate maps of varying completeness have been prepared for several species of urodeles. There being no sharp differences among them, the amblystoma may be described as typical.

A. Immigration

The first surface indication of the new phase of development is a change in the shape of certain yolky cells below the equator on the

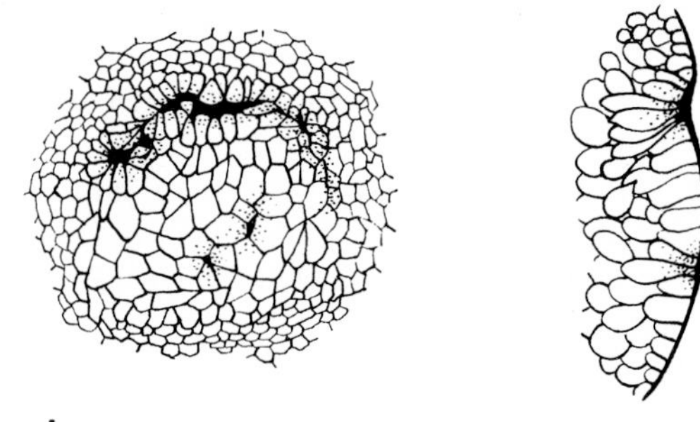

A. SURFACE VIEW AND SAGITTAL SECTION OF PROSPECTIVE BLASTOPORE REGION OF THE AMBLYSTOMA

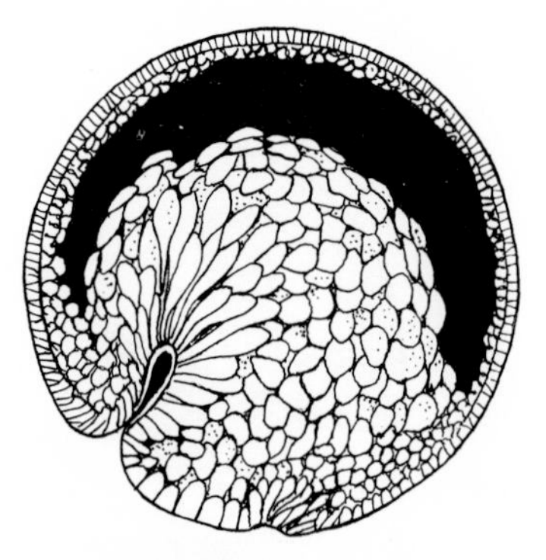

B. SAGITTAL DISSECTION OF YOUNG GASTRULA

Fig. 7–4. Bottle cells and first invagination in the amblystoma.

(After Holtfreter, 1943.)

side of the former gray crescent (Fig. 7–4). Transferring most of their cytoplasm and their nuclei to the interior, these cells convert themselves from a flattened polygonal shape into the form of inverted flasks or bottles. Their external surfaces, still tied to the surface coat, become much contracted and their pigment is thereby concentrated into local dark spots. Neighboring cells are pulled toward them and become "bottle cells" in their turn.

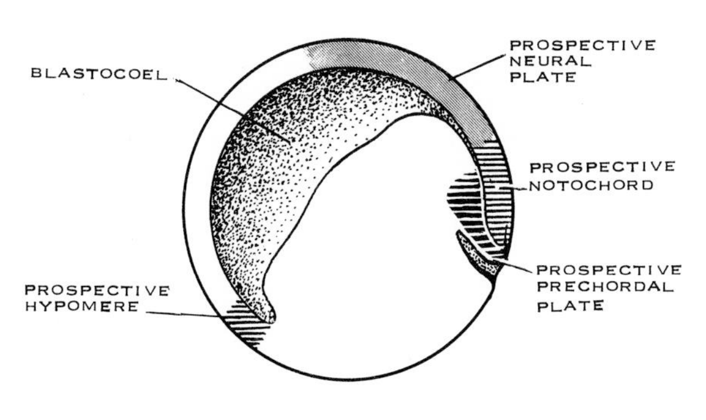

A. EARLY GASTRULA

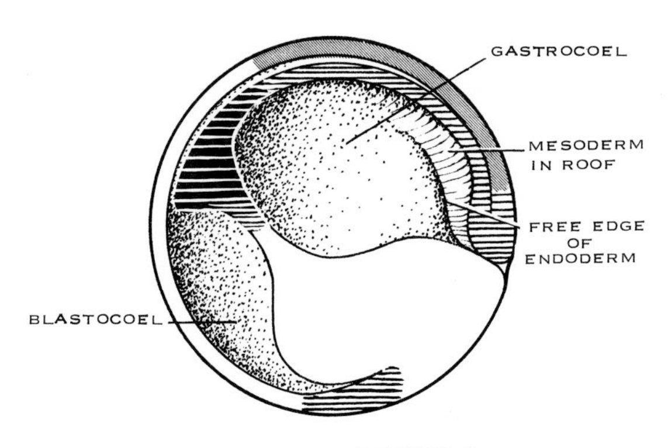

B. MIDDLE GASTRULA

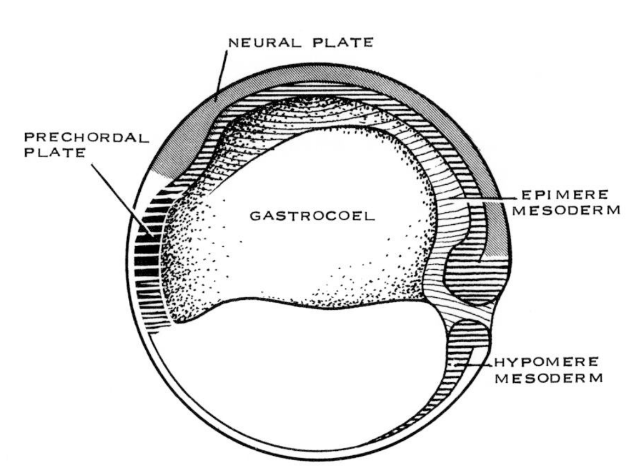

C. LATE GASTRULA, EARLY NEURULA

Fig. 7–5. Progress of gastrulation in a urodele. (After W. Vogt, 1929.)

As the process spreads, the surface pigment spots concentrate into weaving streaks, and finally into a dented crescentic rim, which is the first hint of the **dorsal lip of the blastopore.** More and more of the vegetal cells become involved in the inward stretching, so that the crescent becomes a half-moon and finally a full circle. By this time however, the earliest bottle cells have become extremely elongated, and the dented rim to which they are attached deepens into a real pocket. As this pocket rapidly balloons into the interior, bottle-cell formation virtually ceases and surface cells merely wheel in around the blastopore lips. In other words, what started as an immigration effort has turned into a genuine epithelial invagination (Fig. 7–5).

The embryo itself is now a **gastrula.** The newer internal cavity is the **gastrocoel.** Its wall pushes into the blastocoel, and in a matter of a few hours it has become the larger of the two cavities, probably by absorbing the blastocoel fluid. The lining of the gastrocoel is directly derived from the original surface coat of the blastula, contracted at the blastopore and then much expanded again in the interior. It retains its property of non-adhesiveness, so that even when its walls are pushed flat against each other they do not fuse together. Spots of vital stain printed on cells anywhere near the early crescentic blastopore are rapidly stretched out toward it and are subsequently found, outside-in, on the lining of the gastrocoel.

B. Surface Movements: Epiboly, Convergence, Extension

Since the original surface cells are all tied together by the surface coat, it might be expected that when movement is started in one area there must be movements of adjustment everywhere else. Epiboly cannot take place on the spherical surface of the gastrula without concurrent invagination, or else puckering will result. If the surface is not to be torn, the space vacated by the invaginating cells must be occupied by spreading of the rest of the surface cells. In fact, all the movements are precisely coordinated.

During epiboly the thickness of the blastocoel roof diminishes from 3 or 4 cell layers to 1 or 2, and the animal hemisphere becomes a bit blotchy as the paler cells from the interior become interspersed with the darker ones of the original surface. Also, these cells increase their surfaces at the expense of their individual thickness. In such ways, the animal hemisphere cells expand to cover the entire vegetal hemisphere as well. This epiboly is obvious without experiment in the pigmented amphibian embryos, because in a few hours the whole surface of the gastrula becomes the color of the original dark animal hemisphere.

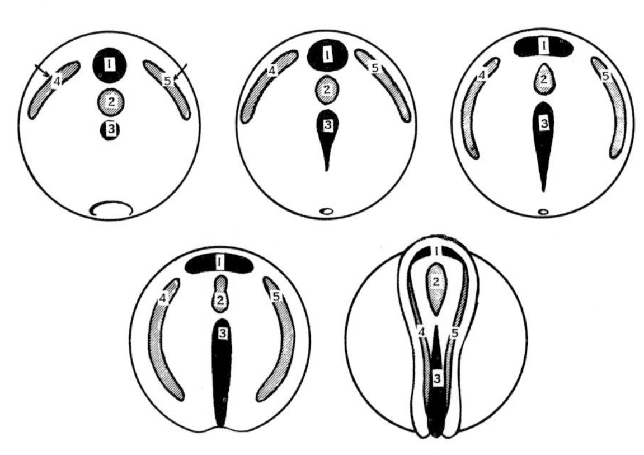

Fig. 7–6. Movements in the prospective neural plate area.
(After Goertler, 1925.)

Vital stains reveal other details. A spot printed on the animal pole (No. 1 in Fig. 7–6) remains there, and does not change shape at first. A round spot placed 45 degrees down toward the equator on the gray crescent side elongates somewhat toward the blastopore, becoming pear-shaped. A similar spot placed on the equator (No. 3) pulls out to a sharp point. This shows that there is a gradient of the extension tendency, increasing with distance from the animal pole toward the equator. Moreover, the extending spots are symmetrically distorted by a convergence tendency, toward the dorsal lip of the blastopore and toward the axis of symmetry, from both right and left sides (spots No. 4 and No. 5).

When the convergence of various points on the surface is plotted it becomes clear that there is a gradient of this tendency also. The closer the cells lie to the dorsal lip of the blastopore, the greater is their convergence, with the conspicuous exception of the huge yolk-laden cells that fall inside the blastopore ring and hardly move at all. The result is that all of the cells of the chordamesoderm area of the fate map, and most of the prospective epimere or somite mesoderm cells, reach the dorsal lip and crowd into the embryonic axis (Fig. 7–7).

But there is also fairly strong convergence in the prospective neural tissue (Fig. 7–6). Before the movements start, the neural area is in the form of a broad crescent more than twice as wide from left to right as it is long from anterior to posterior. Within a matter of a few hours it has become about twice as long as wide, by the packing of its cells toward the embryonic axis. The extension movement is a natural complement to the convergence: each makes the other possible. It should be noted in passing that convergence does not add cells to the true midline. The cells of the original sagittal plane of bilateral symmetry undergo epiboly, and many of them invaginate, but cells that end up in the midline have been in the midline from the start.

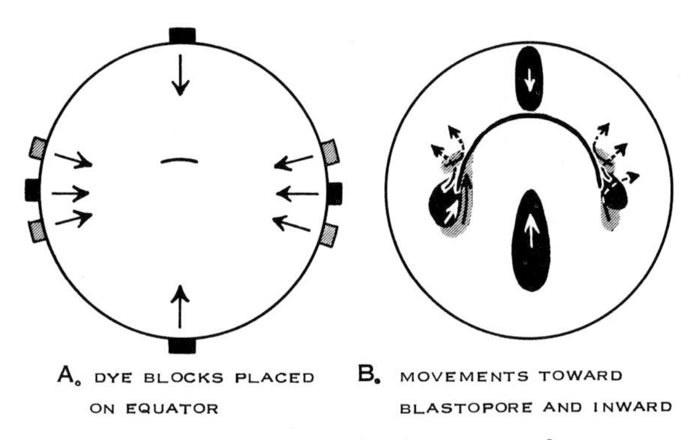

Fig. 7–7. Movements in the areas of prospective mesoderm and endoderm, seen from the vegetal pole.
(After W. Vogt, 1929.)

During the early stages of all these movements there is no change in the shape of the embryo, since invagination of the presumptive chordamesoderm not only proceeds simultaneously with the patterned epiboly–convergence–extension of the presumptive neural area, but also makes room for it. But when the chordamesoderm has taken its definitive position directly under the neural area, a new phase of convergence and extension activity is set in motion on the surface, which brings into existence the neural folds and neural tube, and very greatly increases the length of the embryo along its axis. This development, together with a group of late and special morphogenetic movements, will be described in the next chapter.

C. Interior Movements: Invagination, Convergence, Extension

In the urodele, invagination starts sooner and proceeds faster on the dorsal than on the ventral side. The first invagination occurs just below the line of junction of the prospective chordamesoderm and the prospective endoderm on the fate map, so that only endoderm is involved in the very earliest slit-blastopore stage (Figs. 7–5, 7–8). Soon however the prospective chordamesoderm starts to cross the dorsal lip. At the half-moon stage, mesoderm is turning in over both dorsal and lateral lips, and at the stage when the blastopore is a small circle all the prospective endoderm has pivoted inside, and mesoderm is invaginating over the entire circle. The mid-dorsal mesoderm—the presumptive notochord—has a head start, and it swiftly extends forward below the prospective neural area, reaching the vicinity of the animal pole long before the rest of the mesoderm does.

It has been mentioned that the morphogenetic movements bring into contact cells from very different parts of the embryo. One conspicuous example of this is a result of the wheeling movements of the prospective somite-mesoderm areas (Fig. 7–9). These right and left areas converge sharply toward the dorsal and dorsolateral lips of their own sides of the blastopore before invaginating, so that a belt of cells, which originally wrapped halfway around the equator of the

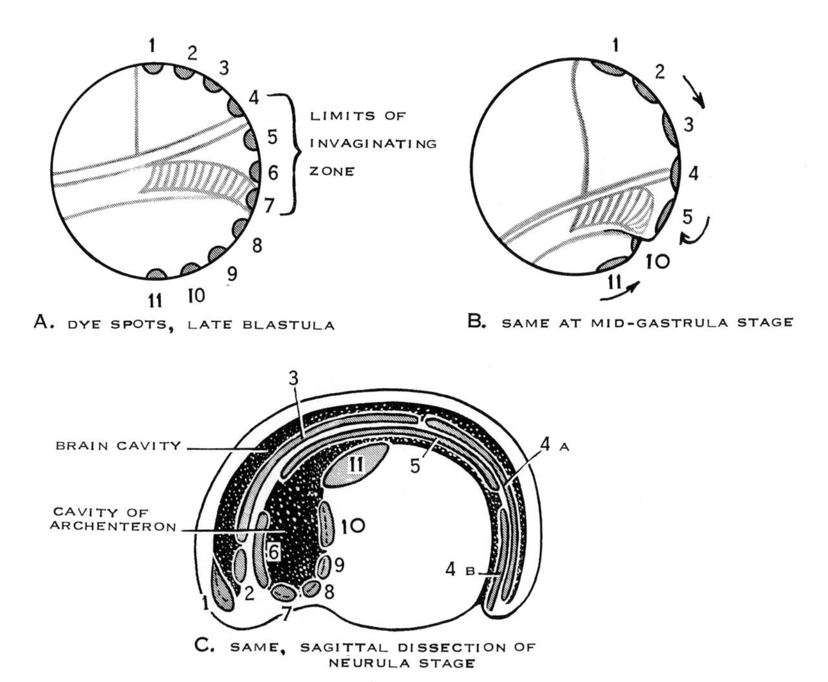

Fig. 7–8. Movements in the plane of bilateral symmetry.
(After W. Vogt, 1929.)

blastula, all gets concentrated close to the mid-dorsal line in the interior.

Also, the material for each particular somite invaginates all at once but in such a way that the cells which lay closest to the original point of invagination are pivoted into a dorsal position while those which lay farthest away come to be ventral; the cells which were originally on the outer surface of the blastula become the internal surface of the somites (next the nervous system and notochord); and those that were originally on the inner (blastocoel) surface come to lie next the skin.

That in the urodele the earliest point of invagination is slightly within the prospective endoderm zone, indicates that the gastrocoel is for a very short time completely lined by endoderm. Due to subsequent swift inrolling of the prospective chordamesoderm area, the rest of the roof of the ballooning gastrocoel—probably three-quarters of it at greatest extent—is lined by prospective mesoderm (Fig. 7–8).

The anterior endodermal part of the gastrocoel roof, called the **prechordal plate** (Fig. 7–5) deserves to be remembered though there is little in its appearance to distinguish it at this stage. Its cells were some of the first to invaginate. It subsequently thins out, becomes mesenchymatous, and takes a leading part in the organogenesis of the anterior part of the head.

In this fleeting moment, the urodele embryo is in a two-layered condition, consisting of an outer shell of prospective ectoderm and mesoderm, and an inner bag of prospective mesoderm and endoderm. In a matter of hours, during the period of formation and closure of the neural folds, it is converted into a three-layered condition by a slipping apart internally of the prospective mesoderm and endoderm where they were originally joined in a continuous sheet. Their

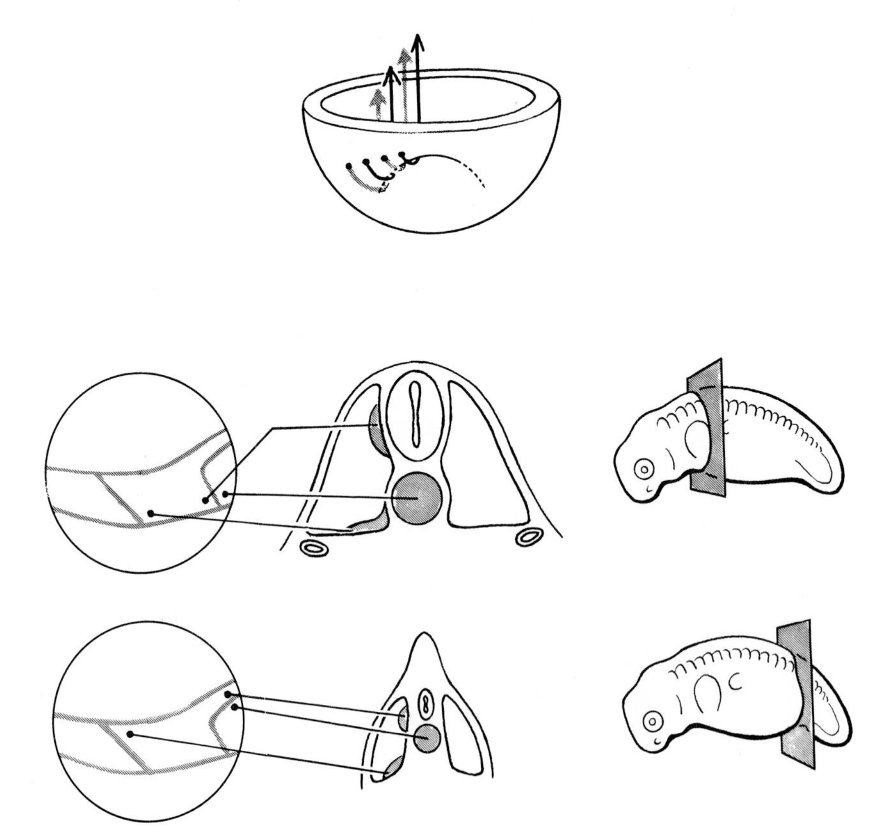

Fig. 7–9. Wheeling movements during invagination.
(After Goertler, 1925, and Pasteels, 1942.)

free edges then move in different directions. (Figs. 7–10, 7–11).

This slipping first arises because the endoderm cells do not share in the strong convergent movement of the chordamesoderm The former merely pivot inward, the latter drift strongly toward the dorsal and lateral lips of the blastopore. As clear evidence that this disjunction takes place, a colored patch placed on the endoderm-mesoderm boundary near the lateral lip of the blastopore will be cut in two by the invagination process, so that originally contiguous cells will pass to two different parts of the interior (cf. black patch on the left side of Fig. 7–7 B).

Further disjunction results in the separation, a little at a time, of the prospective-mesodermal roof of the gastrocoel from the prospective-endodermal sidewalls and floor. The two endodermal edges, thus freed, immediately converge to the sagittal plane dorsally, and fuse with each other (Fig. 7–10). This movement progresses quickly from the prechordal plate backward toward the blastopore, and has completed itself before closure of the neural folds. The result is exclusion of mesoderm from the gastrocoel and the final separation of **three germ layers.** The gastrocoel is still the same cavity, but now, being lined exclusively by endoderm, it may be renamed the **archenteron,** or primitive gut.

The posteroventral endodermal cells, visible for some time at the vegetal pole as a narrowing **yolk plug,** are finally covered up entirely by continued epiboly, and they spread themselves out on the floor of the archenteron (Figs. 7–5, 7–11). The prospective neural area becomes marked on the surface by the thickening and raising of the **neural plate.** All this time, prospective mesoderm of more posterior and ventral regions of the embryo continues to invaginate over the lateral and ventral lips of the blastopore.

It is important to note that *all* mesoderm cells, once inside, move directly toward the anterior end of the embryo without further convergence or divergence (see arrows, Fig 7–11). One corollary of this fact is that the convergence movement, by which the endoderm is now completing the archenteron, is *at right angles* to the movement of the mesoderm. Another is that the meso-

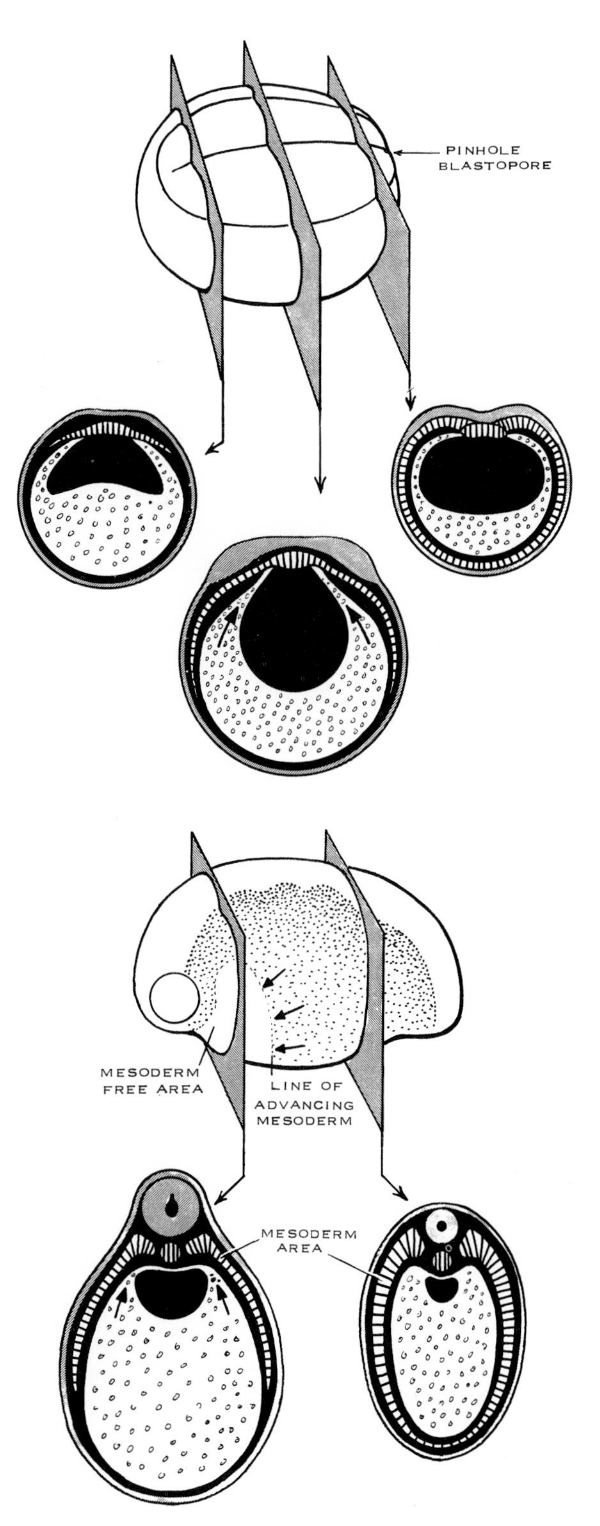

Fig. 7–10. Germ layers in early and late neurula stages of the amblystoma.

derm which will later clothe the ventral part of the belly does not arrive there by the divergent (dorsal to ventral) spread of mesoderm already lined up along the body axis near the midline, but by late invagination over the ventral lip of the blastopore (posterior to anterior). The mesoderm which will produce notochord and somites gets a swift start over the rest of the prospective mesoderm by invagination over the dorsal lip. For a long time after the axial mesoderm is definitively placed, there exists an anteroventral mesoderm-free area on the embryo. It is only slowly being invaded from the direction of the ventral lip (Figs. 7–10, 7–11).

The contact between endoderm and ectoderm that persists in this mesoderm-free area is finally broken by the belated arrival, through delayed anterior extension, of the mesoderm of the future heart and anterior coelom. In amphibia, the precursors of the structures of this region cannot be located on the surface of the blastula by vital stains, probably because their cells are originally internal, in the thick lining of the blastocoel at equatorial level. Such cells undergo the same internal anteriad extension as the other mesodermal cells, but without the necessity for invagination through the blastopore.

D. Appearance of the Primordial Embryo

When the blastopore has narrowed down to a slitlike opening, the blastocoel has all but vanished. The gastrocoel is almost completely roofed by endoderm, and mesoderm is lacking only from a small area of the anteroventral belly region. Morphogenetic movements are by no means yet completed, but cross-sections at most levels of the embryo show clean separation of three germ layers, and differentiation is beginning to appear in each of these.

1. The ectodermal cover has begun to differentiate into a **neural area** and an area of **epidermis** (Figs. 7–6, 7–10). The prospective neural

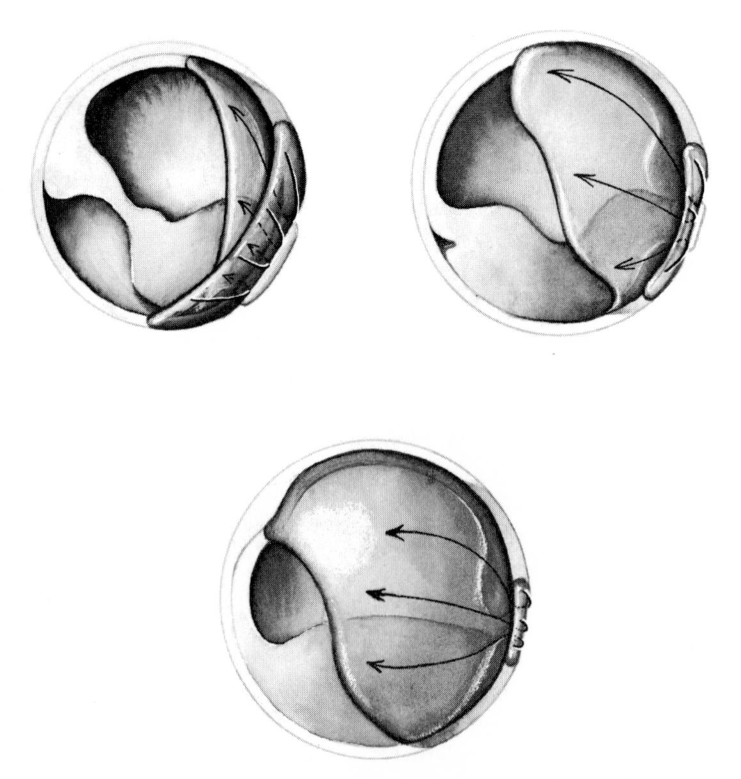

Fig. 7–11. Movement of the prospective mesoderm from the outside inward and then forward.
(After W. Vogt, 1929.)

cells elongate proximodistally and contract their external surface, while the prospective epidermal cells have the opposite tendency, to thin and spread. Within a few hours, the neural area thickens and elongates as a **neural plate,** and its edges elevate as **neural folds** and roll dramatically toward each other (cf. end-paper, back cover).

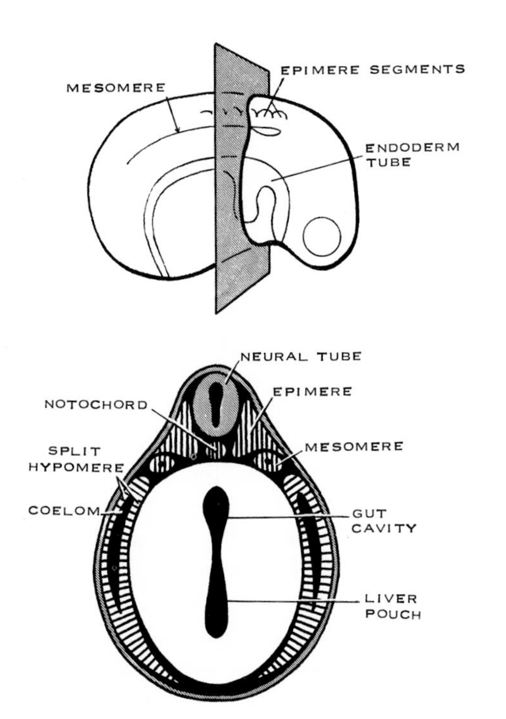

Fig. 7–12. Germ layers of the urodele primordial embryo.

2. The mesodermal sheet shows a mid-dorsal **notochordal strand,** neatly rounded and cleanly separated from the rest. On either side of it are bilaterally symmetric strands of dorsolateral **epimere mesoderm,** beginning to segment into paired **somites** from anterior to posterior (Fig. 7–12). There is also a broad lateroventral **hypomere** envelope, not quite separated from the epimere strips but beginning to split into inner and outer layers forming the **coelomic cavities.** Until the delayed forward extension of this envelope along the midventral line, it consists of partly separated right and left lobes, which are often referred to as **lateral plates.**

3. The endoderm-lined archenteron has a uniformly thin roof throughout the trunk levels, and a floor piled high with giant yolky cells. At its anterior end lie the specially active cells which pioneered the invaignation process. The first of these now form a midventral **liver pouch.** Others form the thin walls of the **pharynx** space. A patch of **prechordal plate** cells forms the roof.

As indicated by the fate map of the one-layered blastula (Figs. 7–1, 7–13), the presumptive mesoderm girdle intervened between the areas of presumptive endoderm and ectoderm. Again in the three-layered primordial embryo, mesoderm intervenes between endoderm and ectoderm, but in a totally different topographical sense: the knife-edge contacts of their presumptive zones on the blastula surrface are replaced by the laying of sheet upon sheet inside the completed gastrula (Fig. 7–12). Smooth gradients of differences between cells existed in the blastula, but now the parts are so rearranged that cells of each layer have come into contact with cells that came from quite distant places. Intercellular reactions of utterly new sorts are now possible. While this chapter follows the story of development no farther than the primordial embryo, this is not a moment when the embryo pauses; rather, it explodes into new activities.

II. CAUSAL ANALYSIS OF THE MORPHOGENETIC MOVEMENTS

All this knowledge of the maneuvering of cells from their positions at the end of the cleavage stage to their location in the three layers of the primordial embryo is the fruit of three generations of observation and experiment. If the job of science is to learn to predict and to control, only the first of the two objectives has been attained here. The new knowledge raises more questions than it settles. Why do the predictable cellular movements have to take place? What sets them off after a period of passive cleavage, and what controls their pattern? Why do certain cells move to the interior while others merely spread over the surface to take their places? What causes convergence, and what, extension? Inquiry into such questions was begun in the 1870's, but the techniques of manipulating live embryonic tissue have developed slowly, and up to now only tentative hypotheses have been achieved. The principal advance has been to narrow the search to the dynamic properties of the individual cells, and to find out what factors are *not* involved.

Epiboly and extension would be easily explained if it could be shown that rapid cell division or growth were taking place in the zones from which the spread took place. Unfortunately, cell division is not abundant or notably concentrated in such areas, and the spread takes place in a time when there is little if any true growth.

Various simple theories of invagination, for instance the notion that invagination cells are sucked inward by an osmotically produced partial vacuum in the blastocoel, are spoiled by the fact that invagination continues in the lower half of an amblystoma embryo after the roof of the blastocoel has been widely opened [3].

It was an attractive idea that differences between the internal and external environments of the blastomeres might create a differential of surface tension forces, causing certain sensitive cells to expand their inner surfaces and contract their outer ones, thus oozing inside. This has turned out to be inconsistent with what is known of the magnitude of such forces and the amount of work involved [4].

It might be thought that the invaginating cells are pushed in by the forces of convergence and epiboly behind them. It has been shown however that if a lump of vegetal-pole cells is set in the bottom of a culture dish and a few dorsal-lip cells are laid upon them, the latter will promptly invaginate, in the absence of convergence, epiboly, blastocoel, and blastopore [3].

New techniques for analytic work with amphibian embryos have provided some stimulating clues to the cause and basic nature of the morphogenetic movements. It is possible to raise small clumps of cells, or even individual cells, from blastulae or gastrulae and watch their behavior for a number of days in sterile isotomic salt solutions. One can make combinations of darkly and lightly pigmented masses or sheets of cells, or of blue-stained and unstained ones, and follow their interactions. In five or ten minutes of treatment with a dilute solution of potassium hydroxide, all the cells of a gastrula or a neurula can be made to let go of each other and fall in a heap. Though they are disaggregated and disoriented they are not badly hurt; and if the pH is dropped to normal they will reaggregate, sort themselves out, and continue differentiating.

Experiments with such techniques show that even blastula cells have some regionally different behavior tendencies. Small pieces of presumptive general ectoderm tend to spread along surfaces, the individual cells becoming shallower and broader. In lesser degree, so do presumptive endodermal cells if they are provided with a surface coat. On the other hand, uncoated presumptive endoderm cells dug out of the interior will not spread over a surface. Certain isolated cells from other parts of the embryo show tendencies for elongation and directed migration in an axial direction. These differences may derive from the cleavage process which allots the heterogeneous cytoplasms of the egg to different blastomeres; or they may be produced during the cleavage and blastula stages by localized ripening processes. The source and the nature of these differences is a key problem for the future.

When small masses or sheets of coated ectoderm or coated endoderm are placed in contact with mesoderm or uncoated endoderm in culture dishes, a two-layered condition is soon produced, for the coated cells actively spread to form a continuous surface epithelium and the mesoderm cells or uncoated endoderm cells actively dig themselves in, either by individual ingression or by group invagination. The result is produced by a specific locomotion tendency in each cell, as can be seen by dissociating the two tissues in potassium hydroxide, stirring the cells into a random mixture and studying their reaggregation in normal culture fluid. The two classes of cells in such a jumbled mass move past each other as individuals, in opposite directions, and join together in the same inner and outer layers that they had previously belonged to [5].

This experiment incidentally reveals attributes of both the prospective epidermis and the coated endoderm cells that would not be suspected from normal embryology. The epidermal cells here insist on *emigration* from the interior, which is a response to a situation that never existed in normal embryos. As to the coated *endoderm* cells, they do not normally spread on the outside of an embryo for the reason that they would then be competing with coated ectoderm cells, which spread more actively and give them no chance there. Nevertheless, if the vigor of the ectoderm's spreading is reduced by poisoning with lithium salts, the prospective endoderm of the amphibian embryo may spread outward instead of rolling inward through the blastopore, producing an **exogastrula.**

Still another unexpected cell migration tendency is seen in culture combinations of presumptive mesoderm with presumptive ectoderm or endoderm, either as sheets or as disaggregated cells randomly mixed. The mesoderm cells immigrate to the interior of an ectodermal combination, as might be predicted, but they also bury themselves inside a lump of endoderm cells! If a neurula is experimentally deprived of its ectodermal covering, a complete reversal of the two remaining germ layers takes place, and further differentiation produces masses of muscle cells jumbled in the interior and intestinal glands on the outer surface.

If prospective ectoderm cells are added to a jumbled mass of prospective mesoderm and endoderm cells, the mesoderm migrates to a position intermediate between surface ectoderm and internal endoderm, as in the normal embryo.

Prospective central nervous tissue behaves in these tissue combinations much like general skin ectoderm, if taken from the blastula or young gastrula. However during later gastrula stages it acquires a new tendency to invaginate to a position intermediate between skin and endoderm. This tendency remains in later stages. It has been demonstrated in randomized mixtures of dissociated epidermal and endodermal cells with dissociated cells of the neural tube from the primordial amphibian embryo or even with brain cells from the young larva. As these mixtures sort themselves out, the neural cells clump together in an intermediate position and tend to form themselves about central cavities like proper brain ventricles.

An even more dramatic demonstration of this capacity for self-organization has been obtained [6] by dissociating and scrambling the cells of differentiated liver or kidney or skin of a chick fetus and culturing a suspension of them on the chorioallantoic membrane inside another egg. In a few days the cells sort themselves out, and the original histologic pattern is re-established.

Such findings suggest that the morphogenetic movements originate in different tendencies that reside in, or develop in, individual cells, according to the parts of the embryo they arise in. The cells not only have their own compulsions for directed movements, they come to rest only in certain preferred spatial arrangements with respect to other kinds of cells. Some of these differences may be inherent in the part of the egg the cells arise in, but others certainly gradually ripen in them and are not present from the beginning. The experiments merely point the way to further research, with the focus narrowed upon individual cells. Much progress will have to be made before a general theory is available as to what upsets the equilibrium of the blastula and coordinates the complex set of movements that smoothly achieves the germ-layer pattern of the primordial embryo [7].

III. COMPARATIVE ASPECTS OF THE MORPHOGENETIC MOVEMENTS

A. Holoblastic Embryos

The lines leading to modern urodeles and anurans may have diverged from their common ancestors as much as 300 million years ago, and the gnathostome vertebrates from the Agnatha at least 100 million years before that. All this time, evolutionary forces have been at work on their embryos. Nevertheless the resulting differences in the patterns of morphogenetic movements seen in modern holoblastic embryos of these groups are not very great.

Fate maps have been worked out for various species of frogs, treetoads, and toads. The areas of cells which will form the future axial organs (nervous system, notochord, somites, gut tube, etc.) occupy the same positions relative to each other in these as their homologs do in urodeles (cf. Figs. 7–1 and 7–13). There are only minor differences in their relative sizes, and in the rates of the movements which they undergo.

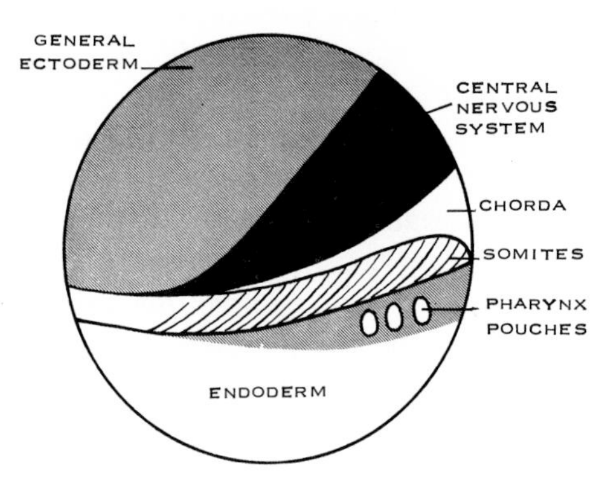

Fig. 7–13. Fate map for an anuran blastula (*Bombinator*, a toad).
(After W. Vogt, 1929.)

The anuran blastopore arises entirely in the area of prospective endoderm, rather than on the boundary between the prospective endoderm and mesoderm cells as in urodeles. One result of this is that there is no stage in the anuran, comparable to that in the urodele, during which the roof of the gastrocoel is temporarily mesodermal. A frog embryo passes from the one-layered condition directly to the three-layered.

Also in the anura, the blastopore becomes a circle almost at once, the middle layer invaginates faster, and the mesoderm-free area below the head is filled in sooner. It may be noted that these are mostly differences in timing (Fig. 7–14). They affect the appearance of the formations of maneuver, but the pattern finally achieved by the primordial embryo is the same. The tailbud stage of a frog is mostly belly, and that of a salamander is mostly back (Fig. 7–15), but this is because the frog has relatively more yolk and its notochord is a little slower in straightening out. Anatomically, such differences are trivial.

In spite of the enormous evolutionary gap between Agnatha and the gnathostomes, the holoblastic blastula of the Mediterranean sea lamprey has yielded a fate map similar to that of the modern amphibia (Fig. 7–16), and its morphogenetic movements are comparable, with only minor variations [8].

B. Meroblastic Anamniotes

Our knowledge of the morphogenetic movements in the elasmobranchs and the teleosts is still fragmentary, but affords a picture of the same anatomical end results being obtained through very different formations of maneuver, though by similar movements. In neither of these groups of fishes is a blastopore formed, nor does a gastrocoel precede the formation of an archenteron A segmentation cavity appears, but in con-

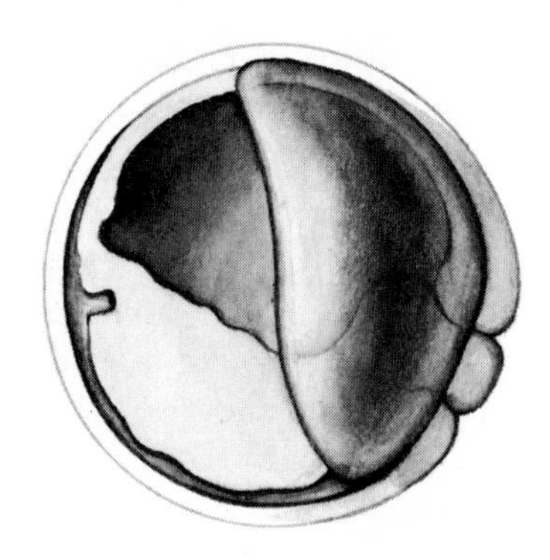

PLEURODELES, URODELE

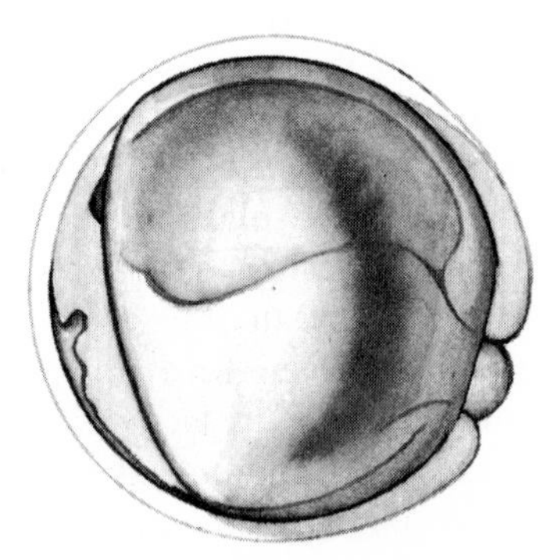

BOMBINATOR, ANURAN

Fig. 7–14. Two embryos with small yolk plugs, showing differences in time of mesoderm ingression.
(After W. Vogt, 1929.)

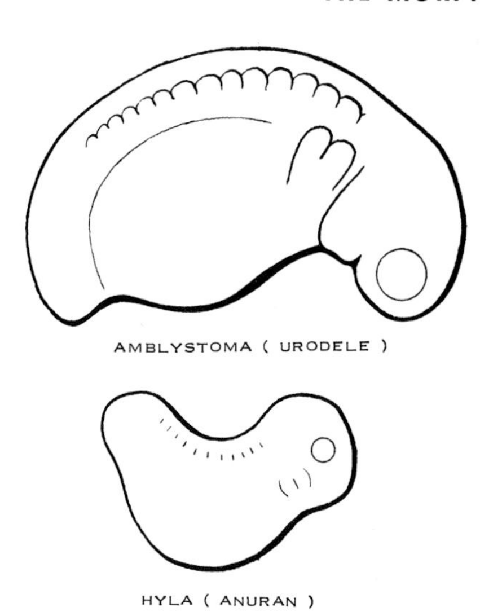

Fig. 7–15. Tailbud stages.

trast to that of the holoblastic anamniotes its floor is not cellular. Instead, it lies over an extremely thin membrane that encloses the fluid yolk. This **yolk pellicle** is presently invaded by free nuclei, forming a yolk syncytium. In teleosts, these **periblast nuclei** form a special and conspicuous embryonic organ of uncertain function [9].

Only the blastodisc of the fish egg is composed of cleaving cells, and this gradually moves out and around the yolk mass, preceded by the periblast nuclei. Its epibolic spread eventually encloses the yolk in a yolk sac, but resemblance of this to the closure of the amphibian yolk plug is only superficial.

Teleosts have another embryonic organ, the **enveloping layer,** a single surface layer of cells which differentiate apart from the rest of the blastomeres after eight or ten rounds of cleavage. It plays a key role in the epibolic covering of the yolk mass. Though it takes no part in the movements that assemble the embryonic axis, development seems impossible without its presence.

If spots of vital dye are printed upon the blastodisc of these fish eggs at about the time the segmentation cavity is forming underneath them, they are soon seen to change their shape and position in bilaterally symmetrical patterns of morphogenetic movement. Experiments of this sort have been done with the eggs of the salmon [10], the killifish *Fundulus* [11], and a shark, *Scyllium* [12]. By correlation of the eventual location of these spots in organs and tissues of the formed embryo with their original position on the blastodisc, fate maps have been constructed. The technical difficulties leave many details uncertain, but as might be expected the fate maps for the flat blastodiscs of the meroblastic fishes bear some resemblances to the way the spherical fate maps of holoblastic amphibian blastulas would look in polar projections.

This means that in spite of the vast differences in the organization of the eggs and the presence or absence of special formations of maneuver, all these embryos undergo comparable morphogenetic movements.

Though the fish yolk is a fluid enclosed in a pellicle, rather than granules imprisoned in cells,

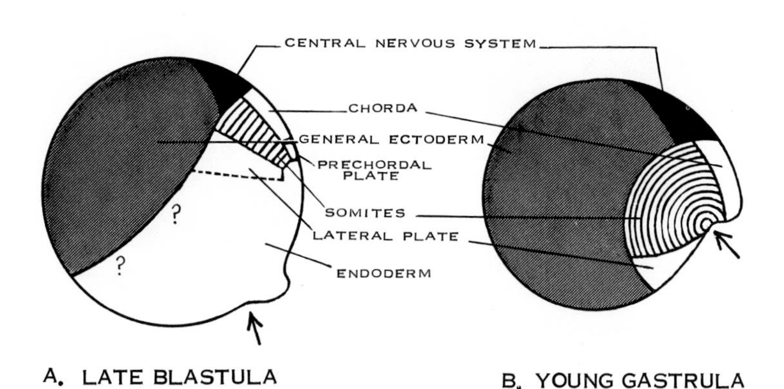

Fig. 7–16. Lamprey fate maps.
(After Weissenberg, 1936, and Pasteels, 1940.)

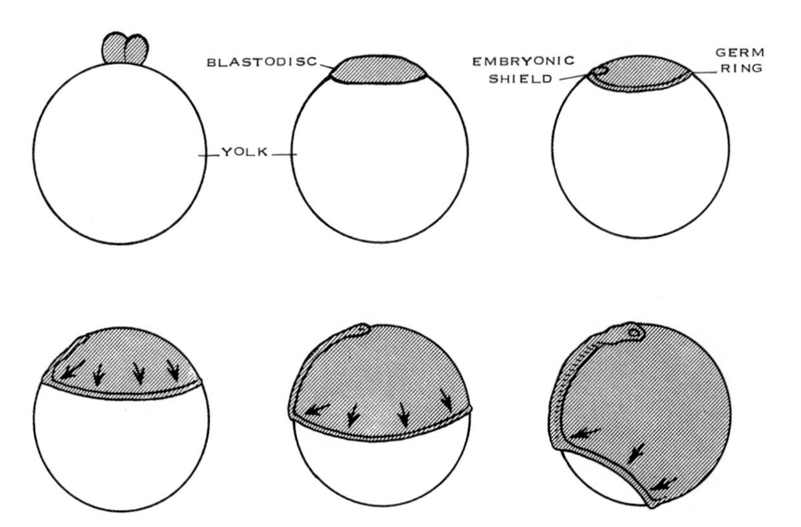

Fig. 7–17. Trout development, first ten days.

the blastodisc performs an *epiboly* (shown by the arrows in Figs. 7–17, 7–19), and eventually swallows it up. In spite of the absence of a blastopore through which an invagination can take place, inner germ layers are established by other methods. Marked *convergence* and *extension* movements then occur in all three germ layers, indicated by the white arrows of Figure 7–19.

In elasmobranchs, the central nervous tube arises as in amphibia, by inrolling and closure of neural folds. In teleosts, the tube is simply created by rearrangement of cells after they have been closely packed into a neural keel by a convergence movement. In other words, the same result is accomplished, but the neural groove and neural folds are omitted. The formations of maneuver need not be the same, but the primordial-embryo pattern nevertheless emerges from the meroblastic eggs (Fig. 7–20), much as one saw it in the holoblastic embryos (Fig. 7–12). To be sure, comparison of the cross-sections of these primordial embryos reveals several differences; but these also are temporary,

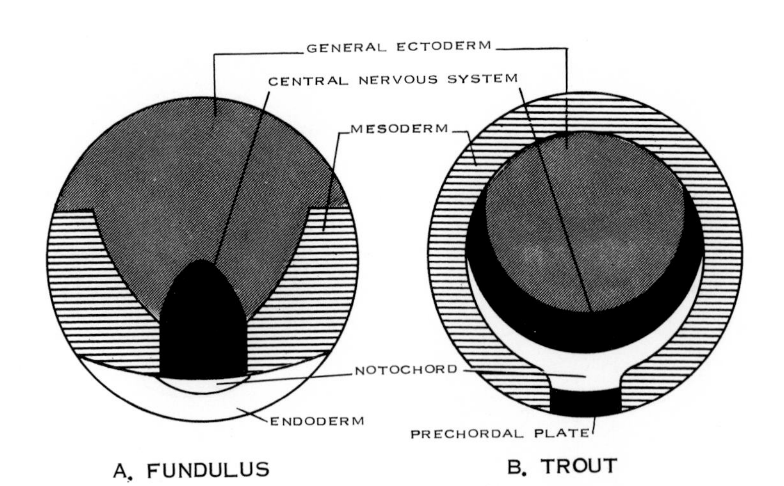

Fig. 7–18. Fate maps for teleost blastodiscs.
(After J. Oppenheimer, 1947, and J. Pasteels, 1936.)

like the contrasts in the formations of maneuver. Whereas the yolk of the holoblastic forms resides inside blastomeres, particularly inside the ventral cells of the intestine, the liquid yolk of the meroblastic fishes is enclosed within the periblast envelope, which becomes enveloped finally in a **yolk sac** through the epibolic spread of the blastodisc. In teleosts, the endoderm does not take part in this spread, but shapes itself into a tube as soon as it is in place in the embryonic axis. Thus, a two-layered yolk sac arises, from which there is no way for the yolk to get into the gut tube. It must be exploited entirely by way of the blood stream.

In elasmobranchs, however, all three germ layers take part in the epibolic spread, and the anterior and posterior parts of the gut tube are later formed by rolling up of the narrow strip of endoderm that lies under the notochord. Until this process is completed in very late fetal development, yolk can still pass into the midgut directly from the three-layered yolk sac, as well as being drawn up through the yolk-sac blood circulation.

These are not merely formations of maneuver, they remain as genuine anatomical differences between established embryos at the pharyngula stage. Yet, after the yolk has been used up, no trace will remain to indicate whether the species had no yolk sac, or a two-layered one with no opening, or a three-layered one communicating

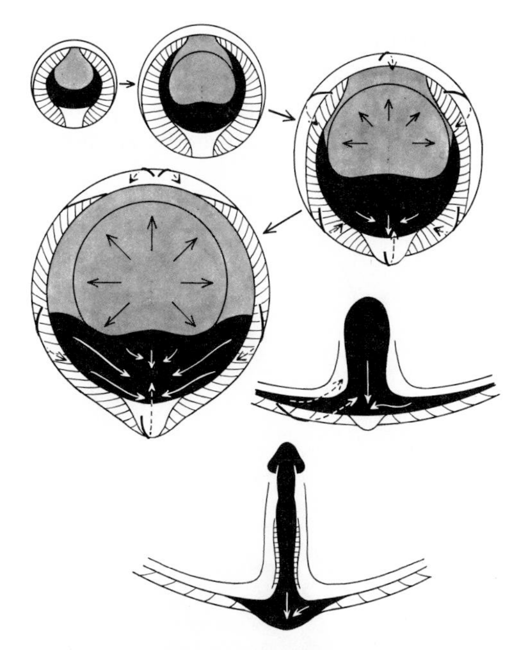

Fig. 7–19. Morphogenetic movements on the trout blastodisc.

(After Pasteels, 1940.)

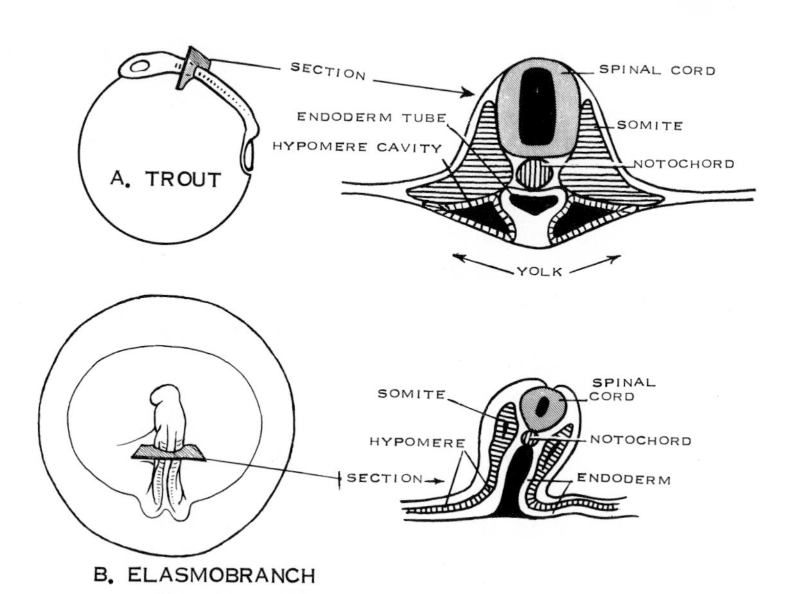

Fig. 7–20. Germ layers in primordial embryos of fishes.

(After H. E. Ziegler, 1902.)

with the gut cavity. These are purely embryonic adaptations, superimposed on the common vertebrate heritage of morphogenetic movements and primordial-embryo patterns.

C. Meroblastic Amniotes

At least 350 million years of evolution in a separate branch of the phylum have produced a whole cluster of new features in amniote embryos which are not found in any anamniotes. It is not only that these animals have protective and nutritive devices in the form of fetal membranes or scaffold tissues (discussed more fully in Chapter 11). In addition, they rearrange their blastomeres through entirely new formations of maneuver during the establishment of the germ layers. Nevertheless, if such *structural features* are recognized as temporary, and adaptive to the requirements of depositing and incubating eggs on land, it can be seen that the underlying *dynamic processes* persist in these peculiar embryos, still serving the function of marshalling the heap of blastomeres into the successive patterns of the primordial embryo and the pharyngula.

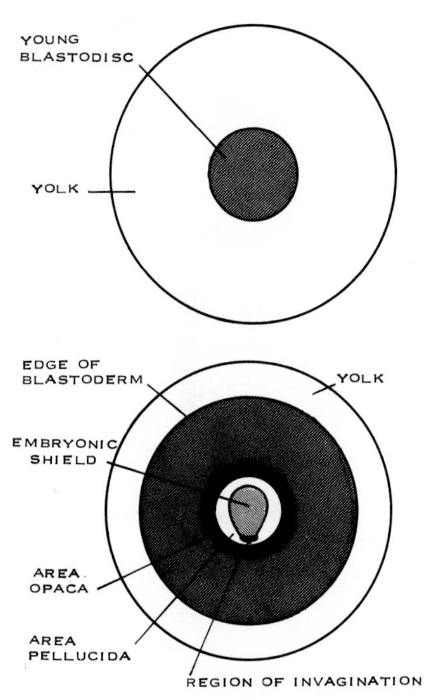

Fig. 7–21. Early and late blastula stages of turtle.
(After Pasteels, 1936.)

A reptile or bird egg, like that of a shark, consists mostly of a very large reservoir of fluid yolk, over which a thin blastodisc slowly spreads. The germ layers are first established, and the embryonic axis arises, in a central area which becomes translucent, floats on a pool of liquefied yolk (blastocoel?) (Fig. 6–8), and is called the **area pellucida** (Fig. 7–21). When endoderm and mesoderm layers have been put in place by the principal morphogenetic movements, they share the epibolic spread of the surface layer, forming an expanding **area opaca** which is attached to the yolk and slowly covers it, producing a three-layered yolk sac, as in the sharks.

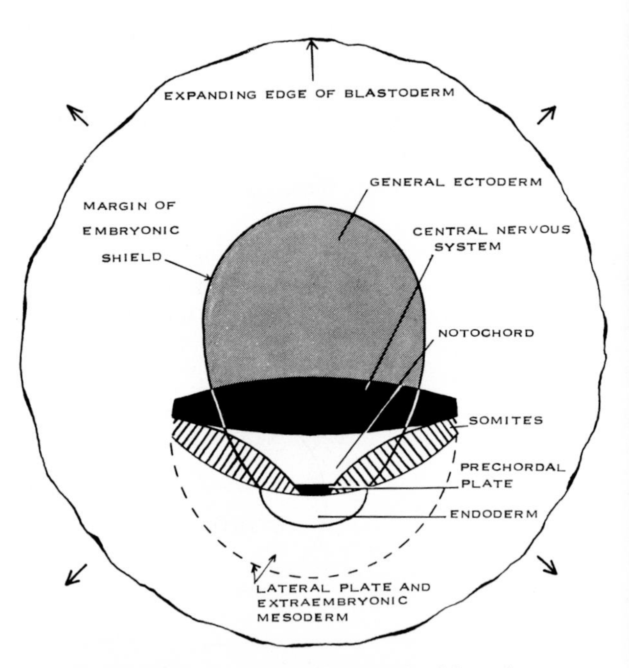

Fig. 7–22. Fate map for turtle blastula.
(After Pasteels, 1936.)

Vital-stain marking experiments [10], augmented by a technique of fixing small spots of animal charcoal to the surface of the embryo, have been used to prepare fate maps of the early blastodisc of a turtle, and the chick (Figs. 7–22, 7–23). They show the same areas in the same order along the axis of bilateral symmetry as the anamniote fate maps do: an anterior zone of presumptive general ectoderm, followed successively by zones of presumptive neural ectoderm, chordamesoderm, prechordal plate and (in the turtle) endoderm. Presumptive somite mesoderm flanks these in bilaterally symmetrical areas.

One distinctly new feature in amniotes is that this mapped area, which is elevated as a visible **embryonic shield** in the turtle (Fig. 7–21) and includes the cells from which the tissues and organs of the embryonic axis are fabricated, is centrally located in the area pellucida, separated by the expanding area opaca from the edge of the blastodisc (Fig. 7–22). Immigration of the mesoderm and endoderm takes place within the disc, and not on its periphery; and this makes room for a new area of presumptive mesoderm which wraps around the posterior end of the embryonic shield in a wide crescent. Most of these cells are designated **extraembryonic mesoderm** because they will pass into the yolk sac and the other fetal membranes, but some, by forward extension in the interior, become lateral plate or hypomere mesoderm. Outside the shield area there is also an expanse of **extraembryonic ectoderm** which will line most of the scaffold tissues: yolk sac, amnion and chorion.

If one makes allowance for certain regular deformations of the area pellucida which do not contribute directly to the pattern of the embryonic axis, the vital-stain experiments show that the turtle and the chick follow patterns of morphogenetic movements which are similar to those of the anamniotes, though with differences in timing and in the formations of maneuver. The forces of *epiboly* are mostly transformed into the production of fetal membranes, but the whole embryonic shield does widen and lengthen. Strong patterns of *convergence* are seen, involving both the prospective mesoderm and the cells of the future central nervous system. Endoderm and mesoderm cells, originally on the surface of the blastodisc, arrive at their proper layers by *ingression.* The formations through which this happens are quite new and peculiar, but the *processes* are familiar. And as in the anamniotes the cells of all the layers undergo a strong *extension* while they are being put in place along the embryonic axis.

So far as the formations of maneuver are concerned, sharp differences have been reported between turtle embryos and those of various birds. Quite early in development, the area pellucida achieves two layers, the **epiblast** and the **hypoblast.** In the turtle [10], the hypoblast apparently arises by ingression of cells through a crescentic groove or a pair of irregular furrows in the posterior sector of the epiblast. In the chick and the pigeon, modern workers find the hypoblast arising by the detachment of scattered cells from

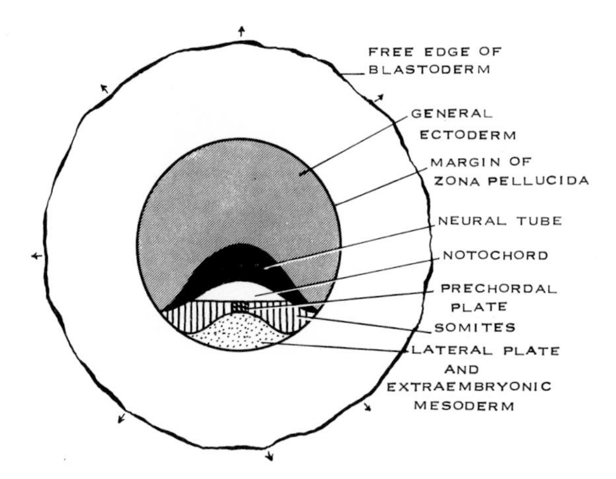

Fig. 7–23. Fate map for epiblast of unincubated chick blastoderm.
(After Pasteels, 1937.)

the lower surface of the posterior sector of the epiblast, without any localized furrows or pits. This has also been noted in the duck [13], but there is also a report that a sheetlike inrolling of cells takes place along the posterior edge of the blastodisc in this species [14]. At first in the chick the hypoblast is exceedingly thin and found only under the posterior half of the epiblast, but before the egg is laid there is a definite hypoblast throughout the area pellucida. The fate map is drawn only on the epiblast.

Mesoderm immigration takes place after the hypoblast is in place, and this also involves novel formations of maneuver. In the turtle, presumptive mesoderm cells of the epiblast converge on a new pore which deepens into a blind tube or **blastoporal canal** that extends forward in the plane of bilateral symmetry under the simultaneously converging presumptive neural area (Fig. 7–24). Presently its floor splits and the edges disperse to the sides, converting it into a mesodermal sheet in which notochord, somites, etc., shortly appear (Fig. 7–25). The endoderm sheet is reconstructed from the hypoblast layer.

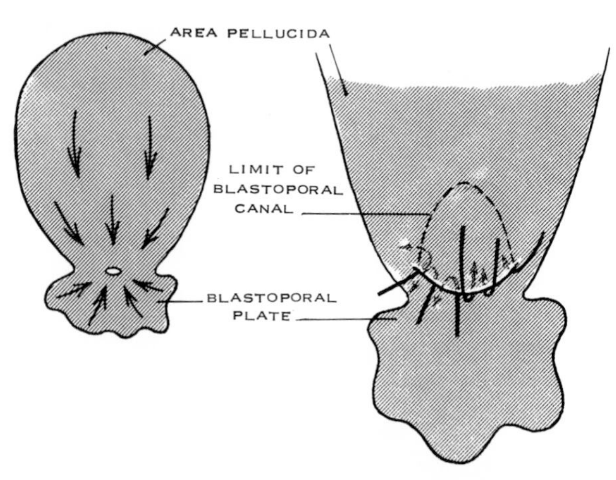

Fig. 7–24. Convergence and invagination in the young gastrula of the turtle.
(After Pasteels, 1936.)

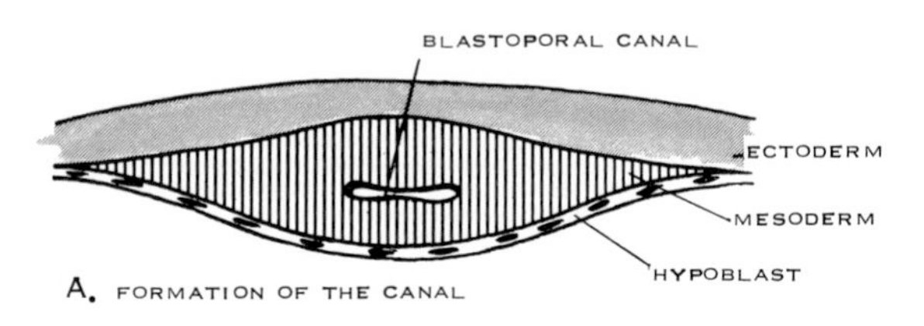

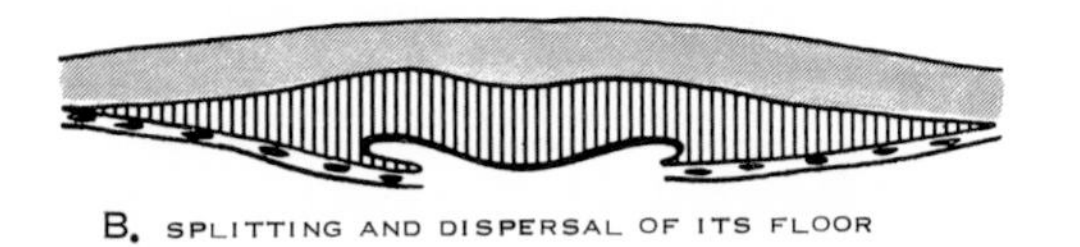

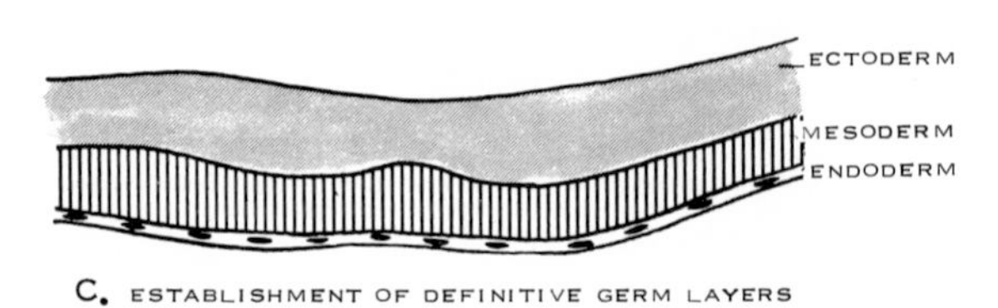

Fig. 7–25. History of turtle blastoporal canal, seen in transverse sections.
(After Pasteels, 1936.)

In birds, still another formation of maneuver appears during the early pear-shaped deformation of the two-layered area pellucida. It is the **primitive streak** (Figs. 7–26, 7–27, 7–28), which appears in the posterior midline of the epiblast. In the first 18 hours of incubation, it grows to nearly three-quarters the length of the area pellucida itself. The presumptive mesoderm cells start a general convergence movement toward it from both sides (Fig. 7–27), burrow down into it (Fig. 7–26), lose their contact with the surface epithelium, and migrate anterolaterally from it as a middle layer. In the fate map, Figure 7–23, and in A of Figure 7–27 (at 12 hours), these cells are shown in the epiblast. In B, C and D of Figure 7–27, the epiblast is cut away to indicate diagrammatically the spread of mesoderm between epiblast and hypoblast at 15, 20, and 28 hours of incubation. There is evidence [15,16] that some of these cells burrow farther and locate themselves in the hypoblast, later being found in the foregut. Thus, carbon grains placed at spots marked x in Figure 7–26, C, are carried into the hypoblast along the arrow lines.

Most of the notochordal material passes down to the middle layer from a sharply marked **primitive node** at the anterior end of the primitive streak, and extends forward underneath the simultaneously converging tissue of the presumptive neural area as a visible strand, the **notochordal process.** (The old name for this strand, "head process," is not recommended since very little of the head is formed from it.) The notochordal process of the duck embryo is penetrated by a fine tube-like space, reminiscent of the blastoporal canal of the turtle, and this happens also in some mammals.

The primitive streak lengthens while the lateral arms of the presumptive mesodermal areas of the fate map are closing in toward it. As more and more of these cells reach the streak, immigrate through it, and spread laterally in the definitive mesodermal layer (Fig. 7–27 C, D), the streak shortens again. The primitive node drifts backward with this shortening (Fig. 7–28), and at the end of the immigration period both streak and node fade from sight in a swollen center of proliferation called the **sinus rhom-**

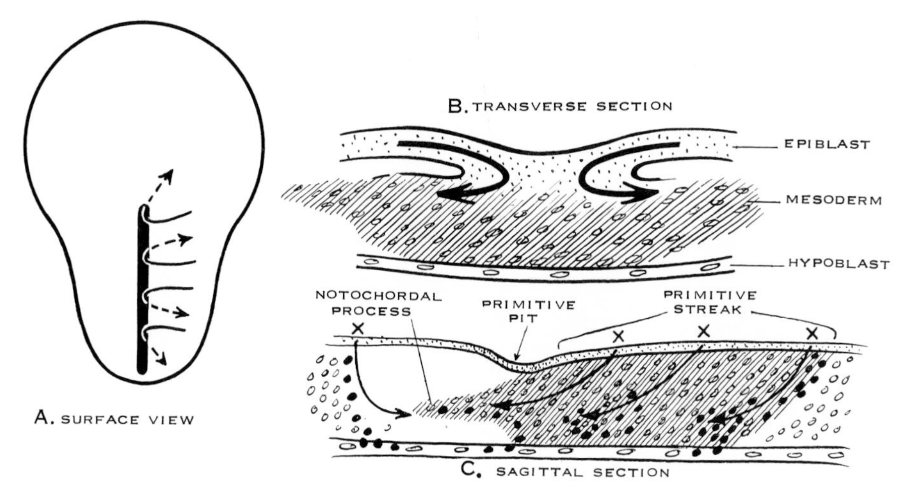

Fig. 7–26. Movements toward, through, and away from the primitive streak of the chick.
(After Pasteels, 1937, and Fraser, 1954.)

boidalis, through which much of the material of the posterior trunk and tail are assembled. The changes indicated in Figure 7–28 occur during about six hours.

The notochordal process lengthens commensurate with the shrinkage of the primitive streak and when it has reached it full anterior extent it makes contact with and adds cells to a thickened anterior crescent of the hypoblast, which is the definitive **prechordal plate** material.

The chick's endoderm layer now begins to gather itself into a **gut tube** along the midline. How much of it is formed from original hypoblast cells, and how much from cells which later immigrate through the primitive streak from the epiblast, is still in dispute [16]. Most of the hypoblast merely contributes to the yolk sac [17].

D. Mammals

Morphogenetic movements have not been rigorously studied in any mammalian embryos, because of great technical difficulties. The only

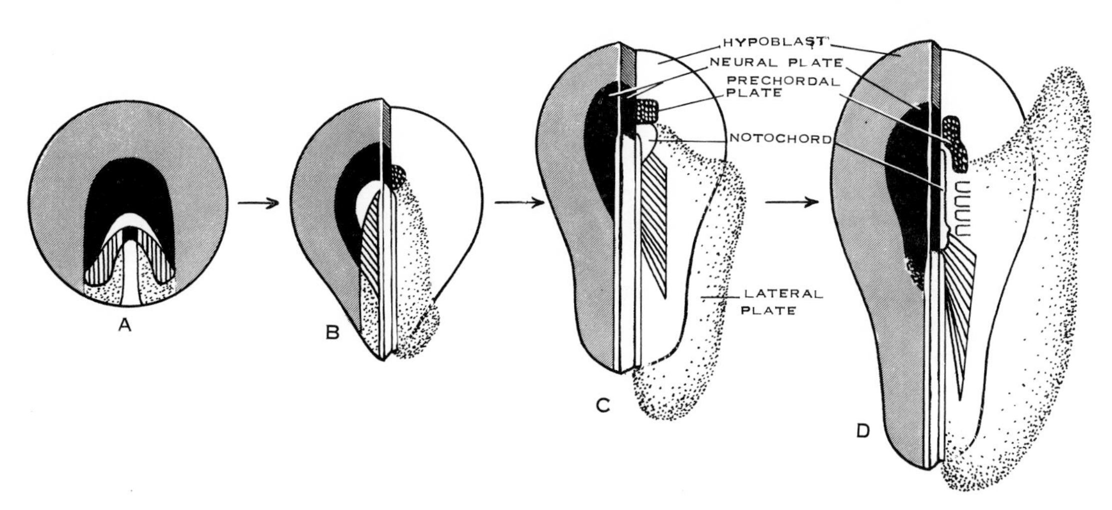

Fig. 7–27. Convergence, ingression, and extension movements on chick blastoderm during first day of incubation. Deep layer exposed on right side.
(After Pasteels, 1937.)

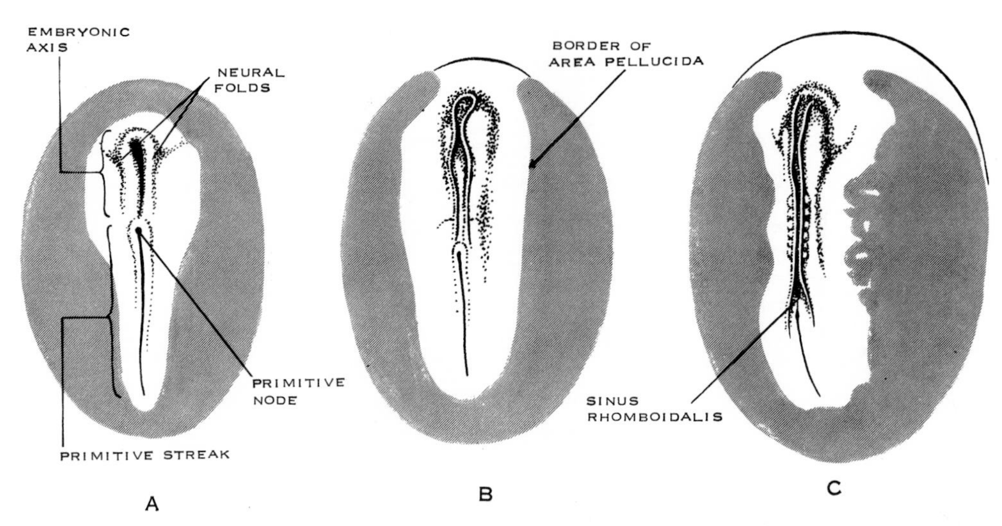

Fig. 7–28. Regression of the primitive streak.

fate maps which have been published for them are merely records of scholarly guesswork. The eggs of monotreme mammals are filled with yolk and laid in a shell, and they develop like those of reptiles. On the other hand, the embryos of eutherian mammals are yolkless, and in their early formations of maneuver they show a great variety of new features, unlike anything else in the animal kingdom. But as usual the same over-all effect is achieved: the lump of cleaving cells is rearranged into the three germ layers from which the standard patterns of the primordial embryo and the pharyngula emerge.

The morphogenetic movements can be described in reptiles and birds with relatively little reference to the formation of scaffold tissues. This is not so with the eutherian mammals, for their nearly yolkless embryos are under the necessity of establishing apparatus for getting food from the mother very soon, and their fetal membranes are being prepared even during the early cleavage stages. These structures are formally dealt with in Chapter 11, but some reference will have to be made to them here also, because of their precocious formation.

First, events will be described as they occur in the pig embryo, for this species has been studied in great detail[18] and has not departed as far from the early developmental patterns of the meroblastic amniotes as most mammals have. Secondly, variations presented by human and rat embryos will be mentioned as examples of other evolutionary experiments in the mammalian class.

Six days after fertilization, the pig egg has cleaved to 40 or 50 blastomeres, and these have arranged themselves around a cavity with a concentration of cells at one pole. This is the **blastocyst** stage, with its **inner cell mass** and **trophoblast**, as discussed in the last chapter (Fig. 6–9). During the following day the trophoblast cells which lie directly outside the inner cell mass withdraw to the sides so that the mass itself is incorporated into the surface as a flattened **germ disc** (Fig. 7–29). Cells become segregated at the inner surface of this disc to form an endoderm layer, and some of them wander out so as to line the whole blastocyst. The two-layered germ disc will furnish all the cells that form the embryo proper, while the two-layered wall of the rest of the blastocyst is involved in formation of fetal membranes.

In the next few days the blastocyst of the pig embryo rapidly elongates as a thin-walled tube, while the flat germ disc, transforming from circular to oval, remains near its middle. What is to become the posterior end of the disc thickens as a rounded mass that gradually takes shape as a **primitive streak,** and from this area mesoderm cells spread as a middle layer throughout the germinal area and out into the rest of the

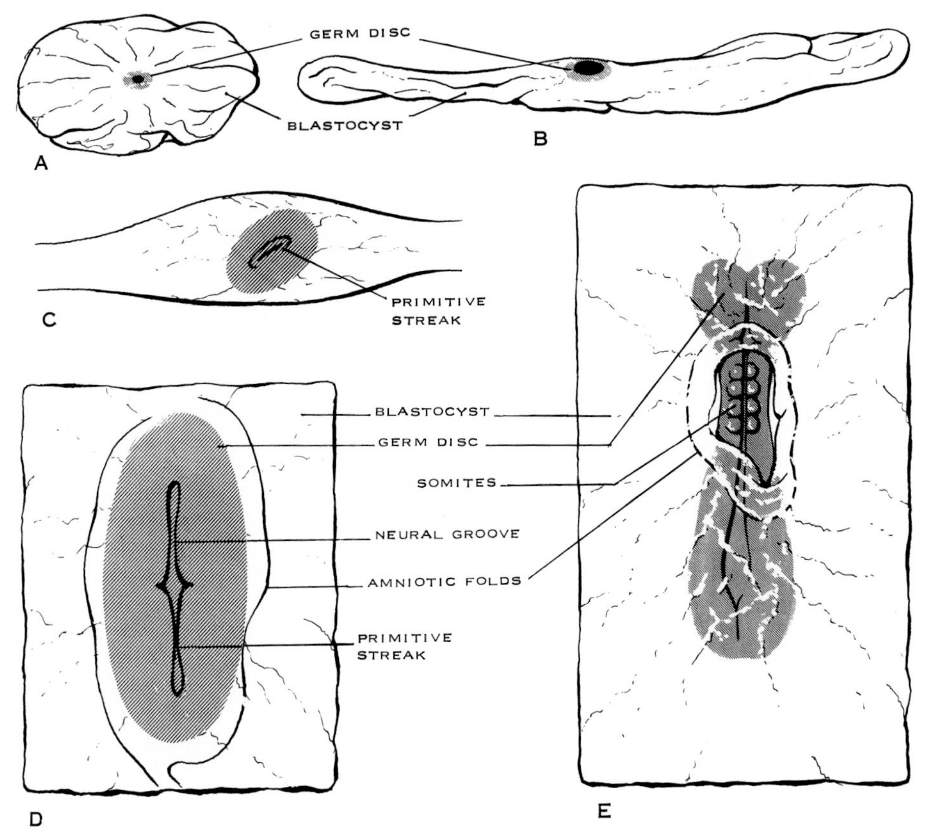

Fig. 7–29. Early development of the pig (2) (continued from Fig. 6–9).
(After Heuser and Streeter, 1929.)

blastocyst. Just anterior to the primitive streak there is a conspicuous **primitive node** whose particular function is to give off a train of notochord cells that pass forward under what shortly takes shape as the neural area.

Once the three germ layers are in place in the elongating germ disc, the primitive streak and the primitive node vanish like the similar formations of maneuver in the meroblastic amniotes, and the localized characteristics of the primordial embryo begin to show up. Although experimental data are totally lacking, there is no reason to doubt that these results have been produced by the usual pattern of *epibolic, convergent, ingressive,* and *elongating* cell movements. Except for the absence of yolk, the early aspects of pig development are not unlike those of birds and reptiles.

Some other mammals are more peculiar at these stages. In the early human embryo a blastocyst is formed, with trophoblast and inner cell mass, but its main cavity becomes filled almost at once with a loose mesh of mesenchyme-like cells called the **extraembryonic mesoderm.** This happens *before* there is any middle layer in the germ disc and even before the segregation of an endoderm layer. An endodermal "yolk sac" is formed, not by migration of endoderm cells along the inside of the trophoblast as in the pig, but by simple cavitation in the inner cell mass (Fig. 7–30). A considerable space continues to exist between this endodermal "yolk sac" and the trophoblast layer, occupied by the extraembryonic mesoderm. These differences between early human and pig embryos are striking in appearance, but may perhaps be dismissed as oddly timed formations of maneuver.

A primitive streak and primitive node are es-

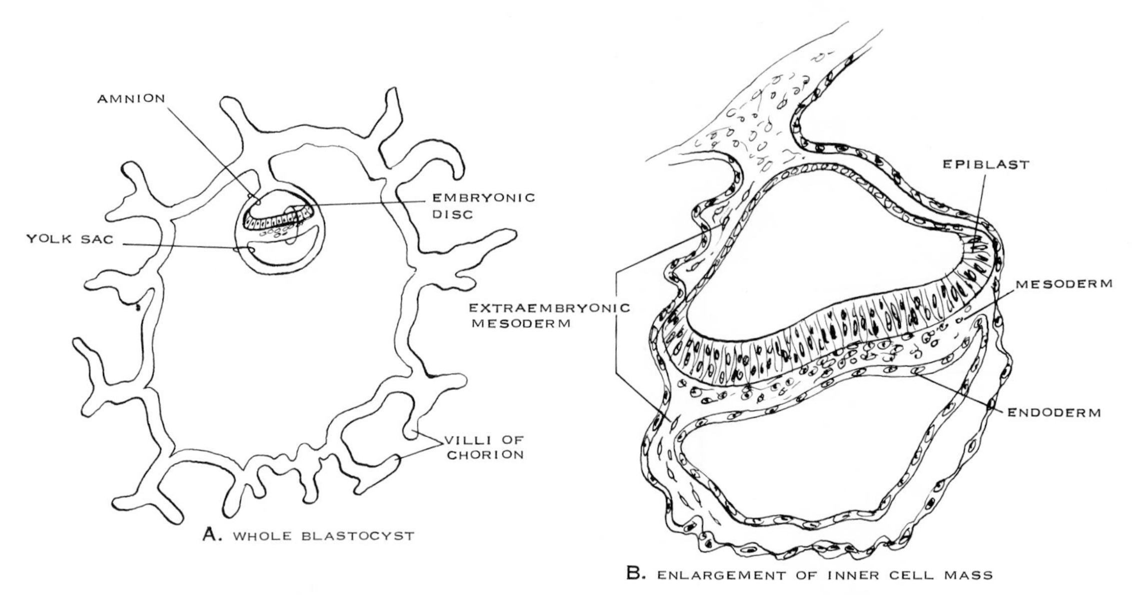

Fig. 7–30. Diagram of a human blastocyst and its embryonic disc at about sixteen days.

(After Heuser, Rock, and Hertig, 1945.)

tablished on the human germ disc. When mesodermal ingression is well under way through these structures, a **notochordal canal** may be formed in the primitive node, extending downward and forward. Pigs do not show this feature though they remain primitive in most other respects. It is somewhat variable in the human embryo, though seen regularly in some other mammals, and in the duck. The human notochordal canal may even perforate temporarily into the "yolk sac" cavity, reminiscent of the turtle's blastoporal canal. It is a temporary formation of maneuver associated with the ingression of chordamesoderm cells.

In early embryos of rats and mice, structural arrangements are odd indeed [19]. The inner cell mass, instead of taking its place as a flat germ disc at one pole of a spherical blastocyst, hangs down as a long pendant in a trophoblastic tube (Fig. 7–31). Most of the length of the pendant is composed of cells which will be involved in the formation of fetal membranes and temporary extraembryonic structures, and only its free tip is destined to contribute to the anatomy of the embryo itself. Even here, the endoderm does not appear as the lower layer of a flat germ disc, but as an outer bag of cells which enclose the prospective embryonic ectoderm and mesoderm. The primordial embryo, in fact, develops inside out at the bottom of the pendant, and only turns itself right side out when a dozen or more pairs of somites have been laid down and the neural folds are beginning to close.

The significance of these bizarre modifications is unknown. Not all rodents have this inversion of germ layers; in fact some of them have quite conventional and primitive early stages. It is worth noting again however that these evolutionary experiments concern merely formations of maneuver. Almost, it seems, in spite of them, the layers of the primordial embryo and their local specializations and the tissue and organ patterns of the pharyngula stage are re-created just as they are in other classes and orders of the vertebrates.

IV. SUMMARY REMARKS ON THE PERIOD OF MORPHOGENETIC MOVEMENTS

A. Anatomical Diversity

In this early period of development, the underlying similarities are not easily expressed in terms of visible structures. The holoblastic an-

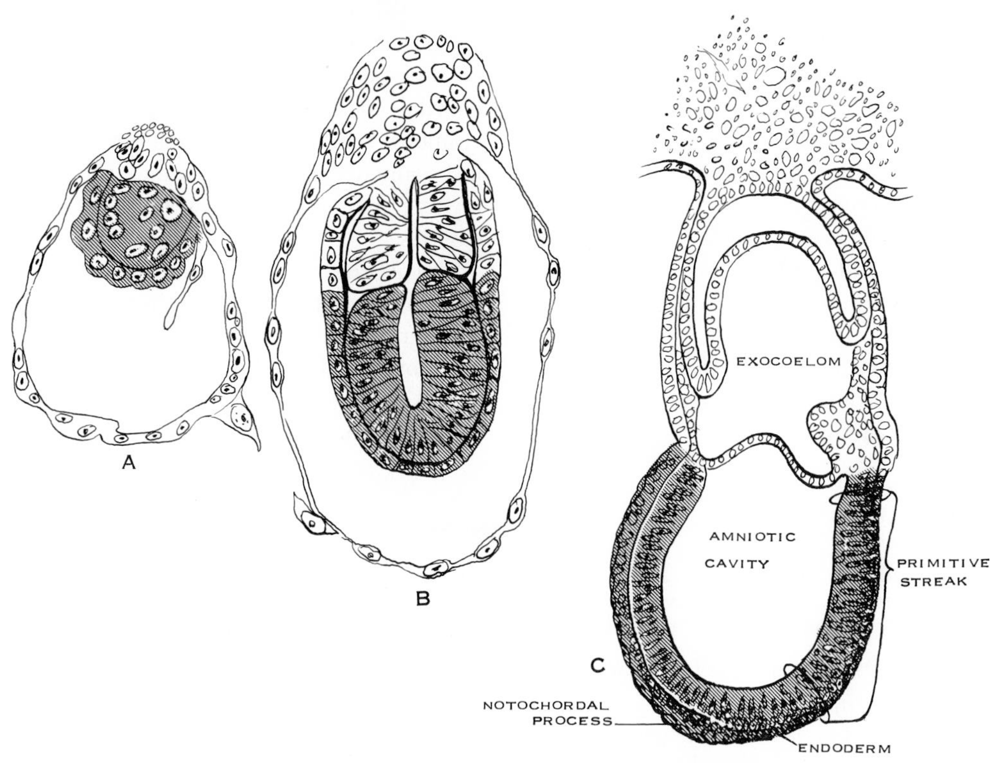

Fig. 7–31. Early development of the mouse.
(After G. D. Snell, Biology of the Laboratory Mouse, 1941, by permission of McGraw-Hill Book Co., Inc.)

amniotes have a blastopore and a gastrocoel, the meroblastic ones do not. Yolk may be held within cells, or may be tanked in a two-layered or a three-layered yolk sac, or may be practically absent. Blastula surfaces may be spheres or nearly flat discs. There may be an invagination of cells bound to a surface coat, or a mere ingression of de-epithelized cells, either at the edge of a blastodisc or in toward the center of it. Some groups of vertebrates show a primitive streak, others have a notochordal canal, and most have neither. Endoderm and mesoderm may be invaginated simultaneously through the same structure, or these things may occur separately in time and place. The amniotes are engaged in the formation of fetal membranes at these stages, the anamniotes are not.

But these structures are functional adaptations to particular ways of embryonic and fetal life, or they are formations of maneuver. They neither interfere with the underlying morphogenetic processes nor leave significant marks on the anatomy of the grown individual.

B. Dynamic Similarities

It is in the processes, rather than the structures, of these early stages in morphogenesis, that the common heritage of vertebrates is revealed. The following generalizations are probably true of all vertebrates:

(a) When there has been enough cleavage to cut the blastomeres down to a certain size, all the cells are set in motion with respect to each other.

(b) These movements, or at least the ones destined to contribute to the formation of the primordial embryo itself, are bilaterally symmetrical about a midline axis, and are polarized in the anteroposterior sense.

(c) The embryonic area is temporarily a single thick layer of cells, including within it not only presumptive ectoderm but also presumptive endoderm and mesoderm. Then they sort out into separate layers, which usually involves movement of many presumptive mesoderm and endoderm cells from the surface to the interior by invagination or ingression.

(d) The embryonic axis becomes defined by right and left convergence movements toward the midline, in all three germ layers. This is accompanied and followed by marked extension movements which rapidly elongate the axis.

(e) Dispersive movements of the cells farthest from the embronic axis close up the yolk in a yolk sac of some sort, or set up a scaffold of fetal membranes, or both.

(f) While the middle germ layer is becoming separated from the endoderm after invagination or ingression, it separates into a midline notochordal strip, paired and segmenting strips of epimere, and sheetlike hypomere mesoderm. The last named quickly splits into inner and outer layers which contain between them the coelomic cavities.

(g) At the same time the presumptive central nervous system segregates from the rest of the ectoderm by a convergence movement and forms a hollow midline tube.

(h) The endoderm cells shape themselves into a longitudinal tube below the notochord.

REFERENCES

1. Vogt, W., 1929. *Wilhelm Roux' Arch. Entwicklungsmech. Organ.* 120: 385–706. Every embryology student should examine this classic at first hand.
2. Pasteels, J., 1942. *J. Exptl. Zool.* 89: 255.
3. Holtfreter, J., 1943, 1944. *J. Exptl. Zool.* 94: 261 and 95: 171. A penetrating study, revealing above all how little the process of gastrulation is understood.
4. Costello, D. P., 1955. Cleavage, blastulation and gastrulation. *In* B. H. Willier, P. A. Weiss, and V. Hamburger (eds.), *Analysis of development.* W. B. Saunders Co., Philadelphia.
5. Townes, P. L., and J. Holtfreter, 1955. *J. Exptl. Zool.* 128: 53.
6. Weiss, P., and A. C. Taylor, 1960. *Proc. Nat. Acad. Sci.* U.S. 46: 1177.
7. Weiss, P., 1947. *Yale J. Biol. Med.* 19: 235. This is a thoughtful and pioneer effort to establish such a theory.
8. Pasteels, J., 1940. *Biol. Revs.* 15: 59.
9. Devillers, Ch., 1961. *Advances in Morphogenesis* 1: 379. Structural and dynamic aspects of the development of the teleostean egg.
10. Pasteels, J., 1936, 1937. *Arch. biol.* (*Liège*) 47: 205, 48: 105, and 48: 381. Comparative studies of morphogenetic movements in trout, turtle, and chick.
11. Oppenheimer, J. M., 1947. *Quart. Rev. Biol.* 22: 105.
12. Vandebroek, G., 1936. *Arch. biol.* (*Liège*) 47: 499.
13. Pasteels, J., 1945. *Anat. Record* 93: 5.
14. Lutz, H., 1955. *J. Embryol. Exptl. Morphol.* 3: 59.
15. Hunt, T. E., 1937. *Anat. Record* 68: 449.
16. Vakaet, L., 1962. *J. Embryol. Exptl. Morphol.* 10: 38.
17. Fraser, R. C., 1954. *J. Exptl. Zool.* 126: 349.
18. Heuser, C. H., and G. L. Streeter, 1929. *Contrib. Embryol.* 20: 1, *Carnegie Inst. Wash. Publ.* 394.
19. Snell, G. D., 1941. *The biology of the laboratory mouse.* Blakiston Division, McGraw-Hill Book Co., Inc., New York.

8

Early Organogenesis: I

Chapter 7 described the movements of sheets or masses of cells, through which the three-layered primordial embryo was established. Chapters 8 and 9 will carry these processes toward the pharyngula, in a period which sees the drift of sheets of cells gradually quieting down, while new qualities of morphogenetic movements become prominent. More and more, the emphasis is shifted to local transformations in the shapes and arrangements of cells, and it is these which bring the anlagen of organs into sight. This chapter will characterize the new types of development, and focus on some things happening in the endoderm and mesoderm, leaving the ectodermal events for Chapter 9.

There is no sharp break between the main period of morphogenetic movements and the onset of these new and more specialized activities. Organs are being established at the head end of the embryo by the new local rearrangements before the germ layers have been put in place at the tail end by the less complex sheet drifts. Even at the primordial-embryo stage some anlagen are visible, for instance the neural plate, the notochord, and the early somites. But by the pharyngula stage the localized and specialized morphogenetic movements have so broken up and intermingled the germ layers that they are no longer easily recognized. They have been replaced by constellations of organ rudiments, and the basic pattern of verterbate anatomy has become visible.

During this transition period, the subtle and invisible process of **determination** is taking place. This is the action by which the developmental potential of a cell is reduced from its maximum, and narrowed to a single channel. The undivided egg has the ability to form all tissues and all organs. Vital-stain experiments can reveal what the normal fate of each cell is, but other sorts of experiments (cf. Chapter 10) show that a "presumptive muscle cell" at the blastula stage, i.e., one which the fate map predicts will become a muscle cell (though it shows no signs of doing so yet), still retains the capacity to form an epidermal cell, or take part in forming brain, or kidney, or skeleton. However, when this cell has had its fate determined, it can only form a muscle cell.

One has hinted previously that utterly new elements are introduced into development by the juxtaposition of the germ layers. Through the morphogenetic movements new kinds of contact reactions have been made possible between cells of different origins, in all parts of the embryo. As Chapter 10 will show, some types and degrees of determination are already detectable in some parts of the primordial embryo, but in most parts, and in increasing degrees, determination is the fruit of these new interactions between the zones and layers. The new local patterns of morphogenetic movements in the pre-pharyngula stages are, in most if not all cases, visible evidences of the progress of determination.

I. GENERAL CONSIDERATIONS

A. Anteroposterior Course of Development

In all bilaterally symmetrical animals, embryonic differentiation starts sooner and goes to greater lengths at the head end than at mid-trunk or in the tail. Vertebrate embryos show this as clearly as any. After the blastula or blastodisc stage, the first tissues to immigrate to the embryonic axis sector of the interior proceed promptly to the future head region. The first differentiations in the endoderm sheet—the paired pharynx pouches and the liver pouch—arise at the head end. The serially repeated patterns of somites and kidney tubules that break up the mesodermal sheet appear first in the head, and new members of each series are added in anteroposterior sequence.

Anterior organs such as the brain, heart, and liver, commence their growth earlier and more rapidly than others, and quickly become the largest parts of the embryo. Cellular differentiations in longitudinally distributed organ systems start earlier and complete themselves sooner in the head than in the trunk, and sooner in the trunk than in the tail—for instance the vacuolization of notochord cells, the shaping up of nerve ganglia, the extension of the axons and dendrites of neurons, the acquisition of contractility in muscle cells, the condensation of vertebrae, etc.

This general principle that development proceeds in anteroposterior sequence is subject to one reservation so far as modern vertebrates are concerned: there is a slight retardation of development in the most anterior part of the head. The first point of closure of the neural folds is at the midbrain level rather than the tip of the forebrain. When pharynx clefts break through, the second (hyobranchial) pair generally open before the first (hyomandibular) pair. The first somites to form are found just back of the ear vesicle, and the pre-otic somite material may segment later in posteroanterior order or it may never undergo true segmentation at all.

The paired mandibular segment is the first of its series in modern vertebrates, but fossil cephalaspids show another whole pair anterior to that. Certain technical details of the head morphology of recent vertebrates fit with the idea that this premandibular apparatus has been strongly repressed but not altogether wiped out in the evolutionary lines that have survived to modern times.

With these minor reservations, the anteroposterior progression of development is a conspicuous feature of the pre-pharyngula period. It is gradually superseded by localized patterns of differentiation, and is no longer an important characteristic of the whole embryo's development after the pharyngula stage.

B. Continuance of Placement of Germ Layers

The movements of *epiboly, convergence, immigration,* and *extension* continue long after the pattern of the primordial embryo has been achieved. A very conspicuous example is **neurulation,** the process of convergence over the surface which packs the cells of the presumptive neural area closer to the midline and leads to their rearrangement into a neural tube.

The neural area or **medullary plate** of the amblystoma embryo occupies at first nearly a third of the embryonic surface, and its edges are prominently raised as neural folds (see end-paper, back cover). As this plate sinks in, the neural folds roll toward each other. When the folds actually meet, the rim on the right side between the thick neural plate and the thin presumptive epidermis meets that of the left side, and the two pairs of homologous tissues fuse. This not only closes the presumptive nervous tissue into a neural tube but also cuts it off from a now continuous roof of covering epidermis. The neural tube is hollow from the time it is formed, and its lining consists of some of the surface coat that was originally on the outside of the blastula.

Since the first closure of neural folds is at the

future midbrain level and proceeds both anteriorly and posteriorly, the primordial embryo has for a while both an **anterior** and a **posterior neuropore,** where the neural tube opens to the surface (Figs. 7–28, 8–1). Both these formations of maneuver normally disappear before the pharyngula stage.

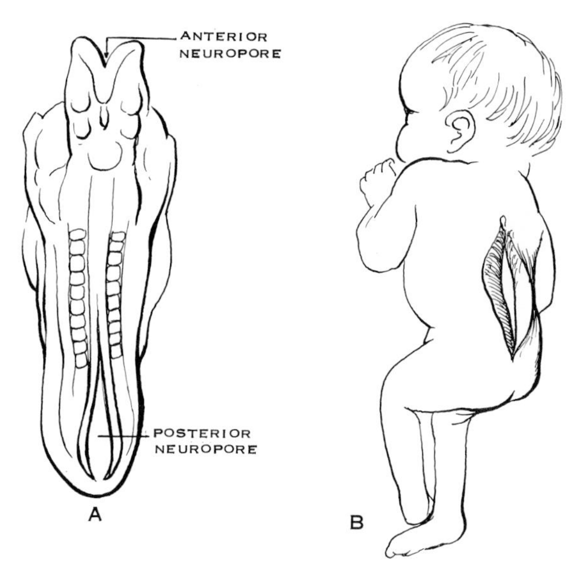

Fig. 8–1. Neuropores and rachischisis in man.
(After F. Payne, 1924.)

Normally the posterior neuropore rather quickly drifts to the end of the trunk and closes there. If it fails to close, the result is an anomaly called **rachischisis** (Fig. 8–1), in which the vertebral column also remains defective, and the spinal cord and its membranes are exposed at the surface. The caudal part of the neural tube is established in a solid tailbud, along with the notochord and the somites of the tail, by a combination of cell proliferations and *extension* movements.

In most vertebrates the neural tube is formed in the way just described for the amblystoma. But in teleosts, which are characteristically barren of formations of maneuver, the prospective neural area does not throw up neural folds. Instead, tube formation takes place quite directly by rearrangement of cells down the length of a solid neural keel (Fig. 8–2).

The mechanics of the neurulation process in the amphibian embryo are as little understood as are those of blastopore invagination, but some of the same factors have been seen at work. The surface coat of the neural plate contracts, and small bottle cells appear at the inner borders of the neural folds (cf. Fig. 7–4). Dissociation and recombination of the cells of the amblystoma primordial embryo show that these neural plate cells have acquired a property which they lacked a few hours earlier, namely that when they are jumbled together with presumptive epidermal cells they prefer and seek the interior position. Also, if the neural plate cells are dissociated and then cultured in a formless

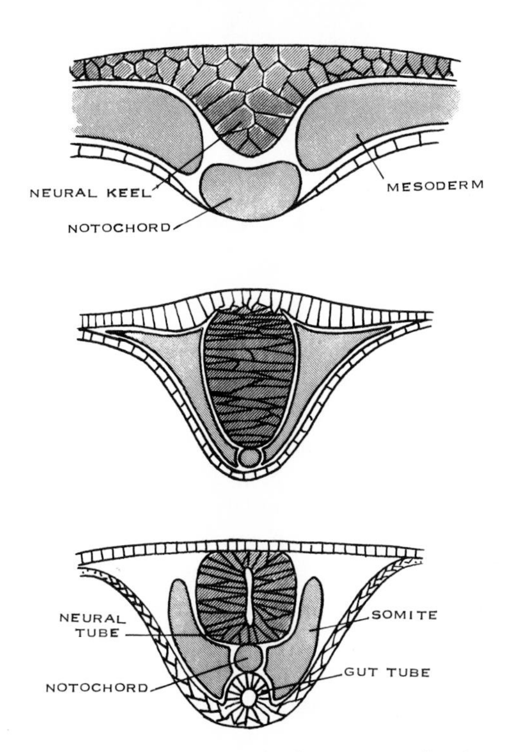

Fig. 8–2. Formation of teleost neural tube.
(After H. V. Wilson, 1889.)

cluster, they will very soon rearrange themselves about fluid-filled cavities resembling the normal neural tube. One may guess that these cell properties are more significant in the normal neurulation process than the more spectacular elevation and closure of neural folds, which teleosts dispense with.

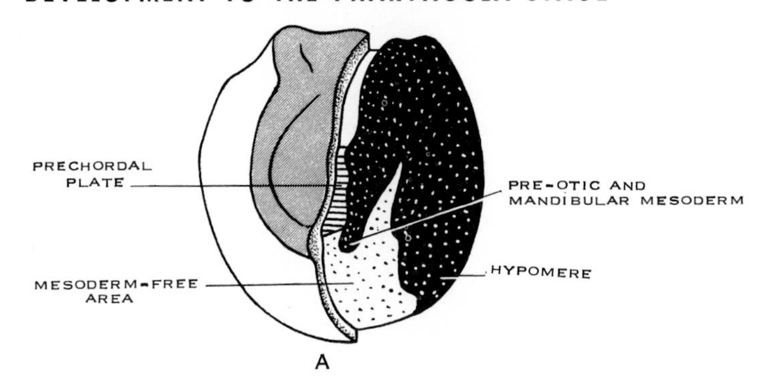

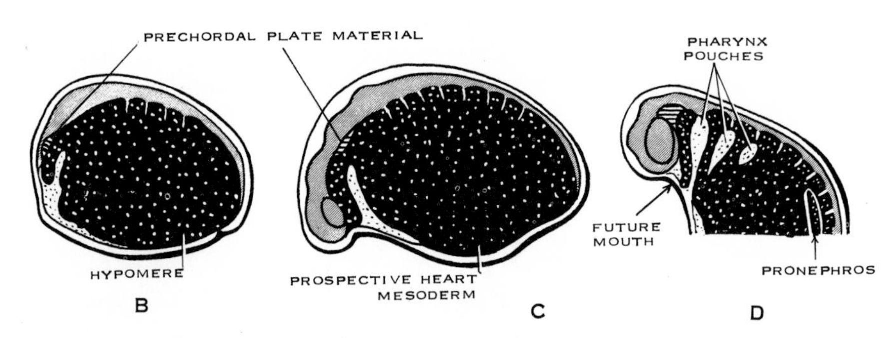

Fig. 8–3. Mesoderm placement in the amblystoma. A. Anterior view of neurula, left side skinned to show mesoderm. B, C, D. Left views, skinned, at 4, 7 and 12 somite stages.
(After H. B. Adelmann, 1932.)

While the neural tube is taking form, the prospective mesoderm sheet is still actively drifting, both on the outside of the embryo and in the interior. Figure 8–3, A, shows the amblystoma neurula with the left side skinned to show its progress within. There is still a large mesoderm-free area in the anteroventral quadrant, i.e., in the future heart–liver area. Figure 8–3, B, shows the 4-somite stage, when the blastopore has closed to a tiny slit. A strip of unsegmented mesoderm lies anteriorly, in line with the first few somites, representing the unsegregated preotic head somites and the mandibular mesoderm. The hypomere, or lateral plate mesoderm, is advancing along the flanks, but a great deal of it, as well as the material for the somites of most of the trunk and all of the tail, is still undergoing active *extension* and *invagination* on the outside of the embryo.

Further extension of the mandibular mesoderm lobes ventrally from the two sides (Fig. 8–3 C, D) brings them into contact with each other in the midventral line, isolating a small anterior patch of the mesoderm-free area from the rest. This patch is never entered by mesoderm, and it is the place where the mouth later breaks through. The advancing hypomere mesoderm gradually fills the more posterior area, by a wheeling together of free lateral plate edges from the right and left sides. The line of fusion of these hypomere sheets contains the presumptive heart tissue.

Similar events take place in other vertebrates, though with differences in timing. A mesoderm-free area gradually narrows down to the mouth region as the mesoderm sheets advance along the two sides. The meeting of these sheets in the presumptive heart area takes place in urodeles at an early tailbud stage, but in anura much earlier, during closure of the neural folds. In the amniotes, even before these lateral-plate edges meet, heart tissues have begun to form in them.

The lateness of the last immigration move-

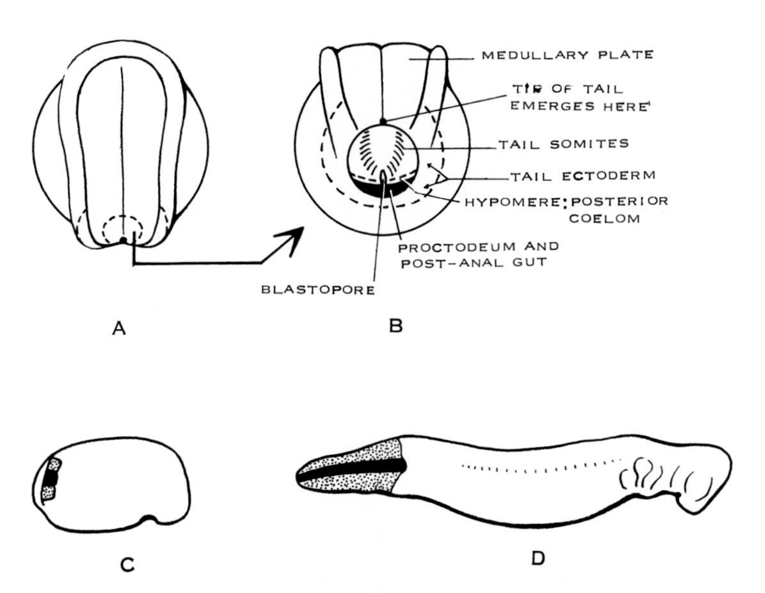

Fig. 8–4. Location of prospective tail materials at the neurula stage in urodeles.
(Amblystoma (A, B) after J. H. Bijtel, 1936. Taricha (C, D) after M. Schechtman, 1932.)

ments was little appreciated until the application of vital-stain techniques. When the amblystoma neural folds have moved halfway to closure (Fig. 8–4 A, B), the material of three quarters of the trunk somites and all of the tail still lies on the surface. These cells can produce a good deal of extension when they move inside and line up along the body axis (Fig. 8–4 C, D). When the primitive streak of the chick has all but disappeared, the presumptive mesoderm of a number of trunk somites and all those of the tail still lie on the surface of the sinus rhomboidalis (Fig. 7–28). The extreme concentration of the materials for the tail prior to invagination shows that a great deal of spreading and growth must take place during the developments of the next few days.

The vertebrate tailbud used to be considered as a special sort of growth center or blastema from which the tail organs were spun out directly, without formal delineation of germ layers. It has been made clear by the vital-stain experiments that this is not so. The presumptive somite and spinal cord materials of the tail can be located on the outside of the amphibian embryo just as their counterparts of the trunk can be. They are brought inside by the continuation of the same morphogenetic movements that act to assemble the trunk section. So far as amphibia are concerned, it was a surprise to find that, when the neural folds begin to arise, the mesoderm of the tail is located across the posterior end of the neural plate (Fig. 8–4). Therefore, this material invaginates through the closure of the neural folds rather than by movement through the blastopore. Once it is inside, it begins to elongate in direct sequence with the trunk somites and in conjunction with the normally placed spinal cord material of the tail. This elongation is what produces the tailbud. It all lies above the blastopore, for the tail does not receive any hypomere mesoderm.

In addition to convergence and immigration, extension movements are also conspicuous following the primordial-embryo stage. The length of the trunk is considerably more than doubled before the pharyngula stage (Fig. 8–5). Cell division is not an important factor in this growth, for the rate of mitosis is only moderate, and not especially increased in the regions which are most rapidly extending. In anamniotes, the swelling and stiffening of the notochord starts at the head end, and progresses rapidly caudad. This straightens the previously curved back and

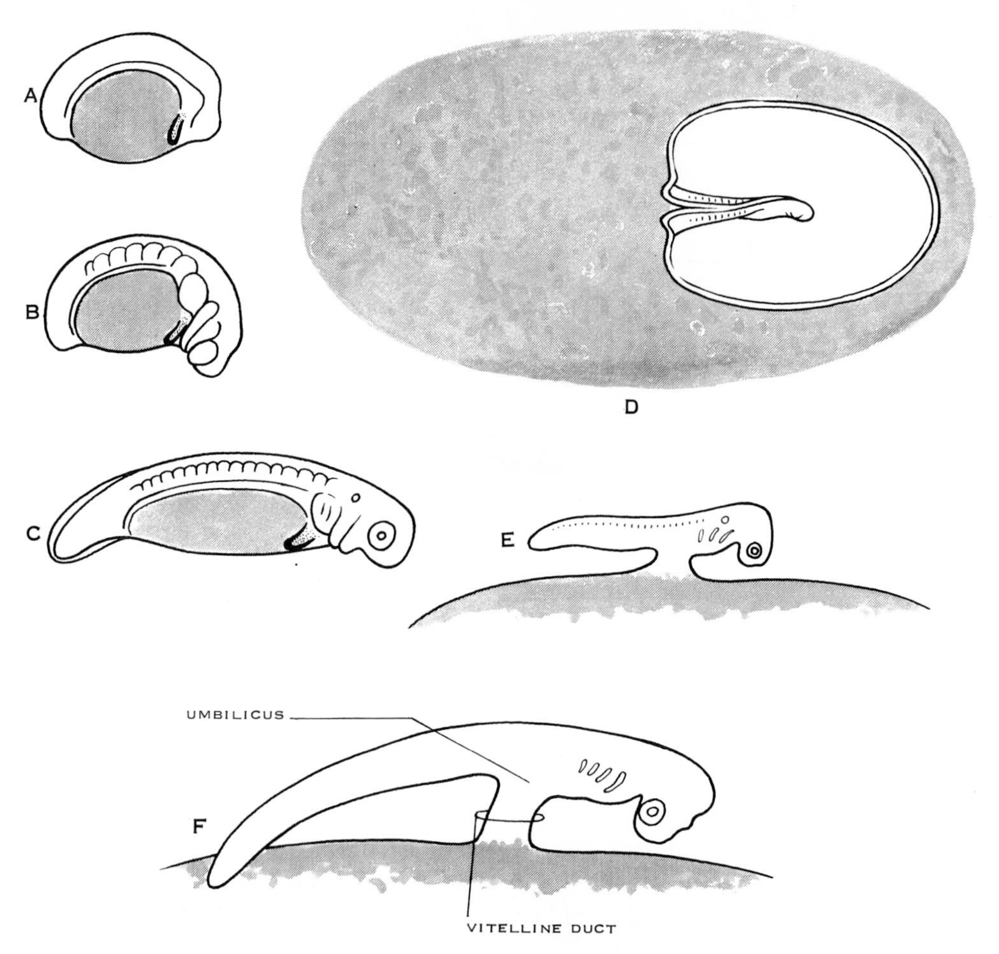

Fig. 8–5. Elongation and undercutting of the body axis in amblystoma and shark.

(Shark after R. E. Scammon, in Keibel's Normentafeln, Vol. 12, 1911, by permission of Gustav Fischer Verlag.)

tail, but all the tissues must share in this extension. The most important element in the lengthening process is undoubtedly the continued convergence and immigration of mesoderm, followed by stretching of the cells as soon as they find their place in the body axis.

One consequence of trunk extension is a remarkable drift of the covering ectoderm. Without great increase in its cell numbers, it not only has to take the place of the late-inturning mesoderm but it also has to cover the relatively enormous part of the trunk and tail produced by this material once it gets inside. As a natural result, round spots of vital stain placed on the general ectoderm at the closure of the neural folds are pulled out into long bands (Fig. 8–6).

Some curious formations of maneuver arise at the posterior end of the trunk during the assembly of the tailbud materials. In most species of anura, the posterior neuropore is finally brought so far back that it is in close proximity with the tiny remaining blastopore and the two openings are enclosed in a common pit by epiboly. Since the blastopore is the primordial anus, leading to the archenteron, there is thus created a passageway that connects the cavity of the central nervous system with that of the gut. It is named the **neurenteric canal.** Oddly enough, a similar neurenteric canal is temporarily opened up in various kinds of vertebrate embryos, in-

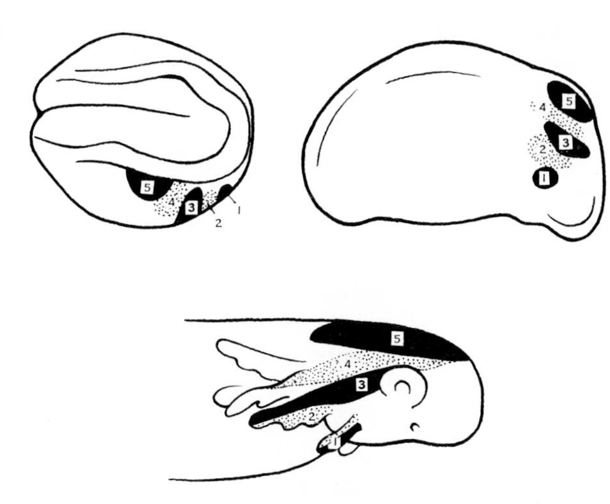

Fig. 8–6. Drift of the amblystoma head ectoderm. Five patches stained at stage 15 and followed to stage 39.
(After E. Carpenter, 1937.)

cluding some which do not have an open blastopore. Perhaps it is the result of tensions on cells in a borderline spot where the sheet-movements of immigration and neuralization contend with each other. As soon as the tail tissues are in place and begin to extend themselves, the neurenteric canal is crowded out of existence.

In most amphibia, the blastopore never closes but persists as a **primary anus.** In some genera of anura, however, it does close, and a secondary anus is produced later by perforation of a midventral area where the endoderm and ectoderm are fused together. In the meroblastic vertebrates which do not have either an open blastopore or a gastrocoel, the anus is always formed by such a secondary perforation.

Due to the close association of the presumptive spinal cord and the mesoderm and epidermis of the tail with the posterior end of the archenteron at the time the tailbud is being assembled, it is not surprising that a slight prolongation of the endoderm, called the **post-anal gut** is also drawn into the base of the tail with them when they begin to extend. This small blind tube is apparently an accidental and valueless by-product of the morphogenetic movements of tailbud formation. It appears and as quickly disappears, in all vertebrates.

Certain other maneuvers of the germ layers in the period of early organogenesis remain to be mentioned but will be discussed in later chapters. These include the establishment of fetal membranes in the amniotes (Chapter 11), and the closure of the gut tube in both amniotes and elasmobranchs. The gut tube of holoblastic anamniote embryos is formed quite simply as a result of the conversion of the gastrocoel into an archenteron by dorsomedial extensions of the endoderm, excluding mesoderm from the roof (Fig. 7–10). In teleosts the narrow strand of endoderm cells merely rearranges itself into a tube as it separates from the mesoderm (Figs. 8–2, 8–7). In the sharks and amniotes on the other hand (Fig. 8–5), the endoderm is at first

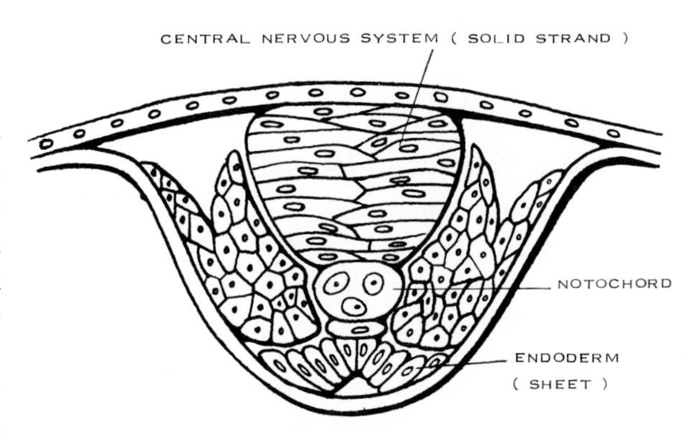

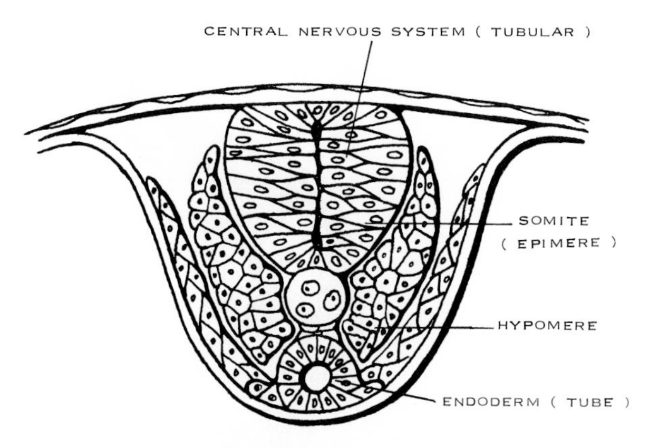

Fig. 8–7. Neural and gut tube formation in a teleost. Cross-sections of trunk of sea bass embryos at 39 and 45 hours of development.
(After H. V. Wilson, 1889.)

a flat sheet extending out over the yolk mass, and it has to be modeled into a tube by an undercutting process, which takes place at the same time that the rapidly elongating head, trunk, and tailbud are being lifted up and extended beyond the yolk mass.

This conversion of the endoderm sheet into a tube starts first at the head end and progresses caudad. Later it starts at the anterior border of the future cloaca and progresses craniad. There are thus two blind sections of gut being formed separately, a **foregut** and a **hindgut**, and as they extend toward each other the originally wide contact of the future gut with the yolk mass is gradually restricted to a narrow umbilical opening, which eventually has to be closed. The yolk sac, which is being gradually emptied by the conversion of its supply into food for the growing embryo, comes to dangle from this opening by a tube, the **vitelline duct** (Fig. 8–5).

C. New Patterns of Movement

While these movements of sheets of cells are running their course, local activities become increasingly evident. All of the smaller organs become visible through the assembly and rearrangement of minor groups of cells. Even some tissue differentiations, for instance the maturing of neurons and of muscle fibers, involve marked changes in the shape of individual cells, and therefore are partly morphogenetic movements. In fact, if all such pattern-creating and pattern-adjusting processes are included in the term, one can say that the new localized kinds of morphogenetic movements persist throughout the life of the individual. Several of the new types may be mentioned.

1. Segmentation. The essence of the movement of segmentation is the breaking of a continuous strip of epimeric mesoderm cells into a longitudinal series of somite blocks, each arranged around a common center. This is an important event in the development of many invertebrate phyla as well as the vertebrates, but practically nothing is known about its causation or mechanics. Some amphibia regularly produce only a few dozen pairs of somites, some produce several hundred. The number produced in some fishes can be altered experimentally by controlling temperature [1].

When the somites are first formed, the cells group themselves about central foci which may (according to the species) be large open cavities called **myocoels**, at first in open communication with the unsegmented coelomic cavity (Fig. 8–8); or they may be closed spaces, or collapsed but virtual cavities. Sometimes their centers are merely suggested by a cluster of pigment where the cells come together. Myocoels, which are formations of maneuver, soon disappear without a trace.

The **primary segmentation**, which consists in

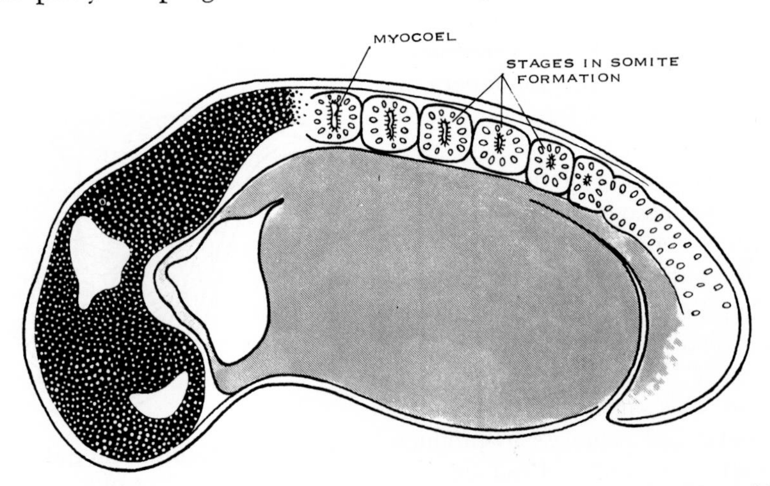

Fig. 8–8. Primary segmentation. Parasagittal section of a stage 29 amblystoma.

formation of paired somites, sets in motion other processes which result in **secondary segmentation** of some of the surrounding tissues and organs. Thus, at the pharyngula stage, the spinal nerves and their ganglia, and the blood vessels of the flanks, have secondarily acquired a segmentation from their association with the somites.

2. *Tube Formation.* Many epithelial cells show a tendency to assemble in the form of tubes. It is not clear why. Examples of this have already been seen in the gut endoderm and neural plate. Smaller and more localized tubules are formed in considerable numbers in the kidneys and in the anlagen of various glands. The primitive kidney duct of each side spins itself out from the head region all the way back to the cloaca, starting shortly after the primordial-embryo pattern has been defined. In both the amphibia and birds it has been shown that this is not accomplished by growth or by accretion from the successive segments through which it passes, so much as by a process of extension; i.e., it is a true morphogenetic movement [2].

The most ubiquitous example of tubule formation is the assembling of mesenchyme cells to form the linings of blood vessels. Nothing is known about the mechanics of this process, either.

3. *Invagination and Evagination.* The central nervous tube has hardly closed before a pair of substantial pouches grow out from the ventrolateral walls of its forebrain region. These evaginating **optic vesicles** pinch away from the brain on **optic stalks** and form conspicuous bulges on the side of the head. They do not contain an unusual ratio of dividing to non-dividing cells, so that their formation must be attributed to local morphogenetic movements rather than to the pressure of growth following mitosis. The same can be said for the paired endodermal pouches which push laterally from the pharynx walls at a slightly later period. These evaginating **pharyngeal pouches** are matched on the outside of the embryo by more or less distinct invaginations called **branchial grooves.** Each pouch tends to press through the intervening unsegmented lateral-plate mesoderm and meet its corresponding groove to form a two-layered **closing plate,** which may break through to form a pharyngeal cleft (Fig. 5–10).

Another conspicuous case of evagination from the endoderm is furnished by the midventral liver pouch. In amphibia (Fig. 7–12) and lampreys this is first composed of thick yolky cells, but in other vertebrates (Fig. 8–11) it is turned out as a very small patch of thin epithelium. Little is known about the cause or mechanics of such local pocketings.

4. *Assembly by Migration.* Certain organs are formed by cells that leave the neural plate or neural tube and penetrate casually into the mesoderm to form localized clusters, for instance the spinal ganglia. Certain thickened areas of the head epidermis, called **placodes,** serve as the sources for similar migrations. For instance the small sense organs called **neuromasts,** of which the lateral line system of fishes and amphibia is composed (Fig. 15–2), arise in head placodes and migrate long distances through predetermined paths just under the epidermis, trailed by the nerves that supply them [3]. Other head placodes, which form the olfactory sense organs, the lenses of the eyes, and the ear vesicles, never lose their epithelial arrangement during their inward movement, and partake more of the nature of local invaginations.

5. *Dispersal.* Multitudes of cells break away individually from their sheets of origin, scattering among the nascent organs by ameboid movement. Such **mesenchyme,** or embryonic connective tissue, arises from most parts of the mesodermal layer, e.g., the prechordal plate, the somites, and lateral plates. Another and liberal source of mesenchyme, quite unsuspected by earlier generations of embryologists, is the edge of the medullary plate, the **neural crest.** Figure 8–9 shows this material emerging from the neural tube of the amblystoma, in cross-sections (*A* and *B*) and in side view (*C*). Many of these cells are assembled as nerve ganglia, but many of them scatter throughout the body as mesenchyme which will be converted into a variety of specialized cells. There are thus two main sources of mesenchyme, and it is useful to give the name

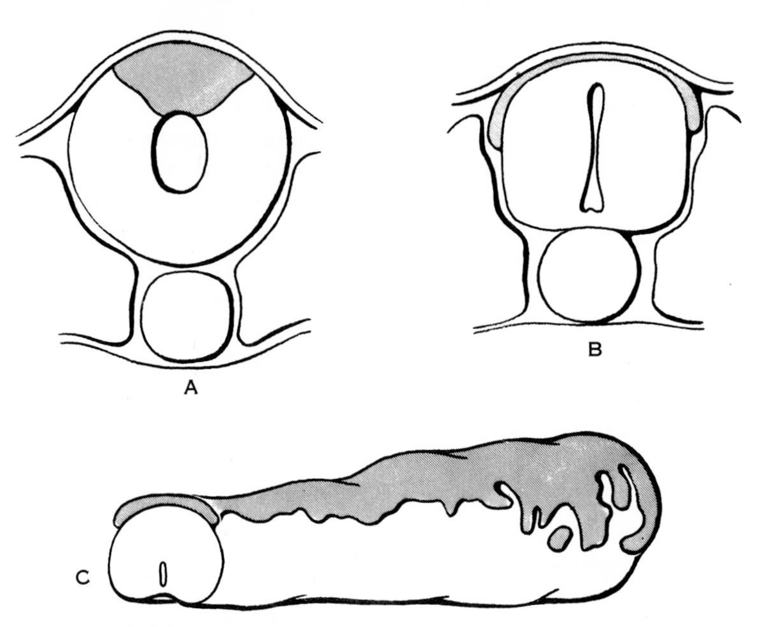

Fig. 8–9. Dispersal of neural crest in amblystoma embryos. A and B. Cross-sections through third somite at stages 22 and 29. C. Reconstruction of spinal cord and spreading mantle of neural crest cells at stage 29.
(After S. R. Detwiler, 1937.)

mesectoderm to what is derived from the ectoderm layer, to distinguish it from what is mesodermal in origin.

6. *Coating.* Mesenchyme cells in increasing numbers lose their tendency to disperse after breaking away from their parent layer. They then settle down and add themselves as special layers to other organs. Both mesectoderm and true mesoderm form layers that enclose the brain and spinal cord. Mesenchyme from various sources forms tough fibrous **dermis** coats on the inside of the **epidermis,** completing the definitive skin. Protective envelopes are laid down on all the muscles. Mesenchyme from the inner layer of the hypomere condenses in successive layers of smooth muscles and specialized binding tissue around the gut tube (Fig. 4–17). All the blood vessels acquire muscular and fibrous coats, from similar sources. A special category of cells migrating from the neural crest, called sheath cells, selectively coat the nerve fibers (Fig. 4–13).

It is gradually being appreciated that these coating activities of the mesenchyme cells furnish not only passive protection and insulation for the organs to which they apply themselves, but can also furnish the stimulus and the direction for their differentiation [4]. As soon as the anlagen are coated with these cells, the new cellular interactions that are thus made possible set going new types of differentiation.

II. DEVELOPMENTS IN THE ENDODERM

Most organs arise as anlagen from one germ layer only, though in the end they include tissues from two or three. We turn now to the methods by which organs arise primarily from the endoderm.

A. Pharyngeal Developments

When endoderm first invaginates into the region of the animal pole in the amblystoma embryo, it makes contact with presumptive ectoderm over a broad area. Subsequent invasion by the mesodermal envelope breaks this primary contact except for three places. One of these is an anterior midline area that becomes isolated from the general mesoderm-free area by the meeting of the right and left lobes of the mandibular mesoderm (Fig. 8–3). This has already been mentioned as the future mouth area. The other two are on the posterior borders of the right and left mandibular lobes, and here the hyomandibular closing plates are formed by primary contact of the first of the paired pharyngeal pouches with the ectoderm. The second, third, and later pouches evaginate after the arrival of the lateral-plate mesoderm and have to push their way through it. Thus, their closing plates are formed by secondary contact with the ectoderm.

The pharynx pouches make their closing-plate contacts in similar fashion in all the vertebrates, but differences exist in the extent to which they achieve the full status of pharyngeal clefts by subsequent rupture. In urodeles and many fishes, the first or hyomandibular pair never open at all, and in other forms they are reduced in size or open briefly. In amniotes, the more posterior pouches are repressed in various degrees, and may fail to achieve even closing plates. The resulting contrasts at the pharyngula stage have already been noted (Figs. 5–9, 5–10). The pillars of lateral-plate mesoderm that are isolated from each other by the formation of these closing plates or clefts have been called pharynx segments, but it should be noted that their method of formation is quite different from the primary segmentation of the epimere mesoderm.

Each pharyngeal pouch forms a closing plate with its outer rim only. On its dorsal and ventral rims (Fig. 8–10), the endoderm tends to throw off trains or nodules of epithelial cells into the surrounding mesenchyme, which form **thymus** and **parathyroid glands** (cf. Chapter 17). This is a relatively late activity, starting at the pharyngula stage but culminating later when the pouches are specializing (as they do in fishes) or when they are pinching off from the pharynx and collapsing (as they do in the amniotes). Cyclostomes show none of this gland-forming activity. In some elasmobranchs all the pouches share in it, in some mammals only two pairs do.

In some fishes and the tetrapods, the most posterior pair of pharynx pouches produce little evaginations called **ultimobranchial bodies.** Usually one of these disappears and the other persists as a ciliated cyst in the mesenchyme near the point of formation of the dorsal aorta. It has no known function. In some mammals, ultimobranchial body epithelium apparently contributes to the thyroid gland.

In all the gnathostomes, the endodermal floor of the pharynx sends down a midventral evagination from which the **thyroid gland** is formed (Fig. 8–10). The outgrowth is from a small spot just back of the point of junction of the mandibular arches. It extends posteriorly through the mesenchyme, breaks loose for short further migration, and differentiates directly into thyroid tissue. Hagfishes and lampreys are quite aberrant in this respect (cf. Chapter 17).

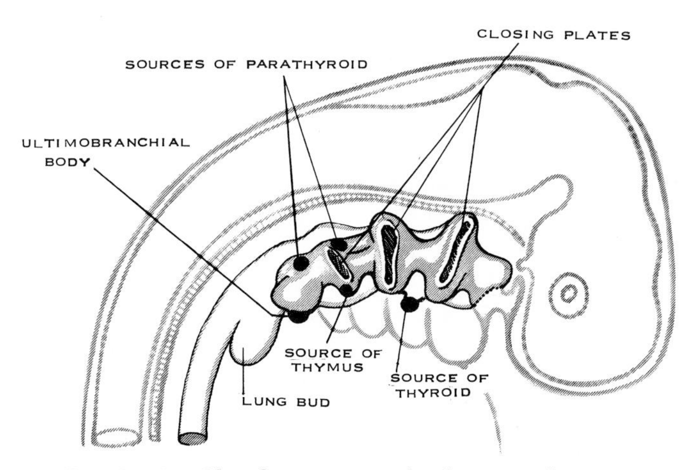

Fig. 8–10. Gland sources in the human pharynx.
(Redrawn from B. M. Patten, Human Embryology, 1946, by permission of McGraw-Hill Book Co., Inc.)

B. The Great Glands

In all vertebrates, **liver** and **pancreas** tissues arise by evaginations from a ring of endoderm in a part of the alimentary canal called the **duodenum.** They become encased in mesenchyme as they grow out, but retain one or more of their connections with the duodenal canal as definitive ducts.

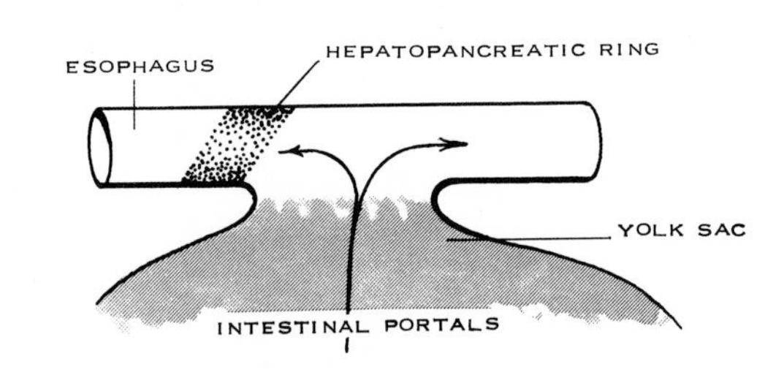

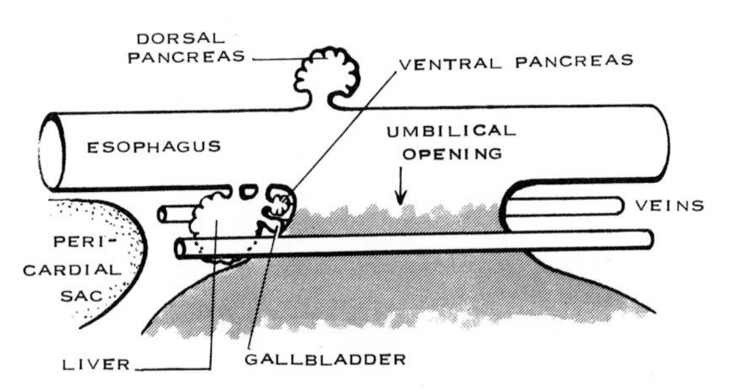

Fig. 8–11. Origin of the great glands in amniotes.

The liver may show fleeting indications of paired origins, but continues its development as a single organ. The anteroventral wall of the large liver pouch of the amphibian primordial embryo (Figs. 7–12, 8–13) actually forms liver tissue. It quickly puts out a thick proliferation of epithelial cords that penetrate the vitelline veins, breaking them up into a braided system of capillaries. The main cavity of the pouch is narrowed down to form the gall bladder and the main bile duct, while the epithelial mass is penetrated by finer branching bile ducts at a much later stage. In the amniotes (Fig. 8–11), there is no such great liver pouch, but a tiny liver evagination occurs in the front wall of the opening from the intestine to the yolk sac. The epithelial proliferation and interpenetration with mesenchyme and blood vessels occurs as in the amblystoma. The burgeoning liver lies directly posterior to the heart, and blood from it flows directly to the sinus venosus.

This liver–heart relationship is standard in the embryos of elasmobranchs and amphibia and all the amniotes, and in their adults also. To find, then, an entirely different relationship in teleost embryos comes as rather a shock, as though some morphologic law had been broken. Here one sees the liver firmly pressed up against the somites of one side or the other, high above the yolk sac and a long way from the heart, its blood sent not directly to the sinus venosus but out in braiding capillaries over the yolk. This novel arrangement is, however, not as radical as it seems. It is a temporary embryonic adaptation consequent upon the location of the liquid yolk. As development proceeds and food stores are diminished the yolk sac shrinks and finally disappears. Only this is required to bring the liver into the normal vertebrate position directly behind the heart. The blood vessels which had been sprayed out over the yolk retract and reveal themselves as hepatic veins, crossing the septum transversum from liver to sinus venosus, just as in other adult vertebrates.

C. Lung Buds

In amphibia and the amniotes (Fig. 8–10), lung buds arise from the endoderm of the posterior end of the pharynx, as late pre-pharyngula evaginations. Frontal sections of amphibian embryos at these stages show *two* lung buds, looking much like a final pair of pharyngeal pouches, extending posteriorly along the sides of the esophagus rather than laterally toward the ectoderm. In amniotes, a *single* shallow pouch or even a short tube arises from the pharynx–esophagus border in the midventral line, and from the end of this arise the two lung buds, stretching along the ventrolateral surfaces of the esophagus. In this position they come into relations with the coelom, described below.

D. Primordial Germ Cells

The principal generalization of Chapter 5 was that practically all the organs common to all vertebrates are present as visible rudiments in the pharyngula stage. Ovaries and testes do not quite fit with this rule, for their two principal components, the **structural elements** which are provided by the intermediate mesoderm, and the **germinal elements** which generally come from the endoderm, are usually still separate. During the pre-pharyngula stage the germinal elements

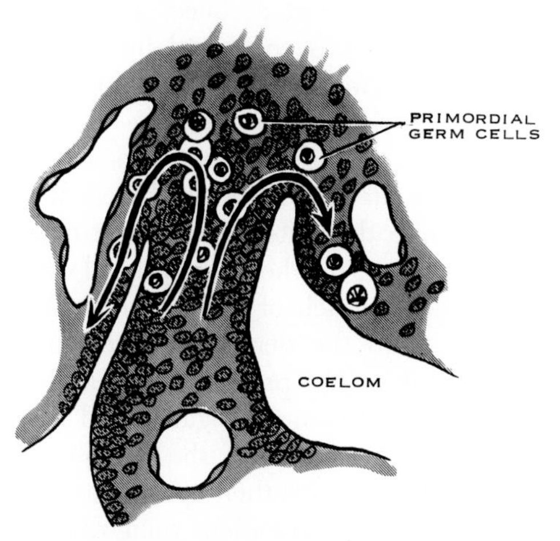

Fig. 8–12. Primordial germ cells in dorsal mesentery of turtle embryo.
(After A. P. Dustin, 1910.)

appear as conspicuously large **primordial germ cells,** variously scattered along their routes of migration from their sources toward the eventual sites of the gonad ridges.

The original locations of the primordial germ cells are remarkably varied. In anura they are described as lying in the endoderm below the blastocoel cavity at the time invagination starts. In urodeles [5] they are apparently not in the endoderm at all, but are first seen in medial hypomere mesoderm. In lampreys they are in the more posterior endoderm, and in teleosts likewise near where the trunk–tailbud arises. In the meroblastic forms they are generally lined up at the junction of extraembryonic and embryonic endoderm, but grouped laterally in elasmobranchs, in an anterior crescent in birds, in a similar but posterior crescent in turtles and mammals, or scattered in the yolk sac endoderm of other reptiles.

By plotting the location of these cells in older and older embryonic stages of a given species, a picture is achieved of their gradual migration (indicated by arrows in Fig. 8–12) by their own ameboid vigor—or in birds and some reptiles possibily by way of the circulatory system—toward the dorsal midline of the intestine in mid-trunk, where they enter the mesoderm and eventually congregate in the definitive gonads.

III. DEVELOPMENTS IN THE MESODERM

A. Midline Structures

The **prechordal plate,** which is formed in clear association with the endoderm but becomes mesenchymatous in nature as soon as it has been excluded from the roof of the pharynx, disperses around the surface of the forebrain, enveloping it in skull-forming tissues (Fig. 8–13). Although this tissue does not differentiate much before the pharyngula stage, experiments to be described in Chapter 10 show that it exerts strong formative influences on all it touches, and in fact is a leading agent in determining the pattern of the anterior part of the head.

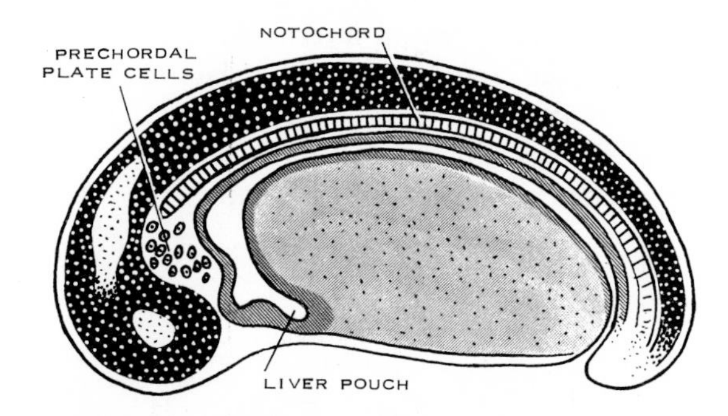

Fig. 8–13. Notochord and prechordal plate of a stage 29 amblystoma.

The notochord cells become vacuolated soon after they are segregated in the midline. In amniote embryos they then at once begin to lag behind in their growth, but in the anamniotes they produce a turgid rod that may rival the spinal cord in size and acquires several connective tissue envelopes. In any case, the notochord is incorporated into the vertebral column and skull base that develop after the pharyngula stage.

B. Somites

In all vertebrates, the epimere mesoderm shows true segmentation as far forward as the ear vesicles, and sometimes beyond.

Whether or not the pre-otic part of the system develops into visible segments, it always behaves in the same way after the pharyngula stage, by differentiating into a family of six or more eyeball muscles (cf. Chapter 14). Post-otic somites of the head region are always formed, but usually disperse early and completely in mesenchyme, or contribute to the formation of certain neck muscles, or contribute elements to the back part of the skull. It is in the trunk and tail regions that the behavior of the somites becomes relatively uniform.

The mesoderm of the trunk region is segregating in three zones at the primordial embryo stage: median **notochord,** paired strips of epimeric **somites,** and **lateral plates** of the hypomere (Fig. 7–12). The myocoels of the somites are shown with quite varying degrees of definiteness depending on the species and on the level of the trunk, and there may already be a visible segregation of a strip of **intermediate mesoderm** between the somites and the lateral plates, which is destined to produce kidneys and gonads. Neither the intermediate mesoderm nor the hypomere extends into the tail.

The history of any one somite during the pre-pharyngula period is much like that of all the rest (Fig. 8–14). Mesenchyme cells loosen and disperse from its whole periphery. Most of this material comes from the medioventral part of the somite, which is set apart as the **sclerotome,** or skeleton-forming tissue, from the remaining muscle-forming part, or **myotome.** Sclerotome material is used in the formation of the **dorsal aorta** almost at once, and after the pharyngula stage it is converted into **vertebrae** and the mesodermal coat of the spinal cord, which is called the **dura mater.**

If there is a well-developed myocoel in the rest of the somite, its inner wall becomes the myotome, while the outer wall is distinguished as the **dermatome,** on the assumption (which is partly true) that much of the mesenchyme that differentiates into the dermis layer of the skin is derived from it. The presumptive muscle cells of the myotome become elongated and fuse together in multinucleate units, the muscle fibers [6]. These rapidly synthesize their specific contractile protein, myosin, and complete their differentiation of myofibrils and striated bands. Finally they become organized in groups, as **muscles.**

The connective tissue that invests the muscle-forming masses may hold them permanently in the myotomic arrangement, as in most fishes. Or the muscle fibers may continue to elongate, so that the appearance of segmentation is rapidly obscured, as in most amniotes.

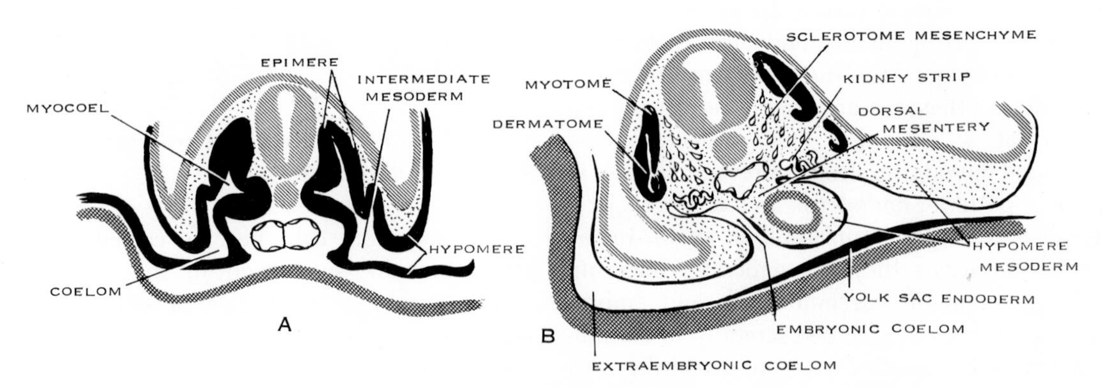

Fig. 8–14. Early mesoderm differentiations in the snapping turtle. A. Cross-section of embryo incubated 13 days. B. Incubated 25 days.

C. Hypomere Mesoderm

In amniotes and elasmobranchs, while the intestine is in communication with the dangling yolk sac through an umbilical opening, one can make a proper distinction between intra-embryonic and extra-embryonic divisions of the hypomere mesoderm. Since the latter is chiefly concerned with fetal membranes, it will be considered in Chapter 11. The hypomere of the embryo itself may be divided into three sections for consideration: the peritoneal, the pericardial and the peripharyngeal.

1. *Pharynx-Segment Mesoderm.* The peripharyngeal mesoderm is passively carved up into segmental masses by the endodermal pharynx pouches. This part of the hypomere is different in two respects from the rest, in being solid and in being segmented. There are exceptional vertebrates in which the coelomic split that occurs in the pericardial and peritoneal divisions makes tentative intrusions into the pharynx zone, but this is never more than temporary. The segmentation, it will be recalled, is not like that of the epimere, nor do these two segmented systems usually coincide.

The pharynx segment mesoderm contributes to the formation of aortic arches (Fig. 5–13), in pre-pharyngula stages, and also in most cases will later condense into muscle-forming rudiments, the most important of which will work the jaw apparatus (Fig. 5–10).

2. *Coelom.* In all vertebrates, the hypomere cells of the pericardial and peritoneal regions divide into two sheets almost as soon as they have reached their position in the interior (Figs. 7–12, 7–20). The outer **somatic** or parietal layer and the inner **splanchnic** or visceral layer enclose between them a continuous **coelomic cavity** from the very first, or, as in amniotes, paired cavities are formed in the lateral plates which subsequently coalesce (Fig. 8–14).

This behavior of the hypomere cells is constant and its cause is completely unknown. Each layer develops a non-adhesive surface turned toward the coelom, and a coating surface turned away from it. What acts to polarize the cells of the two layers in this opposite sense? Why should the tendency to split into layers not show up also in the epimere and in the peripharyngeal hypomere? Most major phyla of animals show coelomic or pseudo-coelomic cavitations like these.

3. *Mesenteries.* The splanchnic section of the peritoneal hypomere on each side moves medially, coating the gut tube and contributing to it various muscle and connective tissue layers. In the space between the dorsal aorta and the gut (Fig. 8–15), these two sheets of peritoneum meet and create a fused continuous sheet of **dorsal mesentery,** enclosing the blood vessels and nerves that extend to the intestinal tissues from above.

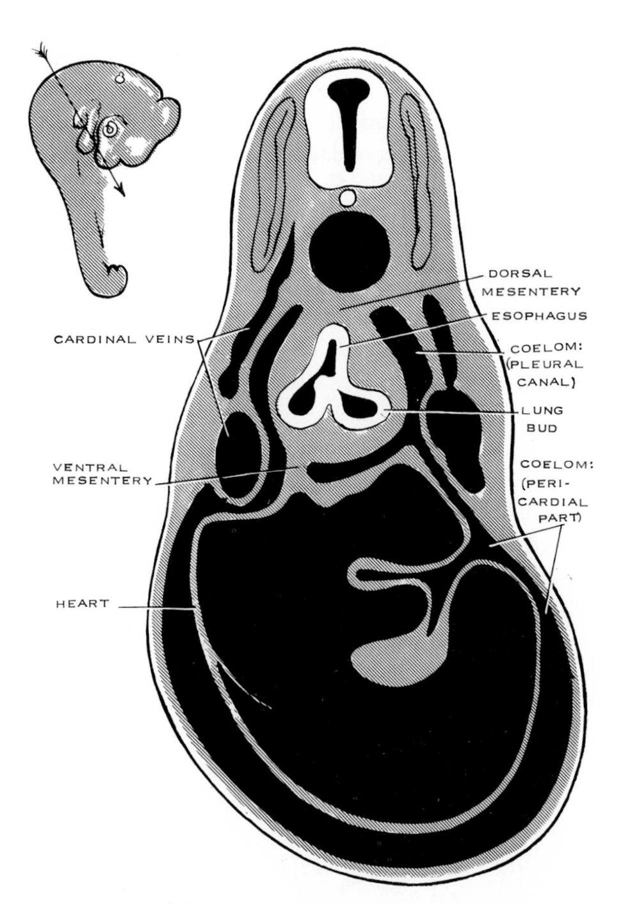

Fig. 8–15. Coelom and mesenteries of stage 18 chick.

In amphibian embryos, the mesoderm mantle of the belly is completed by late invagination of a continuous hypomere sheet, never broken by an umbilical opening (Fig. 7–11). Since the coelomic split occurs through the whole of the peritoneal and pericardial regions of this mantle, in the ventral midline as well as at the sides, there is never any primary **ventral mesentery** formed below the intestine. In amniotes and the elasmobranchs however, because the lateral plates are spread flat on a huge yolk sac at first, separate right and left hypomere cavities are formed, which secondarily swing together as the gut tube is formed (Fig. 8–14). In these, a small piece of ventral mesentery (Fig. 8–15) is formed anterior to the umbilicus. It may survive as a **falciform ligament,** attached to the liver.

4. Heart and Blood Vessels. In most vertebrates the heart is formed by the borders of right and left lateral plates of the hypomere as these are wheeling together to fill the mesoderm-free area (Fig. 8–16). The cells of these borders acquire a tube-forming compulsion at a certain time, and if they have met in the midline by then (as they do in amphibia), a single heart tube is formed. But in amniotes, the right and left anlagen have started to form heart tubes independently before they are brought together. A single heart is then formed by a fusion of the two tubes and their remodeling into one.

In either case, the first formation is a thin **endocardial tube** of flattened cells. The visceral layer of the pericardial end of the coelom envelops this on each side, and provides it with a coating of mesoderm called the **epimyocardium.** This is what later differentiates into heart-muscle fibers covered by a shiny outer layer of **epicardium.** Any fragments of mesentery which may be formed during this envelopment (Figs. 8–15, 8–16) usually disappear with continued growth.

The youngest heart tube is fairly straight, with both anterior and posterior ends forked (Fig. 8–17 A). Vital-stain experiments reveal that only the definitive ventricle and bulbus cordis are present in this midline tube so far (Fig. 25–1). The future unpaired atrium and sinus venosus exist as paired rudiments in the right and left parts of the posterior fork, and are gradually brought together by a morphogenetic tissue-remodeling movement. They take their places in the sequence of unpaired chambers some time after the ventricle has started to beat (Fig. 8–17 B). Both the remaining parts of the posterior fork and the branches of the original anterior fork extend themselves by the continual coales-

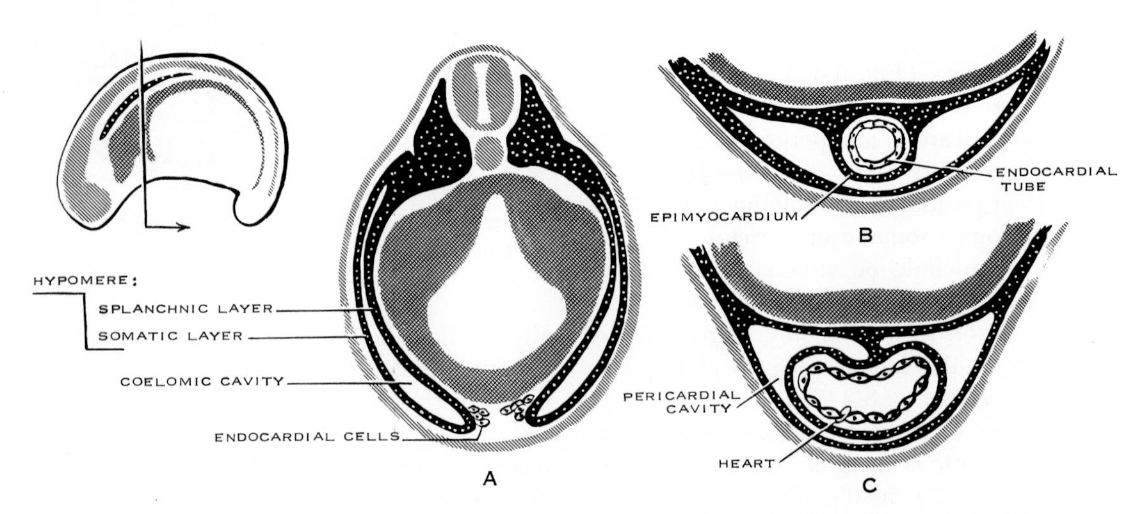

Fig. 8–16. Formation of the heart tube in a urodele. A. 16-somite stage. B. 20-somite stage. C. 26-somite stage.
(After S. Mollier, 1906.)

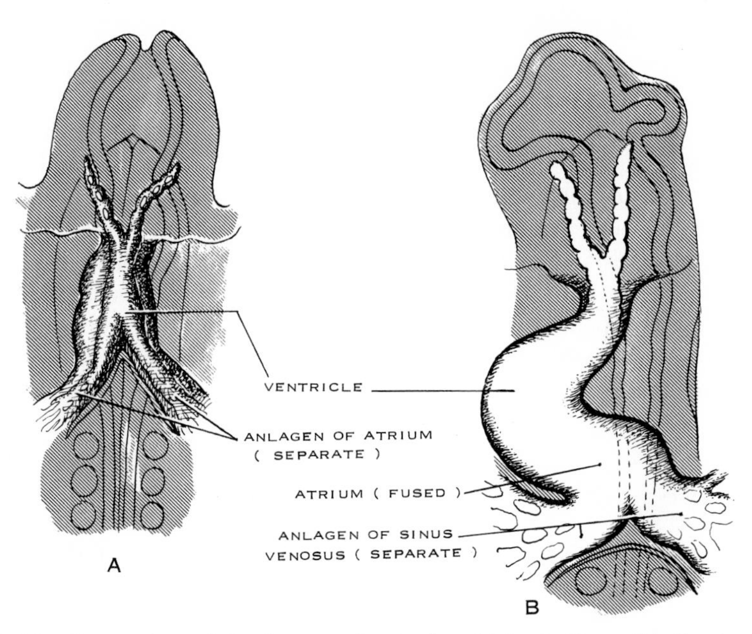

Fig. 8–17. Formation of the heart tube in the chick. A. Stage 10, first heart beat. B. Stage 12, first blood flow.
(After Patten and Kramer, 1933.)

cence of tube-forming mesenchyme cells around their tips. Anteriorly the product of this extension is the branching pattern of aortic arches that penetrates the pharynx segments of the two sides. Posteriorly it is the right and left vitelline veins that extend out over the yolk region but also come at once under the influence of the liver.

As soon as the heart tube starts to differentiate, it lengthens more rapidly than the pericardial cavity that contains it, and is thrown into a series of bends. However it is not the cramped quarters that cause the bending, since this will occur even when a heart rudiment is floated by itself in culture fluid where it has unlimited freedom for expansion [7]. The bending is a reaction to influences which neighboring cells bring to bear on the prospective heart cells during the time they are being determined. Mirror-image reversal of the normal asymmetrical bends of both the heart and the stomach can be produced experimentally by local injury to the mesoderm or the endoderm in this region, even as late as the primordial-embryo stage in the amblystoma [8]. This reversal, called **situs inversus viscerum,** is a fairly common anomaly in man and many other vertebrates.

As soon as the heart tube begins to bend, it shows a series of zones of rapid expansion alternating with rings of more internalized growth. The expansions produce the four familiar chambers of the pharyngula heart (Fig. 5–12); and the constrictions, the relatively stout **endocardial cushions** which will form the valves between them. The ventricle is the first chamber to start beating, followed later by the atrium and the sinus venosus. In Figure 8–17, *A* represents the chick heart at stage 10 when the ventricle starts to beat; *B* is 12 hours later, at stage 12, when blood starts to flow.

While the heart is forming, blood vessels are independently appearing in many parts of the embryo by direct aggregation of tube-forming mesenchyme cells. They can be detected by delicate micro-injection methods while still empty. It is not until a little while after the first pulsation of heart muscle that the heart tube, the aorta and aortic arches, the cardinal veins, etc., are interconnected so as to allow a true circulation. Even then, the fluid which is pumped around may for a short time be a colorless cell-free plasma.

5. *Blood Islands.* The first blood corpuscles to reach the embryonic circulation develop in special nests, called **blood islands,** quite separate from the heart or the main blood channels. In amphibia (Fig. 8–18 A) and lampreys, there is a single Y-shaped blood island of hypomeric mesoderm on the belly, its stem in the mid-ventral line and its arms opening toward the liver pouch. The presumptive blood cells free themselves from the splanchnic lining of the coelom in this area and lie pressed in pockets against the yolk endoderm. At the proper time, blood vessels tap these reservoirs and the corpuscles drain off and finish their development while circulating in the blood.

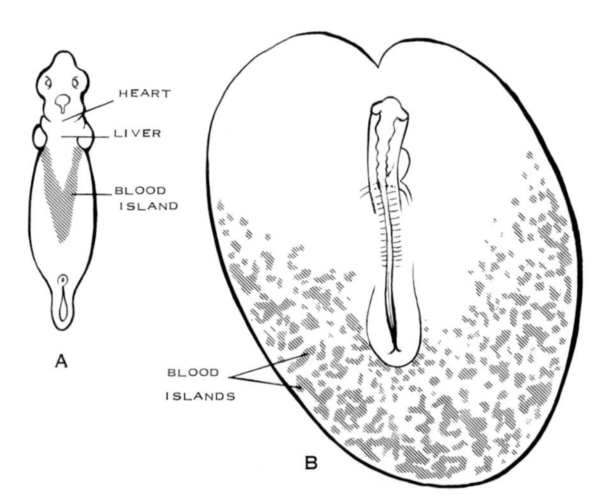

Fig. 8–18. Sites of primary erythrocyte production in the amblystoma and the chick.
(Amblystoma after C. M. Goss, 1928.)

In some fish embryos, colorless blood may circulate vigorously for several days before the red blood corpuscles are released into it from the blood islands. It has proved possible for one species of teleost, living in the frigid depths of the ocean, to go through life with such colorless blood [9].

In meroblastic vertebrates (Fig. 8–18 B), blood islands arise in the extraembryonic mesoderm at the sides of the trunk and posterior to the embryo, before the undercutting of the body axis has begun. Since these regions are later folded under to form part of the belly wall, the principal difference here, in comparison with the holoblastic forms, is the extremely scattered nature of the blood islands.

Before the pharyngula stage the blood islands have all emptied themselves, and their function is thereby finished. The continual new supply of corpuscles which the individual must maintain throughout his life comes from secondary centers of proliferation that are established in various tissues of the body later in development (cf. Chapter 26).

6. *Septum Transversum.* At the time when the heart and the liver are first forming, the coelom is a continuous cavity, and distinctions between peritoneal and pericardial parts can only be made with knowledge of future developments. By the time the pharyngula stage is reached, these two parts of the coelom have been all but separated from each other, except in teleosts, whose peculiar yolk arrangement delays the process. The agent in this separation is the **septum transversum,** a partition of mesenchyme that has spread between the heart and the liver (Fig. 8–19).

The paired **common cardinal veins** (Figs. 5–15, 5–16) are always involved in the establishment of this septum. They form broad bridges across the coelom as they descend on each side just back of the pharynx-segment mass to enter the sinus venosus. At the time the circulation is being established, these veins and the mesenchyme that accompanies them break the broad communications between the future pericardial and peritoneal parts of the coelom on each side, dividing each into dorsal and ventral passageways.

The ventral passageways are promptly stoppered up by the liver, which bulges forward in the midline (Fig. 8–19) and makes adhesions with the body wall on both sides. The definitive septum transversum is thus formed in most vertebrates by the joint activity of the liver in the ventral midline and the common cardinal veins at the sides.

The right and left dorsal passageways between the pericardial and the peritoneal cavities lin-

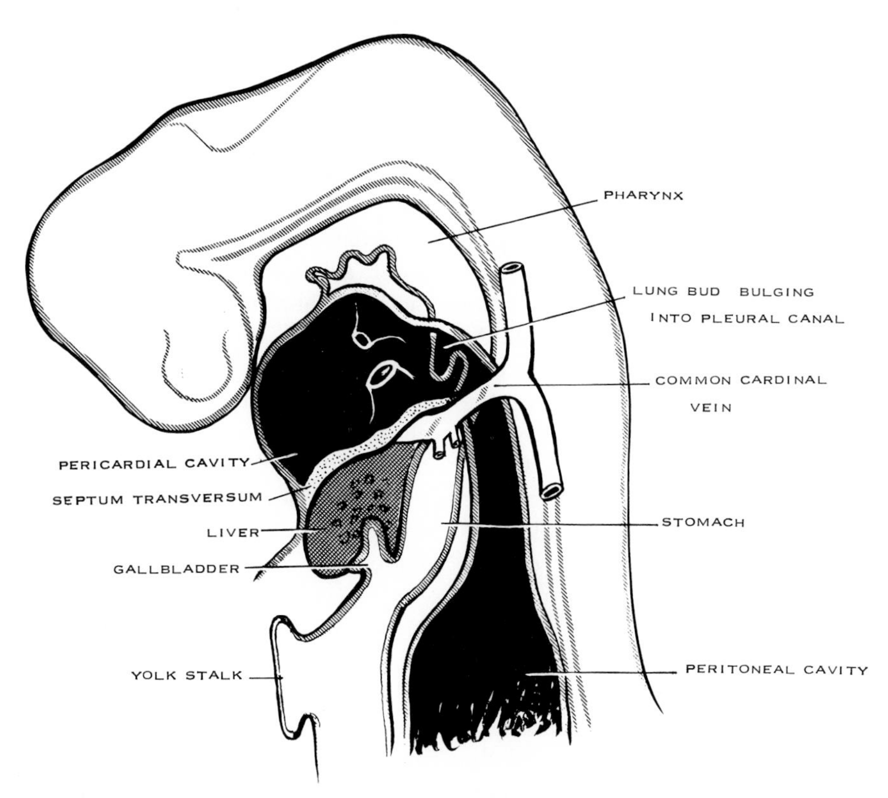

Fig. 8–19. Septum transversum in a 4-millimeter human embryo. Sagittal diagram, heart removed.
(After W. His, 1885.)

ger somewhat longer, usually appearing at the pharyngula stage on either side of the esophagus or its mesentery, dorsal to the septum transversum. In amniote pharyngulas, these dorsal passageways are entered by the lung buds (Figs. 5–16 B, 8–19), which is why they have been called **pleural canals.** Later transformations of this rather standardized arrangement lead to some marked contrasts in the coeloms of higher vertebrates (Chapter 24).

D. Intermediate Mesoderm

A strip of **intermediate mesoderm,** which is interposed between the epimeric somites and the split hypomere on each side, extends from the level of the pectoral limb buds to the base of the tail. It produces most of the urogenital system. The genital part develops late. In prepharyngula stages, two contrasting but associated activities spread from anterior to posterior in each of these intermediate mesoderm strips. The first leaves behind it a continually increasing number of tiny **uriniferous tubules,** each more or less transversely disposed, and each formed from the cells of its own segmental level. The second, which uses almost exclusively a cluster of cells derived from several of the most anterior segments of the intermediate mesoderm, spins out a longitudinal **primitive kidney duct** that collects the product of the successive tubules and empties with its antimere at or near the cloaca.

The process of tubule formation has barely started by the time the primitive kidney duct has reached the cloaca, and continues for a long time thereafter. The localized morphogenetic movements that create the successive uriniferous tubules vary a great deal from species to species, and also from one level to another of the same embryo's trunk. The intermediate mesoderm of some kinds of vertebrates is clearly segmented and primarily epithelial throughout the trunk, and in others it consists of unsegmented mesenchyme, and there are all manner of intergradations between these states. The epithelium of the tubules may be derived directly from the coelomic epithelium, either with or without persistent connections, or it may be assembled from mesenchyme which was either budded from the epithelium or never connected with it at all. As noted in Chapter 5, page 84, there are also great differences among the species as to the rate and time of tubule formation. Some of these differences will be further discussed in Chapter 27.

A representative uriniferous tubule, as it lengthens and coils, evaginates a hollow sac or **glomerular capsule** into the mesenchyme near its medial end, and this is approached by an arterial loop which forms a capillary ball or **glomerulus** (Fig. 8–20). One can either describe the glomerulus as pushing into the capsule or being enveloped by it. The glomerulus and the capsule together constitute a **renal corpuscle.** Waste from the blood may be filtered through to the fluid in the capsule, and the urine so formed may then be passed along to the longitudinal duct.

Once a kidney tubule has established itself, it may also bud off another tubule, which will elongate, coil, and form a renal corpuscle in the same fashion. The secondary tubule which thus arises may empty into the lateral part of the primary one, or achieve its own connection with the primitive kidney duct. It may later bud off a tertiary tubule, and tubules of still higher order are formed within the kidney strips of most vertebrates, the more elaborate arrangements being usually found at more posterior trunk levels. In most vertebrate embryos, with the passage of time, the kidney tubules formed at the anterior ends of the intermediate mesoderm strips are functionally replaced by more posterior ones. In most amniotes they have already begun to degenerate at the pharyngula stage.

E. Limb Buds

Paired limb buds are formed in the prepharyngula stages of all but a few vertebrates, and simultaneously or soon afterward a similar pair of pelvic buds arise. The source of the mesodermal cells from which these buds are assembled is not always easy to discover. The pectoral limbs grow out external to the anterior ends of the kidney strips, bulging the surface ectoderm just below the line between epimere

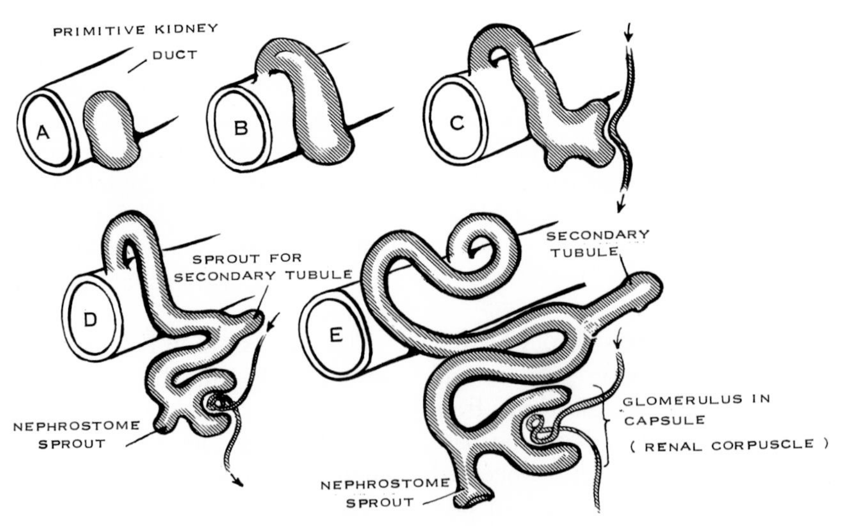

Fig. 8–20. Development of a kidney tubule in a urodele.
(After P. Gray, 1932.)

and hypomere. In elasmobranchs and some amniotes, segmental muscle processes can be seen growing ventrad from the myotomes (epimere) and sending trains of cells into the limb buds. However in amphibia and some other vertebrates there is never at any time an indication of segmentation in the limb buds, nor of a contribution to them from the somites. They contain only mesenchyme, presumably derived from the parietal layer of the coelomic lining (hypomere). These amphibian limb buds, and those of birds, can form complete limbs if transplanted away from the myotomes, or if left in place after removal of the myotomes. In the salmon, the pectoral-fin bud develops by itself from mesenchyme, much as in amphibia, but the pelvic limb receives sprouts from myotomes, as in the elamobranchs.

Recent experiments have further complicated the question of the source of limb-bud material. In urodeles [5] it has been found that the *splanchnic* layer of the hypomere can make passable limb buds if the yolky endoderm is entirely removed. And cultured masses of prospective epimeric *somite* mesoderm above a certain size will frequently develop limb buds [10]. Perhaps a more challenging problem than the source of limbs is the question why limbs are formed in these four particular areas when neighboring groups of apparently similar cells do nothing of the sort. And why should there be almost always two pairs of limbs and never normally more?

REFERENCES

1. Taning, A. V., 1952. *Biol. Revs.* 27: 169.
2. Fraser, E. A., 1950. *Biol. Revs.* 25: 159.
3. A 1960 symposium on cell movement and cell contact discussed from many angles the question of how cells are able to migrate in oriented paths. See particularly the summary comments by P. Weiss. *Exptl. Cell Research,* Suppl. 8, 1961.
4. Grobstein, C., 1954. In D. Rudnick (ed.), *Aspects of synthesis and order in growth* (13th Growth Symposium). Princeton University Press, Princeton.
5. Nieuwkoop, P. D., 1947. *Arch. néerl. zool.* 8: 1.
6. Wilde, C. E., 1959. In D. Rudnick (ed.), *Cell, organism, and milieu* (17th Growth Symposium). Ronald Press Co., New York.
7. Bacon, R. L., 1945. *J. Exptl. Zool.* 98: 87.
8. von Woellwarth, C., 1950. *Wilhelm Roux' Arch. Entwicklungsmech. Organ.* 144: 178.
9. Ruud, J. T., 1954. *Nature* 173: 848.
10. Muchmore, W. B., 1957. *J. Exptl. Zool.* 134: 293.

9

Early Organogenesis: II The Ectoderm

As soon as the presumptive neural area has been segregated as a closed and continuous tube, experiments show that its fate has become more or less rigidly determined, not only as a whole but as a mosaic of subordinate regional parts, each with a special part to play in the central nervous system. Morphogenetic movements of masses of cells still occur, but they are increasingly local and minor in importance. Two theoretically separable but intertwined processes take over the future developments. These are **growth** and **differentiation.**

It is *growth,* at a specifically different rate for each region, that quickly transforms the simple tube into an intricately sculptured collection of vesicles, ventricles, and flexures. It is *differentiation* which transforms this organ into a mechanism for commanding and controlling the whole body, recognizing the outside world, determining proper adjustments to it, and remembering. Only the growth phase, and its results in the anatomy of the embryonic central nervous system, will be considered here. The general nature of the very complex differentiation processes will be mentioned later in this chapter, and the story of their interdependent accomplishments will be resumed in Part IV, Chapter 18.

I. GROWTH OF THE NEURAL TUBE

The growth rate of the brain exceeds that of the spinal cord from the start, and produces three primary swellings called the **forebrain** (prosencephalon), the **midbrain** (mesenchephalon), and the **hindbrain** (rhombencephalon) (Fig. 9–1 A). The forebrain, which is influenced by the underlying contact of the prechordal plate, develops a very different pattern from that of the hindbrain and spinal cord, under which lies the notochord. The midbrain shows intermediate effects.

When the anterior neuropore closes (Fig. 8–1) there is at first a simple forebrain vesicle containing a ventricular chamber, but the roof, floor, and side walls and the anterior end of it soon show their own characteristic patterns of growth. To facilitate description, two zones may be defined in it (Fig. 9–1 B). The more anterior one, the **endbrain** (telencephalon) becomes primarily associated with the olfactory sense organs, whose placodes will develop against its outer surfaces (Figs. 9–1 C, 9–10). The cerebral hemispheres will bulge out from this part. The more posterior zone, the **interbrain** (diencephalon), acquires associations with the hypophysis and the

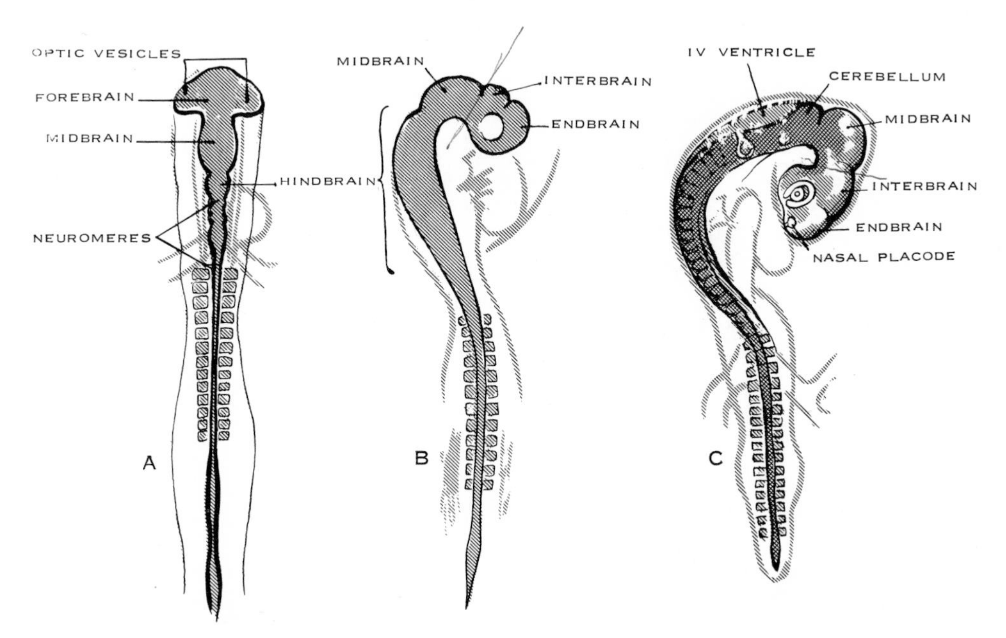

Fig. 9–1. Development of the chick brain (1). A. Stage 11. B. Stage 14. C. Stage 18.

eyes. The three chick embryos shown in Figure 9–1 were incubated 40 hours, 50 hours, and 75 hours, respectively.

The telencephalon is a rather simple tube when the neuropore first closes, and contains a cavity that is broadly continuous with that of the rest of the central nervous system. A pair of pouches grow out laterally from its anterior part, each of them differentiating into an **olfactory lobe** and a **cerebral hemisphere** (Fig. 5–2 B). Usually the two hemispheres contain extensions of the median ventricle, called the **right** and **left ventricles** (PNA). Between these two evaginations, the median part of the telencephalon bears for a time a thin spot marking the point of closure of the anterior neuropore. The wall anterior and ventral to this spot is the **lamina terminalis,** which provides a useful landmark in the comparative descriptions of later stages, when the median part of the telencephalon tends to be engulfed by hemisphere developments.

Later developments in the cerebral hemispheres will concern two clearly separate action systems, one dominated by the olfactory sense and conspicuously built up in fishes, and the other more broadly generalized and non-olfactory, reaching great prominence in amniotes. To facilitate description, the parts concerned with the olfactory action system are collectively termed the **rhinencephalon.**

The ventrolateral walls of the diencephalon evaginate very early, to form the **optic vesicles** (Fig. 9–1 A). Their connections with the brain gradually narrow down to optic stalks. The tissue in the side wall just above each of these is designated the **thalamus.** The thalamic areas become sensory relay and association centers of some importance in amniotes. The roof of the diencephalon remains thin, and sends out a small dorsal midline evagination called the **epiphysis** (Fig. 9–2). This has become a conspicuous epithelial sac in all pharyngulas except those of mammals, in which its formation is somewhat delayed.

The floor of the diencephalon, called the **hypothalamus,** remains thick but sends down a funnel of thinner tissue called the **infundibulum** (Fig. 9–2). Before the neural tube begins to bend (Fig. 9–1 A), the infundibulum lies anterior to the prechordal plate and in contact with the surface ectoderm of the future mouth region, where the placode arises which will

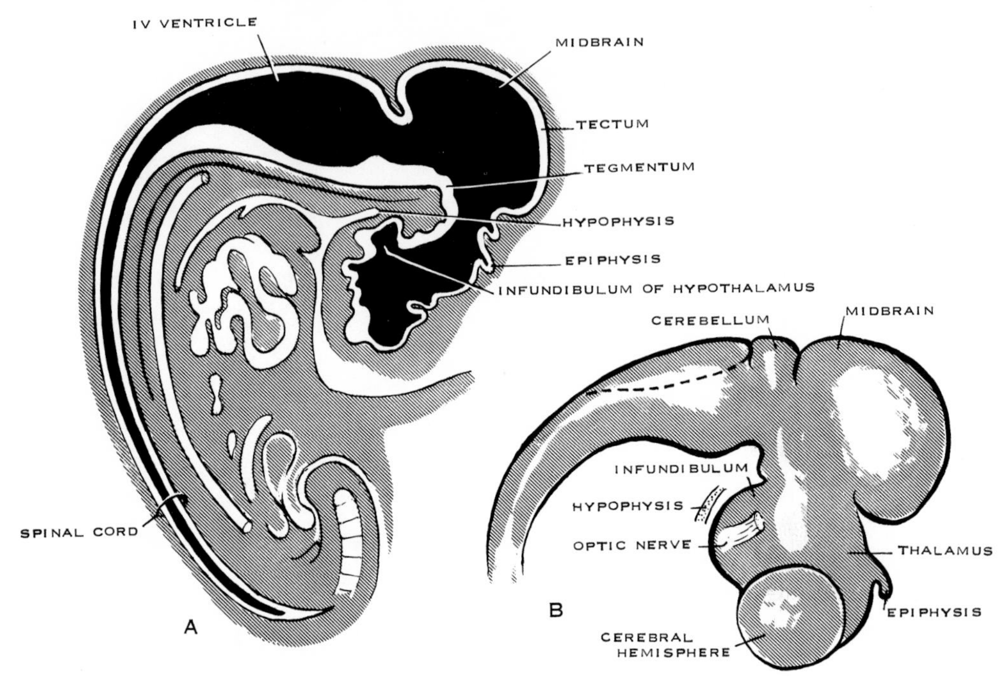

Fig. 9–2. Development of the chick brain (2). A. Sagittal section at six days. B. Side view, brain only.
(After M. Duval, 1889.)

form the hypophysis. Elongation and bending of the neural tube (Fig. 9–1 B, C) then brings it internally and gives it a posterior direction. After dispersal of the prechordal plate in mesenchyme, the funnel also lies close to the tip of the notochord. As will shortly be explained, it is associated with the formation of the pituitary gland.

By the time the pharyngula stage has been reached, the midbrain area has become inflated into a spheroid form, bulging dorsally and containing a ventricular enlargement of the central canal. Its roof or **tectum** (PNA) becomes the destination of axons growing in from the two optic nerves. Its floor is called the **tegmentum.**

The hindbrain and spinal cord are involved in the elongation of the notochord-dominated structures of the embryonic axis. Unlike the spinal cord the hindbrain becomes inflated by a very large expansion of the central canal, but this differs from the ventricles of the midbrain and the telencephalon in that its roof becomes stretched out as a non-nervous epithelium, a translucent window visible on the dorsal surface of the embryo.

Late in the pre-pharyngular period (Figs. 9-1 C, 9–2 B, 9–3), rudiments of the cerebellum arise in the dorsolateral walls of the anterior end of the hindbrain. They and their associated ventral area are then defined as the **afterbrain** or metencephalon The rest of the original hindbrain is then called the myelencephalon or **medulla oblongata.** These last two cumbersome terms are often replaced by the word **bulb** to facilitate description of neuron tracts.

All the primary ventricles of the brain are continuous with each other and with the central canal of the spinal cord. The names **III ventricle** and **IV ventricle** have been carried over into vertebrate embryology from human anatomy, and applied to the spaces in the diencephalon and the myelencephalon. This is rather inappropriate, since all vertebrate embryos, including the human, have a mesencephalic ventricle lying

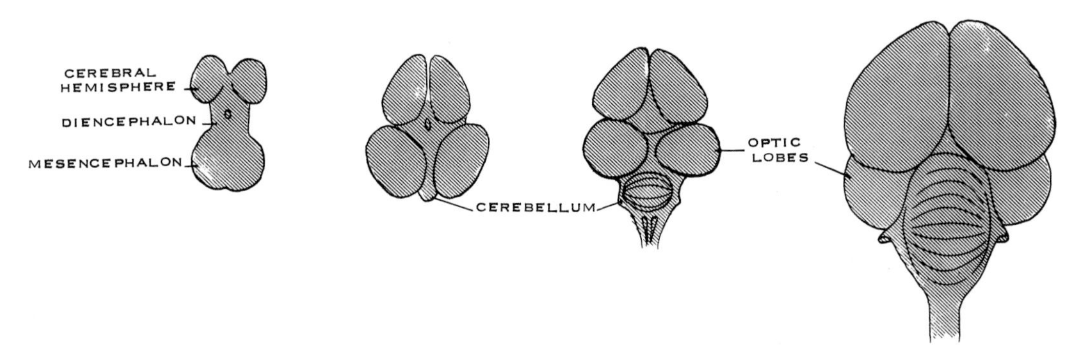

Fig. 9–3. Development of the chick brain (3). Dorsal views at 5, 9, 12, and 20 days. (After A. L. Romanoff, The Avian Embryo, 1960, by permission of The Macmillan Co.)

between III and IV. It is not numbered because it happens to be reduced to a pin-sized passageway during the fetal growth of the human brain. Also, in most vertebrates (but not in mammals) a ventricle develops within the cerebellum.

Telencephalon, diencephalon, mesencephalon, metencephalon, and myelencephalon are all one continuous tissue together with the spinal cord, and are definable merely on the basis of surface contours. The boundary between hindbrain and spinal cord cannot be defined even after the major brain landmarks have appeared, since it is determined by the plane of the joint between the skull and the first vertebra, and these structures appear after the pharyngula stage.

While these primary brain zones are taking shape, a sharp bend called the **cephalic flexure** arises in the tube just anterior to the tip of the notochord (Fig. 9–2 A), so that the parts underlaid by the prechordal plate are turned ventrad almost at right angles to the hindbrain. A **cervical flexure** also develops in the large-brained embryos of amniotes. It is a gentle curve rather than a sharp bend, and it involves chiefly the spinal cord of the neck region. In mammals, and to a less extent in some others, a **hindbrain flexure** also appears in the base of the brain under the cerebellum, with its concavity dorsad. The factors which bring about these bends have not been analyzed experimentally. Though prominent at the pharyngula stage (Figs. 5–1 to 5–4), the flexures are largely obliterated by later growth.

In addition to the primary brain zones and the flexures, there also arise differences in thickness of the walls of the neural tube, in both transverse and longitudinal arrangements. About a dozen **neuromeres** (Fig. 9–1 A) make their fleeting appearance as transverse thickenings, particularly in the hindbrain. They bear no relation to the segmented epimere mesoderm, but are said [1] to be constant in all classes of vertebrates, and to have definite relation, at least, to the nerves that arise from the hindbrain. They are obliterated by later developments.

Of more significance are the longitudinal patterns of thickness, which appear throughout the part of the neural tube underlaid by the notochord. The spinal cord normally develops a lumen which is flattened toward the sagittal plane (Fig. 9–4 A), and has a **roof plate** and a **floor plate** which are much thinner than the side walls. Transplantation and culture experiments with amphibian neural tubes [2] indicate that this cross-sectional pattern is not intrinsic to the spinal cord but impressed upon it by reaction with other neighboring tissues. Figure 9–4 B, for instance, shows the form taken by the cord when it grows on a substrate of muscle rather than notochord, and C shows what happens in the absence of both notochord and muscle. The floor-plate groove ends anteriorly at the midbrain where the notochord ends.

The thickened right and left sidewalls of the hindbrain each become scored by a longitudinal groove on the ventricular surface, called the

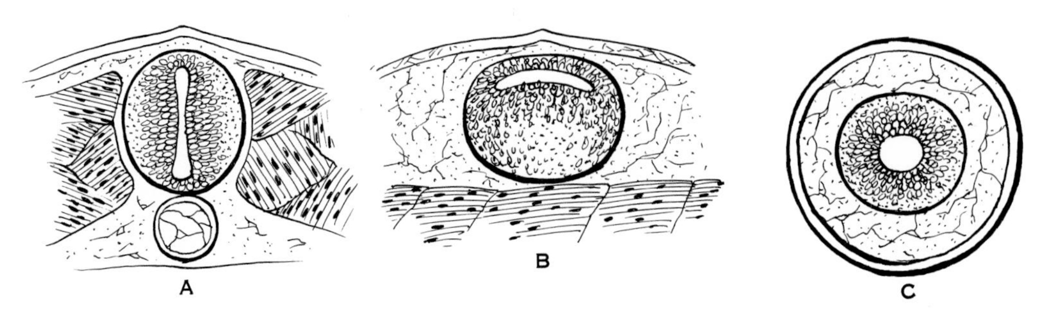

Fig. 9–4. Factors influencing the shape of the spinal cord. A. Normal relationships. B. Underlaid by muscle without notochord. C. No muscle or notochord present. (After Holtfreter, 1934.)

sulcus limitans (Fig. 9–5). The two sulci extend through the hindbrain and midbrain, dividing the walls into dorsal **alar plates** and ventral **basal plates** of thick neural tissue. Each of these may be subdivided by a fainter longitudinal groove. These four pairs of strips of material will later (page 157, and Chapter 18) be associated with categories of functional activity. The sulcus limitans, like the floor-plate groove, fades out anteriorly beyond the notochord, and all the brain anterior to the midbrain seems to be a continuation of the alar plate material. Where the IV ventricle becomes broadest in the hindbrain, the alar plates are spread so that they lie lateral rather than dorsal to the basal plates, and the roof plate is stretched extremely thin between their originally dorsal edges.

All these local differences in the shape and thickness of the originally simple neural tube have been spoken of as the result of differences in growth rates. Scarcely a beginning has been made in sorting out the factors in particular situations, but it is already clear that many kinds of phenomena are involved, each with

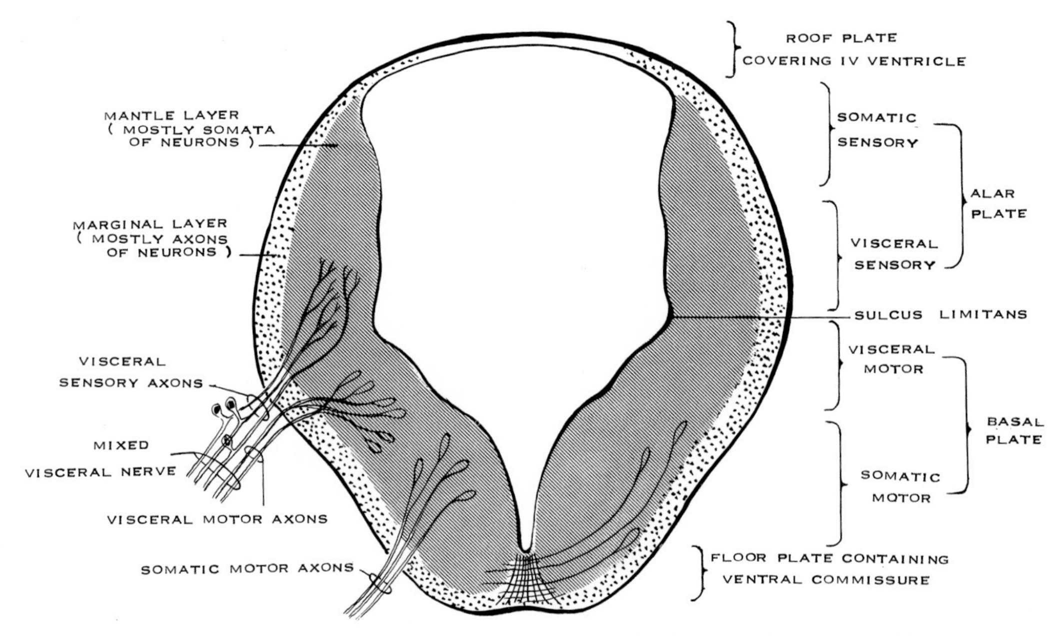

Fig. 9–5. Topography of a fetal human hindbrain seen in cross-section. (After His, 1887.)

causes yet to be analyzed. For instance, one area may become relatively smaller than another simply by not growing as fast. What controls the growth rates? Or it may even become absolutely smaller, either by the migration of its cells elsewhere, or by the wholesale death and removal of many of its cells [3]. Such cellular epidemics are little understood but seem to be a common factor in morphogenesis, found in many parts of the embryo, including certain parts of the central nervous system [3].

In the early neural tube, cells are quite uniformly distributed, and mitoses are found in all parts. Later the cells regularly move in against the basement membrane bordering the central canal to do their dividing. The rate of mitosis in this layer is known to vary from place to place in the neural tube at any given stage, and the pattern of these rates changes with time. Why?

The cells dividing near the central canal may either stay there as part of an organized **ependymal layer** of ciliated epithelium, thus contributing to the expansion of a ventricle, or they may migrate peripherally, contributing to the thickness of the **mantle layer** of differentiating cells (Fig. 9–5). Pressure from the cerebrospinal fluid, which is first secreted into the neural canal by ependymal cells, may be a factor in the ballooning of the early brain ventricles.

Growth in the outer parts of the neural tube may occur either by the enlargement of the cells that are already there, or by the addition of more cells migrating out from the mitotic layer, or by congregation of cells at one region of the mantle layer, depleting neighboring areas. As more and more cells differentiate into neurons and send their long axons in various directions through the central nervous system, these processes build up a sparsely nucleated **marginal layer** in the regions through which they pass, lying outside the predominantly nuclear mantle layer. Their paths are not uniformly distributed, and, especially in the forebrain, the marginal layer becomes quite thick in some areas and remains undeveloped in others. Since many of the axons later acquire white myelin sheaths, the marginal layer becomes **white substance;** the mantle layer remains **gray substance.**

II. DIFFERENTIATION WITHIN THE NEURAL TUBE

A. Cellular Differentiations

The late morphogenetic movements arrange the cells of the future brain and spinal cord into a neural tube. Growth phenomena of many kinds then change the simple tube into a pattern of vesicles, ventricles and flexures. Then begins the third and final sort of development, the differentiation of the cells. At first these are rather generalized and uniform, and although they are

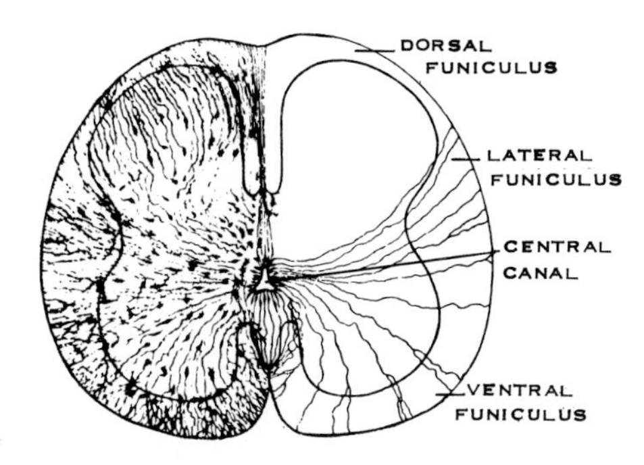

Fig. 9–6. Neuroglia in the spinal cord of a 4.5-month human fetus. Neurons not shown. Those on right side shown anchored in ependyma. Those on left have come free.

(After von Lenhossék, 1890.)

classed as **spongioblasts** or **neuroblasts** according to the paths of specialization they will take they are indistinguishable in appearance.

1. **Spongioblasts** differentiate into connective-tissue–like elements which either keep their nuclei at the inner wall of the tube, extending processes radially and cooperating to form inner and outer limiting membranes for the tube (Fig. 9–6, right side); or else they separate from the ependyma and distribute through all parts of the tube like the matted tissue of a sponge, tying together the whole organ, coating its blood vessels, and forming insulating layers upon many of the neurons (same figure, left side). The collective name for the specialized descendants of the spongioblasts is **neuroglia.** There are possibly more glia cells than neurons in the central nervous system.

2. **Neuroblasts** transform into neurons by protoplasmic extension (Fig. 4–12), one after another and in rapidly increasing numbers. At first there is a reservoir of neuroblasts near the central canal, some of which at any given moment may be found contracted down to the ependymal layer in stages of mitosis, but after they move into the mantle layer and send out their axons and dendrites they do not divide any more, and the reservoir is gradually used up. For instance, there is no further proliferation of neuroblasts in the central nervous system of the chick after the 8th day of incubation. In contrast to blood cells and many epithelial cells which have short lives and are constantly replaced, the neurons are apparently permanent parts of the structure of the individual. Nevertheless, their chemical constituents and their molecular structure are in constant flux, and their overt stability of form is like that of the oft-cited waterfall, or candle flame, which maintains a constant appearance though composed of new materials at every instant.

3. *Categories of Neurons.* **Sensory neurons** generally have their cell bodies or somata located in ganglia, they have long peripherally directed axons with dendritic zones (page 57) in the tissues where they end, and they send nerve impulses into the central nervous system (Figs. 9–5, 9–9). On the other hand, the **motor neurons** in general have their cell bodies and dendritic zones within the brain or spinal cord, sending axons to the periphery. Cells and cell processes with such direct sensory and motor function account for only a very small fraction of the central nervous tissue, which is principally composed of neurons that are neither sensory nor motor in the above senses, since they are totally contained within its walls. In the traditional concept of reflex arcs, these intermediate or **central neurons** bridge the gap between sensory axon and motor cells (Fig. 4–15). They also combine or balance the stimuli from many sources in ways that produce coordinated and purposeful acts.

The central neurons are numbered literally by billions in a single individual, and are spun out in countless shapes and sizes. It is their organization which usually establishes the kind of response that a specific external stimulus or a combination of experiences will elicit. They determine the behavior which is characteristic of the species.

B. Tissue Differentiations

1. *Structure of White Substance.* The cells of the mantle layer produce axons and dendrites of greatly varying length and complexity. The longer processes tend to run together in functionally related groups, and with suitable techniques these bundles or **tracts** can be traced through serial sections so that maps can be made of them. Only the largest and most superficial tracts can be distinguished in dissection, even in the most advanced mammalian brains. Tracts are so named as to indicate where their cells of origin are, and where they end, e.g., the cerebellospinal tract, the spinothalamic tract, the tectobulbar tract, etc., etc.

Whatever proportion of a given section of a particular brain may be occupied by identifiable tracts, the rest of the white substance, and the gray as well, is blanketed in a feltwork of shorter processes of smaller neurons, called **neuropil.** A very primitive brain, such as that of the amblystoma [4], consists chiefly of neuropil, in such a disorderly tangle that it has not been analyzed into functional systems and virtually nothing is known about what happens in it. In more highly differentiated brains much of the neuropil takes on the quality of **reticular substance** as described on the next page.

The long axons, which run anteriorly or posteriorly through the white substance in identifiable tracts, usually cross from one side of the central nervous system to the other during their course. This is called **decussation.** A tract may make a massive decussation all in one place, or the individual fibers may wander across at intervals along their lengthwise path.

Some cells have the special function of communication between paired centers of activity. They produce dendrites on one side of the central nervous system and send strong axons across the midline, to synapse with neurons of a similar group on the other side. They are called **commissural fibers.** Most of the floor plate of the neural tube from the anterior midbrain to the far end of the spinal cord comes to be laced with such axons, comprising the **ventral commissure** (Fig. 9–5). Special commissures are developed between the two halves of the cerebellum, between the two optic lobes of the midbrain, and interconnecting various paired centers of the forebrain (Fig. 18–20).

Not all the tracts are built up from axons of central cells. Some, more conspicuously in higher vertebrates, are axons of cells from the spinal and cranial nerve ganglia, i.e., **primary sensory fibers.** They usually make synaptic connections in the gray substance at their points of entrance, but also divide into branches which run varying distances anteriorly and posteriorly in the white substance, collecting in **primary sensory tracts** according to their particular kinds of sensation. The maximum segregation and forward prolongation of these primary sensory tracts is found in mammals.

The tracts develop gradually, like the peripheral nerves, by the addition of new neurons which follow paths picked by pioneer fibers. This multiplication of units brings new sources of stimulus to centers which are already functioning, and provides them with more extensive outlets for directive activity. Meanwhile the complexity of the neuropil is increasing vastly.

The sprouting of processes on all these neurons changes the gross anatomy of the neural tube in two ways. First, it adds to the thickness of the white substance in particular areas, not in others. For instance, the tracts avoid the roof plate and the floor plate, but group themselves in large longitudinal strips or **funiculi** (Fig. 9–6) on the sides of the alar and basal plates. A prominent group of ascending sensory tracts in such a funiculus is called a **lemniscus.**

Secondly, the tracts push through the rather homogeneous tissue of the gray substance of certain areas of the brain in thousands of small bundles, interwoven in a three-dimensional maze. This converts part of the original mantle layer into a patchwork, or in some places a fairly regular gridwork, of gray and white tissues, called **reticular substance.** Even in lower vertebrates this tissue becomes prominent in the hindbrain, midbrain, and diencephalon, but in the groups with the most elaborately specialized behavior and coordination (teleosts, birds, mammals), the reticular pattern appears in most parts of the central nervous system, everywhere intergrading with the less structured matting of neuropil.

The reticular substance contains a great range of neuron types, with almost hopelessly complex interneuronal relationships. Nevertheless, *general* functions, as distinct from the *specific* rapid faithful transfers of information along the principal brain tracts, are discovered within it: functions such as sleep or arousal, the facilitation or inhibition of behavior, and decisions as to the general direction in which activity is to be channeled.

2. *Structure of the Gray Substance.* In a cross-section of the embryonic hindbrain (Fig. 9–5), the mantle layer is spread out on the floor and side walls of the IV ventricle, and divided into four strips, the two **basal plates** and the two **alar plates.** The boundaries between these strips are marked by the median ventral groove and the sulcus limitans of each side. Not forgetting that most of the cells in both alar and basal plates are neither sensory nor motor, but are either central neurons or neuroglia, it should now be noted that the cell bodies or somata of the **motor neurons** all lie in the **basal plates,** medioventrally, and that the incoming axons of the **sensory neurons** terminate in relation to neurons of the **alar plates,** dorsolaterally. Further, it is important to recognize two kinds of sensory, and two kinds of motor neurons, each of which makes its own connections within the central nervous system.

The basal plate contains two fairly distinct strips of motor neurons The more medial **somatic motor column** (Fig. 9–5) gives rise to nerve fibers that supply derivatives of the epimeric myotomes; the more lateral **visceral motor column** gives rise to nerve fibers that supply the muscles derived from the pharynx-segment hypomere. The nerve fibers of these two categories of motor neurons actually emerge at the surface of the hindbrain along two different lines on each side, the somatic motor ones medioventral to the visceral motor ones (compare Fig. 9–5 with Fig.

of epimeric rather than hypomeric origin. (2) Their cells of origin lie in the somatic motor column of gray substance, close to the median ventral neural groove. (3) Also, with the exception of the IV nerve, they emerge from the central nervous system along a special line parallel to the one marked by the roots of the visceral motor neurons, but closer to the ventral midline (Fig. 9–10). Unlike any other cranial or spinal nerve, either sensory or motor, the IV nerve leaves its ventral nucleus of origin and makes a long detour to emerge on the *opposite* side and the *dorsal* surface of the brain. This illogical arrangement is quite unexplained, but is found in all vertebrates.

In correspondence with the rather late development of the eyeball muscles, cranial nerves III, IV, and VI have barely begun their outgrowth at the pharyngula stage.

In some amniotes, one more primarily motor cranial nerve is counted. Supplying muscles that are formed from the most posterior pharynx segment, it is at first seen as a visceral motor branch of the vagus nerve X. In this condition it remains in most vertebrates, but if it becomes separated from the vagus in post-pharyngula development it becomes known as the **accessory nerve,** XI.

(c) *Mixed cranial nerve group.* The rest of the cranial nerves are primarily visceral, and are both sensory and motor. Though each has its own peculiarities, the group displays a repetition of pattern in relation to the pharynx segments (Fig. 5–11). The visceral sensory components arise from epibranchial placodes, one of which perches just above each one of the pharynx segments posterior to the mandibular. The visceral motor components, when they emerge from their own column of gray substance in the myelencephalon (Fig. 9–5) are directed into all the pharynx segments, including the mandibular. The sensory and motor components related to each segment join together to form the definitive nerve of that segment. The visceral sensory dendrites apply themselves to the endodermal lining of the pharynx immediately adjacent and a little anterior to their own segments, while the visceral motor fibers supply the muscles developed from their own strips of the hypomere mesoderm.

Thus arise the four mixed nerves of each side of the head. The **trigeminal nerve** V, in addition to supplying the mandibular segment, develops extensive somatic sensory branches from ganglion cells of the neural crest and placodes. One of these joins the visceral motor component, forming the **mandibular branch** of the trigeminal, which distributes along the lower jaw. Another spreads to the snout below the eye and along the upper jaw, as the sensory **maxillary branch.** A third grows into the snout dorsal to the eye. This last, called the **deep ophthalmic branch,** or the **profundus nerve,** arises from a separate placodal ganglion in all the vertebrates, and in the lamprey remains a separate nerve throughout life. The **facial nerve** VII, besides supplying its own hyoid segment, sends visceral sensory branches forward through both the roof and the floor of the mouth cavity. As earlier noted, the **glossopharyngeal nerve** IX supplies the third pharynx segment, and the **vagus nerve** X supplies all the rest.

REFERENCES

1. Bergquist, H., 1952. *Acta Zool.* 33: 117. The neuromeres.
2. Holtfreter, J., 1934. *Arch. exptl. Zellforsch* 15: 281.
3. Hamburger, V., 1952. *Am. N. Y. Acad. Sci.* 55: 117. A review of many factors known to operate in shaping up the nervous system.
4. Herrick, C. J., 1948. *The brain of the tiger salamander, Ambystoma tigrinum.* University of Chicago Press, Chicago.
5. Stone, L. S., 1933. *J. Comp. Neurol.* 57: 507.
6. Hörstadius, S., 1950. *The neural crest.* Oxford University Press, London.
7. Yntema, C. L., 1937. *J. Exptl. Zool.* 75: 75 (ganglia of VII, VIII). Also 1943. *J. Exptl. Zool.* 92: 93 (ganglia of IX, X).
8. Triplett, E. L., 1958. *J. Exptl. Zool.* 138: 283.
9. DuShane, G. P., 1935. *J. Exptl. Zool.* 72: 1.

10

Analysis of the Differentiation Period

The biologists of today look at essentially the same developing chicks and frogs and sharks that Aristotle described more than two thousand years ago, but their way of thinking about and describing them has changed radically since the 1930's. Entirely new concepts have come into morphology from new ways of manipulating and culturing embryonic tissues, and from the application of chemical and physical techniques to biological problems. Old questions reappear in entirely new terms, and as usual it is discovered that nature is more complex and more interesting than was previously imagined. This chapter will review some of the general concepts and new kinds of questions that have come from the analytical approach to development [1].

Experiments with amphibian embryos will dominate the discussion. The analysis of amphibian development has progressed much farther than that for birds or fish or other vertebrates simply because many experiments which can be done with amphibia are practically impossible with others. What can be found out depends on what can be done.

I. PRELIMINARY ANALYSES

A. Experiments with the Prospective Chordamesoderm

Amphibian embryos are extremely soft and sensitive in the cleavage and blastula stages, but as young gastrulas they may easily be divested of all their membranes and raised in dishes of spring water at room temperatures. If they are carefully washed and kept in sterile and slightly salted water, surgical operations may be done on them. Pieces may be removed or transplanted with fine needles or iridectomy scissors. Even large wounds close themselves promptly, and transplanted pieces heal in place in a few minutes. If either the host embryo or the donor is stained with a harmless vital dye, the boundaries of a grafted piece can be recognized for some days. If grafts are made from one species to another (heteroplastically) or between animals of very different kinds (xenoplastically), the tissues or even single cells of host and donor can often be identified in serial sections by differences in pigment, nuclear size, or other characteristics. Pieces of the embryo may be cultured by themselves for many days, revealing their intrinsic capacities for development.

1. Regulation. When the dorsal lip of the blastopore first appears, the prospective chordamesoderm can be located by reference to the published fate map (Fig. 7–1), as a broad symmetrical crescent at the equator just above the furrow. It is a simple matter to remove a large piece from the middle of this crescent. The wound quickly closes and despite the loss it is possible for the embryo to develop into an *anatomically normal individual.* In biological ex-

Inductors for all these structures are present in both forms. Prospective belly epidermis of the salamander, transplanted to the jaw region of the anuran embryo, is induced to form a balancer (Fig. 10–7, right). Prospective belly epidermis of the anuran, transplanted to the stomodeal region of the salamander embryo, is induced to form horny denticles and adhesive organs (Fig. 10–7, left). In both cases the prospective fate of the graft is changed by a *host* inductor, but in a direction which is characteristic of the *donor* species and genetically impossible for the host's own ectoderm.

Differences of competence also exist within a genus or within a species. There are two amblystoma species, one of which (*Ambystoma maculatum*) regularly forms balancers while the other (*A. tigrinum*) regularly fails to do so. Reciprocal grafts between their embryos show clearly that both possess the required inductors, and that the skin of the former lacks the competence to respond. In transplants of pigment-forming neural crest derivatives between black and red breeds of the domestic fowl, the *color* of pigment formed is determined by the genetic competence of the transplanted cells, though the *pattern* of pigment laid down in the feathers is determined by the inductive actions of the host tissues.

E. Non-Inductive Tissue Interactions

When a group of competent cells has been subjected to an adequate inductor, its fate is determined and it proceeds to differentiate. This determination can also arise spontaneously, as in the presumptive endoderm and chordamesoderm of the amphibian gastrula. But the cellular differentiation that follows is not necessarily accompanied by self-organization into a functionally meaningful pattern of organs and tissues.

Self-organization has been spoken of as one of the properties of a developmental field, and it is one of the principal unexplained phenomena of embryology. In order to form an organ, cells not only have to differentiate along a number of different lines, but also they have to arrange themselves in proper groupings and adjust their growth to one another. When non-living inductors act on competent gastrular ectoderm in isolation cultures, they may bring about a wide assortment of cellular differentiations, but these are often so lacking in the capacity for self-organization that they develop into scrambled patches of cells and tissues without axis, without bilaterality and without order, resembling nothing so much as a living beef stew wrapped in a wrinkled epidermis.

The cooperative interactions of tissues in self-organization can best be appreciated in situations where they have been prevented from occurring. Presumptive endoderm will differentiate into recognizable intestinal cells in isolation, but is only able to form a jumbled mass. The epithelial arrangements characteristic of the intestine seem to be impossible unless mesoderm is present. If mesoderm is included in such a culture an endodermal epithelium is formed, but the mesoderm burrows to the center of the mass and the epithelium is inside out. Ectoderm also seems powerless to maintain an epithelium without a substrate of mesoderm-like connective tissue.

While the inductions and differentiations are taking place the factors that produce directed movements and selective adhesions of cells continue to act vigorously and are undoubtedly important in local organization. This is shown by disaggregation and recombination experiments [12]. Until their connective tissues become fibrous, amphibian embryos may be caused to fall into heaps of single cells by temporary subjection to a potassium hydroxide solution at pH. 9.8. Swept up into random mixtures these cells may be returned to proper culture fluid at pH. 8.0 and will reaggregate as highly disorganized but living embryonic fragments. At neurula stages, after the normal morphogenetic movements and primary inductions of gastrulation, patches of neural ectoderm, belly epidermis, endoderm, and chordamesoderm have been cut from the embryo, assembled in all the possible combinations of two or three cell types, and subjected to the jumbling and reaggregation process.

Within twenty-four hours the cells of such a jumbled mass have crawled amongst each other and joined up, like with like, each cell type taking up a preferred location with respect to the others. The result is always the same for each combination of cell types and in some cases is comparable to what had previously happened in the normal gastrulation, though here the co-ordinating effect of the surface coat had been eliminated by the action of the alkali.

Neural plate cells, after being jumbled with ventral ectoderm cells (Fig. 10–8), join together in one or more masses in the interior of the clump, with the ventral ectoderm cells in a covering layer. Jumbled with endoderm cells, the neurogenic cells again bury themselves and join together in the interior, though in this case the situation is quite without parallel in normal embryology. In both cases the neuro-genic cells tend to arrange themselves about fluid-filled spaces, comparable to the normal neural-tube cavity, but not formed in the same way.

When ectodermal and mesodermal cells are experimentally jumbled together, they migrate individually until all the mesoderm is buried in the interior, as in normal gastrulation. In this case the buried ectodermal cells have simul-taneously migrated to the outside, which of course has no parallel in normal morphogenetic movements. When mesoderm is stirred up with endoderm it again moves to the interior, in a complete reversal of the normal relationship. Only in a combination of cells from all three germ layers do the individual mesoderm cells come to rest in the normal middle position.

In all these combinations the cells of each type selectively adhere to one another, and clefts or well defined tissue interfaces develop between the masses of cells which are of unlike origin. The factors which produce these patterns of behavior are poorly understood, but are un-doubtedly operating in more and more local and specific ways, in the establishment of anlagen and tissues, long after the times of induction and determination.

Embryo surgery provides numerous examples of effects of this sort. The control of the shape of the spinal cord by the surrounding somites and notochord (Fig. 9–4), and the imposition of

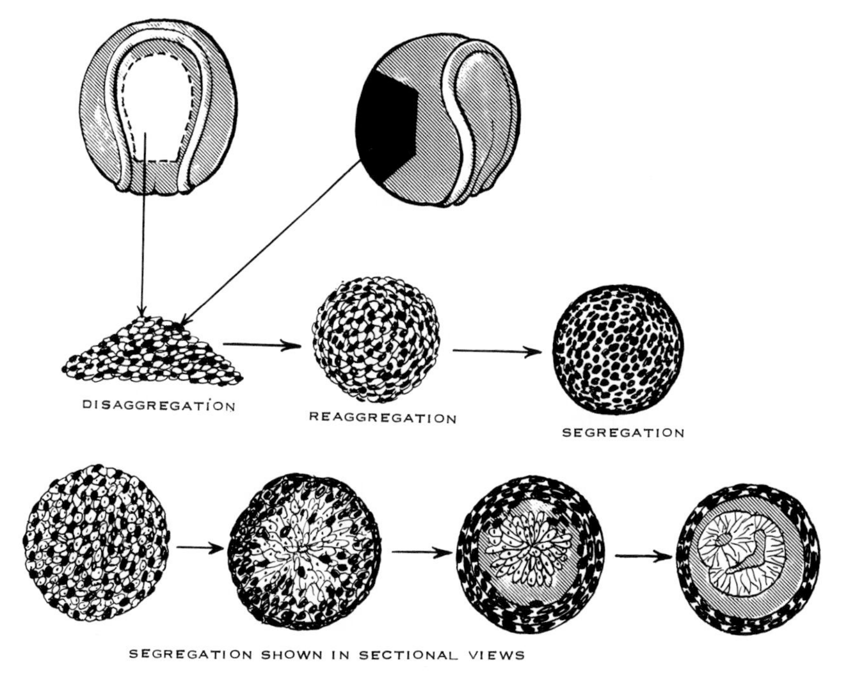

Fig. 10–8. Disaggregation and recombination of neural plate and epidermis cells.

(After P. L. Townes and J. Holtfreter, 1955.)

bling the nervous parts of the retina; 8-hour– and notochord-process–stage grafts show not only these two types of cells but stratification of the retinal cells, and the older ones show them better. Transplants of the already formed optic vesicles of the 33-hour stage differentiate into eyes closely resembling the normal.

(b) For some time after the eye field has been established and the material through which it operates will undergo self-differentiation in explants or transplants, one finds that the determination is general and not at all specific for details. For instance, after the amphibian optic vesicle has started to grow outward, and has acquired the ability to self-differentiate when transplanted to the belly, its parts are not yet determined in detail. It can be turned through 180 degrees and replanted so that the prospective location of the chorioid fissure (a normal feature of the ventral side of the eyeball) is now dorsal, yet a chorioid fissure will presently develop on its *new* ventral side, in harmony with local surroundings. A somewhat older vesicle is unable to regulate in this way.

When the optic vesicle has become an optic cup, its two layers (the prospective retina and prospective pigment epithelium) can be separated and transplanted to favorable sites, where the prospective retina differentiates into both retinal and pigmented layers, and the prospective pigment layer can form a miniature eye cup containing retinal cells. Similar regulations have been achieved in experiments with the chick embryo as late as the 36-somite stage.

At a still later stage, the prospective retina is determined for retina, but if it is turned inside out, reversing the order of the prospective visual and ganglion-cell layers, regulation to the normal histology is possible.

3. *Subordination of Fields to the Whole Embryo.* (a) *Size.* When the embryo is converted into a mosaic of special local developmental fields, each of these has capacities for self-differentiation and self-organization, but is by no means independent. Influences of unknown character come in from the whole organism, regulating various qualities. For instance, the size of a field is not fixed in absolute terms, but relative to that of the whole embryo. When the ventral half of an amphibian embryo is pinched off at the early blastopore stage, leaving a whole chordamesoderm induction system in a half-sized individual, a small but normally proportioned larva may develop. If half the forelimb field district is removed at an early stage, or two field districts are fused together, a normal-sized limb develops nevertheless.

(b) *Polarity.* Equally mysterious influences are at work in the establishment of polarities. All the organs of the body have asymmetrical features, the disposition of which can be described along several axes. The central nervous system, for instance, has been subdivided into fore-, mid-, and hind-brain and spinal cord along an anteroposterior axis. Differences between its roof and its floor were noted along a dorsoventral axis. Mantle and marginal layers are distributed on mediolateral axes which run in opposite directions toward the two sides from the center. The parts of the neural field acquire these polarizations gradually, through the action of the primary inductor system, and transplantation experiments can demonstrate the rather precise times at which the various axes are determined. This is probably true for all the developmental fields. As mentioned earlier (page 145), the way in which the heart tube bends is determined by nearby mesodermal and endodermal tissues. The cue as to where to form a chorioid fissure is brought to the eye field from its environment. The most complete studies on the origin of polarities have been focused on the limbs and the ears of the amblystoma; these will be discussed in later chapters. All of the organs acquire polarities which are in harmony with the pattern of the whole organism.

4. *Subordinations within Fields.* (a) *Inhibition of Peripheral Development.* Once the size of the field has been suitably regulated, a further control is exerted over what part will undergo differentiation toward the proper organ and what will not. This control presumably operates within the field itself, but the mechanism is quite unknown. A normal-sized heart can be obtained from either the right or the left half of the presumptive heart tissue, and if the two halves

are prevented from joining by the interposition of a block of inert tissue, both of them may form hearts, each the mirror image twin of the other (Fig. 10–10). By subdivision of the presumptive heart mesoderm, as many as five hearts have been produced in a single individual from its own substance. Obviously there is enough material in the field to form a grotesquely oversized organ, yet this does not happen.

The same thing can be illustrated in the limb district. As previously mentioned, the amblystoma forelimb field occupies a disc at least the diameter of 5 somites, but the anlage that emerges from it has only the diameter of 3½ somites. If the smaller disc is removed, the cells of the outer ring can still form a normal limb. There is no well-established theory as to how the peripheral parts of the field, which possess this potency, can be held inactive, but the limb which develops is never twice too big. A potentiality exists within the larger disc, for development of two normal-sized limbs side by side, and this can be released experimentally, though it is realized only by the rarest of accidents in nature.

Fig. 10–10. Twin hearts in a toad, produced by introduction of blocking tissue between the two halves of the heart anlage.
(After G. Ekman, 1925.)

(b) *Achievement of Harmonious Proportions.* The brain always fits the skull, the blood vessels that supply a leg are big enough to suit its requirements, and one does not find a biceps muscle twice too long for the arm it is supposed to move. The harmonious proportions are already determined in the embryo, and not much is known about how this is achieved.

Monsters do occasionally arise in embryonic development, and are regularly eliminated from the breeding stock of the species by their own ineptness. One might suppose that normal harmonious proportions are automatic expressions of a successful inheritance of a harmonious assemblage of genes. Many mutations are known which change proportions and affect disharmonies. But to say that genes are responsible merely restates the problem. In what way do the genes exert their control?

Interactions do take place within developmental fields which insure harmony in the presence of potential disharmony, by controlling growth rates and proportionate differentiations and arrangements of parts. Such mechanisms are not discoverable in normal embryology, but can be revealed for example in reciprocal transplantations between species that differ in sizes, proportions, or growth rates.

Two common amblystoma species are available for such experiments. *Ambystoma tigrinum* is fast growing, *A. maculatum* much slower. Their embryos are of comparable size, and reciprocal grafts can be made without being destroyed later by host antibody reactions. At the end of three months' growth, the *tigrinum* larva may be six inches long, the *maculatum* only 2½ inches long, with parts in proportion. When tissues of both species are combined in a single field, either conditions of *dominance* or of *mutual interaction* may emerge.

If optic vesicles together with their covering of lens-ectoderm are exchanged between the two species at an early period, the transplanted eyes that develop are of normal anatomy and about the same size as they would have been in the donor species, though out of proportion in relation to the host head. This shows that the operation itself and the strange new environment have not prevented the transplanted field districts from realizing their normal potentials in their new locations. But since the mesodermal coats of the transplanted eyes have been contributed in thicknesses of harmonious proportions from the hosts, the ectodermal tissues of the large transplanted *tigrinum* eyes have clearly called for greater differentiation and faster growth of the chorioid, sclerotic and corneal layers from the *maculatum* host mesoderm, and those of the small *maculatum* eyes for less differentiation and slower growth from the *tigrinum* host mesoderm. This is a relationship showing complete dominance of one tissue over others (Fig. 10–11 A).

If however the optic vesicles are transplanted without lens-ectoderm, or if they are left in place and an exchange of lens-ectoderm is effected between the embryos of the two species, combinations of the eyeball of one with the lens of the other are produced. In this case, mutual interactions are discovered (Fig. 10–11 B).

Assuming that the tissues of these chimaeric eyes were to develop at the rates characteristic of their species of origin, the *tigrinum* lenses would soon be far too large for the *maculatum* eyeballs, and the *maculatum* lenses would be absurdly small for the optical requirements of the *tigrinum* eyeballs. Instead of this happening, in the one combination the slow-growing lens is speeded up and exceeds its normal size while the fast-growing eyeball is held somewhat in check. In the other combination, the fast-growing lens is somewhat inhibited and the slow-growing eyeball becomes somewhat larger than normal. In both combinations the result is a substantial reduction in the expected disharmony of proportions. Either combination can be grown in the head of either species, and the result is the same.

Reciprocal exchanges of ectodermal ear vesicles between the two species furnish other examples of mutual interactions within a field.

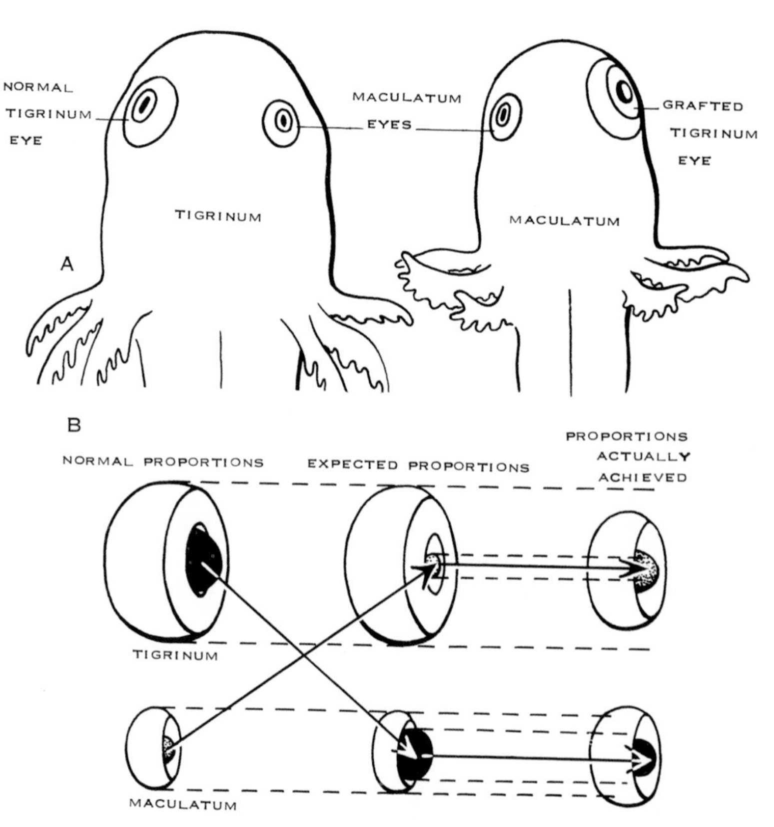

Fig. 10–11. Achievement of harmonious proportions. A. Transplantation of whole eyes: growth rates unaffected. B. Adjustments in chimaeric eyes. (After Harrison, 1929, and Ballard, 1939.)

The host mesenchyme is induced to form a cartilaginous capsule around the ectodermal vesicle. In one host the vesicle would be expected to be too big, the capsule too small, and in the other host, vice versa. What happens in this case also is a mutual regulatory effect, resulting in intermediate proportions of a more harmonious sort.

When half of the *A. maculatum* forelimb district is combined with the other half of one from *A. tigrinum*, the limb which is produced from the regulated field is of intermediate size and its parts are in proportion. This would not have happened without the controlled alterations of the numbers of cells differentiating in all categories, or the controlled alteration of the growth rates of cartilages, muscles, blood vessels, and the covering skin. The demonstration that this extraordinarily pervasive control can exist in experimental combinations implies that it exists in the normal field. Gene-controlled or not, it is of crucial importance for the establishment and maintenance of an adequate anatomy and can be adjusted to circumstances.

B. The Functional Period and Later Field Phenomena

A review of the diagnostic features of the embryonic fields shows that most of them are temporary and fade out with the emergence of the anlagen and their further differentiation. When the heart begins to beat, the limb to walk and the gill to carry blood, the period of functional development is reached and many new and mostly unknown factors begin to shape the anatomy of the parts. Most cells have already become irrevocably determined and only lesser categories of new structures are arising, and at decreased rates. Differences in the relative growth rates of the parts begin to change proportions of the animal toward those characteristic of the order, the family and the species.

In poorly understood ways, function becomes a factor of development at these later stages. For instance, more active life strengthens the heart, poorer aeration increases the size of the gills, removal of one kidney brings about compensatory increase of the remaining one, and the diet may make minor modifications in the structure of the intestine.

Also the nervous system takes over certain maintenance functions. Some tissues, the limb muscles for instance, which are able to establish their full anatomical pattern in complete isolation from nerves, now become extremely dependent on them, withering away if disease or surgery removes them. Other tissues acquire similar dependence on endocrine secretions from the pituitary, the thyroid, or the sex glands.

During the operation of all these new factors, integrating influences resembling those of the embryonic fields still operate so as to hold the multitudinous cells and tissues of the separate organs and parts of the body to normal sizes and patterns. When sudden changes in growth rates or new patterns of differentiation occur, as in the sexual cycles, puberty, pregnancy, or metamorphosis, all the component tissues of organs that are affected react in a coordinated way. These later field effects may be a persistence of those set up in the embryo. Fields precisely similar to the ones known in the embryo reappear in larvae or adults of vertebrates which have strong regenerative powers.

"Physiologic regeneration," which is the replacement of worn-out cells or of larger units such as pancreatic islands, uterine glands, epidermis, teeth, hair, feathers, etc., is a common phenomenon, normally occurring at appropriate rates. "Reconstitutive regeneration," which is the replacement of whole missing organs or regions, occurs in various invertebrates including the tunicates, but few vertebrates retain the ability to any important degree. Exceptionally, salamanders can restore eyes and limbs and other parts after almost total removal. In such cases, after the wound has closed there appears a special accumulation of apparently undifferentiated cells called a *blastema*. Almost a perfect replica of the missing parts differentiates out of the blastema. For a time it has all the properties of an embryonic field. It grows very rapidly at first, but as the regenerated part approaches an appropriate size and proportions, its growth rate slows down to fit the pace of the whole animal.

The controls which cells place upon each other

is an incomplete skull in itself, forming part of the neurocranium and most of the splanchnocranium. The osteocranium (Fig. 12–3) mostly forms a sheath of flat scalelike bones over the jaws and the brain box, but is also in process of replacing some of the cartilage. (It is shown solid black in Fig. 12–1 B.) Both the chondrocranium and the osteocranium take shape in late embryology by the joining of separate elements formed in a fixed time and pattern. One of the functions of this chapter is to consider the processes by which the cartilage and bone tissues differentiate, and another is to analyze the patterns of these elements which contribute to the finished skeleton. The skull-forming process is generally comparable throughout vertebrates, but lends itself to innumerable variations in detail.

II. LANDMARKS

In comparing the very different skulls of vertebrates with each other, certain landmarks will continually be referred to. Skulls of adult vertebrates can become most remarkably adapted in shape and proportions, but they can be analyzed easily if it is remembered that these relationships, which are established in the pharyngula, are somehow maintained. For instance, nasal organs associate with the forebrain, eyes with the midbrain, and ears with the hindbrain. The otic capsules of the differentiated skull often have close associations with hyoid-arch derivatives. This was foreshadowed by the location of the otic vesicles above the hyoid segments in the pharyngula. The anterior end of the notochord, which lay just below the boundary between forebrain and midbrain in the pharyngula, is later found embedded in the base of the skull just back of the spot where the pituitary gland itself has become embedded.

In the analysis of a new skull, it helps to locate a certain few landmarks at once: the **nasal capsules**, the **orbits** or spaces where the eyeballs lie, the **otic capsules,** and the **pituitary.** One also easily finds the **foramen magnum,** the big hole in the posterior end of the skull through which the brain is continuous with the spinal cord; also the **jaw joints,** between upper and lower jaws. However conspicuous the foramen magnum and the jaw joints may be, they are not the stable landmarks that they seem. Evidence will be presented in later chapters that different elements have been used in their construction in different stocks of vertebrates.

III. HISTOGENESIS IN THE HEAD MESENCHYME

A. Meninges

The central nervous system and the roots of the cranial nerves acquire a delicate and tight-fitting cover of fibrous tissue called the **inner meninx** (Fig. 12–4), which carries blood vessels that penetrate the nervous tissue. Outside this and separated by a space in which cerebrospinal fluid moves, a tougher fibrous layer is laid down, which follows the contours of the brain less faithfully and may even become widely separated from it. This **outer meninx** remains undivided in fishes, and only becomes split locally in amphibia, but in amniotes it is readily separable into a **dura mater** associated with the central nervous

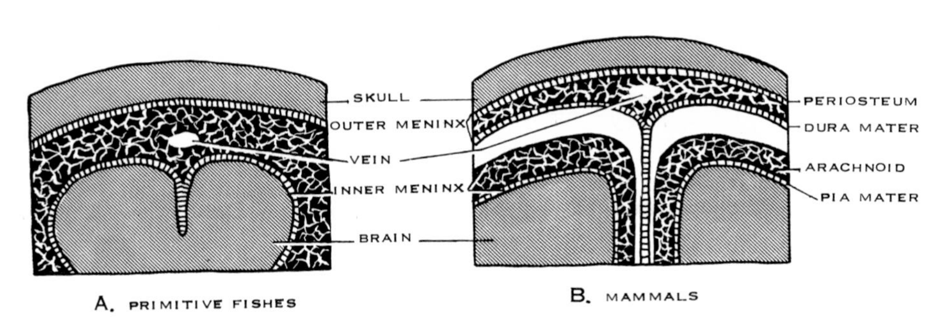

Fig. 12–4. Meninges.

system and a **perichondrium** or **periosteum** associated with the skull.

Experimental evidence from some vertebrates has suggested that the neural crest is the source of most of the inner meninx. The outer one apparently comes mostly from regular mesoderm [2].

In teleosts, birds, and mammals the inner meninx separates into an inner component, the **pia mater** or **leptomeninx,** which is firmly attached to the brain, and an outer mat of wispy fibers called the **arachnoid layer** (Fig. 12–4).

B. Chondrogenesis

The first indication of the formation of cartilage is the condensation of clusters of mesenchyme cells into recognizable zones and masses of procartilage (Fig. 12–1). These cells, called **chondroblasts,** then secrete about themselves an abundant watery intercellular matrix which hardens due to the synthesis within it of complexes of mucopolysaccharides with collagen and other proteins. This occurs in a constellation of spreading centers. The number of spots of true cartilage increases for a time, and the size of each piece increases. Then many of the separate elements begin to merge together, but others retain their individuality and form joints with each other. When the pattern has stabilized, each piece of cartilage is seen to be wrapped in a tight limiting membrane of connective tissue, the **perichondrium.** Blood vessels do not usually enter the cartilage. The trapped cells get their food and oxygen and pass on their wastes by diffusion. Growth is partly interstitial and partly appositional; i.e., the cells within the matrix continue to divide and produce more interstitial substance, and other cells join the cartilage mass by transformation from the perichondrium.

Each of the cartilage pieces can be identified by its relationship to the previously existent pattern of cranial nerves, pharynx segments and other structures (Fig. 12–6). The pattern of cartilages is constant for each stage for each species, and the individual pieces can be named and homologized more or less consistently throughout the gnathostomes [3].

Not so with the agnathous fishes, however. In the lamprey larva, a peculiar tissue called **mucocartilage** is formed, from which a head skeleton of cartilage plates arises after long delay. This cannot be securely homologized in any detail either with that of the hagfishes or with those of gnathostomes. It has been mentioned that the cells which form the cartilage centers in the upper and lower jaws, the hyoid and branchial arches of the amblystoma are derived from the neural crest. This observation has been confirmed for various other gnathostomes, and also for the lamprey [4]. But neither the lampreys nor the hagfishes ever produce any jaws; and their branchial skeletons are entirely different, both in their structure and in their relationships to branchial muscles and blood vessels, from those of the gnathostomes. This is a very ancient evolutionary divergence, revealed very early in development.

C. Osteogenesis

In the elasmobranchs and holocephals, cartilage formation progresses until it has produced a complete skull. In higher vertebrates, however, the cartilage usually fails to complete its spread over the top of the brain, and even where it becomes established it may fail to maintain itself after the fetal period. Spots of degeneration develop in predictable places, and are invaded by blood vessels. In these areas, special bone-forming cells called **osteoblasts** begin to operate. All these specialized cells are derived from mesenchyme, and it is not known what causes some of them to form cartilage or others to form bone, or what it is that determines their life span as individuals.

With the regression of cartilage and the spread of these centers of ossification, casual observation would perhaps suggest that cartilage is being *converted* into bone. Instead, it is being *replaced* by bone which, for a while at least, takes the same shape as the precursor tissue. Such bones may thus be said to be "pre-formed in cartilage." They are cataloged as **endochondral bones** or **replacement bones** (cf. the articular bone in Fig. 12–1 B).

In other parts of the head, particularly in the spaces between the chondrocranium and the skin or the roof of the mouth, osteoblasts accumulate in superficial sheets and there lay down a pattern of spots of bone, quite independent of the cartilage. These are called **membrane bones** or, in some cases, **dermal bones,** since the membrane in which they are formed is at first indistinguishable from the dermis layer of the skin (cf. parietal, squamosal, and dentary bones in Fig. 12–1 B).

All these ossification centers arise in a species-specific pattern, and entensive resemblances can be made out between the patterns of all the higher vertebrates. The individual bones can be identified by their relationships to the chondrocranium and the soft parts of the head, and they have been the object of extensive homology studies. On the assumption that two bones cannot be homologous unless they are formed in the same way, the distinction between membrane bones and replacement bones has been much emphasized, though the actual bone-forming process is the same in both cases and the distinction can be seen only in early stages of development. Both types grow by the addition of bone cells (osteocytes) from a **periosteal membrane** of osteoblasts, in the one case within an eroding cartilage mass, and in the other case floating in soft connective tissue. Confusing intergradations occur in bony fishes, for there are examples of membrane bones which invade cartilage, and replacement bones which extend into the overlying membrane.

When bone is about to be formed in a new ossification center, the osteoblasts link themselves together by a network of tendril-like processes enclosing a watery intercellular substance containing fibrils. Poorly understood synthetic processes involving alkaline phosphatase then imprison these cells and fibrils by turning the intercellular substance into a hard matrix of calcium phosphates and carbonates. This activity takes place always at a certain small distance from blood vessels which are spreading through the mesenchyme, so that the bone itself tends to spread in spicules and small plates and bars from the original center, enclosing a network of unossified but vascularized connective tissue spaces. This results in what is called **spongy bone** (Fig. 12–5).

Almost as soon as a center of spongy bone has been established, along with its growth by the apposition of new bone from the periosteal membrane, a process of bone dissolution and reorganization is started. Conspicuous large cells called **osteoclasts** appear in the areas where bone is being dissolved, but what they actually do or how the bone is cleared away is in dispute. However there is no doubt that healthy-looking bone is being resorbed, its place being taken by new tunnels containing connective tissue and blood vessels, and that presently new bone is

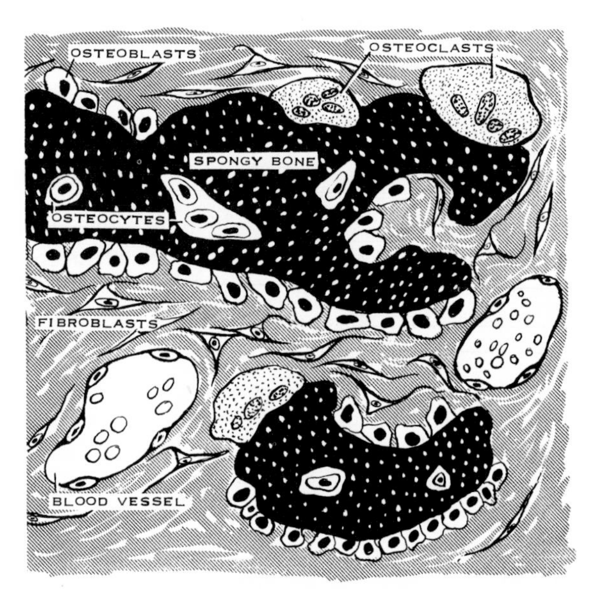

Fig. 12–5. Components of developing spongy bone.

deposited in these same places, but in new patterns, with the entrapped fibrils oriented in new ways, and with greater compactness and strength.

This simultaneous growth, dissolution, and reorganization makes bone one of the liveliest tissues in the body. Every individual bone follows its own locally established instructions, enlarging and strengthening in appropriate ways. The size of the braincase, and the diameters and directions of its foramina, must continually change to fit the expanding brain, cranial nerves, and blood vessels. The two bones which replace the cartilaginous capsules formed around the human otic vesicles become firmly embedded in the middle of the fetal skull base, yet as the head grows all during childhood the angle formed by the intersection of their axes is continually changing. The skull is not only rigid, it is plastic.

The reorganization of spongy bone into new **compact bone,** and the continual alteration of this during further growth, is accomplished by the addition, subtraction and substitution of microscopic bony units called **osteons** (Fig. 4–6). One of these units appears in cross-section as a central **vascular canal** carrying one or two blood vessels and a small amount of connective tissue, surrounded by concentric rings of bony matrix regularly interspersed with small lacunae in which the trapped osteocytes lie. The tendrils by which these cells had established a network with each other, before the matrix was hardened, remain in **canalicules** which form communications between the lacunae. There must be lively transport of substances through the canalicules, since the cellular processes they contain are the only pathways between the central blood vessels of the osteon and the concentric rings of osteocytes.

When an osteon is laid down, the first layer of bone is formed at the periphery, along, but at a distance from, the central blood vessels. Successive rings of osteocytes take their position concentrically on the interior of this shell, gradually diminishing the mesenchymatous interior until there is little left in the vascular canal except the blood vessels. Lengthwise, the osteon follows the branching or anastomosing of its blood vessels, and the bone acquires its compactness by filling all the connective tissue spaces of the precursor spongy bone with osteons, built around the blood vessels that branch and anastomose in those spaces.

While new layers of bone are being deposited on the outer surfaces of the skull bones from the periosteal membranes, older bone is being resorbed and reorganized by the endosteal membranes on the inner surfaces. In addition, new osteons are constantly being built at the expense of older spongy bone, and old osteons are being resorbed and new osteons laid down in new orientations in the temporary connective tissue spaces so created. It is not known what dictates absorption of bone in one area and deposition of bone in an area just next to it, nor is it known what directs this complex shufflng of highly organized materials to the result that the skeleton is always playing its proper role in the whole animal.

In the large heavy skull bones of land vertebrates, a structural pattern is gradually worked out, of inner and outer "tables" of compact bone, separated by an inner mass of spongy bone arranged in pillars and struts, interspersed by blood-filled marrow spaces. The outer table shows a number of superimposed lamellae of bone laid down parallel to the surface by the periosteal membrane, inside which there is a thicker zone of reworked and tightly packed osteons. In birds and some reptiles, the interior of certain skull bones is pneumatized, i.e., filled with a froth of tiny interconnected air cells, each walled off by thin bone partitions, and all communicating with the ear or nose by air passages. In large mammals, similar but more extensive sinuses are created by air spaces that invade the tissue between inner and outer tables, in certain bones of the face, forehead, and ear regions.

IV. THE CHONDROCRANIUM

The anterior and posterior parts of the brain are formed under different inductive influences, from the prechordal and notochordal tissues respectively. The anterior and posterior parts of the skull are likewise formed in different patterns. There have been evolutionary lines of vertebrates in which these two parts of the skull never joined up. In crossopterygian fishes an intracranial joint characteristically formed between them.

The first indication of the formation of the posterior part of the skull is always the deposition of a rod of cartilage on each side of the anterior end of the notochord under the hindbrain (Fig. 12–6 A). These two **parachordal cartilages** subsequently broaden and fuse in the midline, enclosing the notochord in a **basal plate** (Fig. 12–2 B). A small but variable number of cartilage arches also arise posterior to the basal plate on each side, looking like the rudiments of vertebrae. In fact they are derived like vertebrae from

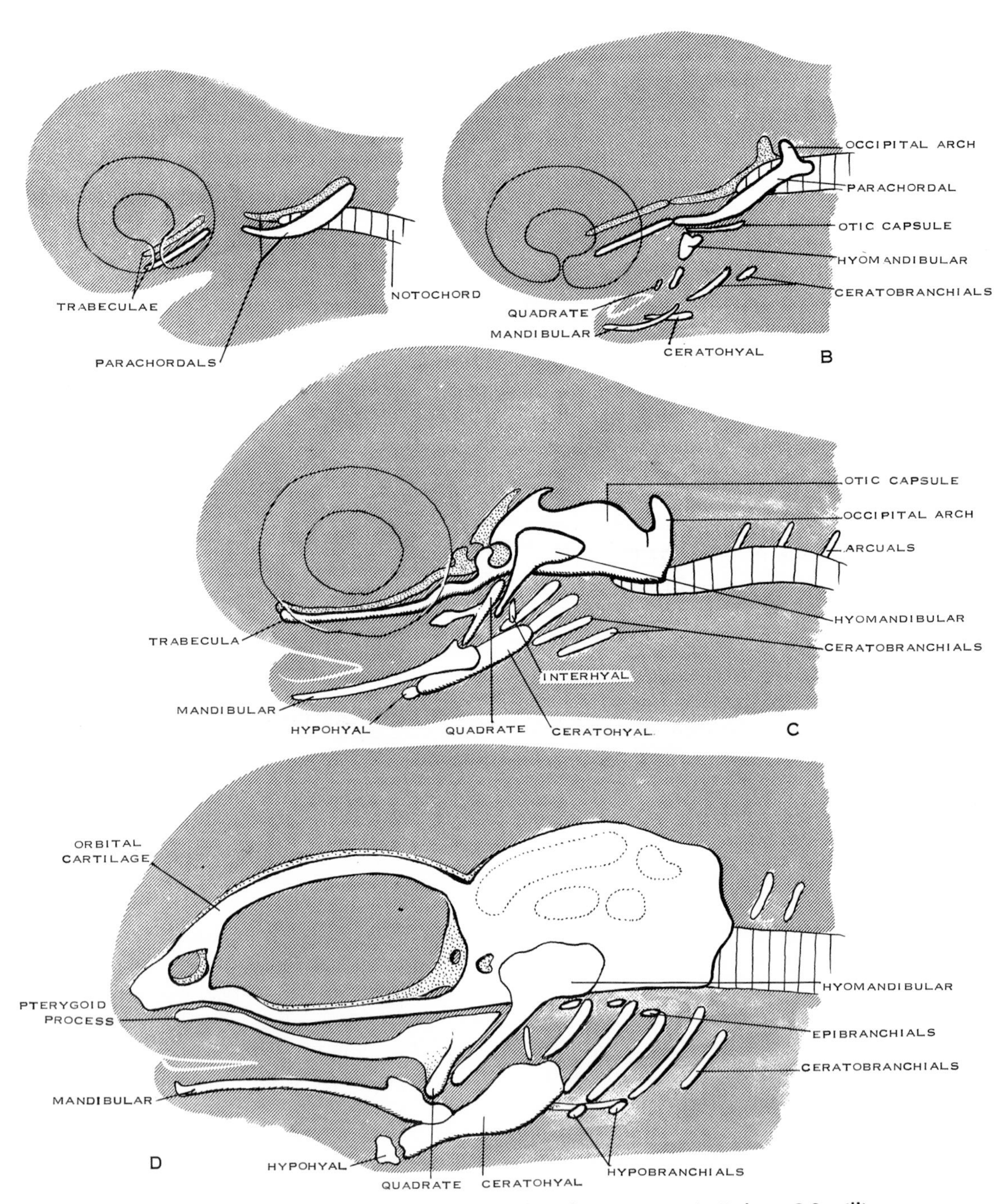

Fig. 12–6. Development of the trout chondrocranium. A. Embryo 9.2 millimeters long. B. 10.8 millimeters. C. 12.3 millimeters. D. 16.5 millimeters.
(After G. R. de Beer, 1927.)

the sclerotomic parts of the first few post-otic somites (cf. page 142). Except in cyclostomes these **preoccipital** and **occipital arches** soon unite with the basal plate, and the last ones produce one or more **occipital condyles** with which the first vertebra forms a joint. (There is only one occipital arch in the trout, Fig. 12–6.)

While this is happening, the otic vesicle of each side has become invested with a cartilaginous **otic capsule,** which becomes united to the basal plate by a series of bridges running transversely between the roots of the cranial nerves that arise from the hindbrain. By the time that the hindbrain has been provided with a floor and sidewalls of cartilage through confluence of all these elements, a strip of cartilage called the **synotic tectum** usually spreads over the top between the two otic capsules as a sort of diminutive roof. The posterior part of the chondrocranium has now taken shape.

In the meantime, a pair of cartilages called **trabeculae** have been differentiating from neural crest cells, anterior to the notochord and the hypophysis, below and along the sides of the forebrain (Fig. 12–6 A, B). They subsequently unite into a **trabecular plate** (or **ethmoid plate**) across the midline. (Only a single trabecula is formed in the midline in mammals.) A pair of **orbital cartilages** arise dorsal to the trabeculae and soon become united to them by straps of cartilage developed between the roots of the cranial nerves II to V (Fig. 12–6 D). Thus, there are formed skeletal sidewalls for the forebrain, and these are soon augmented by the incorporation of the capsules forming around the nasal sense organs. More or less prominent **antorbital processes** grow out from the anterior parts of the trabecular cartilage on each side to form walls between the orbits and the nasal capsules. **Basitrabecular processes** grow out from their posterior ends lateral to the hypophysis. The establishment of these cartilages has given rise to the anterior part of the chondrocranium.

The recently discovered coelacanth fish *Latimeria* is the only surviving vertebrate in which the anterior and posterior parts of the skull have not fused. It still reproduces the archaic and probably useless intracranial joint of the crossopterygian fishes [5]. In the modern vertebrates, variable but extensive fusions take place between the trabecular plate and the basal plate, and between the orbital cartilages and the otic capsules, bringing the whole chondrocranium into one complex brain box. Cartilages formed by neural crest cells in the mandibular and hyoid segments of the pharynx wall may later form joints with this box, or even fuse with it, but this is a subject for Chapter 16.

The chondrocranium is formed more or less in the same way throughout the gnathostome vertebrates, but there are multitudes of minor variations. Conspicuous differences occur in the trabecular region, in correlation with differences in the relative size and position of the eyeballs and the forebrain. Elasmobranchs, amphibia and some others have relatively small eyes and a long forebrain. In these groups the trabeculae are far apart (Fig. 12–2 B), and the orbital cartilages are small and arise in common with them. In the big-eyed bony fishes and birds, the trabeculae may be much closer together and quickly fuse into one piece (Fig. 12–6 C, D). The orbital cartilages may then become pressed together into an interorbital septum anteroventral to the relatively short brain. In mammals the single trabecula that appears in the midline is quite small, and is functionally replaced by expansion of the orbital cartilages.

Chondrocranium formation has not progressed far before constellations of replacement bones and membrane bones begin to appear. Only in exceptional vertebrates, such as elasmobranchs and quite primitive bony fishes, does the chondrocranium form much of a roof. The top of the brain gets adequate protection from the shingling of membrane bones.

V. THE OSTEOCRANIUM

A. General Features

The modern cyclostomes and the elasmobranchs and holocephals produce no bone at all. Very little of the chondrocranium is replaced by bone in chondrostei, but in many teleosts nearly all of it is. Similarly among amphibia there is little replacement in urodeles but a great deal in

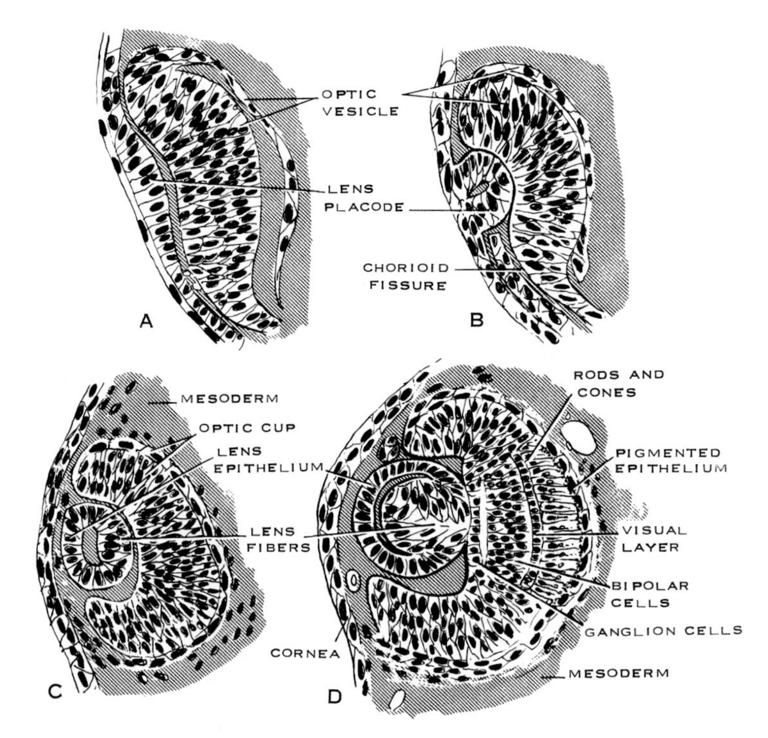

Fig. 14–3. Development of the amblystoma eye. Stages 32, 35, 37, 40. (After Rabl, 1898.)

epithelium pressed tightly against the part that lines the cavity of the eyeball. The latter becomes very thick and its cells differentiate into the light-sensitive and sense-transmitting tissues that are collectively known as the **retina.**

Mitotic figures are scattered throughout the retinal layer at first, but soon are confined to its outer rim, which thus acts as a germinal zone. The new cells that are added to the retina from this zone are gradually sorted out into three layers (Figs. 14–3 D, 14–4 B). From the brain side toward the lens side these are the **visual layer,** the **bipolar layer,** and the **ganglion-cell layer.** The cells of the visual layer send out highly specialized cytoplasmic processes shaped like rods and cones toward the pigmented epithelium. It is in these **rod-** and **cone-cells** that the chemical and nervous reaction to light originates. The bipolar cells transmit the excitation from the rod- and cone-cells to the ganglion cells, which in turn report it to the brain through axonic processes which they send to the floor of the diencephalon along the original stalk of the optic-vesicle evagination. The ganglion cells of the retina are, in other words, the source of the **optic nerve.**

During the time when the retina and lens are differentiating, the open ventral part of the optic cup begins to close together. Its ventral defect is called the **chorioid fissure.** While this still remains open it is the path both for the optic nerve fibers to leave the retina and for the blood vessels and mesenchyme to enter the cup. If it fails to close, it produces an eye defect called **coloboma.** About the time it closes, the interior of the eyeball becomes filled and expanded by the formation of a colloidal jelly called the **vitreous humour.** The lens and retina are thereby separated from each other by the interposition of the **vitreous chamber** (Figs. 14–3 D, 14–4 A).

General head mesenchyme condenses about the developing eye cup, adding an inner nutritive layer called the **chorioid** and an outer stiffening layer called the **sclera,** to the outside of the pigmented epithelium. It also moves across the inner surface of the ectoderm from which the lens placode had separated itself—the future **conjunctival layer of the cornea**—and lays down the fibrous tissue of the cornea, between it and the lens. Presently also the mesoderm and the retinal ectoderm collaborate in producing an **iris** membrane, that draws in between the lens and cornea but fails to complete itself, so that an opening called the **pupil** is left for the entrance of light to the lens and retina (Fig. 14–4).

None of these developments of the mesenchyme will take place in the absence of the ectodermal optic cup, nor will the optic vesicle form a two-layered optic cup in the absence of the mesenchyme. The ventral location of the chorioid fissure is determined not by the retinal cup but by the mesenchyme. Many other highly localized and highly specific tissue interactions

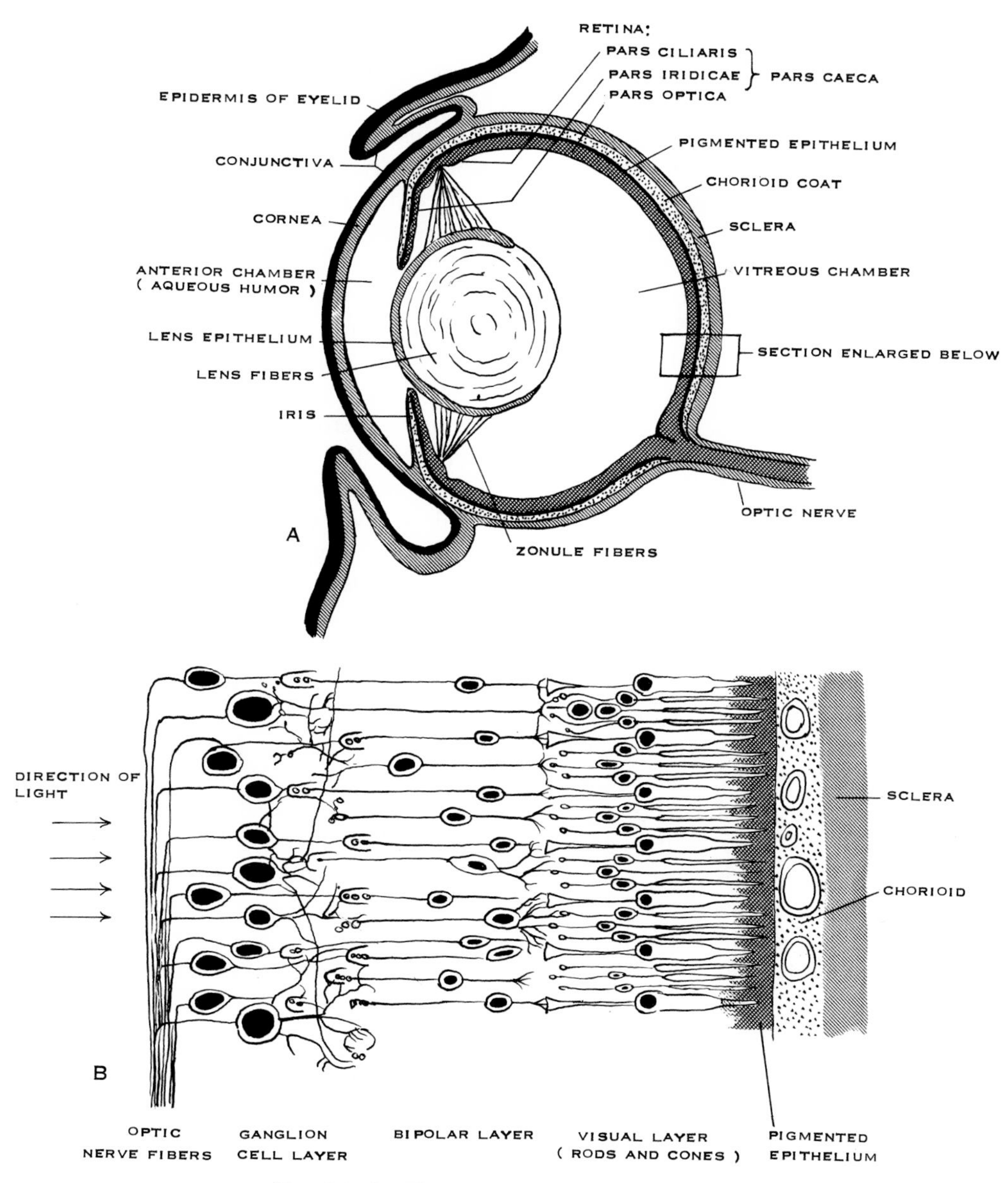

Fig. 14–4. The eye and retinal detail.

take place in the development of the eye. For instance the *corneal* mesenchyme spreads completely across the outside of the eye and becomes transparent; but the *iris* mesenchyme does not attempt to close the aperture of the pupil, and it develops dense pigmentation. Almost any of the surface ectoderm seems to have the competence to form a transparent conjunctival layer, but only that which is in contact with the eyeball does so.

All of the parts of the eye which have been mentioned so far can be distinguished in representative vertebrates of all the surviving classes. Most of them can be recognized at the pharyngula stage, before any of the adaptive features of the adult eyes of particular species have become defined. There is an extraordinary range of such adaptations in later development, to diurnal or nocturnal habit, to the requirements for pursuing swift prey, etc., all utilizing the basic plan but exploiting variations of detail. Some of the histologic adaptations will be discussed next, grouped according to the germ layers from which they arise.

B. Adaptive Specializations

1. Ectodermal Components: Retina, Pigmented Epithelium, and Lens. The proliferating cells of the germinal zone at the outer rim of the retinal layer differentiate according to their position as rod- and cone-cells, or bipolar cells, or ganglion cells. Each one of them is at first capable of differentiating in any of these directions, and the specific determiners are unknown. Collectively, they form the visual part of the retina, distinguished as **pars optica.** Later, cells from the same germinal zone spread over the inner surface of the iris, forming **pars iridicae,** and a ring of them at the border between the optic and iridic parts may also differentiate as a mooring for the lens (**pars ciliaris**) (Figs. 14–4 A, 14–9). The non-visual parts of the retinal sheet (pars ciliaris and pars iridicae) are collectively termed **pars caeca.**

It is usually assumed that the clear jelly, called **vitreous humour,** that fills the vitreous chamber between the lens and pars optica is a secretion of the retina. Evidence also suggests that the watery fluid, called **aqueous humour,** that fills the space external to the lens and on both surfaces of the iris, is secreted by pars ciliaris.

(a) *Retina.* It should be noticed that the vertebrate retina is installed inside out, at least from an engineering standpoint. The light has to traverse optic nerve fibers, ganglion-cell layer, bipolar layer, and the layer of nuclei of the rod- and cone-cells before reaching the rods and cones themselves, where the light-sensitive reaction takes place (Fig. 14–4 B). This requires almost complete transparency of the cell layers through which the light must pass. Then the nervous impulses are sent in the reverse direction, away from the brain, toward the light source, until they reach the vitreous surface of the retina, when they double back along the optic nerve fibers, through the chorioid fissure toward the brain.

This curious arrangement is understandable if it is assumed that the prospective light-sensitive cells on the neural plate of the embryo have an external–internal polarity which they maintain during their enclosure in the wall of the neural tube, and during their later movements in the wall of the optic vesicle and optic cup. The original external surface forms the light-sensitive elements; the internal surface, the neural processes (Fig. 14–5 A).

The paired eyes of cephalopod molluscs, which closely mimic the principal structures of vertebrate eyes, have retinas which form by a direct in-sinking from the general ectoderm (Fig. 14–5 B). The original external–internal polarity of the light-sensitive cells is retained here too, but with the production of visual elements that are directed outward toward the light source. Although this is a more logical arrangement than that of the vertebrates, the molluscs have not exploited its possibilities as cleverly.

The vertebrate retina has two visual functions, one operating best in moderate and dim light, and the other in bright light. The former seems to be carried on mostly by rod-cells, the latter by cone-cells. Rod-cells secrete a family of light-sensitive pigments called rhodopsins. These vary somewhat in their sensitivity to different wavelengths according to the species. The swift breakdown of rhodopsin in light is associated with the seeing of relatively fuzzy black-gray-white images. The pigmented epithelium cooperates with the retina in its regeneration of the bleached rhodopsin [4].

Vertebrates which live in the dark or are most active in dim light, whether fish, fowl or beast, have a high preponderance of rods in their retinas. On the other hand, diurnal vertebrates are apt to show many more cones than rods in their retinas, and some species have no rods at all. The mechanism of color vision has been a subject of endless controversy, but it is a traditional assumption, consistent with many observations, that impressions of color and sharp images in bright light arise from the sensitivity of the cones.

Both the rod- and cone-cells pass their excitation to cells of the bipolar layer by synapse. One of the bipolar cells may be connected with a large number of the rod-cells and vice versa, so that there is a great summation of many weak stimuli over an appreciable area, with some resultant blurring of the image as the nerve impulses spread toward the optic nerve. On the other hand, each cone-cell usually synapses with a very few bipolars, or even only one, so that sharp pinpoint vision is attainable from them, but only in bright light. Most vertebrate eyes, containing a preponderance of rods but plenty of cones also, may be thought of as consisting of a dim-light retina superimposed on a bright-light one.

In many species representing most of the classes of living vertebrates, special provisions are made for exploiting the acute vision obtainable through cone-cells. A spot called the **area centralis** (Fig. 14–6 A), though its location is not usually central, is developed on the retina of each eye, in which cone-cells are crowded tightly together, often to the total exclusion of rod-cells. Since a pure-cone district requires a much higher proportion of bipolar and ganglion cells in its cross-section, the area centralis is easily detected by its thickness. The shape of the area varies from circular to oval to bandlike, and its location always makes sense in respect to the location of the eyes on the head and the optical needs of the individual. If an animal looks forward with both eyes while hunting, for instance, the two areas are usualy found to have been shifted from medial to posterior positions so that they can be focused at once binocularly on the prey.

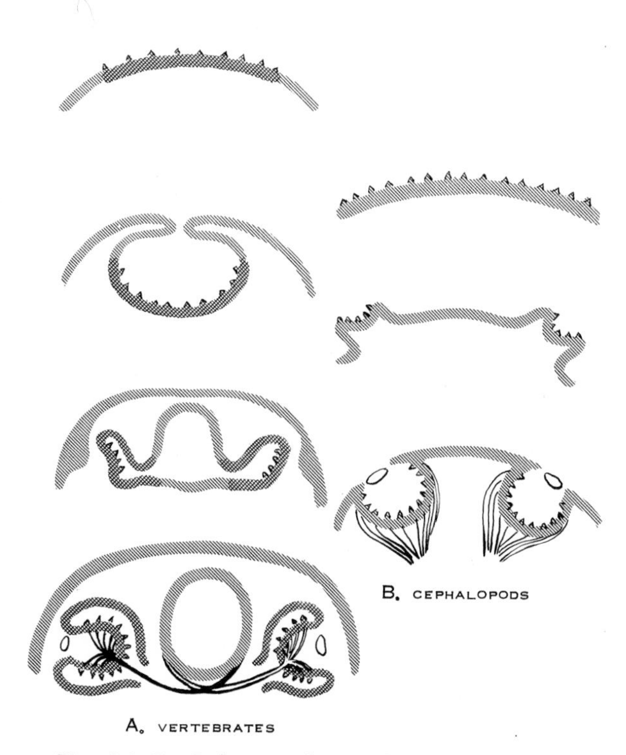

Fig. 14–5. Polarity of visual cells in eye development. A. Introverted retina of vertebrates. B. Extroverted retina of cephalopods.

Not uncommonly, part of the area centralis may be further specialized by the pushing aside of bipolar and ganglion cells, which forms a pit or furrow in the retina called a **fovea.** Exclusive pathways between single cone-cells and single ganglion cells through single bipolar cells may occur here. The highest concentration of cone cells is also reached in foveas, as many as a million per square millimeter being reported in birds. Though foveas are rare among mammals, they occur in the humans, and a man normally focuses the image of the object of his primary interest simultaneously on the foveas of his two eyes, the rest of his retinae giving him only blurred peripheral vision.

Some birds have two foveas in each eye, one centrally located and the other on the temporal side of the retina (Fig. 14–6). Assuming binocular vision toward the front using the two temporal foveas, there results a "visual trident" of acute vision in three directions at once, and this, added to the outstanding efficiency of the bandlike area centralis of each eye, produces an unrivaled visual power.

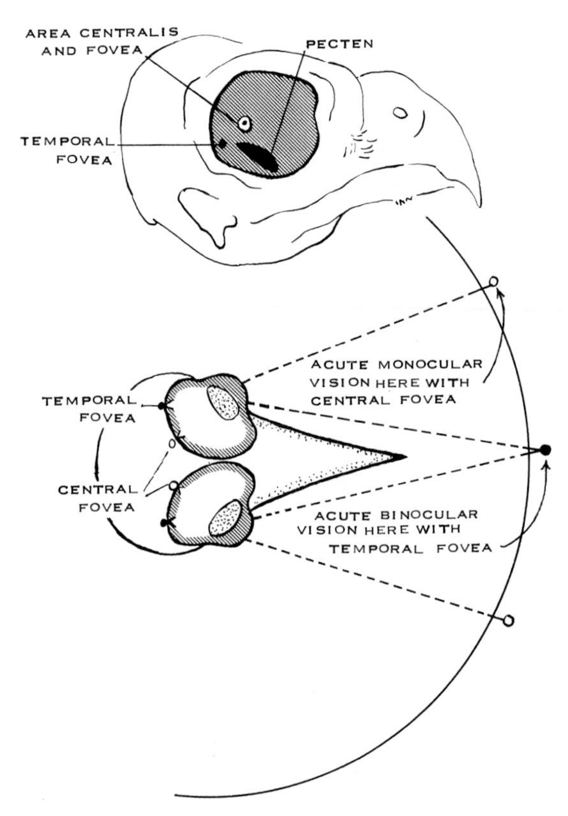

Fig. 14–6. Eye structures and vision in a falcon. A. Dissected eye. B. Field of vision and the "visual trident."

(Suggested by Rochon-Duvigneaud, 1950, in Traité de Zoologie, by permission of Masson et Cie.)

The transmitting axones of the ganglion cells stream over the inner surface of the retina (Fig. 14–4 B), and gather together as the **optic nerve** at the chorioid fissure. Since there is no room for rod- and cone-cells at the point where they leave the retina, this is a **blind spot,** which becomes especially large in the diurnal species that have the great number of ganglion cells necessary for direct sharp vision. Independently, some predacious teleosts, birds and certain squirrels have avoided the dangers of a seriously enlarged blind spot by transforming it into a narrow strip along the length of the chorioid fissure.

In some reptiles and birds a mass, cone, or ridge of neuroglia-like ectodermal cells and pigment rises into the vitreous cavity from the blind spot. Since it is highly vascularized it probably functions as a supplementary nutritive device for the retina. In most birds this becomes a highly pleated crest called the **pecten** (Figs. 14–6 A, 14–8 A). In most teleosts, a similar vascular mound of mesodermal origin grows in through the chorioid fissure. Other vertebrates, including a few teleosts, snakes, and the mammals, bring arteries directly inside the eyeball through the chorioid fissure, from which center they ramify over the inner surface of the retina, or even within it.

The optic nerves of the two eyes grow back from the retinas along the stalks which mark the paths of original optic-vesicle evaginations, so that they approach each other at the base of the diencephalon. When the skull finally forms, it encloses the optic nerves in **optic foramina** in the medial or posteromedial walls of the orbits. In non-mammalian vertebrates all these nerve fibers then grow straight on to end in synapse with neurones of the midbrain roof *of the opposite sides* of the brain. The axones of the two optic nerves must therefore cross each other in the midline, forming the **optic chiasma.** This is a constant feature of vertebrate anatomy, located at the base of the diencephalon, anterior to the hypophysis.

In mammals, many optic fibers reach the chiasma and turn back with the crossed fibers from the opposite eye, ending in the midbrain *of their own side.* The proportion of uncrossed fibers ranges from a few up to 50 per cent in the different species, roughly proportional to the degree of overlap of the right and left visual fields. In man, practically all of the 50 per cent which remain uncrossed arise from the temporal side of the retina. This means that the visual impressions from the left side of the visual field (nasal side of left eye, temporal side of right eye) are reported to the right side of the brain, those from the right side of the visual field to the left side of the brain.

(b) *Pigmented Epithelium.* The cells of the outer layer of the optic cup form multitudes of pigmented specks in most vertebrates, and these are carried down amongst the outer elements of the rod- and cone-cells on cytoplasmic streamers (Fig. 14–4 B). Both the rods and the pigmented streamers may acquire the ability to stretch out in strong light, and the cones to contract; the reverse takes place in darkness. Such **photomechanical movements,** which are particularly rapid and extensive in teleosts and birds, favor the maximum function of cones in brightness, but unmask the rods for their maximum exposure in twilight.

(c) *Lens.* In the most primitive vertebrate eyes (Fig. 4–18) the lens is merely propped in place between the vitreous humour and the cornea, with the iris applied around its equator. Usually however it acquires a washer-shaped **zonule** of radially arranged fibers which moor it to the pars ciliaris of the retina (Figs. 14–4 A, 14–9, 14–10). This attachment becomes highly specialized in the amniotes. Pars ciliaris may throw out a large number of radially arranged and vascularized epithelial folds called **ciliary processes** which may even fuse with the lens epithelium in some reptiles. The lens epithelium itself, especially in lizards and birds, may produce a conspicuous **annular pad** of high columnar cells to which the zonule fibers attach (Fig. 14–10). Mammals form very soft simple lenses but clothe them in elastic capsules which are firmly bound by zonule fibers to pars ciliaris. These variations are correlated with sharply contrasting mechanisms for focusing the eye (see below).

The organ here discussed as *the* lens (PNA) is often referred to as the *crystalline* lens in ophthalmology in recognition of the fact that other parts of the eye have lens properties in the physical sense, i.e., the ability to shift the direction of light as it passes through. In air (but not in water) the cornea-conjunctiva of amniotes is often a stronger lens than the (crystalline) lens which lies inside it. Some of these animals, particularly mammals, have flattened (crystalline) lenses whereas the lenses of fish eyes are generally round.

2. *Mesodermal Components: Uvea, and Sclera.*

(a) *Uvea.* After the ectodermal part of the eyeball has taken shape, the mesoderm deposits two tissue layers upon it, the **chorioid** and the **sclera** (page 244). The inner one of these is sometimes compared with the inner meninx of the brain, because it becomes heavily vascularized. Unless the retina is directly supplied with arteries through the chorioid fissure the whole nourishment of the visual cells presumably takes place through it by diffusion. The chorioid layer expands to form the mesodermal part of the **iris** and a special zone, called the **ciliary body,** which joins and strengthens the pars ciliaris of the retina in supporting the zonule fibers of the lens. Chorioid, ciliary body, and the mesodermal part of the iris form one continuous and usually heavily pigmented layer, collectively called the **uvea.**

Fishes which live in deep or muddy waters, and many kinds of noctural animals, have independently developed special uses for the uveal pigment. Mirror surfaces may be formed on the inside of the uvea, sometimes of crystalline deposits, sometimes of connective tissue fibers, which reflect back the light that has entered the pupil and penetrated the visual layers of the retina. This presumably increases the ability to see in very dim light. Such eyes gleam brilliantly at night by reflection. Many fish larvae are almost perfectly transparent, and in these the uvea is usually coated with opaque materials on its outer surface so that the images produced by light coming through the pupils will not be blotted out by what comes through the surrounding orbital tissues.

(b) *Sclera.* If the uveal coat of the eyeball can be compared with the inner meninx of the brain in its nutritive function, the auter coat or sclera can be compared with the outer meninx which is involved in skull formation. Like the outer meninx, the sclera is laid down first in fibrous form, and may then chondrify, and later be replaced by bone. A few fishes, the snakes, and all the higher mammals retain the fibrous condition throughout life, the eyeball then remaining practically spherical under the influence of fluid pressures from within.

In the rest of the vertebrates the sclera adopts many cartilaginous and bony modifications, and can hold the eyeball to some oddly adaptive shapes. In all the sauropsida except the snakes and crocodiles, for instance, the outer rim of the sclera is armored with a ring of small overlapping **sclerotic bones,** which form in the skin and sink in secondarily (Fig. 14–10). Their effect is to deform the eyeball from a spherical shape to one in which the **anterior segment** (from the zonule and lens outward) has a much shorter radius of curvature than the **posterior segment** (vitreous chamber, retina, chorioid, and sclera) (Fig. 14–8 A). These bones also furnish a rigid support for the thick ciliary body which firmly grasps the annular pad of the lens, and they serve to anchor the perimeter of the protruding cornea-conjunctiva dome.

3. *Components of Ectoderm and Mesoderm Combined: Cornea, Lids, Spectacles, Iris, and Ciliary Body.*

(a) *Cornea.* This layer becomes almost perfectly transparent under the influence of the eyeball-lens contact. If the eyeball is experimentally removed, the transparency is lost and the tissue acquires the blood vessels, pigment and glands of ordinary skin. In various vertebrates with degenerate eyes (hagfishes, abyssal or cave fishes, cave salamanders, some burrowing lizards and snakes, and moles) the cornea either fails to differentiate or later undergoes regression toward the condition of ordinary skin.

The cornea of fish eyes has nearly the same index of refraction as water, so that it would be optically inactive even if it were curved outward in the form of a lens; in fact it is usually flat, or curved only enough to conform to the streamlined shape of the head. In air, the optical situation is quite different, and in many sauropsida the bulging "anterior segment" of the eye may serve as a stronger lens than the crystalline lens itself.

(b) *Eyelids and their Lubricating Glands.* No true fishes develop lacrimal glands, and few have lids, but all the amniotes do. Amphibia which metamorphose and live in air develop similar apparatus abruptly at the end of their larval period. Most amniotes develop a third eyelid on the nasal side of the eye, called the **nictitating membrane,** which is movable and often transparent in sauropsida, but rudimentary in mammals. All the lids are formed by epithelial ingrowths which undercut the normal surrounding skin, whereupon the skin folds extend out over the front of the eyeball by relative growth rates. They commonly fuse together when they first make contact with each other, and the line of fusion secondarily breaks down during a late fetal period. The thin transparent epidermis which lines the lids and the cornea is called **conjunctiva.** The space formed between the lids and the eyeball is the **conjunctival sac.**

Palpebral glands form by ingrowth of epithelial cords from the conjunctiva into the orbit. Most tetrapods form separate masses of them on the nasal and temporal sides of the eyeball. The nasal one often has a thick oily secretion, and is prominent in aquatic birds and mammals but absent in man. The temporal one is the **lacrimal gland** (PNA). The salty fluid that it pours into the conjunctival sac lubricates the lids and is drained into the nose by a nasolacrimal duct (page 235).

(c) *Spectacles.* A good many vertebrates have eyes that are capable of free movement inside transparent fixed layers called **spectacles.** Three different kinds of these are found, and they have been evolved independently a number of times.

Primary spectacles (Fig. 14–7 A) arise when the corneal mesoderm fails to adhere to the inside of the conjunctival ectoderm, though both layers become transparent. This happens in lampreys and anuran tadpoles, and persists in a very few strictly aquatic adult frogs. If the eyeball moves, the cornea moves with it while the conjunctiva remains fixed to the surrounding skin.

Secondary spectacles (Fig. 14–7 B) are produced by a split in the cornea, separating an outer mesodermal layer which remains fixed to the conjunctiva, and an inner one which attaches to the sclera of the eyeball and moves with it. Such spectacles are common in fishes which grub along the bottom, or which come out on dry land. In dissecting fishes, one can often make such a split in the cornea where it does not naturally occur, in a zone of loose connective tissue that allows the eyeball and inner cornea to move under a stationary outer cornea.

Tertiary spectacles (Fig. 14–7 C) are produced from eyelid tissue, in all snakes and in many burrowing, sand-dwelling or nocturnal crawling lizards. The lids form and fuse together in the usual way, but then they fail to separate but turn glassy transparent, remaining as a closed window outside the transparent cornea of the movable eyeball. Temporary tertiary spectacles are created in various genera of other lizards and a few turtles by transforming a spot of tissue in the lower eyelid into transparent tissue, which can be held over the center of the eyeball by special muscles. The nictitating membrane functions in this way in birds and some frogs.

(d) *Iris and Ciliary Body.* These are two organs formed by the cooperation of pars caeca of the retinal layer and the external part of the uveal mesoderm.

(1) The outer layer of the **iris** is continuous with the chorioid, and shares its pigmented and vascular qualities (Fig. 14–4 A). The inner layer, the pars iridicae of the retina, may also be pigmented, and the color of the iris may be due in different species to the pigment of either layer, or to refractive effects of the superimposed layers. It is an odd and impressive fact that many fishes, amphibia, and reptiles have independently hit upon the device of laying a stripe of color along the face which continues unbroken across the iris. The eye would otherwise be a conspicuous glittering object, risky for either predator or prey. The disruptive pigment pattern tends to conceal it.

In most fishes the iris is motionless, and the pupil is of fixed size. In amniotes, and in urodeles and anura at the time of metamorphosis, two kinds of iris muscles are formed, a radially arranged dilator system and a more substantial sphincter. These dilate or constrict the pupil in reflex response to changes in the amount of light entering the eye. Both sets of muscles are formed from the ectodermal part of the iris, except in snakes, and are unstriated, except in birds and some reptiles.

(2) In amniotes (except snakes) a strong and complete ring of muscle is formed from the uveal mesoderm in contact with the pars ciliaris of the retina (Fig. 14–9), and the latter becomes elaborated into **ciliary processes** which reach out

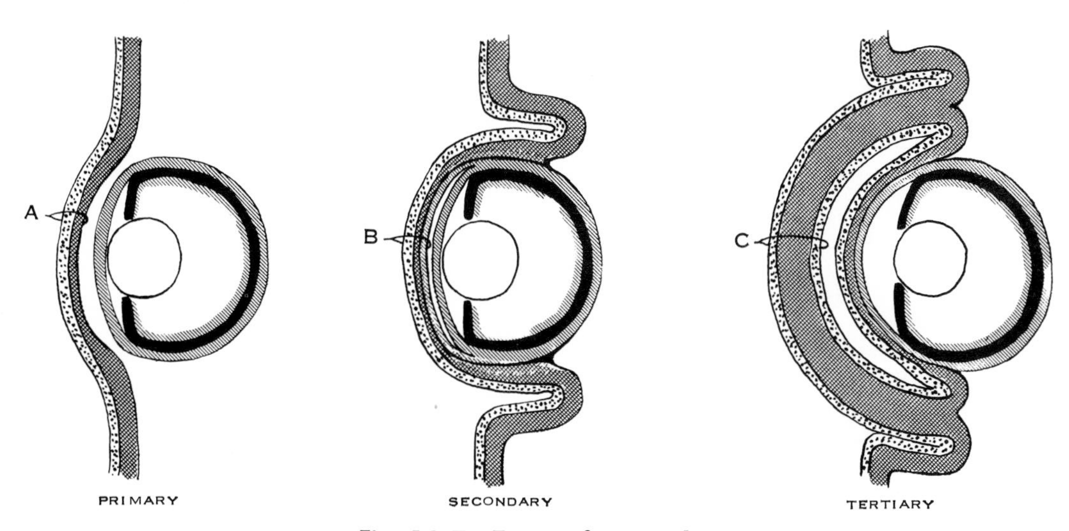

Fig. 14–7. Types of spectacles.
(After G. L. Walls, The Vertebrate Eye, 1942, by permission of Cranbrook Institute of Science.)

toward the lens like the teeth on a bevel gear (Fig. 14–10). This combination of tissues forms the **ciliary body** and, except in snakes, acquires the ability to change the shape of the lens, thus focusing the eye to different distances under voluntary control. The lens in these animals is quite soft and is suspended by the zonule fibers inside the iris. In most fish and aquatic amphibia, the lens is hard and lies in the pupil, and the ciliary body is not significantly developed.

4. Nocturnal and Diurnal Adaptations. Many kinds of vertebrates live in dim light, for instance fishes of the oceanic abyss, cave-dwelling or burrowing tetrapods, and preferentially nocturnal fishes, lizards, and mammals. They all tend to show similar modifications of the eyes. The typical nocturnally adapted eye is unusually large, with a broad and often bulging cornea, a wide pupil, and a big deep-set lens which is nearly or quite spherical (Fig. 14–8 A, owl eye).

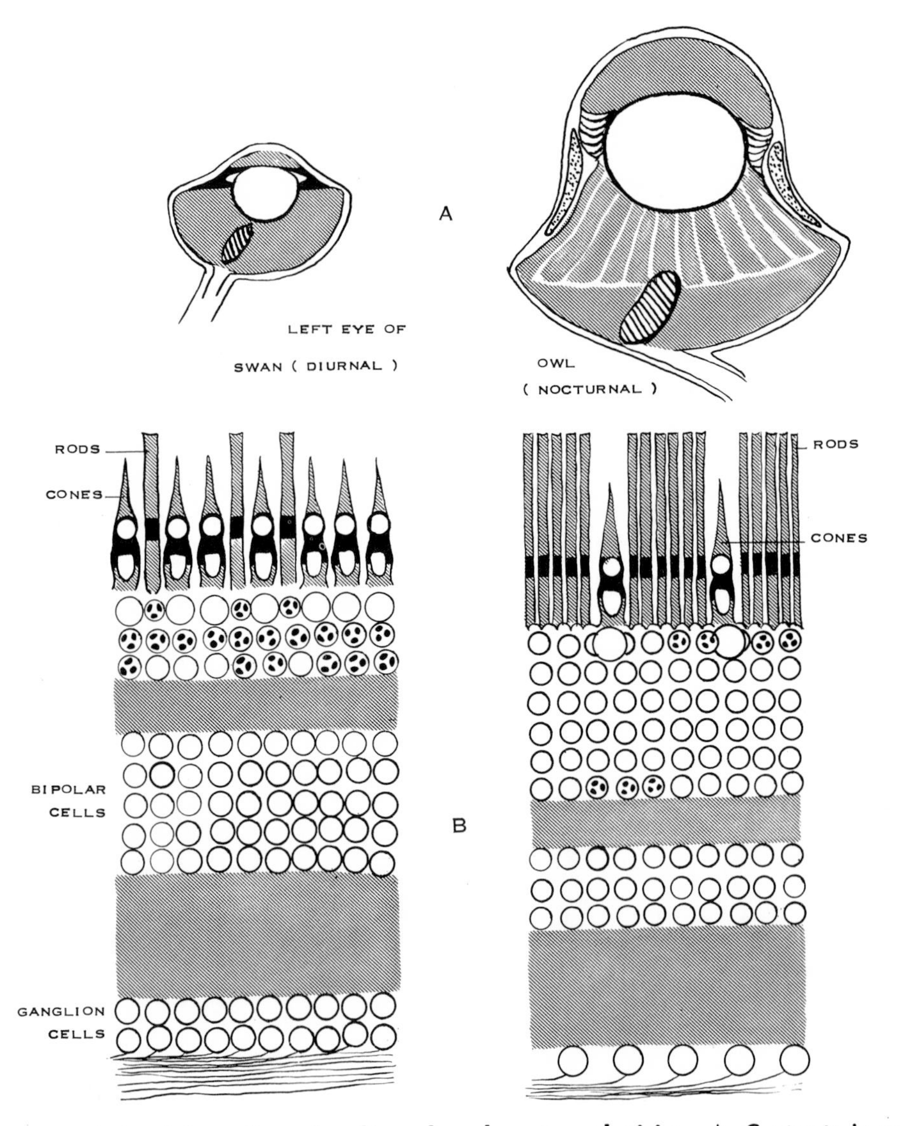

Fig. 14–8. Adaptations for diurnal and nocturnal vision. A. Contrasts in eye proportions. B. Contrasts in retinal components.
(After G. L. Walls, The Vertebrate Eye, 1942, by permission of Cranbrook Institute of Science.)

All these features combine to produce a small bright retinal image, making the most of what light is available. Parallel examples are known among fishes, birds, and mammals in which the effort to expand the eyeball to match the lens and cornea has been abandoned, with the production of peculiar "tubular eyes" having the requisite sensitivity but a much restricted field of vision.

In these dim-light creatures, the visual layer of the retina contains rod-cells predominantly, though pure rod retinas are rare. Summation of the stimuli arising in the rods is notably great, there being relatively few bipolar cells (Fig. 14–8 B). In some nocturnal retinas, both through the normal spread of dendrites of the bipolar cells and through the agency of special horizontal cells in the bipolar layer, as many as several thousand rod-cells may funnel their stimuli into a single optic nerve fiber.

To make the most of the light, mirrors to reflect it back into the visual layer tend to be substituted for the usual light-absorbing pigment layers. Such mirrors may be produced in either the ectodermal pigmented epithelium or the mesodermal chorioid layer, and a number of types of the latter are known. From the spotty distribution of these mirrors among the classes, orders, and families of vertebrates, it is obvious that such devices have arisen separately many times in past evolution.

Eyes with nocturnal adaptations can also be used in full daylight, since they can be protected against too great light by the development of photomechanical movements in the retina itself, or by sphincter reflexes in the iris, or by the closure of movable lids. However, eyes specially adapted for use in bright light are of necessarily limited use in the dusk.

Diurnally adapted eyes are usually large but with relatively small anterior segments and flattened lenses, so as to produce large retinal images. The visual cells are predominantly cones. Pure cone retinas, almost or quite devoid of rhodopsins, are known in a number of strictly diurnal lizards, snakes, birds, squirrels, etc. As evidence that there is much less summation of stimuli in the optic pathway from the visual cells to the ganglion cells, the layer of bipolar cell nuclei is thicker than the layer for the visual cells; the opposite is true in nocturnal retinas (Fig. 14–8 B).

Another characteristic adaptation for diurnal vision is the thickened retinal **area centralis** (Fig. 14–6 A), in which the rods are less frequent, or absent, and cones are packed tightly together, with displacement of the nuclear layers of the transmitting cells and the hyaloid blood vessels. **Foveas** also occur in the thickest of these areas, in diurnal lizards, birds, and the higher primates.

Animals living in bright light can afford to eliminate some of it in the interests of sharper resolution. The photographer's method of doing this is to use a yellow filter, which screens out a good deal of the haze and glare from scattered light, and at the same time removes some of the fuzzy effects of chromatic aberration. The same method is used by many animals, with slightly yellow corneal tissue, yellow lenses and the yellowish screen provided by a hyaloid network of blood capillaries over the retina.

5. *Focusing Devices.* In some amphibia and a good many bony fishes there are no mechanisms for changing the focus of the eyes, but most vertebrates have one or more devices for the purpose, and a most impressive variety of these has been evolved within the phylum. The anamniotes have discovered at least four different ways of moving the lens nearer to the retina or farther away. The amniotes have specialized in changing the shape of either the (crystalline) lens or the cornea-conjunctiva lens system, or both, in various ways.

(a) *Anamniotes.* Elasmobranchs and adult urodeles produce tiny muscles which drag the lens a slight bit toward the cornea. In the former case the muscle is formed from ectoderm of the dorsal part of the iris, and in the latter case it is from uveal mesoderm and lies against the ventral part of the iris. Adult frogs produce both dorsal and ventral protractor muscles from uveal mesoderm. Teleosts sometimes form little retractor muscles from the iris ectoderm, which run across the floor of the vitreous chamber, pulling the lens slightly inward and downward. The lampreys also succeed in moving the lens inward,

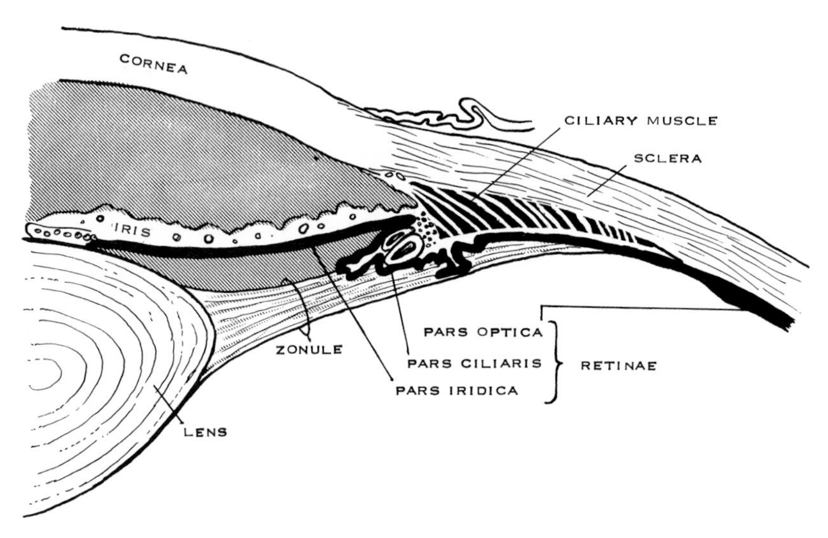

Fig. 14–9. Focusing apparatus in a mammalian eye.

but by the indirect action of a muscle derived from the head myotome series, which pulls on and flattens the dome of the cornea, thus pressing it deeper.

(b) *Amniotes.* Mammals have inherited a ciliary body and focusing mechanisms more primitive than found in any living reptile. The muscles developed in the ciliary body are relatively firmly anchored at the edge of the cornea, and when they contract they pull the whole ring to which the zonule fibers are attached a little bit outward (Fig. 14–9). This relaxes the zonule fibers, whereupon the soft flat lens rounds up slightly under the pressure of its markedly elastic capsule. This brings a change in focus, up to 10 diopters in the best mammalian eyes (i.e., those of man).

In all the sauropsida except snakes the eyeball is made relatively rigid by scleral cartilage and bone, and the musculature of the ciliary body works in quite a different way, actively deforming the lens by causing the ciliary processes to press upon it (Fig. 14–10). The lens is then forced to bulge slightly through the pupil. In some lizards and particularly in birds, some of the ciliary muscle reaches out from an origin on scleral ossicles and inserts into the rim of the cornea so that when it contracts the corneal curvature is increased. The combined action of these muscles on the two lens systems (crystalline and cornea-conjunctival) in birds may produce an accommodation of as much as 40–50 diopters, and this can be done swiftly, since the ciliary musculature is striated.

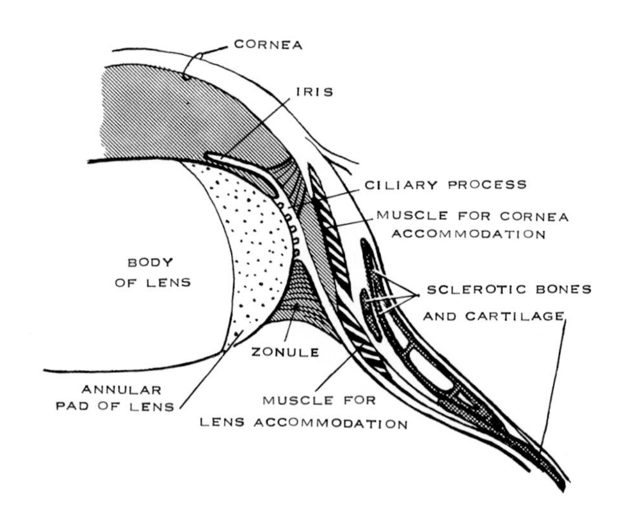

Fig. 14–10. Focusing apparatus in a bird eye.
(After G. L. Walls, The Vertebrate Eye, 1942, by permission of Cranbrook Institute of Science.)

Turtles have still a different way of causing their lenses to round up by directly squeezing them with sphincter muscles of the iris. Snakes, which do not have ciliary processes or the usual pattern of ciliary muscle at all, combine this sort of iris pressure with indirect pressure caused by tightening the whole posterior segment of the eye by contraction of a sphincter which is developed along the line of attachment of the iris to the chorioid. This is only one of a long list of peculiarities that have been noted in snake eyes. To explain their radical design it has been suggested that this group of reptiles underwent extreme optic degeneration during a burrowing or cave-dwelling phase of their evolution, since when they have recovered keen vision, solving all the classic optical problems in quite new ways, starting from the barest essentials of eye structure. Some snakes have a power of accommodation up to 17 diopters.

II. EXTRINSIC EYEBALL MUSCLES AND THEIR NERVES

A. Head Somites

In all vertebrates, the epimere mesoderm shows true segmentation as far forward as the ear vesicles, but more anteriorly the organization is variable. On the one hand, in the lamprey embryo there are already three easily recognized somites in place anterior to the ear vesicle when it first appears, and each is complete with an associated strip of lateral plate mesoderm. Much later, these three somites differentiate into a family of six eyeball muscles which are served by three motor cranial nerves (Fig. 14–11). In the amblystoma, on the other hand (Fig. 8–3), there is never a sign of any pre-otic somites. The cells which represent them are indistinguishable from those of the mandibular lobe. Nevertheless, the same family of eyeball mucles later differentiates, served by the same three motor nerves. Segmentation, as an attribute of the pre-otic mesoderm, is clearly an unessential formation of maneuver.

Other vertebrates range between the amblystoma and the lamprey in this respect. The segmentation of the pre-otic somites can be made out very well in elasmobranchs, less well in primitive teleostomes and reptiles, and not at all in birds. In other vertebrates, including man, it is at best suggested by mesodermal concentrations in the company of small fleeting "head cavities" (myocoels?) anterior to the notochord and lateral to the prechordal plate. But throughout the vertebrates the basic pattern of the six muscles and their nerves is always added to the orbit. The pattern later becomes more complex in tetrapods because additional muscles are split off to move the eyelids.

Four of the basic six muscles arise close together from the skull in the deep temporal or posterior part of the orbit, and insert on the sclera of the eyeball. They are called **rectus muscles** and are distinguished by their insertion on the sclera, as **superior rectus, inferior rectus,**

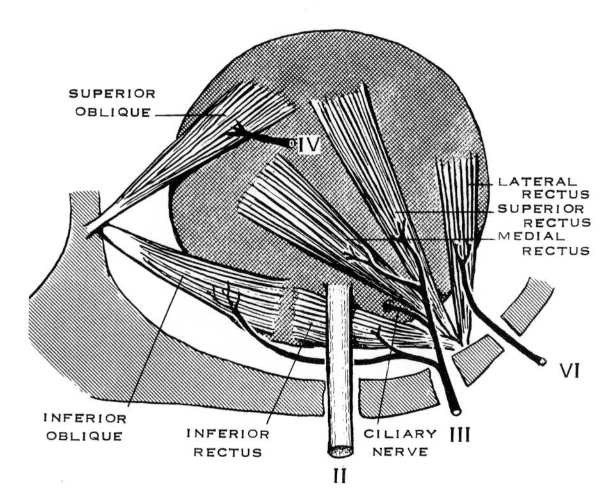

Fig. 14–11. Standard arrangement of eyeball muscles and nerves. Right eyeball, mediodorsal viewpoint.

medial (or nasal or rostral) **rectus,** and **lateral** (or temporal) **rectus.** The two other standard eyeball muscles arise from the skull in the nasal or anterior depth of the orbit and insert respectively on the dorsal and ventral limits of the sclera. They are called the **superior oblique** and the **inferior oblique** muscles (Fig. 14–11).

Of these six muscles, the **oculomotor nerve** (III) supplies four: the superior, inferior and medial rectus, and the inferior oblique. The **trochlear nerve** (IV) supplies the superior oblique, and the **abducens nerve** (VI) supplies the lateral rectus. In species with clearcut pre-otic somites it is clear that each of the three nerves is associated with a single somite, for the muscles served by III all arise from the mesoderm of the first or premandibular somite while the superior oblique and lateral rectus muscles arise respectively from the second and third somites.

The hagfish and a handful of other species with obviously degenerate eyes are the only vertebrates which lack a full complement of six eyeball muscles and their three nerves. Only the lamprey has presented anatomists with fundamental homology quandaries. It has the proper number of muscles and nerves but an anomalous innervation of one or two of them (there are several alternative interpretations). Variations in other fishes are slight and of no importance, though in teleosts some of the muscles are curiously elongated and their tendons of origin pushed far back into tunnels in the skull called **myodomes** (Fig. 14–14).

In tetrapods a seventh muscle of this group appears during development, splitting off from the lateral rectus and retaining an innervation from the VI nerve. Its characteristic arrangement is as a **retractor oculi** (Fig. 14–12) with origin on the base of the skull and insertion on the eyeball near the point of emergence of the optic nerve. Anyone who has handled a frog knows how the eyes can disappear into the head through the action of these muscles. Snakes, bats, and primates lack the retractor oculi. In some mammals it is divided into a bundle of four muscular slips which lie inside of the rectus muscles, alternating with them at their scleral ends.

Tendinous connections are established between the single retractor and the lower eyelid in frogs, and between it and the nictitating membrane in many reptiles and birds, so that when the eyeball is retracted the lid is automatically drawn across it. In other reptiles and birds, the retraction of the nictitating membrane becomes its only function, and it transfers its origin from the skull to the eyeball, and divides into separate bellies called the bursalis and quadratus muscles. In all these clever adaptations the VI nerve innervation is retained.

A new muscle is also frequently produced in mammals by subdivision of the superior rectus, for the purpose of lifting the upper eyelid (hence its name, the **levator palpebrae**) (Fig. 14–12). Like its parent, it is innervated by the III nerve. Other muscles for moving both upper and lower eyelids are developed in various sauropsida, but probably from other sources, since some of them are composed of unstriated fibers, and others must have been derived from the visceral musculature of the mandibular segment, since they are innervated by the trigeminal nerve.

A peculiar novelty found in all mammals is the transfer of the point of origin of the superior

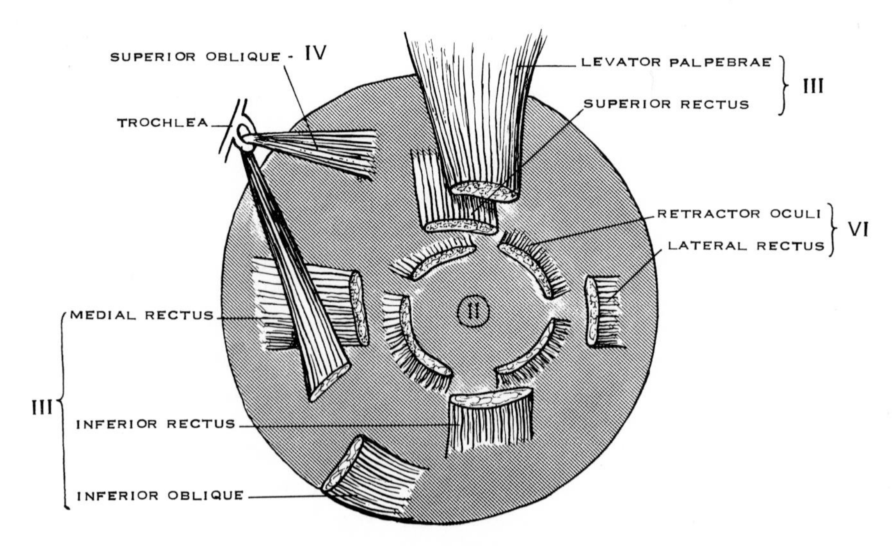

Fig. 14–12. Eyeball muscle arrangements in a mammal. Right eyeball, medial view.

oblique muscle from its normal position on the nasal side of the orbit to a position near the origin of the rectus muscles. However, its angle of approach to the sclera (and therefore its action on the eyeball) is not changed, due to the fact that the muscle passes through a pulley of connective tissue attached to the overhanging frontal bone of the braincase (Fig. 14–12). This pulley (Latin, *trochlea*), which is found only in mammals, is the reason why the superior oblique muscle used to be called the *trochlear* in human anatomy, and why its IV nerve still is.

These variations, mostly of splitting and specializing, are not as impressive as the fact that the original six eyeball muscles and their three nerves appear throughout the vertebrate series. Mutation affecting this anatomical complex must be very rare indeed, and its inheritance has been remarkably stable.

Possession of this apparatus does not necessarily mean that it is used. In some birds the bones that rim the orbit are so tight that the eyeball is held practically immobile, yet the four rectus and two oblique muscles are present. The function of these muscles is to keep the eyeball faced toward the same aspect of a moving field, or to swing the image of greatest interest into the most sensitive part of the retina (a fovea if there is one). In many cases this is actually done by visual reflexes operating through the eyeball muscles, but more frequently it is done by quite different visual reflexes which change the position of the whole head, the eyes remaining motionless within their orbits. Amniotes do this with neck muscles, fishes do it with their trunk.

One teleost, named *Astroscopus* the stargazer, has converted part of its eyeball muscle tissue into an electric organ.

III. NERVES OF PASSAGE, AND AUTONOMIC NERVES OF THE ORBIT

The general sensory nerve supply of the entire front of the head comes from the trigeminal nerve (V) and the facial nerve (VII), and both of these emerge from the skull posterior to the eyes. The trigeminal nerve sends **ophthalmic** branches *dorsally* past the eyes, **maxillary** branches *ventrally* past them, and **mandibular** branches *downward* to the tongue and lower jaw region. All of these trigeminal branches pass through the orbit, unless the eyeball has been displaced to a distance or walled off with unusual thoroughness by skull developments. When branches of the VII nerve spread to the face to supply lateral line organs, as they do in fishes, they usually accompany branches of the trigeminal through the orbit. All these nerves will be considered in the proper context of Chapter 16, but their fairly constant relations in the orbit may be mentioned here.

The ophthalmic division of the trigeminus consists actually of two nerves of somewhat different history and function. The **superficial ophthalmic branch** regularly passes **dorsal** to both the superior oblique and superior rectus muscles, and the **deep ophthalmic** or **profundus branch** passes *ventral* to them (Fig. 14–13). Hence, the IV nerve passes *between* these branches on its way to the superior oblique muscle, except in rare instances. Both of the ophthalmic nerves pass dorsal to the optic nerve and to the other four eyeball muscles. Both the maxillary and mandibular nerves pass *posterior* and *ventral* to the whole set of eyeball muscles.

The oculomotor nerve (III) always divides into a superior ramus and an inferior ramus. The superior ramus innervates the superior rectus muscles and therefore ends *between* the two ophthalmic branches of V. The inferior ramus characteristically forms a long descending loop, hooked around the optic nerve, on its path to innervate the inferior oblique muscle. The abducens nerve VI prefers to enter its lateral rectus muscle near its origin, even when this is displaced far posteriorly in a myodome, as in teleosts.

The constancy of all these minute and functionally inconsequential relationships in the orbits of practically all vertebrates after half a billion years of divergent evolution is a prize exhibit for the theory of homology.

Other neural elements in the orbit are so inconstant as to show even considerable variation within species. The exquisite sensitivity of the conjunctiva, the constriction and dilation of the

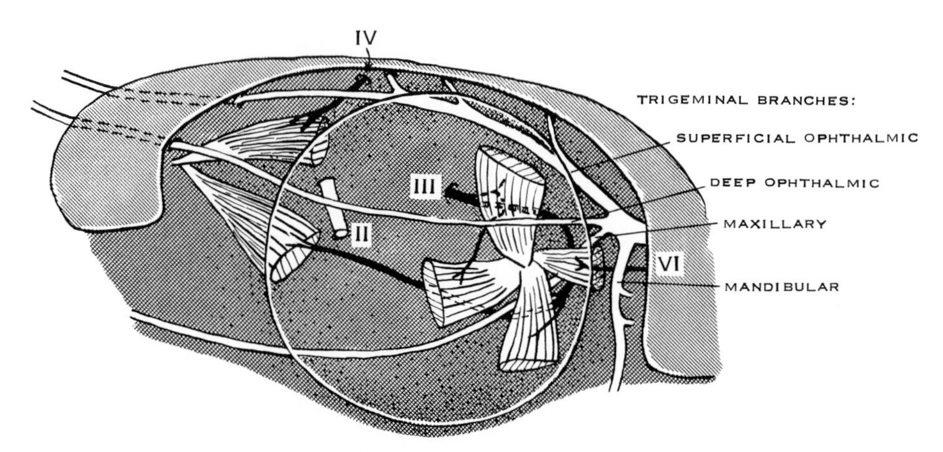

Fig. 14–13. Nerves of the dogfish orbit. Lateral view of left orbit after removal of eyeball.

pupil by the iris muscles, the regulation of eye focus through ciliary muscles and the regulation of pressure and blood supply within the eyeball by control of blood vessels are all mediated through **autonomic nerves** whose connections are highly variable and poorly understood except in mammals. Autonomic motor fibers enter the orbit through the oculomotor nerve III and along blood vessels, and sensory fibers make their way back to the brain along the trigeminal V nerve; some of these are channeled through a **ciliary ganglion** (or several of them) located near the optic nerve, and motor fibers may end in synapse in these ganglia with relay fibers that arise there. Commonly one or more **ciliary nerves** can be found piercing the sclera to ramify within the eyeball after separating from the ciliary ganglion or the III nerve or both (Fig. 14–11). The comparative anatomy of these elements is not well known.

IV. OTHER ORBITAL STRUCTURES

The arteries and veins of the orbit will be reviewed later since they cannot be understood without reference to the entire blood supply of the head.

A. Orbital Fascias

The structures having to do with the eyeball are more or less well segregated from the skeleton and the intruding muscles and other peripheral structures of the orbit by a layer of connective tissue called **periorbita.** It may be so tightly applied over the exposed skeleton as to be indistinguishable from periosteum or perichondrium, but particularly in mammals it seems to have split into an outer periosteum and an inner layer of smooth muscle called the **orbitalis.** The latter is well enough developed in a few species so that it can contract and cause a pronounced bulging of the eyeballs.

A thin connective-tissue envelope called the **vagina bulbi** (PNA) surrounds the eyeball in many vertebrates, attaching to the sclera near its junction with the cornea, and providing a slight cavity just outside most of the sclera. The optic nerve and the insertion-ends of the eyeball muscles pierce this sheath, while their main masses lie outside it.

The room between the vagina bulbi and the periorbita is mostly filled by the eyeball muscles, their nerves and blood vessels, but the rest of the space is often amply packed with loose connective tissue or fat, which makes a shock-absorbent cushion for the eyeball.

B. Myodomes

The tendency for eyeball muscles of teleosts to elongate beyond the orbit, forcing their way into tunnels in the skull called **myodomes,** is as good an illustration as any of the plasticity of the skull under the domination of soft tissues. Myodomes are known to have occurred in some Devonian agnathous fishes, but are absent in modern elasmobranchs, catfishes, and a few others. Practically all the bony fishes have them, and no land animals do.

Sometimes only the lateral rectus muscles, but commonly also the medial recti become much longer than the orbits and push their ends of origin posteriorly (Fig. 14–14). As the skull takes shape around them, they come to lie in myodome tunnels surrounded by the basiphenoid, prootic, and basioccipital bones. The myodomes are entirely ventral to the inner meninx, and entirely dorsal to the parasphenoid, a membrane bone.

If both medial and lateral recti extend backward, the lateral rectus lies dorsal to the medial, and the two may be separated in dorsal and ventral compartments by ingrowth of bony flanges. The abducens nerve (VI) persists in entering its lateral rectus muscle at the end which takes origin from the skull, and has to elongate with it. There are species in which the myodomes are pushed back as far as the foramen magnum or even the first vertebra.

Some fishes also show what are called anterior myodomes. In these cases the ends of origin of the slightly elongated superior and inferior oblique muscles have moved into spaces left between the nasal capsules and the ethmoid regions of the braincase. They are modest spaces indeed, compared with the posterior myodomes.

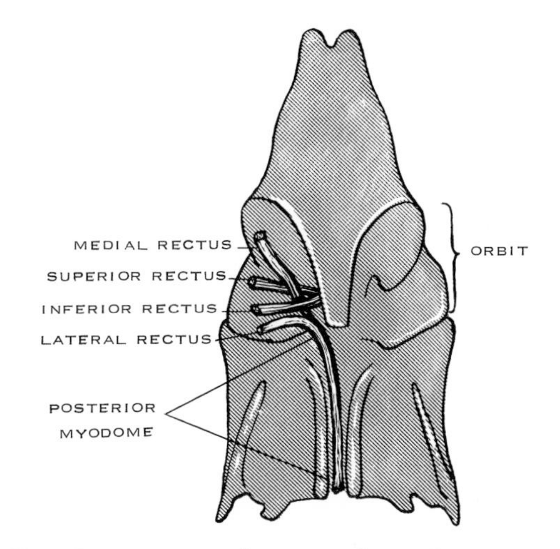

Fig. 14–14. Myodome in the salmon neurocranium, dissected from below.

REFERENCES

1. Walls, G. L., 1942. *The vertebrate eye.* Cranbrook Institute of Science, Michigan. One of several recent monographic treatments of the eye and vision; not the most recent, but the best reading, full of surprising glimpses into natural history.

2. Adelmann, H. B., 1936. *Quart. Rev. Biol.* 11: 161, 284. A comprehensive review of the problem of cyclopia in vertebrates.

3. McKeehan, M. S., 1958. *Anat. Record* 132: 297.

4. Wald, G., 1958. *Exptl. Cell Research,* Suppl. 5: 389. Also Hubbard, R., and A. D. Colman, 1959. *Science* 130: 977.

15

Lateral Line System and Inner Ear

The inner ear is already an internal organ at the pharyngula stage. Its fate is to be buried in the skull, where it will serve as a sense organ for static and dynamic equilibrium, and for hearing. The anlagen of the lateral line system on the other hand have begun to scatter over the skin of the head and down the flanks, and will remain at the surface, for the detection of movements in the surrounding water. Though these two systems of sense organs are topographically scattered, there are good reasons for considering them together.

I. COMPARABLE ASPECTS OF LATERAL LINE AND INNER EAR

A. Common Origin

In every vertebrate, without exceptions, the inner ears appear first as ectodermal placodes before sinking inward as vesicles. The lateral line system, though it fails to appear in amniotes, arises in anamniote embryos in the form of dorsolateral placodes, immediately anterior and posterior to the ears (page 159; Fig. 15–1 B). One might guess that, in some lost ancestral stock of vertebrates, the ear evolved by the sinking in and specializing of a middle member of a linear series of placodal sense organs, and that its new functions in its new position gave it values for survival in terrestrial animals which the superficial members of the series lacked. One might also remember that this kind of guess is not based on evidence, nor is it testable.

B. Dichotomy

The ear vesicle, the pre-otic, and the post-otic lateral line placodes are alike in another respect, namely that in each the cells of the inner and outer parts differentiate in sharply divergent ways. The inner cells form a ganglion and become sensory neurons, while the outer ones remain epithelial and produce sensory end-organs. Nothing is known about how the individual cells decide between these two fates, or how it is insured that the numbers of the two types of cells are in proper balance with each other. All the ganglion cells remain close to their sites of origin and send axons into the hindbrain but retain dendritic-zone contact through lengthening axons with their own end-organ cells while these go on with their subsequent migrations or segregations (Fig. 15–1 B, C).

C. Neuromasts

The sensory parts of the lateral-line placodes wander out from their sites of origin, forming trails on the inside of the surface ectoderm and dropping off at intervals little clusters of cells

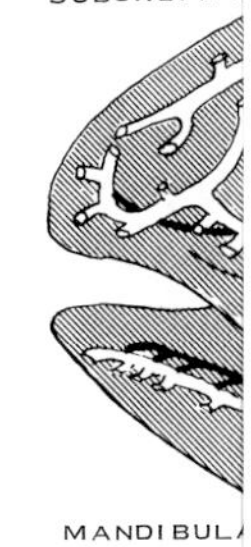

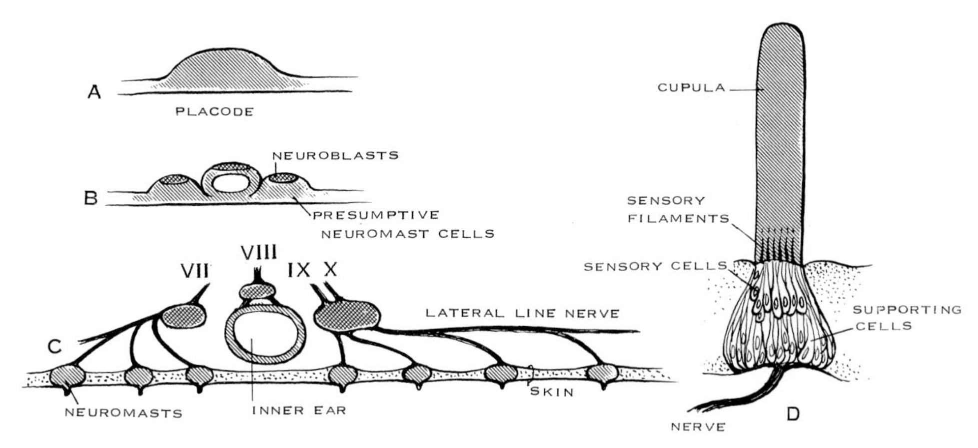

Fig. 15–1. Dorsolateral placode derivatives. A, B, C. Differentiation of placodes. D. Structure of a neuromast.

which differentiate into **neuromasts** (Fig. 9–7). The sensory inner ear vesicle at the same time is becoming complexly modeled into chambers and ducts, and in special areas of these the histological pattern of neuromasts appears again, with variations.

A **neuromast** is a patch of special epithelium laid out between a basement membrane and a fluid medium, and containing both sensory and supporting cells. In the case of the lateral line, the fluid may either be water on the outside of the animal, or mucus filling a tube that communicates with the outside water. In the case of the inner ear it is a tissue secretion called endolymph which fills the epithelial vesicle. The sensory cells send delicate protoplasmic filaments into the fluid, protected by a thin jelly-like coating that often takes the form of a dome or **cupula** (Fig. 15–1). A movement of the fluid can press on the cupula and its filaments, producing an excitation in the sensory cells which is then transmitted to dendritic endings of the sensory nerves across the basement membrane.

Vertebrates have adapted the neuromast device to the detection of many kinds of fluid movements and vibrations, by producing appropriate histological variations of the pattern. Nevertheless the neuromasts of lateral line organs and those of inner ears still have recognizable similarities, both structural and functional. Some fishes are known to hear part of their audible range with the former, and part with the latter.

D. Nerves

The neurons which develop from the inner border of the ear vesicle become organized as the **statoacoustic nerve** * **(VIII)**. Their dendritic zones remain in contact with the neuromast areas of the developing vesicle. Their ganglion cells presently become enclosed in a foramen in the medial wall of the ear capsule, and their axons enter an immediately adjoining dorsolateral area of the anterior part of the hindbrain. The neurons developed from the lateral line placodes send their axons into the same part of

* Borrowing a name for this nerve from human anatomy presents a problem. The BNA list of 1895 called it *N. acusticus*, but since the ear is both an equilibratory and an auditory organ, the INA of 1936 adopted instead the name *N. statoacusticus.* This logical but uncouth name caused protests from traditionalists, so that the 1955 PNA allowed as an alternate the name *N. octavus.* At the Seventh International Congress of Anatomists in 1960, a recommendation of the International Anatomical Nomenclature Committee was adopted, to displace the name *statoacusticus,* to substitute *N. vestibulocochlearis* for it, and to retain *N. octavus* as an alternate. *Vestibulocochlearis,* besides being excessively long, is inappropriate for any vertebrates except mammals, since these alone possess a cochlea. Ancient usage defends the name *N. octavus,* but not even in human anatomy is this actually the eighth cranial nerve. *Nervus statoacusticus,* the statoacoustic nerve, is favored in this text because it expresses function, and is suitable for all vertebrates.

general ectoderm in rather late tailbud stages, it is discovered that both polarities have become rather firmly fixed and the ear simply develops upside down in the head. At the critical stages when the polarities are being established, these rotation experiments often yield very strange ears whose structure indicates that the field was trying to produce mirror-image twins, i.e., to have the polarity both ways at once. The nature of the determining influences, and the molecular basis of the polarities themselves, remain to be discovered [6].

3. *General Pattern.* Except in matters of proportion, no change in the design of the semicircular ducts occurs in the entire range of the gnathostomes. Short wide ones occur in some species, hardly removed at all from the utriculus; in other species they may be slender and soaring. They may open broadly into the central chamber at both ends or have the ampullar ends set off on constricted connecting tubes. In many species, as though in reminiscence of their common origin from the single dorsal ridge of the early vesicle, the two vertical ducts remain joined at their upper ends, emptying into the central chamber by a common stem called the **crus commune** (Fig. 15–5).

In most elasmobranchs the central chamber remains a vaguely constricted "otosaccus chamber," but in other fishes the sacculus is separated from the utriculus by a narrow waist, or even hangs down from it at the end of a long narrow connecting tube. Where separation of the two is thus made plain, the semicircular ducts are clearly associated with the utriculus.

A special area, sometimes appearing as a shallow pit, sometimes as a blind pouch of some length, develops at the posterior corner of the sacculus in all but a very few species. It is called the **lagena** (Fig. 15–4). Though usually insignificant in the ears of anamniotes, it becomes elongated and coiled in amniotes, and the sense of hearing becomes concentrated in it. In many amniotes the sacculus and utriculus are very small in relation to the winding semicircular and lagenar passageways. It becomes appropriate then to borrow the term **membranous labyrinth** from human anatomy, for the whole complex of spaces derived from the embryonic ear vesicle, and the term **vestibule** for the saccular and utricular spaces into which the passageways lead.

While the ear vesicle is being modeled into all these special parts in early post-pharyngula development, its interior fills with the fluid called endolymph, and most of its epithelium spreads out very thin. At the medioventral border of the vesicle however, there is an area of epithelium which is becoming thicker: the prospective sensory tissue. Medially the ganglion cells are withdrawing slightly toward the brain, though preserving dendritic contact with the sensory cells (Fig. 15–1).

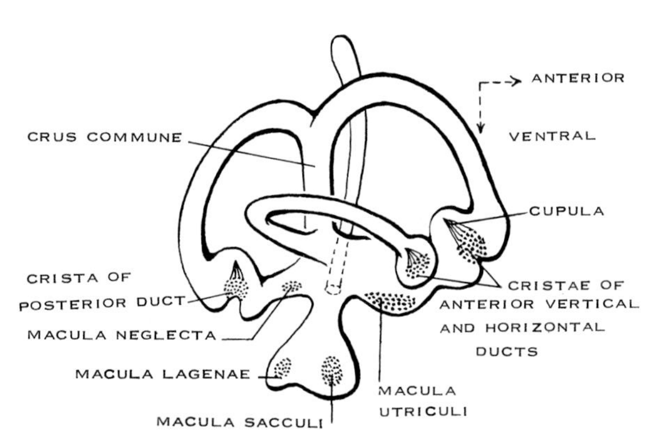

Fig. 15–5. Sensory patches in the membranous labyrinth. Right ear, schematic, for bony fishes and tetrapods.

(After de Burlet, 1934, in Handbuch der Vergleichenden Anatomie der Wirbeltiere, by permission of Urban u. Schwarzenberg.)

The sensory area quickly separates into anterodorsal and posteroventral parts, the dendrites separating likewise, though with some variation, into the future anterior and posterior divisions of the VIII nerve. The anterodorsal sensory area further subdivides into three patches, two of which locate themselves in the ampullae of the horizontal and anterior vertical semicircular ducts and the third one on the anterior floor of the utriculus. The posteroventral sensory area similarly segregates into a patch in the posterior ampulla, one in the lagena and one in the medial wall of the sacculus (Fig. 15–5).

Other patches form with less regularity from the posteroventral sensory area. One, called **pa-**

pilla neglecta, is absent in most mammals, many birds and most amphibia, but present, though curiously variable in location, in the majority of the vertebrates. Another, **papilla amphibiorum,** occurs in all three of the living amphibian groups but in no other vertebrates. A third, **papilla basilaris,** occurs in practically all tetrapods but in no fishes so far as known. It is either found perched at the sacculus end of the lagena pouch (amphibia) or drawn down into its dorsal side (most amniotes). The papilla basilaris comes to have central importance in the augmented sense of hearing developed by the land animals. In mammals it shares in the spiral winding of the cochlea and is re-named the **spiral organ** (PNA).

The sensory patches are named papillae, or cristae, or maculae, according to the shape they take as they complete their development. The three which occupy the ampullae develop into sharp ridges called **cristae,** at right angles to the planes of their semicircular ducts. Just like neuromasts, they have their sensory filaments embedded in a gelatinous **cupula** (Fig. 15–5). When the head moves in any particular direction the membranous parts of the ear move with it, but the endolymph, being fluid and having inertia of its own, may tend to lag behind, like water in a bucket which is suddenly rotated about its long axis. This would cause a relative movement of endolymph past the crista in one or more of the semicircular ducts, pressing on the sensory hairs in the cupulae. This would generate a sense of movement, and the direction of the movement in space could be judged by the degree of disturbance in each of the six differently oriented semicircular ducts of the two ears. The inner ears do in fact give the animal a sense of **dynamic equilibrium,** i.e., of the direction of movement in space, though it is far from clear how the information from the various sensory patches is sorted out and interpreted in the brain [4].

The sensory patches in the lagena, the medial wall of the sacculus, and the floor of the utriculus, are broad flat affairs, and are therefore called **maculae.** They are covered by gelatinous pads, and in many fishes these are weighted down by heavy concretions called **otoliths.** The macula utriculi tends to lie horizontally and the macula sacculi vertically and medially. By comparing his sensations from all of these maculae, the animal can judge his orientation to gravity. This is the source of the sense of **static equilibrium** the awarenes of one's position at rest.

B. The Capsule

During or after the pharyngula stage the ear vesicle induces the surrounding somatic head mesenchyme to condense into a cartilaginous capsule. The experimental evidence comes mostly from amphibian embryos and is not without some contradictions, but in general the capsule will not form in the absence of the ectodermal ear vesicle, and the vesicle can sometimes convert strange mesoderm into capsule cartilage. Vesicle and cartilage seem to be mutually dependent, for further normal development apparently requires a continuing interaction between them. There must also be a complex and progressive interchange of influences between the whole ear and the neighboring head structures.

In elasmobranchs, the capsule becomes complete and solid except for the room already occupied by the previously existing membranous ear itself, the endolymphatic tube, and the VIII nerve. In bony fishes, its medial wall generally fails to chondrify, leaving a defect on the brain side which may be so extensive that in some species the membranous ear seems to float in the cranial cavity outside the outer meninx. However the capsule is always represented by a membrane of fibrous tissue covering such a defect. In cases where subsequent cartilage expansion of the skull makes it look as though either the VII or the IX nerve passes *through* the otic capsule, reference to this surviving capsule membrane shows that the visceral nerve actually still lies *between* the true capsule and the rest of the skull.

Cartilage usually spreads into the spaces between the semicircular ducts and the sacculus–utriculus, forming septa or pillars. Each **semicircular duct** then runs through its own cartilaginous tunnel, which is called a **semicircular canal** (Fig. 15–6).

The cartilage always lies at a little distance from the membranous ear, the intervening space

15–8 B). In mammals, no such short path from cistern to saccus is developed. The two limbs of the perilymph duct that follow the cochlear duct are called *scalae* (stairways) (Figs. 15–9, 15–10). The one that descends from the perilymph cistern (which lies in the sacculus region, a part of the vestibule) is called **scala vestibuli,** and the ascending one, for a reason explained below, is called **scala tympani.**

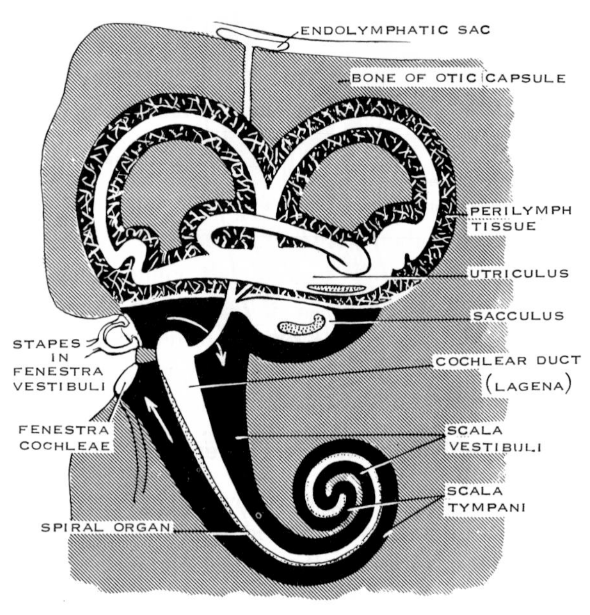

Fig. 15–9. Relations of sacculus and cochlear duct to perilymph chambers in a mammal.
(After de Burlet, 1934 (op. cit.), by permission of Urban u. Schwarzenberg.)

A section of the mammalian cochlea through its axis (Fig. 15–10 A) shows the cochlear duct cut twice for each of its complete turns, and wherever it appears it is pressed between scala vestibuli and scala tympani. The sensory part, the attenuated papilla basilaris or spiral organ, lies on the floor of the cochlear duct and consists of the familiar sensory neuromast cells projecting their fibers into a gelatinous cap, similar to a cupula, called the **tectorial membrane.** The cochlear division of the VIII nerve fills the axis of the cochlear coil. Its ganglion is spread out in a spiral along the inner border of the cochlear duct, and its dendrites reach out to the sensory cells of the spiral organ. Cutting this part of the VIII nerve results in complete deafness. Animals subjected to long-continued deafening sounds show roughly localized degenerations of the sensory cells. The membrane on which the spiral organ rests is set in resonant vibration by sound waves transmitted through the middle ear to the perilymph of the scalae. Many other aspects of the mechanism of hearing remain obscure [8].

The perilymph saccus has so far been mentioned as a pressure-relief device opening out from the perilymph duct either toward the cranial cavity or into the fissura metotica at the base of the skull. It comes in for some remarkable variations and specializations in the tetrapods. In crocodiles, birds, and mammals, coincident with the elaborate lagenar or cochlear developments, its membranous expansion into the cranial cavity is subordinated to that at the fissura metotica. Secondarily, by different means in the different classes, its ending may be transferred laterally and given a floor of bone, so that it appears as a membrane closing a small foramen, visible from the middle ear space, called the **fenestra cochleae.** In an adult mammal, if the middle ear space is opened and the ear ossicle which fits into the fenestra vestibuli is jiggled, compensatory movements are seen in the membranous wall of the perilymph saccus which lies in this fenestra cochleae. It thus acts as a tiny secondary ear drum, or tympanum. It is for this reason that the ascending limb of the perilymph duct, following the line of the spiral organ up the cochlear duct and ending here, is called the **scala tympani.**

3. *Endolymphatic Sac Developments.* In various tetrapod embryos, the endolymphatic ducts grow dorsomedially from the ear vesicles toward the brain, enlarging outside the meninges as **endolymphatic sacs** (Figs. 15–6, 15–9).

After the skull and ear capsules have formed, these provide another answer to the problem of protecting the encased sensory tissues of the inner ears from pressure fluctuations due to movement of the ear ossicles; however there are fishes that show the same arrangement of the endolymphatic sac in the absence of either a fenestra vestibuli or an ear ossicle.

Sometimes these endolymphatic sacs develop

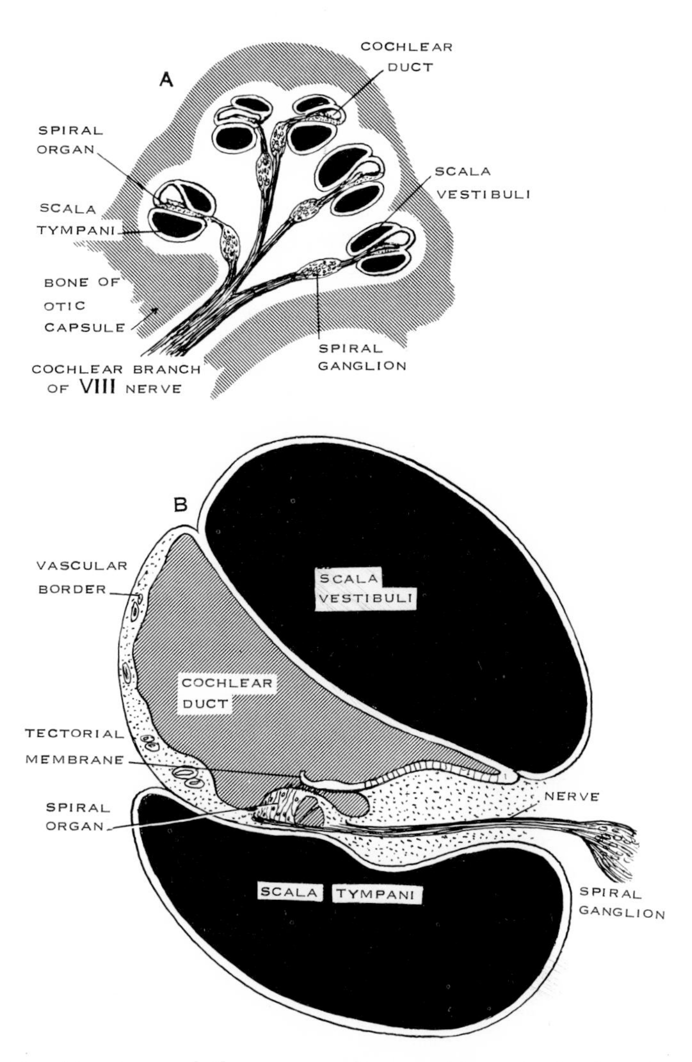

Fig. 15–10. Structure of the mammalian cochlea. A. Section through axis of cochlea spiral. B. Enlarged section of one coil of the cochlear duct.

spectacularly. In urodeles, they vary from simple club-shaped appendages inside the braincase (Fig. 12–1) to greatly expanded sacs completely covering the hindbrain, fused together across the midbrain region and filled with a chalky precipitate. In frogs they expand even farther, and, fusing together both above and below the brain, they pass through the foramen magnum and clothe the whole dorsal spinal cord. In many species they even extend through the intervertebral foramina and envelop the spinal ganglia. The whole of this enormous sac system is filled with white chalk, and provides a reservoir of calcium which is drawn upon at the time of metamorphosis when the relatively huge hindlimb skeleton gets its growth.

In reptiles, the endolymphatic duct often makes a deep bend inside the otic capsule before invading the cranial cavity, and in turtles the saccus is considerably enlarged dorsal to the brain. In gecko lizards the ductus may run out posteriorly from inside the skull, taking a much coiled path as far back as the neck and shoulder region, ending in a folded saccus which extends forward to the roof of the mouth, or even may reach into the orbit and envelop the eyeball. The whole thing is filled with tiny calcareous crystals. Its function is unknown.

In mammals and birds, the ductus endolymphaticus leads merely to a tiny flattened saccus pressed between the dura mater and the skull.

REFERENCES

Four of the following citations are to chapters in the three-volume tome on fishes in the massive *Traité de zoologie,* in process of publication since 1950 under the editorship of Pierre-P. Grassé, Masson et Cie., Paris.

1. DEVILLERS, CH., 1958. *Traité,* Tome XIII, p. 940. Lateral line system.
2. SPEIDEL, C. C., 1950. *In* P. WEISS (ed.), *Genetic neurology.* University of Chicago Press, Chicago.
3. BUDKER, P., 1958. *Traité,* Tome XIII, p. 1033. Skin senses of sharks.
4. LOWENSTEIN, O., 1957. *In* M. E. BROWN (ed.), *Physiology of fishes.* Academic Press, Inc., New York. Vol. 2, p. 155. Acousticolateralis system.
5. DEVILLERS, CH., 1958. *Traité,* Tome XIII, p. 625. Fish skulls.
6. YNTEMA, C. L., 1955. *In* B. H. WILLIER, P. A. WEISS, and V. HAMBURGER (eds.), *Analysis of Development.* W. B. Saunders Co., Philadelphia. Ear and nose.
7. GRASSÉ, P.-P., 1958. *Traité,* Tome XIII, p. 1063. Inner ear and accessories.
8. DAVIS, H., 1957. *Physiol. Rev.* 37: 1. Biophysics and physiology of the inner ear.

16

Derivatives of the Mandibular and Hyoid Segments

I. INTRODUCTION

The pharynx segment zone of the vertebrate embryo has a deceptive simplicity about it. Each side of the pharynx wall is cut up into a series of segments at the pharyngula stage, each similar to its neighbors in the arrangement of its essential parts (Figs. 5–9, 5–10). But during the evolution of vertebrates, so many potentialities have been discovered and exploited, with respect to the differentiation of the pharynx segments, that the whole zone becomes too complex for study as a unit. This chapter will take up only the main part of the two pre-otic segments, postponing the consideration of some of their derivatives which come into inextricable relations with more posterior structures. The thyroid, the tongue, and the first two pairs of aortic arches, for instance, though they belong here, will be taken up with the post-otic segments in Chapter 17.

Even thus reduced, the mandibular-hyoid region is almost unmanageably big for one chapter. It will help to give merely a passing glance at the agnathous vertebrates, for the differentiations of this zone are so aberrant in them as to defy comparison. The few sentences devoted to the Agnatha will attempt nothing more than an impression of how great the contrasts are. In the gnathostomes on the other hand, really convincing homologies are found, but some of them are at first sight almost incredible, the adaptations of comparable pharyngular structures are so divergent. They include, in fact, some of the most remarkable homologies in vertebrate morphology.

For instance, the mandibular segment of gnathostomes invariably produces jaws, but of *four main types*, seen respectively in elasmobranchs, the higher bony fishes, the mammals and the non-mammalian tetrapods. The hyoid segment produces a suspensorium for the jaw in most fishes but *never in tetrapods*, and produces an ear ossicle in most tetrapods but *never in fishes*. Its tissue overflows as a gill-covering operculum in most fishes, and as superficial muscles of the neck or the face in amniotes. The hyomandibular pharynx pouch may form a breathing hole, a degenerate gill, an auditory tube, or nothing. Since none of these differences are yet established at the pharyngula stage, but the rudiments from which they all develop are present in equivalent form at that time, a comparative study of development shows the true relationships underneath adult divergencies.

This chapter and the next will assume familiarity with the pattern of the pharynx-segment zone of the pharyngula, as described in Chapter 5, pages 75–77. It will take up in separate sections (a) the derivatives of the **hyomandibular pouch,** that pharynx pouch which is formed between the mandibular and hyoid segments, (b) the skeletal patterns laid down in these segments, (c) the muscles, and (d) the nerves.

To consider first a mere space, and then to take up separately the skeleton, the muscles, and the nerves of the region in this way does violence to anatomy as it exists. Even more, it distracts attention from the whole acutely living organism in its constant struggle for survival. It is justified only for pedagogical reasons. The muscles do not operate separately from their nerves and their skeleton, and what they accomplish depends on the combination of them. It is the combination that one sees in dissection or surgery, and it is only through their combination that one can understand the feeding and breathing apparatus which they produce. Beyond this, one must remember the living animal, caught between its aspiration and its fate.

In each section, some generalizations will first be expressed about all the gnathostome vertebrates, and then the great adaptive contrasts that exist in the different classes will be explained as alternative lines of specialization based upon the similar structures of their pharyngulas. The special uses which mammals make of this region will be considered at the end of the chapter because they are in many respects radically new.

The agnathous lampreys and hagfishes do, like the gnathostome vertebrates, show a repetition of the pharynx-segment pattern in their early development. In them, as in all the jawed fishes, these segments become outfitted with gill-slits, aortic arches, cartilages, muscles, and visceral branches of cranial nerves. There the resemblance ceases. The adult structures become so different that it is a frustrating experience to try to bring them into a single homology scheme with those of other vertebrates. There is almost as much difficulty in comparing the lampreys with the hagfishes. The most remarkable of the contrasts are found in the pre-otic segments.

Neither lampreys or hagfishes have jaws or jaw muscles. The hagfish (Fig. 2–4) has nothing for a mouth but a soft-walled opening at its front end. The adult lamprey has this mouth hole surrounded by an elaborate muscular sucker studded with horny spines (Fig. 2–3). In lamprey embryos a trigeminal and a facial nerve can be defined by their relation to the mouth opening and the first of the paired pharyngeal pouches, but the muscular and skeletal derivatives of these segments are most peculiar. All the pre-otic cartilage is incorporated into the skull, and the muscles supplied by the trigeminal nerve are powerfully and intricately developed to work the sucker and a huge piston-and-rasper apparatus that extends in the midventral line nearly as far back as the level of the heart, between the right and left sequences of gill pouches.

As for the hagfishes, apparently three pairs of pharynx pouches that are formed between the mouth hole and the first of the gill pouches are obliterated, whereas the lampreys lose only their first (hyomandibular) pair. The homology of particular lamprey cartilages with gnathostome mandibular and hyoid elements is quite uncertain. More remarkably, at present not a single one of the various elements in the cartilaginous visceral skeleton of the hagfish can be homologized confidently with any one in the lamprey. Except for the fact that the piston-and-rasper device is recognizable in both forms, the same homological chaos extends to the pre-otic musculature. Extensive studies of the fossils of agnathous fishes of Silurian and lower Devonian ages (Fig. 2–5) show great variability in the group and provide few convincing solutions to these homology problems [1].

For practical reasons then, pre-otic visceral anatomy of the cyclostomes will be ruled out of the scope of this volume.

Before starting the examination of the gnathostomes it should be noted that the derivatives of the mandibular and hyoid segments are not more primitive in fishes than they are in land vertebrates. The specializations of the amniotes are not built upon and extended from those of anamniotes. Each class of vertebrates sets out along its own direction of specialization soon after the pharyngula stage. In the fishes, the organs and devices that are produced from these two segments are as complex as they are in the mammals, perhaps more so, but developed along different lines. These parts are adapted to the requirements and opportunities of different environments.

II. THE HYOMANDIBULAR POUCH

Every vertebrate embryo produces a pharyngeal pouch on each side between the mandibular and hyoid segments. Perforation of this **hyomandibular pouch** through a closing plate to form a visceral cleft is rather rare. It occurs quite temporarily at the pharyngula stage in sauropsida, but a permanent cleft is formed only in a small minority of fishes. Its highest development as a cleft is in the elasmobranchs, where it may form a breathing hole or **spiracle** (Fig. 16–1). Its highest development as a pouch is in the land animals, where it may enlarge as a **middle ear space,** forming a new kind of closing plate that functions as an eardrum or **tympanic membrane.**

Most fish breathe in through the mouth and out through the gill slits. This would be awkward in the flattened bottom-dwelling skates and rays, for all these openings rest against the mud or sand at the ventral surface. The much enlarged **spiracle** lies on the dorsal side of the head and is equipped with a skin flap which passively opens when the pharynx muscles and skeleton cooperate to suck water in through it, and closes again when the water is being expelled through the gill slits on the ventral side (Fig. 16–1).

The spiracle is of no functional importance in sharks, and different species of them show all stages in its constriction, reduction, or closure. Even when it is completely blocked off by skin during late development however, the pharynx pouch which originally produced it remains like an inverted funnel pushing dorsolaterally from the roof of the pharynx between the upper parts of the skeleton of the mandibular and hyoid arches. Spiracles exist as vestiges in the adult stages of a very few bony fishes (Chondrostei, *Polypterus*), but in most of the rest even the hyomandibular pouches are completely obliterated early in development.

Some of the post-otic pharynx pouches of fishes regularly break through as clefts and form permanent gills in their walls. As though in imitation of this, the anterior, i.e., mandibular, wall of their closed hyomandibular pouch or open spir-

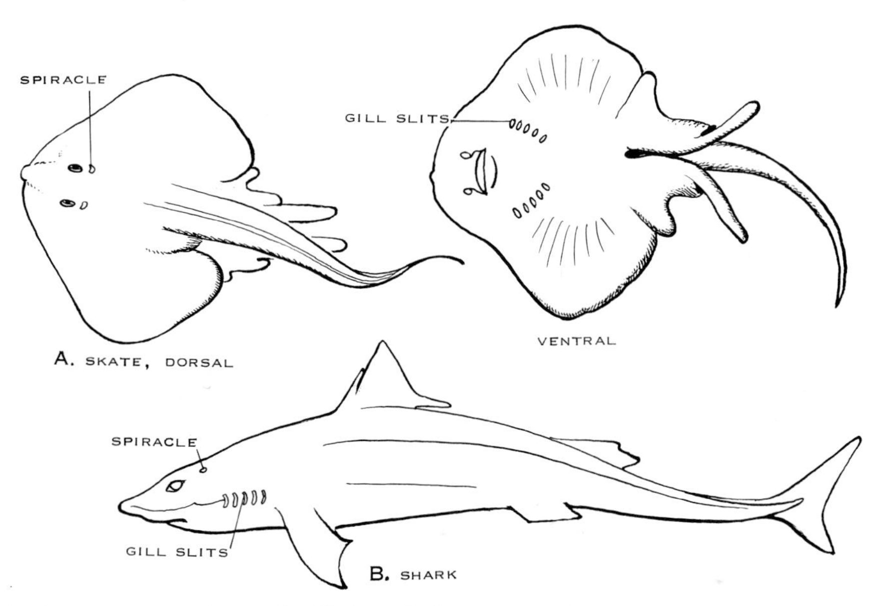

Fig. 16–1. Spiracles and gill slits of elasmobranchs. A. Skate, dorsal and ventral. B. Shark.

acle often develops a little patch of gill lamellae called a **pseudobranch.** If the hyomandibular pouch is subsequently reduced or lost, as in most bony fishes, the pseudobranch may disappear also, but instead it may secondarily migrate to a position near the opening of the first true gill slit (the hyobranchial cleft), on the inside of the base of the gill-cover or operculum.

In the very young fish embryo, the pseudobranch receives blood through the aortic arch of the mandibular segment, but after the first two aortic arches are obliterated it begins to be supplied with freshly oxygenated blood from the top of the first true gill (third pharynx segment). Since this blood passes to the skull and orbit after leaving the pseudobranch, the latter is sometimes referred to as the **eye-gill.**

The pseudobranch only rarely retains this respiratory function. Usually, if it persists, it becomes more and more overgrown by generalized epithelium, and may finally be buried in connective tissue and packed with glandular cells of an unknown function. Its fate, while fixed for given species, varies a good deal even in closely related groups of teleosts.

In tailed amphibians, the hyomandibular pouch is promptly obliterated, but in anuran amphibia and most amniotes, it gets a greater development than in any fishes, as a **middle ear chamber.** This development seems to be independent of the inner ear, for in both frogs and chicks it has been found to occur after the ear vesicle has been removed [2].

Middle ears form soon after the pharyngula stage in the amniotes. Although a temporary hyomandibular cleft is visible at the pharyngula stage in chick and lizard embryos, opening out from the dorsal part of the pouch (like the spiracle of the elasmobranchs), this soon closes up. The middle ear space is a later enlargement of the *ventroposterior part* of the pouch (marked with a star in Fig. 16–2 A).

It is quite otherwise in anura, whose hyomandibular pouch persists as a slender blind tube throughout the tadpole stage and then, except in a few families of frogs, suddenly reaches the skin during metamorphosis, and reacts with it to form a tympanic membrane, placed *high on the dorsal side* of the head. A special nerve, the internal mandibular branch of VII, which passes *dorsal* to the middle ear space of amniotes (Fig. 16–2 B), passes *ventral* to it in the anura (Fig. 16–3). This and some fossil evidence suggests that the middle ear development in the amphibia is not strictly homologous with that of amniotes [3].

The presumptive anuran middle ear cavity is pushed out toward the skin just posterior to the quadrate cartilage, the upper element in the jaw joint. During late larval life this cartilage proliferates a ring of tissue around it, which differentiates into cartilage at metamorphosis and fuses with the crista parotica of the otic capsule. Nothing like this **tympanic anulus** (Figs. 16–3, 16–13 A) is known in any other group of vertebrates. It has been demonstrated to be the

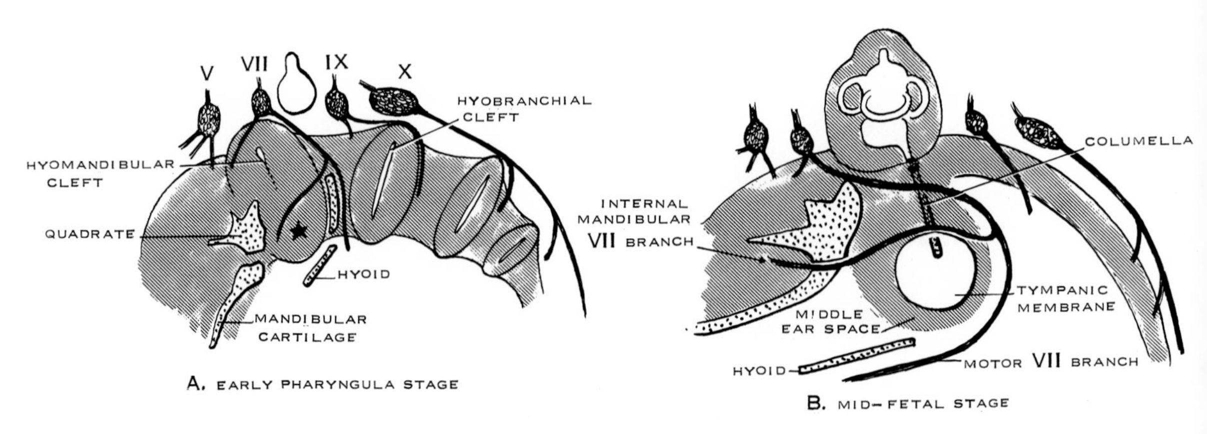

Fig. 16–2. Relationships of the developing middle ear in an amniote.

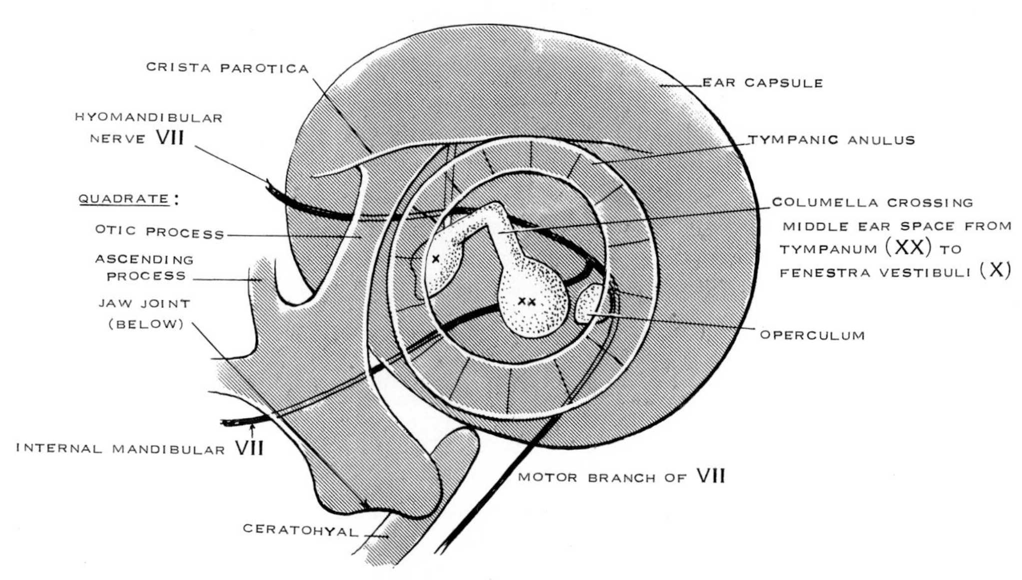

Fig. 16–3. Diagram of relations in the middle ear region of an adult frog.

inducing agent for the formation of the frog's tympanic membrane, and it will act this way whether or not the inner ear is present [2]. If the anulus is removed, no eardrum is developed. If it is transplanted elsewhere in the frog, it can induce an eardrum-like reaction in the skin with which it comes in contact. It is not known whether such an inductor system exists to call forth the formation of a tympanic membrane in the amniotes.

In *sauropsida,* middle ear developments take a variety of forms and achieve different relations with the skull and the musculature. Many of the lizards exceed even the frogs in the size of the enlarged pharynx pouch, so that when one eardrum is opened one can look across a vast head space and see the opposite eardrum (Fig. 16–4). On the other hand there are lizards (Fig. 15–8 A) in which the opening of the middle ear space to the pharynx is narrowed to a slit or a tunnel called the **auditory tube** (PNA). The auditory tubes of turtles open outward into partly segregated lower chambers of the middle ear spaces. In the crocodilia they have crooked paths enclosed in bony tunnels. In birds, secondary folds of the pharynx roof bring the right and left auditory tubes gradually together below the skull so that they finally share a common opening down into the pharynx in the midline.

The middle ear chamber itself varies in its degree of expansion. In the sphenodon, snakes, and some burrowing lizards it fails to form a tympanic membrane because it does not reach the skin and in turtles it forms one that is so thick and leathery that it can have little use as a resonator of audible vibrations. Usually it expands and applies itself against the outside of the otic capsule ventral to the crista parotica (Fig. 15–8 A). In so doing, it envelops the ear ossicle (see page 281).

The middle ear cavity, like the nasal passage (Chapter 13, page 238), is sometimes involved in "pneumatization" of the skull. Practically all the skull bones and the lower jaws of birds become reduced to thin outer and inner tables of compact bone, separated by a froth of interconnected air cells, all derived from the expansion of the middle ear. Similar but far less extensive bone invasions are found in the crocodilia, and in some mammals, for instance in the mastoid region of the human skull.

The tympanic membrane lies flush with the outer surface of the head in frogs, turtles and some lizards (Fig. 15–8 A). In other reptiles, and

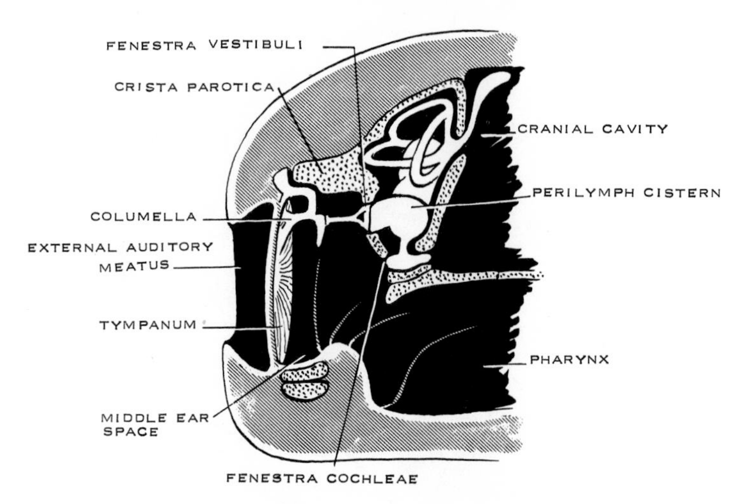

Fig. 16–4. Middle ear structures of a lizard.
(After E. S. Goodrich, Studies on the Structure and Development of Vertebrates, 1930, by permission of Macmillan & Co., Ltd., London.)

in all the birds and mammals, the skin sinks in to meet the outgrowing middle ear chamber, and the tympanum of the adult is found at the bottom of a surface recess called the **external auditory meatus** (Fig. 16–4). Such a meatus is sometimes capable of being closed by a sphincter muscle, as in gecko, lizards, owls, diving mammals, etc. In the crocodilia it is equipped with a special ear-lid, which can be closed tight for cruising under water.

III. THE MANDIBULAR AND HYOID SKELETON

A. Early Differentiation

As previously noted (page 160) the skeleton of the pharynx segments is formed from trains of neural crest cells which migrate down into them from above (Fig. 9–8). Experimental evidence from amphibian embryos suggests that even before these cells enter the pharynx segments their potentialities have become so restricted that those destined for pre-otic segments cannot be substituted for those destined for post-otic ones, and vice versa [4]. The paths of migration are apparently determined by the arrangement of tissues in the pharynx segments since neural crest material transplanted to the ventral part of the head will send trains of cells *up* into the segments.

Skeletal developments in each of the pre-otic visceral segments are easily divisible for descriptive purposes into upper and lower parts, which acquire different functions. In the mandibular segment these are respectively the **upper** and **lower jaw** rudiments, and in the hyoid segment they form the **suspensorium** dorsally, and the **hyoideum** or tongue support ventrally. The upper parts will be considered first.

1. Upper Jaw Rudiment. The maxillary process of the mandibular segment produces a characteristic skeletal element called the **palatoquadrate cartilage** in every gnathostome vertebrate. (It appears in two pieces in mammals.) This is the basic element of the **primary upper jaw,** and actually *becomes* the upper jaw itself in elasmobranchs and holocephals (cf. Fig. 16–6). In the other modern groups of gnathostome fishes (Fig. 16–8), and in the tetrapods (Fig. 16–9), various membrane bones join with the derivatives of the palatoquadrate cartilage to form **secondary upper jaws,** or, in mammals, to replace them altogether.

The palatoquadrate cartilage always comes in contact with the cartilage of the primary lower jaw and forms a **jaw joint** with it. In addition it produces at least two and sometimes as many as four processes extending toward the skull (Fig. 16–5). The four processes are separately identifiable throughout the gnathostomes, each by re-

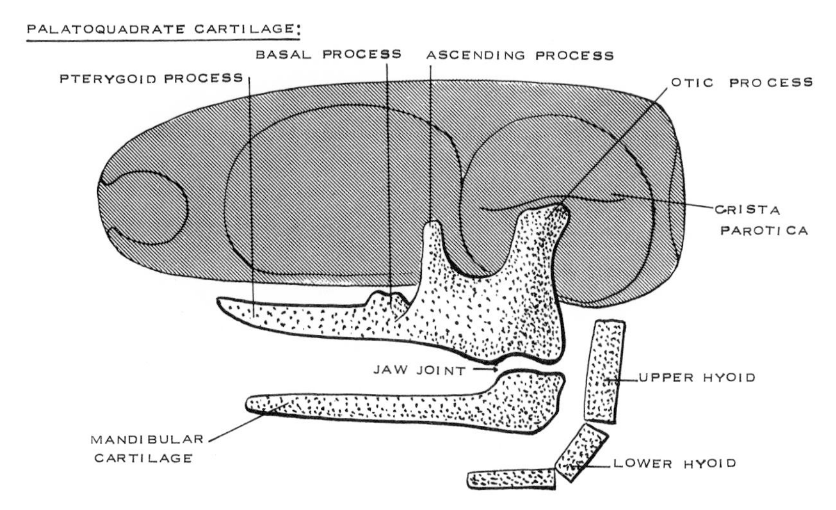

Fig. 16–5. Hypothetical complete palatoquadrate cartilage and some of its relationships.

lation with a particular skull region of the embryo and with particular nerves and blood vessels. In fact their identification in various combinations has been the key to solution of some difficult questions of homology in head anatomy. They are: (a) the **ascending process,** which extends directly dorsad just anterior to the otic capsule; (b) the **basal process,** which extends dorsomedially toward the trabecula just in front of the ascending process; (c) the **pterygoid process,** which extends dorsoanteriorly, nearly parallel to the trabecula; and (d) the **otic process,** which extends dorsoposteriorly toward the otic capsule, posterior to the ascending process. The only one of these which is invariably present in gnathostomes is the otic process. But in some species or other, each of them can be found, sometimes ending free, or in contact with the skull, and sometimes actually fusing with it. Most of the possible combinations of presence-or-absence and freedom-or-fusion of these four processes are known, and evolutionary exploitation of their possibilities for functional adaptation has produced many ingenious devices [5].

Since the reader is aware that his own upper jaw is firmly fused to his neurocranium, it is necessary to observe that the palatoquadrate cartilage always appears first as a free element somewhat removed from the skull (Fig. 12–6), so that for a time at least the possibility of retaining a movable upper jaw exists in every species. Some mobility of upper jaw elements is in fact retained, in one form or another, in the great majority of gnathostomes.

2. *Upper Hyoid Rudiment.* The characteristic skeletal element formed in the upper part of the hyoid segment of *gnathostome fishes* is a large **hyomandibular cartilage,** which makes a joint with the crista parotica of the ear capsule dorsally, acts as a suspensorium for the jaws, and is bound firmly by ligaments to the hyoideum or tongue support ventrally (Fig. 16–6). In the *tetrapods,* there is a striking contrast, for a tiny rodlike cartilage is formed in the upper part of the hyoid segment, which later becomes an ear ossicle (Fig. 16–7, columella). At its inner end it fits into a fenestra vestibuli in the ear capsule, and at its outer end it becomes connected in one way or another to the tympanic membrane (Fig. 15–8 A). With but one known exception, the sphenodon, it loses all connection with the hyoideum at the adult stage, and it often does not even form a temporary connection.

Despite this contrast, the ear ossicle, which will be described below as a **columella** or a **stapes,** is homologous with the hyomandibular element (compare Figs. 16–6 and 16–7). These elements all form in the upper part of their

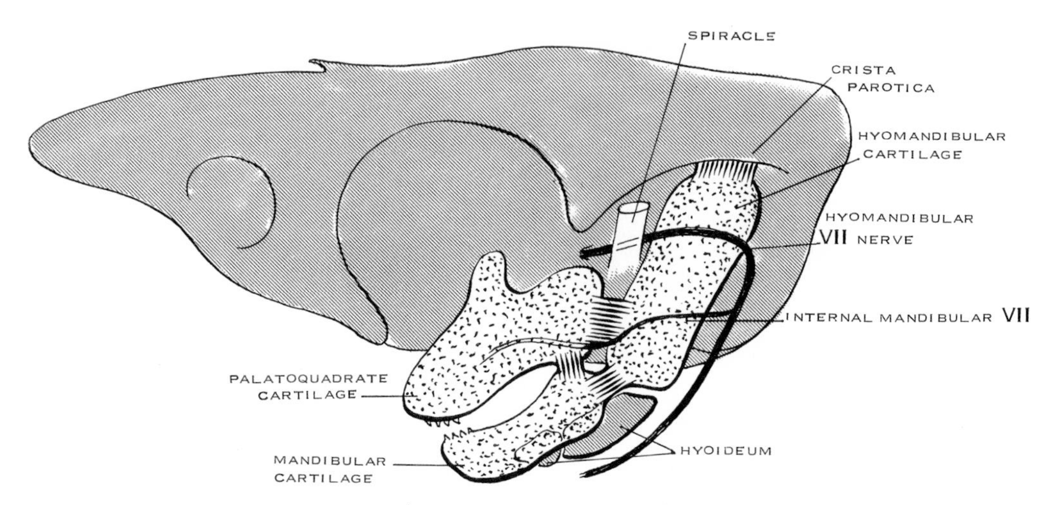

Fig. 16–6. Hyostylic jaw suspension in the spiny dogfish.

hyoid segment, they all arise directly posterior to the hyomandibular pharynx pouch (the columella or stapes therefore becoming associated with a middle ear expansion from the pouch if this occurs), and they all are associated with the ear capsule. Unfortunately, the fossil record is inadequate to show the stages by which the hyomandibular element was transformed into an ear ossicle.

While the hyomandibular cartilage is forming in the fish embryo, a vein is formed which drains blood from the head past it toward the heart. This head vein lies *dorsal* to the articulation of the hyomandibular cartilage with the ear capsule in elasmobranchs, but *ventromedial* to it in bony fishes. The motor branch of the facial nerve VII, descending from the hindbrain into the hyoid segment, crosses *dorsal* to the cartilage in elasmobranchs (Fig. 16–6) and some bony fishes, but there are other species of bony fishes in which it crosses *ventrally,* or passes through the cartilage, or forks around it. The equivalent branches of the VII nerve of tetrapods make similar inconstant relations with the ear ossicles (Fig. 16–7).

Such inconsistencies might be dismissed as species-specific variations in the path of least resistance which would be chosen by the neural crest cells as they wander down into the hyoid segment. Nevertheless they have been a concern to morphologists for a long time, because many anatomical relationships of similar inconsequence have remained immutable through hundreds of millions of years of evolution (Chapter 14, page 257). One hypothesis is that the hyomandibular cartilage always had a tendency to send two processes toward the skull, a lower and an upper one (in resemblance, perhaps, to the basal and otic processes of the palatoquadrate cartilage (cf. Fig. 16–5), and that different stocks of vertebrates make use of either the one or the other.

3. *Lower Mandibular and Lower Hyoid Rudiments.* Usually a single **mandibular cartilage** forms on the mandibular segment on each side, and it makes a joint with the lower surface of the palatoquadrate cartilage. In the lower part of the hyoid arch, the neural crest cells form a chain of small cartilages, held together by ligaments. These form the tongue support, or **hyoideum** (Figs. 16–6 to 16–9, 16–19, 16–22). Since the hyoideum is inextricably tied up with the gill arch apparatus of fishes or the special tongues of amniotes, it will be considered in the next chapter.

B. Variations in Later Development

1. *Bone Patterns.* In the permanently cartilaginous elasmobranchs and holocephals, the palatoquadrate and mandibular cartilages elongate and

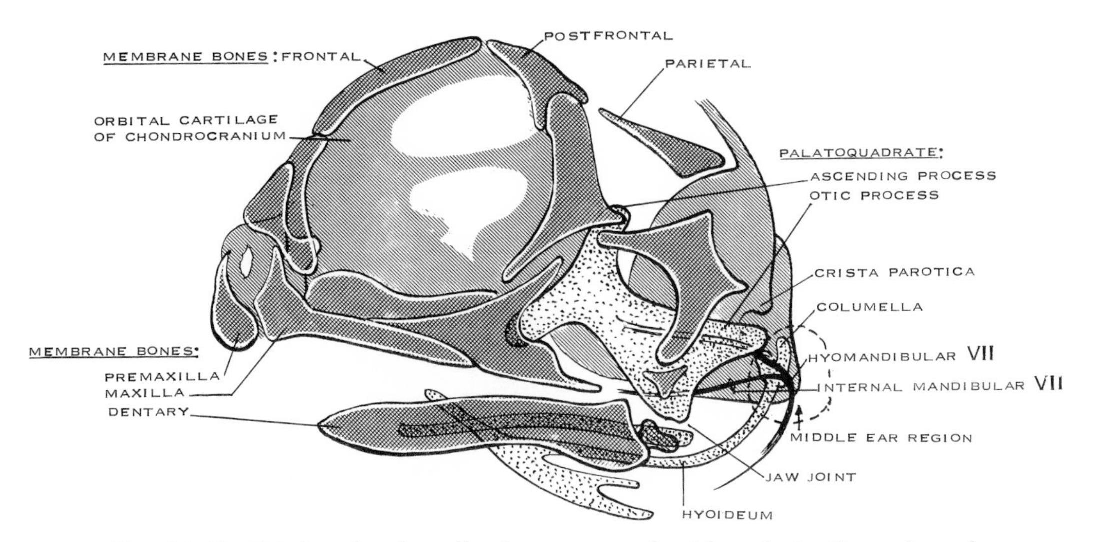

Fig. 16–7. Origin of columella from upper hyoid arch in the sphenodon. Diagram of young fetal head skeleton, left side.
(After Howes and Swinnerton, 1901.)

strengthen to form the definitive upper and lower jaws. Three elements come together at the jaw joint: upper jaw, lower jaw, and hyomandibular cartilage.

In all other fishes (Fig. 16–8) and land vertebrates (Figs. 16–7, 16–9) the palatoquadrate is replaced by at least two endochondral bones and reinforced by dermal bones which line up as the **inner and outer arcades** of the palate and upper jaw. The bone which retains the facet for the jaw joint is called the **quadrate.** The mandibular cartilage lags in growth while an entirely new lower jaw of membrane bone is formed around it (Figs. 12–1; 16–7, 8, 9; 16–19). A replacement bone formed in it at the jaw joint is appropriately called the **articular.**

In the bony fishes (Fig. 16–8), the **inner arcades** appear in the roof of the mouth, diverging from the midline at the anterior end of the snout and ending posteriorly in the quadrates. The bones at the two ends of these arcades (autopalatines, metapterygoids, and quadrates) are produced from separate ossification centers in the original palatoquadrate cartilages. The intervening bones are formed directly in membrane, or in some species the situation is complicated by the fusion of overlapping replacement- and membrane-bones. The **outer arcades** consist of premaxillary and maxillary bones which are usually loosely attached in upper lips and may be separately moved.

The quadrate bone on each side is usually tightly jointed to the bones formed in the upper hyoid arch, but the principal one of these, the **hyomandibular,** makes a movable joint with the outside of the ear capsule. Despite greater complexity of detail, the derivatives and replacements of the same three elements converge on each jaw joint: palatoquadrate cartilage, mandibular cartilage, and upper hyoid arch.

In most tetrapods (Figs. 16–7, 16–9), the inner arcades of the upper jaws contain fewer bones, while the outer arcades are usually more substantial and their bones more firmly knit together. However, there are wide variations within classes and even within orders, and the differences extend not only to the presence or absence of particular bones, but also to the preservation or abolition of the original embryonic condition of mobility in the upper jaws, and to the formation and spread of secondary palates beyond the primary palates which are defined by the original location of the choanae (Chapter 13, page 236). This causes a variable amount of contact between the inner and outer arcades across the roof of the mouth.

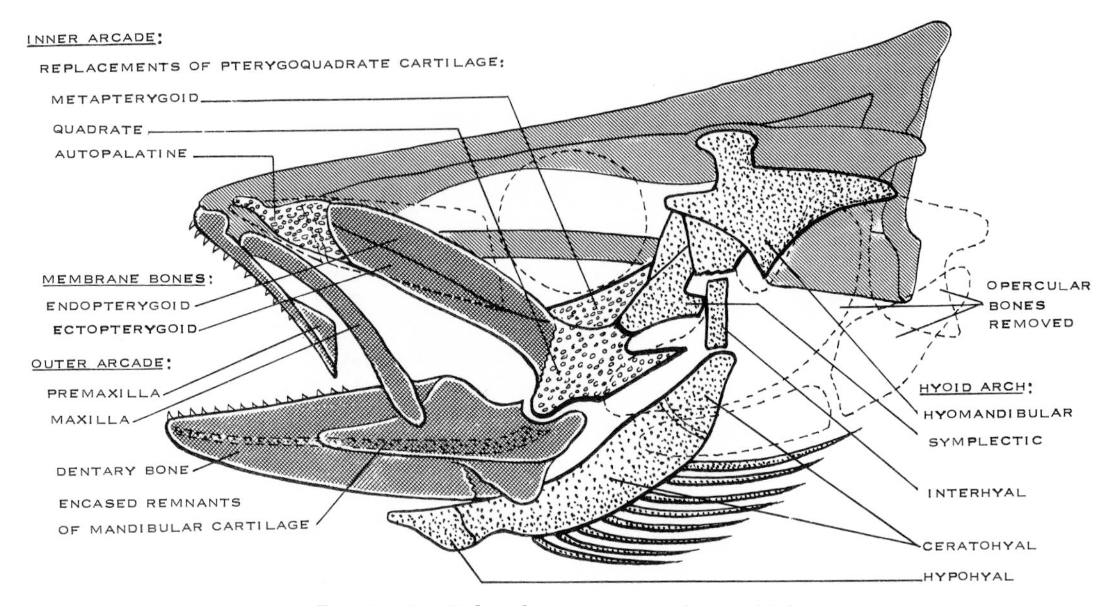

Fig. 16–8. Splanchnocranium of a codfish.

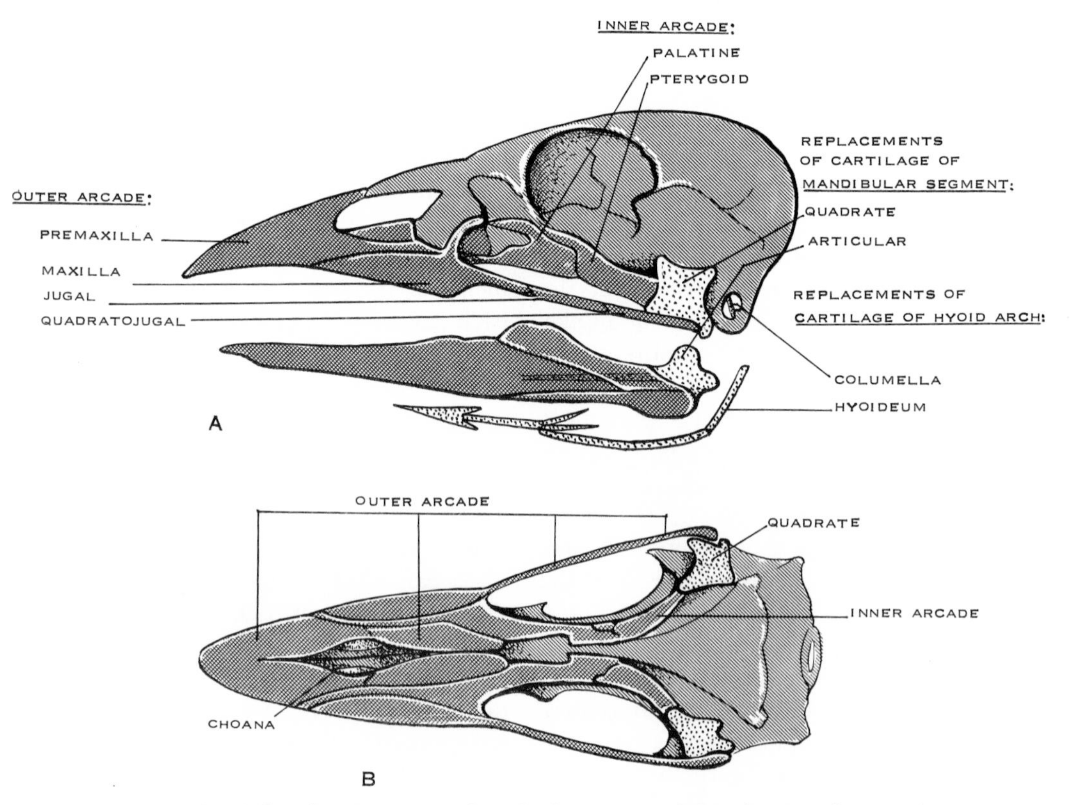

Fig. 16–9. Splanchnocranium of a duck. A. From left side. B. Palate and neurocranium from below.

(After G. Heilmann, The Origin of Birds, 1927, by permission of Meredith Press.)

In comparison with the three elements converging on the jaw joint of fishes, as described on page 283, tetrapods show two changes. First, there is no hyoid involvement, since an ear ossicle has been substituted for the hyomandibular bone (page 281). Second, membrane- and replacement-bones have completed a substitution of inner and outer arcades of bone for the cartilaginous primordial upper jaw (palatoquadrate cartilage). Here in the tetrapods then, the three elements converging on the jaw joint are the lower jaw, and the inner and outer arcades of the upper jaw (Fig. 16–9). The hyomandibular has moved out from involvement posteriorly, and the outer arcade has moved in from anteriorly.

In both the bony fishes (Fig. 16–8) and the tetrapods (Figs. 16–9 and 16–19) the mandibular cartilage loses out relative to the membrane bones that ensheath it. Through relatively slow growth, it becomes a delicate rod of cartilage buried inside the bony secondary jaw. Only its replacement-bone, the articular, peeps out at the jaw joint. The pattern of lower-jaw membrane-bones varies considerably in the different classes and orders.

In the bony fishes, not only are the upper and lower parts of the cartilaginous hyoid arch replaced by numerous bony elements but there are added to these a cheek armature of membrane-bones forming a gill cover or **operculum.** It is augmented ventrally by a **branchiostegal membrane,** supported by the numerous horny plates or bony rays that form in connection with the **ceratohyal bone,** one of the principal elements in the hyoideum chain (Fig. 16–8).

The operculum and the branchiostegal membrane, which are interconnected, serve to protect the gills, aid somewhat in their aeration by flapping movements, and act as breathing valves. When a bony fish is breathing rhythmically, water is drawn in anteriorly by a gaping of the mouth and a dropping of the hyoideum, and exhaled posteriorly by closing of the mouth or special soft lip-valves and simultaneous opening of the gill slits. During inhalation, the operculum and branchiostegal membrane are passively clapped shut, preventing water from coming in at the wrong places. During exhalation they are blown outward by the current of discharged water.

In the extinct acanthodian fishes (Fig. 16–10), apparently all the pharynx segments including the mandibular produced their own opercular flaps stiffened by bone, with the principal array of bone in the mandibular flap. The arrangement in modern elasmobranchs, in which there is a series of overlapping soft flaps developed from all the segments *except* the mandibular, and supported only by cartilage rays, may be thought of as a persistence, in reduced form, of a heritage from the acanthodians. The holocephals produce

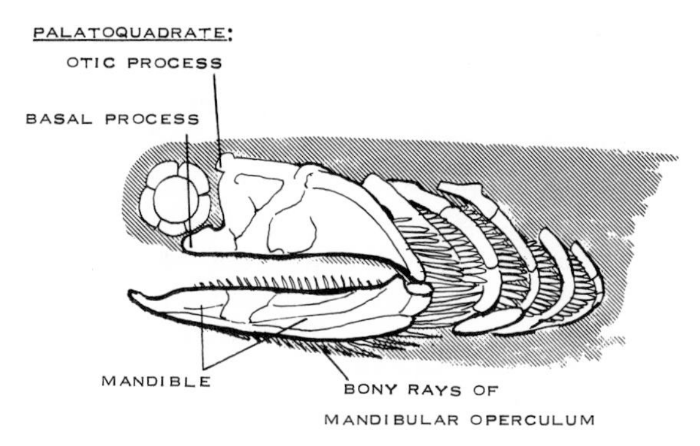

Fig. 16–10. Splanchnocranium of *Acanthodes* (extinct, Permian, reconstructed).
(After D. M. S. Watson, 1937.)

a single soft opercular cover. The elaborate development of the bony operculum and branchiostegal membrane in association with the hyoid arch has become standard in the bony fishes, but all trace of it has been lost in the tetrapods.

2. *Jaw Suspension.* The acanthodian fishes were also noteworthy for an extraordinarily unspecialized condition of the upper and lower jaws, which—even more than those of the most primitive elasmobranch—merely resemble slightly altered gill arches (Fig. 16–10). While it is possible that gnathostome fishes once existed in which the jaws floated in the head wtihout any anchorage to the skull, the acanthodian palatoquadrate element apparently used its otic process for forming a strong joint with the otic capsule. This is only one of a number of methods of jaw suspension which survive in modern vertebrates.

(a) *Autostyly.* When the upper jaw skeleton

forms its own joint directly with the base of the skull, the arrangement is known as *autostyly*. In the case of the acanthodians just mentioned, the joint remained movable. This variant, called **autodiastyly,** is common among tetrapods (Figs. 16–7, 16–9), though the quadrate bones which replace the loose palatoquadrate cartilages may not maintain the movable condition. In the modern dipnoi and amphibia, one or another of the palatoquadrate's dorsal processes may actually fuse with the chondrocranium, producing the condition called **autosystyly** (Fig. 12–1 B). In the holocephals, the primary upper jaw and the skull become completely and indistinguishably fused with the neurocranium, which is the condition called **holostyly.**

Where the jaw suspension is autodiastylic at the cartilage stage of development, the possibility remains open for continued mobility in the upper jaws. This is actually realized in snakes, lizards, and birds, for the quadrate bones which replace the palatoquadrate cartilages form movable joints with the otic capsules. However the extent of motion may be very slight, due to the anchorage of the enveloping membrane bones in the arcades anteriorly. In turtles and crocodilia, on the other hand, the quadrates become firmly sutured to the neurocranium.

(b) *Hyostyly.* A much more common arrangement among modern fishes is for the palatoquadrate cartilage (or its bony derivatives) to make no contact directly with the skull, but to form ligamentous or jointed attachments to the upper part of the hyoid skeleton (hyomandibular cartilage or hyomandibular–symplectic bones), which in turn is jointed to the crista parotica of the ear capsule. In this case, the hyoid is the suspensorium.

Hyostylic suspension occurs in two different forms, which may well have arisen independently in separate lineages. In elasmobranchs (Fig. 16–6), the upper jaw is the palatoquadrate cartilage itself, and although it receives its support entirely from the hyomandibular cartilage, it glides against and in direct contact with the skull. In teleostomes on the other hand (Fig. 16–8), the quadrate and the other derivatives of the palatoquadrate cartilage are propped out at a considerable distance from the braincase, at the end of the hyomandibular–symplectic buttress. The appearance is so different that this variant is often distinguished as **met-hyostyly.**

(c) *Amphistyly.* There is no theoretical reason why a combination of autostylic and hyostylic

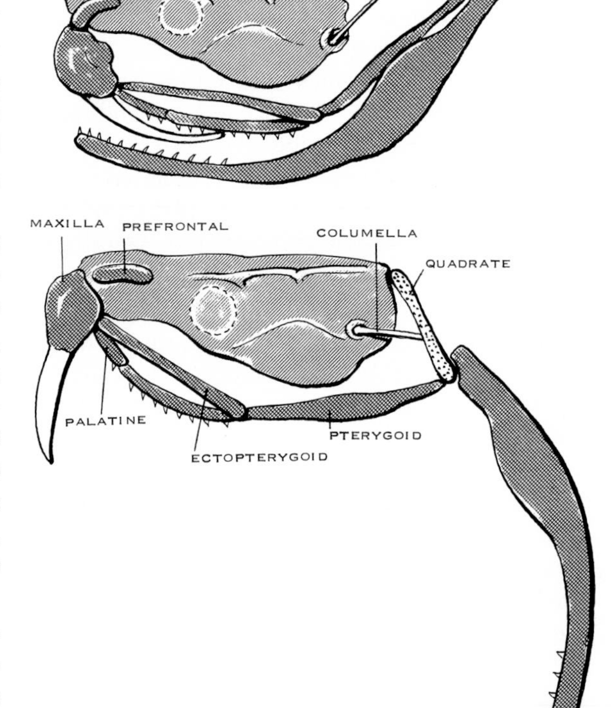

Fig. 16–11. Movable jaws of a rattlesnake.
(Second drawing after L. M. Klauber, Rattlesnakes, 1956, by permission of University of California Press.)

suspensions cannot be developed, and in fact such an **amphistylic** arrangement is known in a few sharks.

It should be noted that although one or another variant of hyostyly has been retained in most of the living gnathostome fishes, while the tetrapods became autostylic, neither group temporarily adopts or recapitulates the arrangement of the other, before developing its definitive type of jaw anchorage. Both start with the same primary parts, the palatoquadrate and mandibular cartilages and the upper hyoid cartilages, and the two types of development are divergent from the time these are established, at or soon after the pharyngula stage.

With extremely rare exceptions, all these parts, and the membrane bones as well, arise separately from each other and from the chondrocranium. They are all present before the chosen course toward the adult specialization is revealed. In both hyostylic and autostylic groups of vertebrates, various possibilities for developing mobile upper jaws have been exploited in later development.

In teleosts for instance, though the quadrate bones are usually jointed firmly to the hyomandibular bone (or the hyomandibular–symplectic), the latter is free to swing in and out on a horizontal joint pivot at the otic capsule, carrying with it the whole inner arcade of the upper jaw. Special arrangements of the upper mandibular and hyoid muscles make use of this freedom, to deepen or flatten the mouth–pharynx cavity for breathing. The maxillary and premaxillary bones can be moved separately from the rest of the upper jaw in sucking and nibbling actions.

Snakes have rodlike quadrate bones which can pivot anteriorly or posteriorly on their joints with the otic capsules, carrying the inner arcades of the upper jaws with them (Fig. 16–11). Neither the two upper jaws nor the two lower jaws are fastened to each other, and all four can be moved independently. Once a snake has struck and caught on to its prey with its incurved teeth, its swallowing technique is to slide first one and then another of the four jaws forward in stepwise coordination. The teeth drag the prey inward as each in turn is pulled back in place. The snake can so extend the gape of its jaws that it can swallow objects considerably larger than its own head.

When a rattlesnake strikes, the quadrates are rocked forward simultaneously with the dropping open of the lower jaws. This automatically shoves the inner arcade bones forward, and these pivot the fang-bearing maxillary bones of the reduced outer arcades, so that the fangs are erected out of their sheaths of mucous membrane in the palate. When the strike has been made and the jaws are clenched, muscles of the inner arcades press upon the enlarged ducts of the poison glands and discharge venom down along the fangs. Thus the venom is injected hypodermically into the prey.

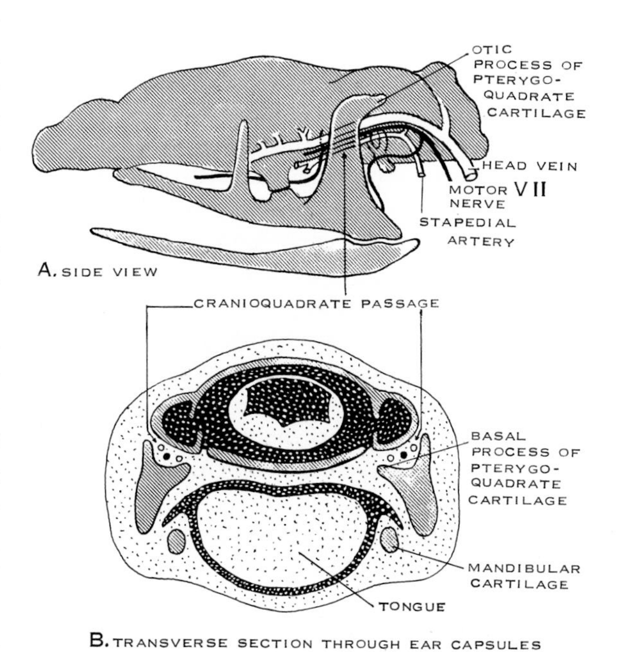

Fig. 16–12. Cranioquadrate passage and its contents in a tetrapod fetus (schematic). A. Side view. B. Transverse section through ear capsules.

The placing of the quadrate against the skull for the suspension of the jaw results in the formation of a characteristic head space in tetrapods, called the **cranioquadrate passage.** In a cross-section of a urodele head (Fig. 16–12 B) this may be seen in schematic form as a crescentic area, its dorsomedial wall provided by the ear capsule, and its floor and lateral walls, respectively, by the basal and the otic processes of the palatoquadrate cartilage. An artery passes forward through this space, and the principal head vein and the motor division of the VII nerve pass backward through it. All three of these regularly identifiable structures lie close to the ear capsule in bony fishes also, but not in contact with the quadrate, which is propped out at the end of the hyomandibular–symplectic buttress. The cranioquadrate passage and its contents appear in typical fashion in young fetal amniotes, but may be obliterated in later developments. They have served as important landmarks in the solution of some famous homology problems produced by the evolution of the middle ear.

3. *Ear Ossicles of Tetrapods.* Although the upper or suspensorial part of the hyoid arch is invariably jointed to the lower hyoideum part in the fishes, such a continuity is only rarely visible in tetrapods, in consequence of the conversion of the hyomandibular cartilage to the service of sound-wave transfer. Evidence of continuity between the upper and lower parts of the arch can be found in earliest procartilage or blastema stages, and this progresses to a ligamentous connection in some lizards and turtles, and even to a temporary cartilaginous connection in crocodilia and birds, but the lizard-like sphenodon, a living fossil, is the only known species in which the embryonic cartilaginous continuity (Fig. 16–7) lasts through life.

In embryos of various tetrapod species, the upper skeletal rudiment of the hyoid arch forks at its upper end into a **medial prong** which differentiates into an ear ossicle, and a **lateral prong** which reaches dorsally in the direction of the crista parotica of the otic capsule. Dipnoi show a similar forked arrangement. The medial prong, which is invariably present, lies ventral to the head vein, like the hyomandibular cartilage of elasmobranchs (pages 281–282). The lateral prong, which cannot be found in all species, lies lateral to the head vein, like the hyomandibular bone of the teleostomes.

The ear ossicle which forms from the medial prong (or the only prong as the case may be) is called **columella** (or **stapes** in mammals). Always in dipnoi, and sometimes in amphibia, the columella subsequently fuses with the ear capsule and is lost as an individual structure. In the rest of the tetrapods it remains free, filling the fenestra vestibuli of the otic capsule (Figs. 15–8, 15–9), even in animals which lack middle ear chambers, such as urodeles (Fig. 15–6), gymnophiona, and snakes.

4. *Operculum, etc. of Amphibia.* In most modern amphibia, a small piece of cartilage called the **operculum** (no relation to the gill-covering operculum of fishes) is cut out of the otic capsule just posterior to the columella, and may remain separately movable alongside it in an enlarged fenestra vestibuli. Or it may fuse with the columella, or either the one or the other of them may subsequently fuse with the capsule. There are no known homologs of this little operculum bone in other vertebrates. It arises early in anura (Fig. 16–3), late in urodeles. Often it is covered by part of a shoulder muscle that takes origin on the ear capsule and inserts on the scapula. It has been suggested—without experimental test—that ground vibrations could be passed from the forelimb through this opercularis muscle and the opercular ossicle to the perilymph cistern of the inner ear, for improved hearing.

5. *The Columella.* In the anura (Fig. 16–3), most reptiles (Fig. 16–4), and the birds (Fig. 16–9), the columella extends across the dorsal wall of the middle ear cavity and makes contact with the inner surface of the tympanic membrane, while its inner end rests at the fenestra vestibuli. During the subsequent expansion of the endoderm-lined middle ear cavity, the columella is not shoved aside but enveloped. As a result it comes to hang in the roof of the middle ear space, in the free edge of a little mesentery. If the mesentery subsequently disappears, the columella extends across empty space without support, but it is still coated with endoderm.

The columella acts as a simple plunger, transferring sound-wave vibrations from the tympanic membrane to the perilymph cistern of the inner ear, through the spot of the membranous sacculus with which it is in contact at the fenestra vestibuli (Figs. 15–8, 16–4). The invention of this mechanism for transferring sound across the middle ear restores to the sense organ of hearing the functionally necessary contact with the outside world which it might have lost by becoming buried deep in the skull. Curiously enough, although the optic cup induces the formation of its own lens, the inner ear has nothing to do with the formation of its ear ossicle. Like the middle ear space itself, the columella forms even in an embryo from which the ear vesicle has been removed [2].

The columella may be formed from two different center of chondrification, and may be incompletely or completely replaced by two ossification centers. But it always acts as a unit. In turtles and snakes it is a simple rod without side processes, but in other reptiles and birds there may be ligamentous attachments or processes built out toward the quadrate bone, or toward the hyoideum. Most of these ornaments have been homologized with various relations developed by the hyomandibular bones of fishes. While the part of the columella that fits into the fenestra vestibuli represents the "medial prong" of the embryonic hyoid arch, the "lateral prong" is sometimes represented by a dorsal process which reaches up from its shaft toward the crista parotica of the ear capsule (Fig. 16–4), or to the otic processes of the quadrate, if this extends far enough posterodorsally to intervene. This dorsal process of the columella may exist as ligament, or as cartilage, or as bone, in particular species.

In mammals, as will be shown later, only the inner end of the columella is developed, and this is known as the stapes.

The artery which runs forward in the cranio-quadrate passage of the fetus is usually enveloped by the columella or stapes. Therefore it is called the **stapedial artery** (Figs. 16–12, 16–20).

IV. THE MUSCLES

Like all pharynx segments, the embryonic mandibular and hyoid masses each contain muscle-forming mesoderm in a strip called a **muscle plate.** During its earliest visible differentiation each muscle plate divides into a dorsal and a ventral part, and these in turn subdivide further into muscles which arrange their fibers in characteristic angles, develop tendons of origin and insertion, and become wrapped in separate connective tissue envelopes [6].

These muscles can be given individual names according to their origin and insertion (e.g., craniomandibularis), or their function (levator mandibulae), or their shape or location or other peculiarities; but there are so many of them and they are so variable in different species that inspection or enumeration of individual ones tends to obscure the general organization of the head. Both man and the codfish develop a dorsal set of muscles from the mandibular segment, but not one of the six muscles produced in this group in man can be identified with any one of the six or more in the codfish, though in a collective sense the two *groups* of muscles are homologous. The following discussion will be limited to muscle groups.

A simple traditional lettering system will suffice for identification. Since all the pharynx-wall muscles collectively squeeze down upon the pharynx cavity when they contract, they are given the general name of **constrictors.** The dor-

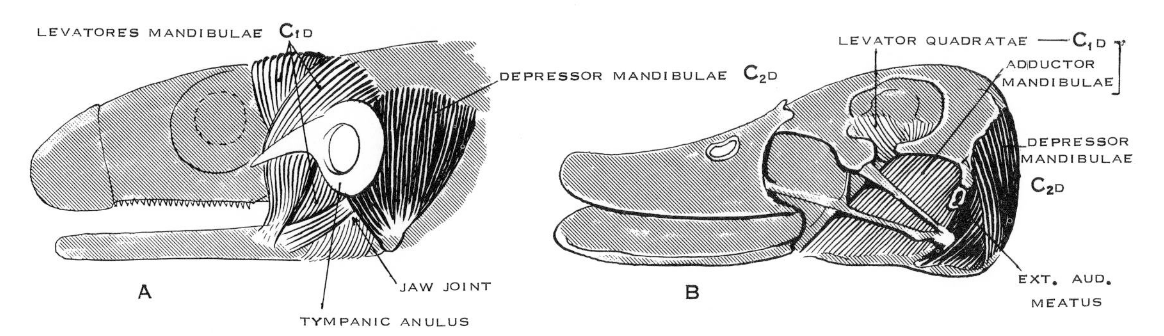

Fig. 16–13. Dorsal mandibular and hyoid muscles of tetrapods. A. Frog. B. Duck.

(After Luther, 1914, and Hérissant, 1752.)

sal and ventral constrictors of the first or mandibular segment are referred to respectively as C_1d and C_1v. They are shown with light lines in Figures 16–13 to 16–15. The dorsal and ventral constrictors of the second or hyoid segment, referred to as C_2d and C_2v, are shown in dark lines in these same figures.

A. Mandibular Arch Muscles

The C_1d and C_1v muscle plates separate widely and differentiate independently. All the derivatives of both are innervated by the trigeminal nerve V, through its motor division, the mandibular nerve.

The C_1d muscle mass becomes subdivided in different ways according to whether the upper jaw fuses with the skull or remains movable. In animals with attached upper jaws—holocephals and dipnoi among the fishes, and most amphibia (Fig. 16–13 A), the turtles and crocodiles —it forms a **levator mandibulae** group of muscles, variously partitioned and placed, but having origin on the skull and insertion on the lower jaw. It operates in closing the mouth or in biting. In animals with movable upper jaws or movable quadrates, the C_1d logically provides two sets of muscles (Fig. 16–13 B). The upper or **levator palatoquadrati** group takes origin from the skull and inserts on the upper jaw, which it can either cause to move, or to freeze in a position of rest. The lower or **adductor mandibulae** group takes origin on the upper jaw and inserts on the lower jaw, and is used to snap the jaws shut. Each of these named masses is variously subdivided in different species. In teleosts (Fig. 16–14), the levator group fans out posteriorly, producing **protractor hyomandibulae** or **dilatator operculi** muscles, while the adductor group spreads far forward along the inner arcade in the floor of the orbit and becomes cut up into many spe-

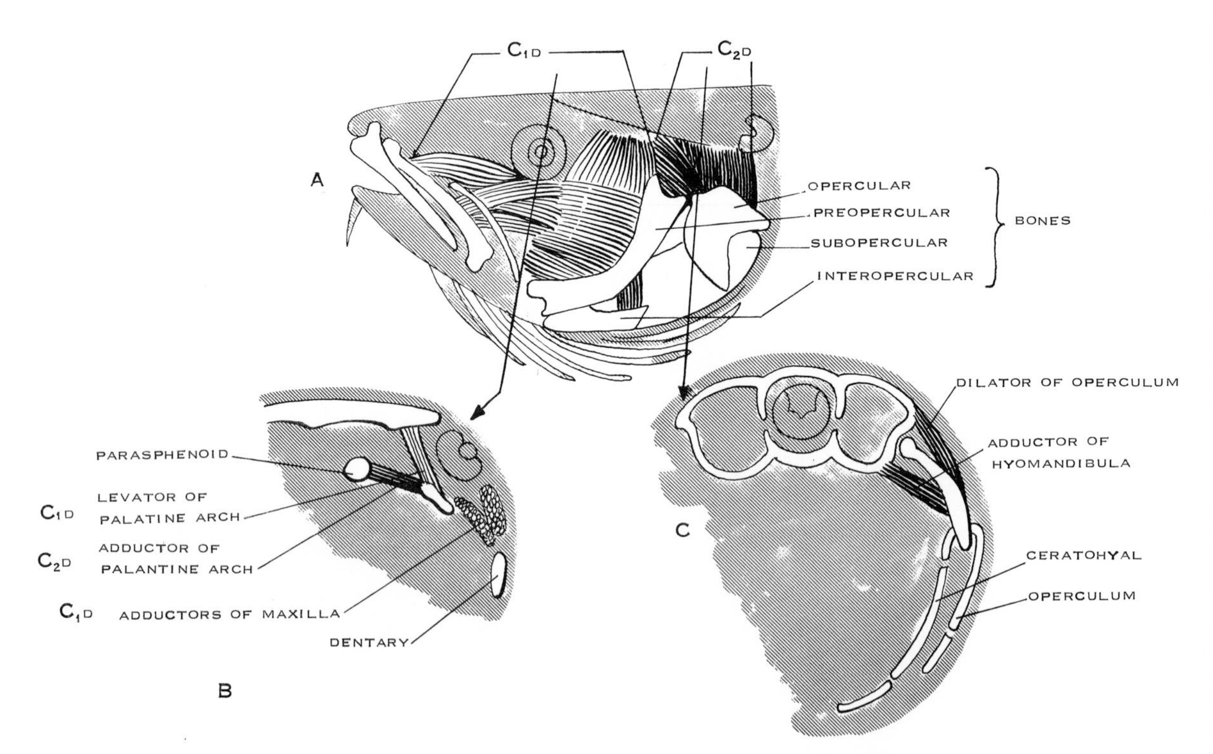

Fig. 16–14. Dorsal mandibular and hyoid muscles of a codfish. A. Left side. B. Transverse section through orbit. C. Transverse section through ear and operculum. (After P. A. Dietz, 1912.)

cialized muscles which move the inner arcade or lip bones. The ultimate in subdivision and specialization of these groups occurs in the highly mobile jaws of snakes.

Another curious use for muscles of the dorsal C_1d is found in the orbits of amphibia and most sauropsida, where little sheets of them cross from skull to upper jaw under the eyeball. They are called **levator bulbi muscles** for the reason that when they contract they cause the depressed eyeballs to pop outward. They are not only unusual as examples of skeletal muscles which do not run across a movable joint, but they develop ingenious tendinous relations for the correlated automatic operation of eyelids.

The C_1v plate differentiates into **intermandibular muscles,** which in their simplest form meet each other in the ventral midline to form a transverse sheet between the two halves of the lower jaw (Fig. 16–15). Commonly also they are subdivided into layers, or into bundles running at different angles. They may make various functional combinations with C_2v muscles, but retain their trigeminal innervation when they do so.

B. Hyoid Arch Muscles

In bony fishes, the C_2d mass differentiates into muscles that take origin from the skull and insert on the hyomandibular bone and its extension, the operculum (Fig. 16–14 A). Some of them, which bear names like **levator hyomandibulae,** lie outside the suspensorium and help swing it laterally, carrying the quadrate and inner arcade with it. Others, variously called **adductor hyomandibulae, adductor operculi,** etc., lie deeper and pull these parts medially (Fig. 16–14 C). It is common for part of the C_2d mass to move anteriorly internal to the suspensorium and become an adductor of the palatine arch (Fig. 16–14 B). That is, it can pull the inner arcade toward the midline, counteracting the effect of the levator hyomandibulae; these muscles can alternate in rhythmic swallowing or breathing actions.

This C_2d mass was deprived of its historic functions when the hyomandibular suspensorium was converted into an ear ossicle in the evolutionary lines that led to tetrapods. Embryos of amphibia and sauropsida do develop a muscle which for a while has the relations of a **levator hyoideus,** taking origin from the skull and extending through the upper part of the hyoid segment, but then it transfers its inserting end to a projection of the lower jaw, posterior to the jaw joint. It thus becomes a **depressor mandibulae,** or mouth opener (Fig. 16–13). (Fish mouths are opened by the contraction of ventral throat muscles which are derived from trunk myotomes.) Sauropsida do retain scraps of C_2d muscle in association with the hyoid arch itself,

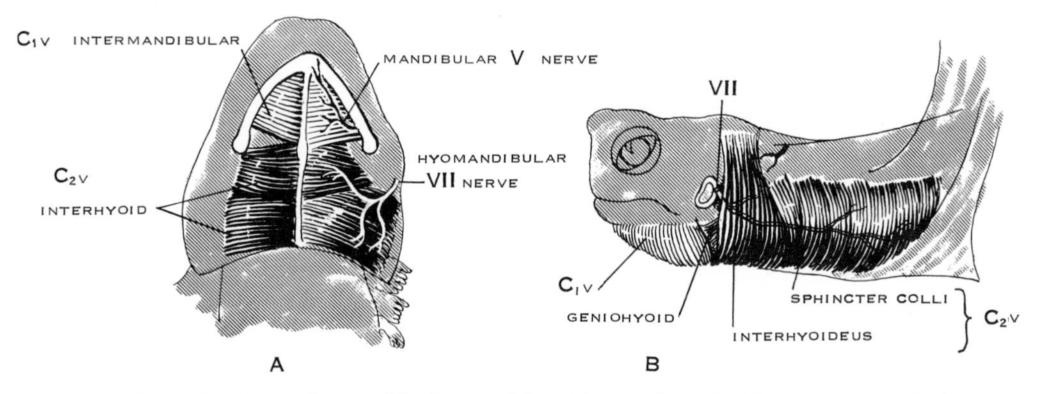

Fig. 16–15. Ventral mandibular and hyoid muscles. A. Necturus, ventral view. B. Turtle.

(After Ruge, 1897, and W. Lubosch, 1933.)

but they are relegated to the middle ear apparatus, and have no importance.

Both C_2d and C_2v of fishes form a number of sets of small short muscles that run across the successive joints between the separate elements in the hyoid arch chain. The equivalents of these can also be found in relation to the tongue skeleton of amphibia and sauropsida. A more massive development from C_2v of the two sides tends to form a transverse **interhyoideus** sheet (Fig. 16–15 A), like the intermandibular sheet of the first pharynx segment. This is subject to countless modifications and subdivisions in different species of fishes and tetrapods. The right and left masses may not join but may take an oblique direction anteriorly, so as to insert on the lower jaws or the intermandibular muscles of C_1v, serving to pull the hyoideum and the tongue forward. Other subdivisions of C_2v tie together and manipulate the branchiostegal rays in breathing.

In tetrapods, with reduction of the hyoideum, the interhyoideus sheet may remain as a sort of sphincter band across the ventral surface of the neck. In sauropsida, the neck usually becomes quite long, and the growth of the interhyoideus muscle more than keeps pace with it. Spreading far posteriorly, it also grows up dorsally on each side until it completes a ring of subcutaneous muscle around the long neck, called **sphincter colli** (Fig. 16–15 B). Sometimes it divides into anterior and posterior divisions, and in snakes it achieves intimate and specialized relations with the skin muscles that move the scales. Wherever it spreads, it carries along its original innervation, the motor division of the facial nerve VII. The same nerve supply goes to all the other muscles derived from the hyoid segment, C_2d, or C_2v.

Where intermandibular and interhyoid sheets are formed across the ventral side of the head, respectively from C_1v and C_2v, they may fuse into one sheet, the anterior part of which is served by the trigeminal nerve, the posterior by the facial. Or the trigeminal part may completely replace the facialis part, or vice versa. Study of embryonic origins and nerve supplies can answer the puzzling questions of muscle classification produced in such an area [6].

V. THE NERVES

The **trigeminal V** and **facial VII** nerves are associated respectively with the mandibular and hyoid segments, and this relationship is revealed at the pharyngula stage when their motor neurons grow out from the hindbrain and down toward their own muscle plates (Fig. 5–11). Since the pharynx wall is technically a part of the alimentary tract, and since this is hypomere mesoderm (Chapter 5, page 82), such motor neurons are classed as **visceral motor,** in contrast to others, for instance the ones in the spinal nerves, which reach out to epimeric muscles and are **somatic motor.** The distinction between visceral and somatic motor neurons is not only apparent in the periphery, it is revealed within the central nervous system, for the cells from which these neurons grow are located in different regions of the gray substance.

But nerves V and VII include much more than visceral motor neurons. Each of them becomes associated with ganglionic masses, developed from neural crest cells or (in the case of the lateral line components) from placodes. These send branches radiating out over the face and cheeks, some of which have already been mentioned as "nerves of passage" in the orbit (Fig. 14–13). Not only do the sensory branches pass well beyond the proper confines of the mandibular and hyoid segments, those of V and VII tend to travel in parallel bundles or to anastomose. Also, particularly in adult fishes, the ganglia of V and VII may fuse. Thus, the separation of the pre-otic mixed cranial nerves was accomplished only after a period of confusion, resolved finally by precise embryological and neurological studies of their functional components.

A. The Functional Components

Parts of the body which are derived from the ectoderm and the mesodermal somites, for instance the skeletal muscles of the trunk or the skin in general, are by definition **somatic** structures. The parts of the brain and spinal cord that send motor neurons to these, and receive sensory stimuli directly from them, are by association called somatic centers. The organs and tissues which are derived from the endoderm and its associated hypomeric mesoderm are defined as **visceral.** Their neurons arise or end in special visceral areas of the central nervous system.

Within the brain, the **somatic sensory areas** lie high in the dorsal part of the hindbrain walls, and in the roof of the midbrain and forebrain. The **somatic motor areas** lie close to the midline in the floor of hindbrain and midbrain. **Visceral sensory areas** lie just ventral to the somatic sensory areas, and the **visceral motor areas** lie between the visceral sensory and somatic motor areas (Fig. 9–5).

Each nerve consists of hundreds or thousands of axons. In properly prepared serial sections these can be traced both to their endings in particular brain areas and to their peripheral connections. The evidence thus gained as to the functional components present in each nerve may be tested by physiological experiments in the living condition.

In the mixed cranial nerves it is useful to distinguish not only between somatic and visceral sensory neurons, but also between general and special categories of each of these. The dendritic zones of **special somatic sensory components** are stimulated by special sensory cells in multicellular sense organs such as the nose, ear, eye, and the neuromasts of the lateral line. **General somatic sensory components** fray out to twigs with free dendritic-zone endings in the skin and other somatic structures. **Special visceral sensory neurons** are associated peripherally with **taste buds,** which are little sense organs somewhat resembling neuromasts but carrying cells that are sensitive to chemical stimuli. **General visceral sensory neurons** have free dendritic terminals in the mucous membrane of the visceral tract. Each of these types of neurons seeks out its own localized terminal area in the brain.

The special visceral sensory category is anomalous in fishes, for taste buds are often found widely scattered over the skin of the head and even of the trunk, in territory which otherwise fully satisfies the definition of a somatic area. In other smaller details too, the classification of components lacks consistency, but the broad usefulness of the concept of functional components is not thereby affected.

B. Trigeminal Nerve V, and Its Four Branches

This was called the "triplet nerve" in human anatomy long before there was much knowledge about the embryonic development or the comparative anatomy of vertebrates. Its upper branch, V_1, is called the **ophthalmic nerve,** because, even in the tightly circumscribed orbit of the human skull, it is a nerve of passage across the eyeball. Functionally it has nothing to do with the eye, but it sends general somatic sensory twigs to the skin of the forehead. The middle branch, V_2, is called the **maxillary nerve** since it runs along the upper jaw, giving general somatic sensory branches to the face and snout. The lower branch, V_3, is the **mandibular nerve.** It sprays out branches to all the C_1d and C_1v muscles, carrying visceral motor and proprioceptive sensory axons to them (proprioceptive sense is information on posture, movement, tension, etc., derived from inside muscles and tendons); V_3 also sends general somatic sensory components to the skin of the lower jaw and chin region.

The terms of human anatomy notwithstanding, morphologists long ago demonstrated that the vertebrate trigeminal nerve is not a triplet; it has *four* main branches (Fig. 16–16). The evidence from embryology and comparative anatomy shows that V_1 is a fusion of a **deep ophthalmic nerve** (the nasociliary, PNA) and a **superficial ophthalmic nerve** (the supraorbital, PNA). In higher vertebrates these two look like branches of the same nerve, but in carefully investigated species it is discovered that they arise from separate ganglia. In crossing the orbit, the former invariably passes *ventral* to the superior rectus and superior oblique muscles of the eyeball, while the latter passes *dorsal* to them (Fig. 14–13). The deep ophthalmic nerve distributes farther out on the snout. It is sometimes consid-

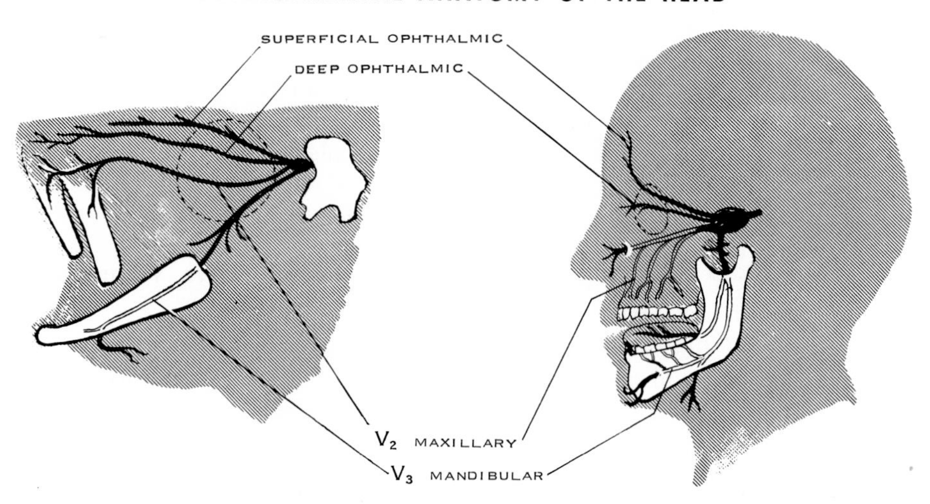

Fig. 16–16. The four branches of the trigeminal nerve in codfish and man.

ered to be the nerve of a lost premandibular segment of the head, only secondarily attached to the trigeminal.

The fibers of proprioceptive sense that pass to the mandibular-segment muscles through the branches of the mandibular nerve are classed with the exteroceptive skin senses in the general somatic sensory category, though in this case the rule seems arbitrary, since the muscles are of visceral origin. These important "mouth-sense" fibers are found constantly in all vertebrates except the jawless cyclostomes, and are unique among sensory fibers because their somata do not lie on a ganglion outside the central nervous system. Instead they lie in a strip in the roof of the midbrain, constituting the *mesencephalic root* of the trigeminal nerve.

The mandibular nerve makes contact with the mandibular muscle plates when they are just beginning to differentiate and subdivide, and this contact is never broken. The neurons lengthen and accompany their own muscle fibers as the latter spread toward their various origins and insertions. There is no doubt that both man and the codfish have mandibular nerves (Fig. 16–16). But just as the resulting subdivisions of the C_1d muscle mass cannot be individually homologized in the two species, so also it is no good trying to compare the branches of V_3 between them.

In general, the mandibular nerve is the only one of the four main branches of the trigeminal which carries visceral components and distributes within the confines of the mandibular segment. However, various exceptions occur. In some bony fishes, the C_1d muscles spread along the palatine arch under the orbit, and it is possible then for visceral motor fibers to reach them conveniently through the maxillary nerve. The addition of lacrimal glands and salivary glands to the orbit or face of amniotes requires the sending of visceral motor fibers to them through ophthalmic, maxillary and mandibular nerves, but these components are part of the autonomic system (cf. Chapter 30) and are added to the peripheral branches in somewhat casual ways without running through the trigeminal roots directly from the brain.

It may be noted that in the general description of the trigeminal there has not so far been any mention of visceral sensory components, though one might think the mucous membrane of the anterior part of the mouth might easily be supplied through the maxillary and mandibular branches. Instead, in fishes, this territory is supplied by the facial nerve, and the only visceral sensory components carried by the trigeminal nerve are fibers for the taste sense. In some species, however, taste buds may occur all over the skin of the face and jaws, and in these, special visceral sensory components may appear in almost any branch of V or VII.

In amniotes, by contrast, the trigeminus captures some of the former VII territory in the anterior part of the mouth (Fig. 16–16). Palatine processes grow medially from the territory of the maxillary nerve and form a secondary palate, and the mucous membrane of this and the augmented nasal passage is then partly supplied through the maxillary nerve. In the floor of the mouth, when a new sort of mobile tongue is developed partly in territory of the mandibular nerve, this nerve acquires a new lingual branch, which contains visceral sensory components of its own.

The branch of the mandibular nerve which reaches toward the chin regularly parallels the mandibular cartilage in its course, in every gnathostome vertebrate. In all the bone-forming gnathostomes except the anuran amphibia, this nerve gets encased in the same membrane bones that ensheath the mandibular cartilage and form the secondary lower jaw. There thus arises the curious spectacle of a principal V_3 branch passing into the lower jaw from its medial side through a foramen just anterior to the jaw joint, coursing down its length through a bony tunnel in the company of the dwindled remnant of the mandibular cartilage, and finally coming out through an external foramen near its tip, in a spray of branches that distribute to the skin in the region of the chin (Fig. 16–24).

C. Facial Nerve VII, and Its Dual Nature

In the anamniotes, the VII nerve, like V, develops two ganglia (Fig. 16–17). One comes from the pre-otic dorsolateral placode and serves the lateral-line system of the head (Fig. 9–7), a *somatic* sense. Rather wishfully some anatomists have considered this ganglion and its three peripheral branches to be a separate cranial nerve ("lateralis anterior"), but it is not found anatomically separate from the VII nerve in any adult living vertebrate. The other VII ganglion lies somewhat more ventromedially and is derived partly from neural crest cells and partly from the epibranchial placode of the hyoid segment. It produces *visceral* sensory components. Only the second of these two ganglia is formed in the amniotes.

To the special somatic and visceral sensory components of the two VII ganglia are added visceral motor components arising in cells of the appropriate zone of gray substance in the hindbrain and emerging near the ganglion as a separate motor root of VII.

By the accident of embryonic fusion of the two ganglia, the VII nerve of anamniotes thus acquires two utterly unrelated sets of components, and branches: *somatic* ones for the lateral line system of the head, and *visceral* ones for the supply of the second or hyoid segment of the pharynx wall. In Figures 16–17 and 16–18 A, the somatic components are shown in dash lines, the visceral components in solid black.

1. Visceral Components. In the VII nerve of some fishes, a triplet-pattern of visceral branches is found, the like of which is repeated in each of the post-otic segments also. This generalized pattern, which will be more extensively illustrated in Chapter 17, consists of (a) a **pharynx-roof branch** visceral sensory, (b) a **pretrematic branch,** visceral sensory, and (c) a **post-trematic branch,** both visceral sensory and visceral motor. The *trema* (Gr., hole) refers to the pharyngeal cleft or pouch which lies anterior to the pharynx segment served by the cranial nerve in question.

The three branches of the VII nerve are lettered on the diagram of the dogfish, Figure 16–17. They are (A) a **palatine branch** which projects forward to supply mucous membrane in the roof of the mouth, (B) a pretrematic or rather **prespiracular branch** which serves the mucous membrane in the anterior wall of the spiracle, and (C) a **hyomandibular branch** which follows down the full length of the hyomandibular cartilage and the chain of elements in the hyoideum. This last branch supplies visceral motor fibers to all the C_2d and C_2v muscles, and visceral sensory fibers to the mucous membrane of the posterior wall of the spiracle or pouch. It also sends an internal mandibular branch to pick up visceral sense from the floor of the mouth. This latter branch has enduring relationships which will be referred to again on page 296; they should be carefully noted at this point.

If the spiracle or hyomandibular pouch is suppressed in the early embryo, as in the codfish and

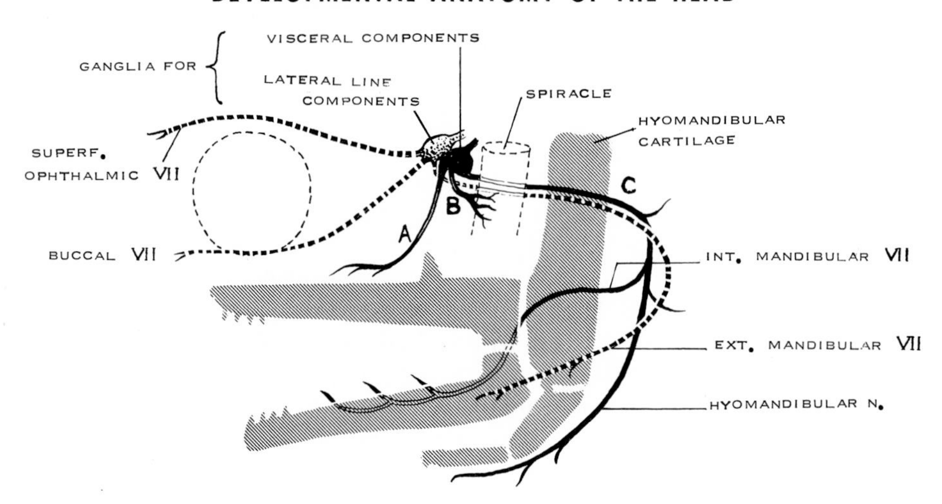

Fig. 16–17. Diagram of the relations of the dogfish facial nerve.

most bony fishes (Fig. 16–18), the pretrematic branch of VII is not separately distinguishable from the palatine branch.

In many teleostomes, the hyomandibular branch of VII borrows general somatic sensory components (which it does not produce from its own ganglia) by way of a short commissure from the trigeminal ganglionic mass, and these are fanned out to the skin over the operculum and branchiostegal membrane.

The special visceral sensory components of taste are distributed in almost any of the branches of the V or VII nerves in one species or another, depending on the distribution of the taste buds themselves. Many teleosts have a special **accessory lateralis nerve,** which leaves the VII ganglion, pierces the skull to the top of the head, and turns posteriorly along the trunk, making a great variety of connections with other nerves it meets on the way (Fig. 16–18, codfish). It supplies chiefly taste buds in the skin.

In tetrapods, the triplet pattern of the VII nerve is more or less disrupted. No pretrematic branch can be distinguished. The palatine nerves of the two sides, which in bony fishes run forward just inside the mucous membrane between the midline parasphenoid bone and the inner arcades of the upper jaw, become reduced and obscured. This is because the pterygoid and palatine bones, in spreading medially to incorporate themselves in the braincase or to form a secondary palate, tend to bury the nerves in bony canals. Simultaneously, the palatine nerves lose part of their ancient territory to the maxillary branches of V, which move into the roof of the mouth and the nasal passages along with the new palatine processes and nasal conchae (Fig. 16–16, man).

The post-trematic part of the VII nerve of amphibia and sauropsida may be expected to repeat the relationship with the columellar ear ossicle (Figs. 16–7, 16–12) that it formerly had with the hyomandibular suspensorium (Figs. 16-6, 16–17), and with very few exceptions it does so. Emerging from the skull just anterior to the otic capsule, it bends posteriorly through a region which is now hemmed in laterally by the quadrate bone (i.e., through the cranio-quadrate passage (cf. page 287), and crosses the columella almost invariably on its dorsal side, before turning ventrad and dividing into the motor branches which supply the C_2d and C_2v muscles. It also gives off at this point a sensory branch whose destination is the floor of the mouth.

This last branch has already been called the **internal mandibular nerve** VII (Figs. 16–6, 16–7, 16–12, 16–17; and see page 295). In fishes it runs parallel but medial to the mandibular V nerve (or that portion of it which is following the mandibular cartilage or buried in the secondary bony jaw). Along this course it gives off visceral

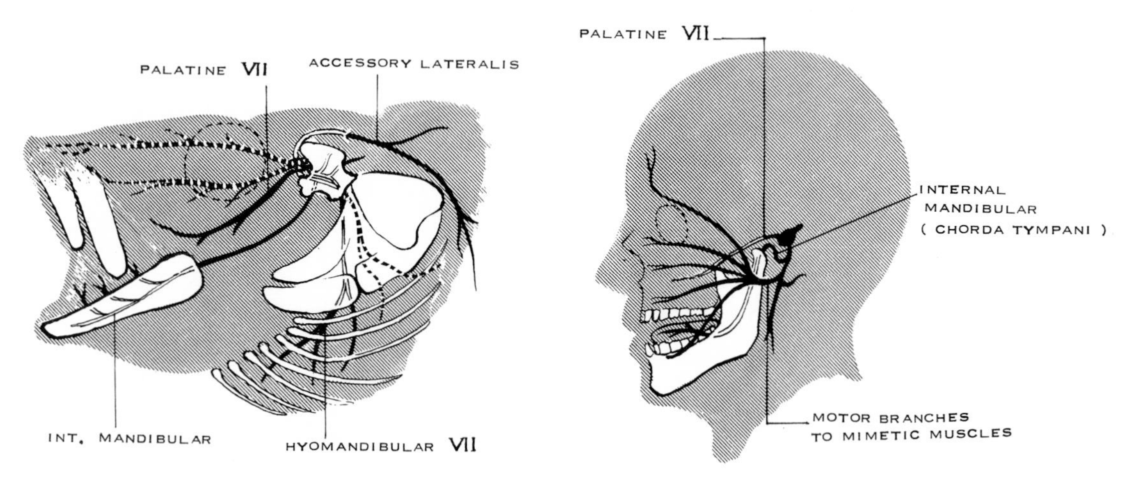

Fig. 16–18. Territory of the facial nerve in codfish and man.

sensory branches to the mucous membrane of the entire floor of the mouth. However, in the amniotes the middle ear pushes out toward the skin just below this nerve. In the dissection of these animals therefore, the nerve is found crossing dorsal to the eardrum or tympanic membrane. For this reason, in human anatomy it is called the **chorda tympani** (Fig. 16–18). In frogs, because the middle ear is formed from a more dorsal part of the hyomandibular pouch, the nerve crosses in its floor, not its roof. The chorda tympani nerve of amniotes, in reaching toward the mucous membrane of the mouth, may find that a lingual branch from the mandibular of V has usurped much of its ancient territory (cf. page 296). The two usually join and distribute together toward the tongue.

The main motor branch of the post-trematic VII nerve no longer follows the hyoideum in adult tetrapods as it did in the bony fishes. Partly this is because the skeleton of the hyoid arch is consolidated ventrally in the service of a new sort of tongue, with a considerable reduction in the intrinsic hyoid musculature. A more important factor in adult long-necked sauropsida is the extensive posterior migration of one of the muscles in its group, the sphincter colli (Fig. 16–15 B). Following this, the VII nerve spreads far down the neck, overlapping in its lengthwise course certain zones occupied by other more transversely distributed post-otic cranial and spinal nerves, and making plexus networks with them. In these animals, the facialis has practically no distribution on the face at all.

2. *Somatic Components.* The three lateral-line nerves given off from the dorsolateral VII ganglion have already been diagrammed (Fig. 15-2, and Figs. 16–17, 16–18). The **superficial ophthalmic VII** and the **buccal VII** nerves closely parallel the **superficial ophthalmic V** and **maxillary V** nerves (Fig. 16–16), and in fishes fuse with them so as to be indistinguishable in dissection. The fusion of buccal and maxillary nerves is sometimes renamed the *infraorbital trunk.* One suspects that the arrangement of tissues in the early embryonic head produced a few especially easy peripheral paths for the first outgrowing pathfinder nerve fibers to select, and that both sets of sensory neurons followed leaders which had picked the same path for the same reason (Chapter 4, page 58). The fusion of the parallel nerves in some species but their failure to fuse in others perhaps indicates differences in the aggressiveness of the coating activity of local mesenchyme cells (Chapter 8, page 138), that bind neurons up into nerves.

The third of the principal lateral line branches from the somatic ganglion of the VII nerve accompanies the post-trematic branch of the visceral part of nerve VII, spraying out twigs to neuromasts on cheek and operculum and finally turning anteriorly along the line of the jaw.

These, or very similar, lateral line nerves arise from the same pre-otic placode in embryonic amphibia, take paths parallel to the same general-sensory nerves and persist throughout larval life. At the same time of metamorphosis the lateral line branches, together with their ganglia and their associated neuromasts, nearly or completely disappear. No such regression occurs in the general-sensory components.

None of the lateral-line apparatus is found at any stage in any amniote.

VI. SPECIAL MAMMALIAN DEVELOPMENTS

The anatomical contrasts between the modern mammals and the surviving reptiles are as sharp in the pre-otic pharynx-segment region as in any part of the body. There are important new developments in each of the four districts considered in this chapter: upper and lower mandibular, and upper and lower hyoid. Mammals have completely redesigned the jaw joint, the ear ossicle system and the tongue, with numerous incidental adjustments in the skull, the walls of the middle ear, the palate and the hyoid musculature.

A. Developments in Upper Mandibular Segment

In the non-mammalian gnathostomes, the palatoquadrate cartilage exists as a *single element* in the upper mandibular segment from the early post-pharyngula stage on. In mammals, it is represented by *two separate pieces,* each of which is replaced by bone and forms a characteristically mammalian element.

One piece, called the **ala temporalis,** has the relationship ordinarily seen in the **ascending process** of the palatoquadrate; i.e., it reaches dorsally toward the sidewall of the chondrocranium between the otic capsule and the orbital cartilage (Fig. 16–19; compare with Fig. 16–7). It is later replaced point for point by an **alisphenoid bone,** and occupies the sidewall of the braincase between the periotic and the orbitosphenoid bones (Figs. 12–9, 16–22). This spot is preformed in cartilage in the chondrocrania of lower animals, and is replaced by the **pleurosphenoid bone:** in mammals the area that might have formed a pleurosphenoid remains membranous. It is as though the mammals, compensating for an unfortunate hereditary defect in

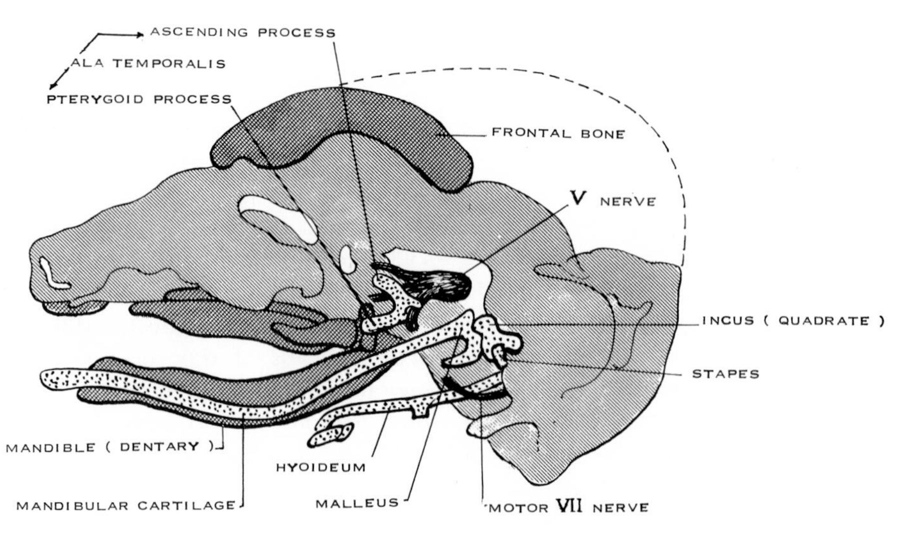

Fig. 16–19. Skull of a 40-millimeter cow fetus.
(After E. Faucett, 1918.)

the skull at this point, have sacrificed part of their upper jaw to plug the gap.

The other piece clearly behaves like a little quadrate. It has a *body* which makes a joint with the mandibular cartilage, and an *otic process* which reaches toward the otic capsule of the skull. At an early fetal period its principal mammalian idiosyncrasy appears in a sudden surprising loss of growth momentum. Merely maintaining itself, and eventually becoming replaced by bone while the rest of the body is multiplying its size enormously, the "quadrate" becomes relatively tiny and survives as the **incus.** How it becomes an ear ossicle will be explained shortly.

B. Developments in Lower Mandibular Segment

Shortly after the pharyngula stage, a mammalian embryo shows a mandibular cartilage in the lower jaw region, quite like that of any other tetrapod, articulating as usual with what looks like a normal quadrate. Only during the mid-fetal period does development take a new direction, but then the lower jaw begins to show three new and uniquely mammalian features:

1. The finished lower jaw consists of only a single membrane bone. The **dentary** (marked 1 in Fig. 16–20) has taken over all the functions of the entire field. It provides support for all the teeth of the lower set. It bears the facet for a new jaw joint. It projects behind that joint for the attachment of jaw-opening muscles, and sends a coronoid process upward to meet the tendons of the jaw-closing muscles anterior to the joint. Lastly it meets its antimere in the midline at the tip of the chin. In recognition of its new eminence, the dentary of mammals is renamed the **mandible** (Fig. 16–22).

2. The *mandibular cartilage* fails to grow commensurate with the rest of the jaw, and splits into proximal and distal parts (Fig. 16–19). The vestige of the distal part lies inside the shaft of the mandible, as in practically all the other gnathostomes, along with the accompanying branch of the mandibular V nerve (cf. dash-line, Fig. 16–22 for cartilage, Fig. 16–24 for nerve). In view of the fact that this nerve supplies the teeth from below, during its passage through the interior of the mandible, and because the teeth fit into sockets called alveoli, this V_3 branch is called the **inferior alveolar nerve** in human anatomy (Fig. 16–24).

The proximal part of the cartilage, which should have become the **articular** bone (Fig. 16–20 A, marked 2) and produced the definitive jaw joint in association with the quadrate, remains tiny and drifts away from the jaw altogether, becoming an ear ossicle called the **malleus** (Fig. 16–19; and marked 2 in Fig. 16–20). Nevertheless, it does produce and maintain a small-scale model of the old jaw joint in association with the quadrate (now the incus) (Fig. 16–20, marked 3).

3. The *angular* bone (Fig. 16–20 A, marked 8), which forms in membrane posterior to the jaw joint and against the mandibular cartilage in most lower vertebrates, fails to appear in the lower jaw of mammals. However, a plausible homolog of it appears just posterior to its normal location, in the wall of the middle ear. This element, called the **tympanic bone** (Fig. 16–20, marked 8), arises as a curved spicule back of the mandible and spreads to a nearly closed ring in relation to the developing tympanum in all mammals. In most species it continues to spread around the middle ear until it forms a shell of bone for the whole cavity (Fig. 16–22), with passages left for the external auditory meatus and the auditory tube.

C. Mammalian Jaw Suspension

In all bony fishes, amphibia, and sauropsida, the jaw joint is invariably between the articular and the quadrate bones (marked 2 and 3 in Fig. 16–20 A and B). In the sauropsida, the quadrate, whether movable or not, lies close below the squamosal bone of the braincase (marked 5). As already mentioned, the articular and quadrate (now malleus and incus, marked 2 and 3) drift away from the jaw apparatus in mammals. At the same time the mandible moves proximally, and, quite naturally, it comes into contact with the squamosal (Fig. 16–20 C,

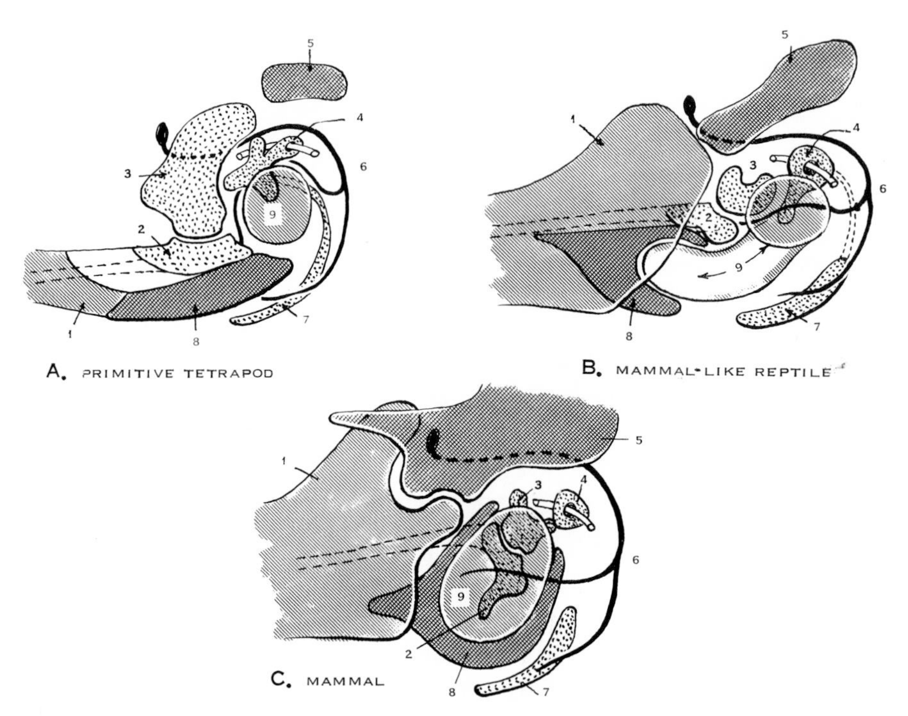

Fig. 16–20. Evolution of mammalian inner ear bones and jaw joint.

1. Dentary ⟶ mandible.
2. Articular ⟶ malleus.
3. Quadrate ⟶ incus.
4. Columella ⟶ stapes.
5. Squamosal.
6. VII nerve giving off internal mandibular branch (chorda tympani).
7. Hyoideum.
8. Angular ⟶ tympanic bone.
9. Tympanic membrane.

(After A. Portmann, Einführung in die Vergleichende Morphologie der Wirbeltiere, 1948, by permission of Benno Schwabe & Co.)

marked 1 and 5), which provides the matching upper facet for a new jaw joint.

The history of the primordial jaw apparatus shows three main trends. (a) In some of the ancient fishes and modern elasmobranchs (Fig. 16–6), the palatoquadrate and mandibular cartilages themselves enlarge and serve independently as upper and lower jaws. (b) In the bony fishes (Fig. 16–8) and in the amphibia and sauropsida (Fig. 16–9), whether or not the hyoid arch is used as a suspensorium, the primary jaws are augmented by a number of ensheathing membrane bones, retaining their own prominence only in the region of the jaw joint. (c) In the mammals (Fig. 16–22), the secondary jaws of membrane bone take over completely, while the ancestral jaw joint (between malleus and incus) is hung from a shelf in the middle ear like a miniature museum piece.

A troublesome question faced by earlier anatomists was how the animals which made the evolutionary transition from reptiles to mammals could have lived through the period during which their jaw joint was being disengaged from their feeding apparatus and transferred to the middle ear. Such an evolution must take thousands of generations to complete itself. Obviously the new joint between dentary and squamosal bones must have been prepared in advance, or the animals would have been crippled and their genetic line would have been extinguished. Yet how could the middle stage, neither good reptile nor good mammal, have had a jaw joint more efficient than the reptile? And if it had been the least bit awkward, where was the selective advantage that could have brought it evolutionary success in competition with its conservative reptilian contemporaries? Such evolutionary dilemmas are among the reasons why some biologists have proposed that quick bold transformations must take place in animal heredity, in ways quite different from the plodding accumulation of the tiny mutations that one usually studies in genetics laboratories.

However, the Permian rocks of South Africa have yielded thousands of fossils of transitional reptiles or pro-mammals from which the answer to this particular question can now be drawn [7]. A number of experimental transformations of various parts of the head seem to have been going on in different lineages of these animals, involving not only the suppression and backward transfer of the articular and quadrate bones, but also the lengthening of snout and jaw. The C_1d muscles were being strengthened so that they overflowed onto the top of the skull (i.e., over the squamosal bone) and farther out along the lower jaw (over the dentary). The whole head was changing from the squat lines of a lizard to the elongated form of a dog. All stages in the transformation of the jaw joint are present in different species of these fossils, including:

1. Articular jointed to quadrate (Fig. 16–20 A);
2. Dentary and articular jointed to squamosal and quadrate (Fig. 16–20 B);
3. Dentary to squamosal (Fig. 16–20 C and Fig. 16–22).

As the articular and quadrate bones diminished in size and importance, they could be loosened and finally dropped off the back, to be absorbed into the expanding middle ear. The transitional animals were powerful and probably aggressive types, to judge from their shapes, and any slight awkwardness of the jaw joint structure was undoubtedly balanced out by the speed and power of the elongated snapping jaws themselves.

Incidentally, some of these mammal-like reptiles showed a notched angular bone at the posterior end of the lower jaw, as though it may have supported a tympanic membrane before it was detached as a true mammalian tympanic bone (Fig. 16–20 B, marked 8).

D. Mammalian Ear Ossicles

All mammals show the three ear ossicles, **malleus, incus,** and **stapes,** jointed to each other and stretching from the tympanic membrane across the middle-ear space to the fenestra vestibuli. No other vertebrates have such a chain. In most of the tetrapods the single **columella** completes the bridge between eardrum and fenestra (Figs. 16–4 and 16–20 B). Since the columella shows embryonic origin in two, three, or more parts in various species, it was long ago suggested that the three mammalian ossicles were derived from different parts of the reptilian columella. Among the hypotheses which were rivals to this a hundred years ago, there was one which was advanced almost without supporting evidence, but which has since been substantiated by a large body of fact from embryology, from paleontology, and from the study of anatomical relationships (Fig. 16–20). There is no longer any doubt that this theory is correct, namely that the malleus and incus are derived respectively from the mandibular and the palatoquadrate cartilages of the mandibular segment. The stapes seems to be a vestige of the inner end of the reptilian columella.

(The names malleus, incus, and stapes, meaning respectively the hammer, anvil, and stirrup, were assigned to the ossicles of the human middle ear by ancient anatomists, and are justified more by tradition than actual resemblance.)

The **malleus** has a "head" and two processes (Fig. 16–21). The head lies high in the dorsal part of the tympanic cavity, in the narrow space between the dorsal rim of the eardrum and the otic capsule, and bears a posteriorly facing joint surface where it meets the incus. One of the processes runs anteriorly, and connects the head with the rest of the mandibular cartilage until midfetal life, when it is pinched off (compare Figs. 16–9 and 16–21). The other process spreads ventrad over the inner surface of the eardrum, to which it becomes fastened by ligament.

The **incus** has a "body" and two processes also. The body bears the joint with the malleus. One of the processes projects posteriorly and is tied by ligament to the overhanging ridge—crista parotica—of the ear capsule. It (or its predecessor the quadrate bone or palatoquadrate cartilage) clearly has had this otic-process relationship with the ear capsule in *all gnathostome vertebrates* (compare Figs. 16–5, 16–7, 16–9, with Fig. 16-21). The other process, called the long leg, projects downward and inward, ending in a joint with the outer end of the stapes. On the reasonable assumption that the stapes is a surviving vestige of the ancient hyomandibular suspensorium of the fishes, this joint can be compared with a hyostylic suspension of the quadrate. Similar connections with the quadrate bone are formed by the columella in many anuran and sauropsidan species.

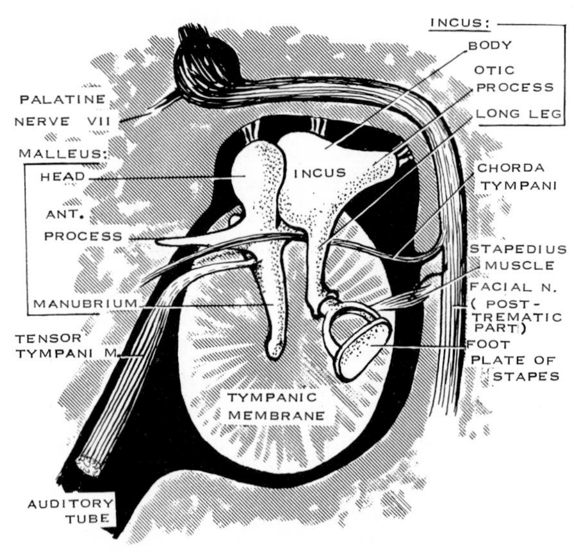

Fig. 16–21. Human middle ear relationships. Right side, looking outward across tympanic cavity toward inner surface of tympanic membrane.

The mammalian **stapes** is a tiny short element, practically confined to the fenestra ovalis in which it has an expanded footplate (Fig. 16-21) but forming a joint with the incus at its outer end. With few exceptions it contains a tiny perforation, the pathway of an embryonic artery which dries up and disappears during development, because its territory is usurped by other arteries (Fig. 16–20). In the few mammalian species (bats, mice) in which this **stapedial artery** (orbital artery of lower vertebrates) persists to the adult stage, it usually still pierces the stapes, just as it always runs through its precartilaginous anlage.

Like the columella of other tetrapods, the stapes is formed in the "medial prong" of the upper end of the embryonic hyoid arch, but unlike the columella it never achieves a meeting with the eardrum. Obviously, the outer half or two-thirds of the ancestral columella has disappeared. In the middle ears of various species of mammals, small isolated pieces of cartilage have been discovered which may be traces of the lost part, but the transformation of the columella to the mammalian stapes is an evolutionary step whose history has otherwise been erased.

Malleus, incus, and stapes are dorsal and anterior to the tympanic cavity when they first form, but as the cavity expands it envelops them so that they may hang in it on little mesenteries. In most human beings the two joints in the chain of three ossicles are movable, and so are the attachments to the overhanging ear capsule and the tympanic bone. In other mammals, however, it is not uncommon to find the joints semirigid or even destroyed by fusion of the ossicles with each other. This may be an improvement with respect to faithful reproduction of the eardrum vibrations in the perilymph cistern through the fenestra vestibuli. However, the anterior process of the malleus also sometimes fuses with the tympanic bone, and cases are known of the fusion of the stapedial footplate with the rim of the fenestra ovalis, which seems less efficient for auditory purposes.

E. Other Hyoid Segment Developments

The stapes develops in the "medial prong" of the embryonic upper hyoid arch. The "lateral prong" is also discernible in the mammalian embryo, though it does not always pass beyond the mesenchymatous or ligamentous stage. As expected, it reaches up to the crista parotica of the ear capsule. Part of it, called the **tympanohyal** element, becomes enveloped in the expanding skull, and part projects downward from this as either a firmly planted spine called the **styloid process** (Fig. 16–24) or a free little rod called the **stylohyal** (Fig. 16–22). The connection between the styloid process or stylohyal and the lower hyoideum is sometimes formed by cartilage or bone, but is more commonly represented by a degenerate **stylohyoid ligament.**

The lower part of the hyoid skeleton is involved in the tongue, and will be described with that organ in the next chapter.

F. Some Consequent Relationships

The reorganization of jaws and middle ear brings about a number of other interesting peculiarities of the mammalian head.

1. When the malleus is separated from the lower jaw and enclosed within the tympanic cavity, a small slip of the C_1d muscle is usually entrapped with it. In the adult it is found as a tiny **tensor tympani muscle,** whose origin is on the ear capsule and insertion on the malleus (Fig. 16–21). In contraction it pulls the malleus inward and indirectly tightens the eardrum. As a consequence of its embryonic origin it is served by a twig from the mandibular branch of the trigeminal nerve.

2. The cranioquadrate passage (Fig. 16–12) reappears temporarily in the mammalian embryo as the space between the quadrate (i.e., incus) and the otic capsule. As in amphibia and sauropsida it contains the head vein, the stapedial artery, and the emerging, backward-projecting stem of the post-trematic VII nerve. As mentioned, after leaving its mark on the stapes the artery usually dries up and disappears. In placental mammals the venous blood is diverted to the interior of the skull, reappearing posterior to the ear through the jugular vein. The nerve is later more or less buried in the expanding bone of the otic capsule so that it acquires a characteristically mammalian curved canal and a secondary foramen of exit posterior to the middle ear.

This new condition obscures the original preotic nature of the facial nerve, particularly since the only other important division of VII, the palatine nerve, has also been hidden in bone over much of its course. The chorda tympani, whose homolog in fishes is given off on the face, quite close to the skin, is here given off from the post-trematic branch inside its new bony canal (compare Figs. 16–6, 16–7, 16–20, 16–21). Nevertheless, swamped though they may be in confusing details, the main branches of VII can be sought out and found to have preserved the same fundamental relationships to the ear capsule and the hyomandibular pouch derivatives in mammals as in fishes.

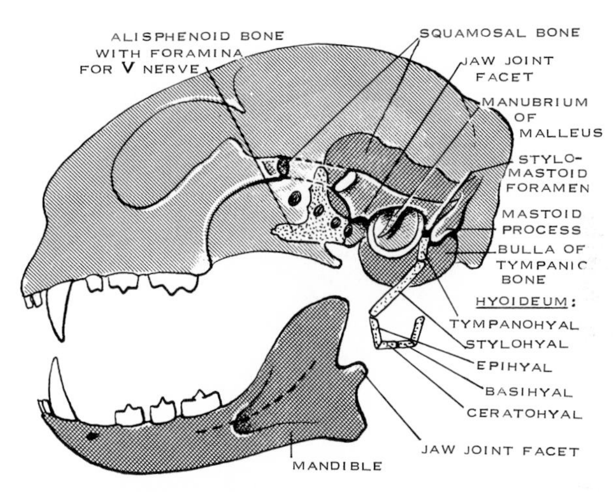

Fig. 16–22. Skeletal derivatives of mandibular and hyoid segments in an adult cat. Incus and stapes are concealed inside the tympanic bulla.

3. In sauropsida and amphibia, the C_2d muscle is mostly converted into a depressor mandibulae by transfer of its tendon of insertion to the posterior end of the lower jaw. This arrangement however is destroyed in mammals by the transfer of the whole posterior end of the jaw itself (articular and angular bones) to the middle ear, as the malleus and tympanic bones. One scrap of this muscle nevertheless remains, running from a nearby point on the skull to an insertion on the stapes. It is called the **stapedius** muscle, and true to its derivation, it receives a motor twig from the post-trematic VII nerve (Fig. 16–21).

4. The *post-trematic motor nerve of the facial VII,* in consequence of being partly buried in new bone by the expanding skull, finally emerges through a new foramen between two characteristically mammalian skull structures: the styloid process ("lateral prong" of the upper hyoid skeleton, fused with the skull), and the mastoid process (a backward projection of the crista parotica of the otic capsule bone). The foramen, not unnaturally, is called **stylomastoid** (Fig. 16-22). From this point, the nerve sends out a great fan of branches over the face, just under the skin (Fig. 16–18).

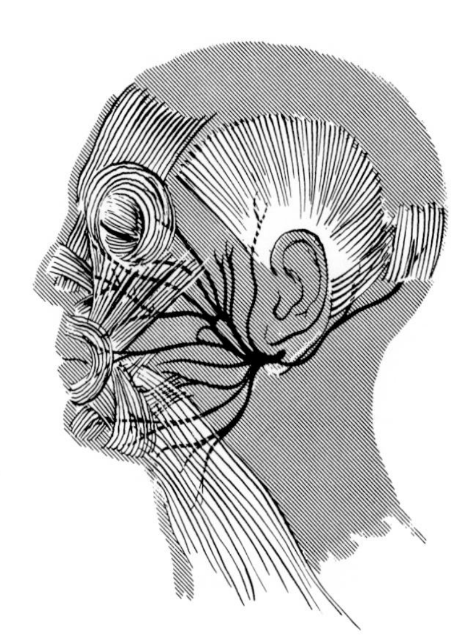

Fig. 16–23. Mimetic muscles and their VII nerve supply in man.

The reason for this extraordinary distribution of motor VII fibers on the face, unlike anything found in other vertebrates, is that the great majority of the C_2v muscle cells have indeed escaped from the normal hyoid-segment territory. Instead of passing down the neck to form the sort of sphincter colli which is common in sauropsida, most of them have spread out anteriorly in superficial sheets, forming muscles of facial expression, the **mimetic muscles** (Fig. 16-23). These consist of striated fibers that arrange themselves in sphincters around the openings of nostrils, eyes, ears, and mouth, strips which radiate from the sphincters, and other general sheets, fastening themselves to each other and to the dermis layer of the skin. They form a greatly variable collection of muscles for moving the lips, cheeks, vibrissae, eyebrows, eyelids, nostrils, external ears, etc. In man and some other species they even spread down the neck and over the shoulders. Having made their permanent connections with nerves before leaving their segment of origin, they bring the branches of the post-trematic VII with them.

The facial nerve acquired its name from this facial distribution of motor branches in man. It has no appreciable facial distribution at all in sauropsida, and can only claim to be a facial nerve in fishes and amphibia because of the preotic lateral-line branches, which of course are sensory. The permanent relations of the facial nerve are with the derivatives of the hyoid segment, not with the face.

5. Most mammals have a pair of **digastric muscles** between the halves of the lower jaw (Fig. 16–24). This is a new device which replaces the lost depressor mandibulae muscles of the other tetrapods (Fig. 16–13). A digastric

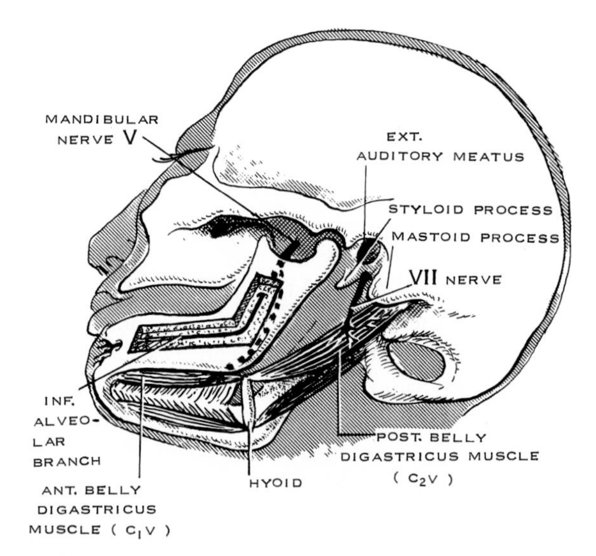

Fig. 16–24. Human digastric muscle and its double nerve supply.

muscle characteristically arises from the base of the skull posterior to the otic capsule and arches down to an insertion on the inside of the mandible at such an angle that, when it contracts, it rocks the bone backward on the jaw joint, opening the mouth. It is named a "double-bellied" muscle because there is usually a constriction in the middle of its length, or at least a strip of tendinous tissue interrupting the muscle fibers there. The "anterior belly" is served by the mandibular branch of the V nerve, and the "posterior belly" by the post-trematic VII nerve, which is an indication of the fact—confirmed in embryology—that it is produced by a fusion of parts of both the C_1v and the C_2v muscle masses. The remainder of the C_1v muscle forms an intermandibularis sheet as in other gnathostomes. The small elements of the C_2v which are not used in the digastric or dispersed in mimetic muscles are involved in the tongue.

REFERENCES

1. Stensiö, E., 1958. In Grassé, *Traité de Zoologie,* Tome XIII (1). Masson, Paris. The best recent summary of information on the long-extinct Ostracoderm groups.
2. Yntema, C. L., 1955. *In* B. H. Willier, P. A. Weiss, and V. Hamburger (eds.), *Analysis of Development.* W. B. Saunders Co., Philadelphia. Pp. 415–428. Ear and nose.
3. Goodrich, E. S., 1930. *Studies on the structure and development of vertebrates.* Macmillan & Co., London.
4. Hörstadius, S., 1950. *The neural crest.* Oxford University Press, London.
5. de Beer, G. R., 1937. *The development of the vertebrate skull.* Oxford University Press, London.
6. Edgeworth, F. H., 1935. *The cranial muscles of vertebrates.* Cambridge University Press, London. Includes a monumental catalog and description of head muscles on an embryological classification scheme. But because of some oddities in Dr. Edgeworth's embryology and neurology, comparisons should be made with the chapters by Luther and Lubosch in Bolk, Göppert, Kallius, and Lubosch, *Handbuch der vergleichenden Anatomie der Wirbeltiere,* Bd. V, 1938. Urban u. Schwarzenberg, Berlin.
7. Watson, D. M. S., 1953. *Evolution* 7: 159.

17

Post-Otic Pharynx Segments Tongue and Throat

I. INTRODUCTION

A. Topography

At the pharyngula stage (Figs. 5–9, 5–11), the post-otic pharynx segments of cyclostomes and elasmobranchs form an extended series of more or less vertical bars on either side of the head. Those of amniotes form a very short and diminishing series, much overhung on all sides, and those of some teleosts (Fig. 5–3) are pressed down obliquely toward the ventral surface of the head and more or less completely hidden against the yolk. These differences aside, the segments are generally comparable in structure, as noted in Chapter 5, page 75. Dorsal to them lie the first few post-otic mesodermal somites, and from these there migrate down some muscle-forming cells posterior to the pharynx segment mass on each side, which then move forward into what may be called the **mesobranchial space** in the midventral line of the head, between the right and left masses of the post-otic segments. Here they will differentiate into the **hypoglossal** or **hypobranchial muscles** (Figs. 17–1, 17–2).

Connective tissue separates the pharyx-segment mass of each side both from the somite-derived muscles that form above it and those that move in below it. Important nerves and blood vessels run through and across these connective tissue partitions, and to facilitate description the names **suprapharyngeal septum** and **subpharyngeal septum** are proposed for them. The former lies between the dorsal borders of the visceral pharyngeal segments and the overlying somatic or epimeric myotomes. The latter lies between the ventral borders of the pharyngeal segments and the hypoglossal or hypobranchial muscles. The suprapharyngeal septum ends anteriorly at the otic capsule, the subpharyngeal septum usually at the ventral limit of the hyoid arch, and the two are continuous with each other at the posterior limit of the pharynx segment mass on each side.

B. Four Lines of Differentiation

The post-otic pharynx segments differentiate along four boldly different lines in vertebrates, seen respectively in hagfishes, lampreys, the gnathostome fishes and the amniotes. Each of these groups produces a variety of special structures not recapitulated or represented at all in the others. The principal derivatives in the first three groups are organs concerned with *gill-breathing*—in three quite different patterns. Besides endocrine glands which are present in fishes but take on new importance in tetrapods, the principal derivatives in the amniotes are the **tongue** and the **larynx.** Amphibia, which develop

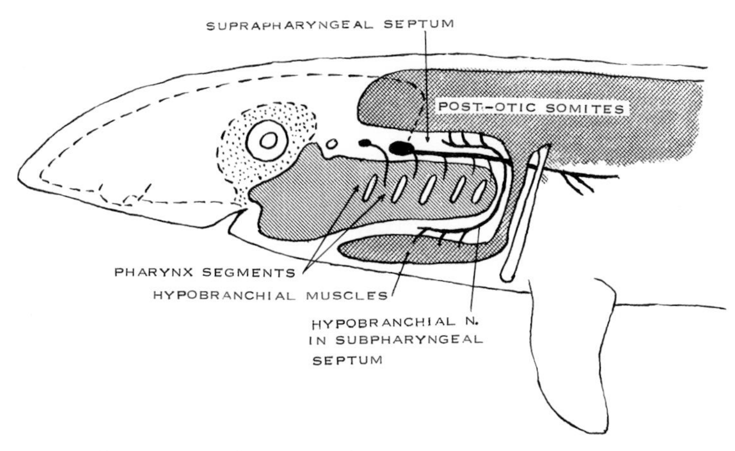

Fig. 17–1. Relationships between derivatives of pharynx segments and somites in an adult shark.

tongue, larynx, *and* gills, may be considered to have a post-otic pharynx-segment morphology which is partly intermediate between that of the gnathostome fishes and that of the amniotes, but they also show uniquely divergent developments. They do not share in the curious dispersal of pharynx-segment materials that occurs during the formation of the **neck** in the amniotes.

C. Numbers of Segments, and their Distribution

The differences in the post-otic segments at the pharyngula stage in various vertebrates are mainly of number and position rather than of structural pattern. There are four post-otic segments (numbered III-VI, counting the pre-otic segments as I and II) in most tetrapods, and five in most teleosts, six or seven in some sharks, and regularly seven or more in the cyclostomes. The embryonic segments show little indication of the sharply divergent developments that are to come (cf. Fig. 5–9).

Nevertheless there are hints. In a shark or a lamprey, the numerous segments are relatively uniform in size, with only a gradual diminution from anterior to posterior, and they trail posteriorly, suggesting their future prominence and relative freedom from the skull. In higher fishes, and especially in the amniotes, the pre-otic segments are enormous, and the successive post-otic segments grade rapidly down to almost nothing, directly below the large hindbrain. In the pudgy

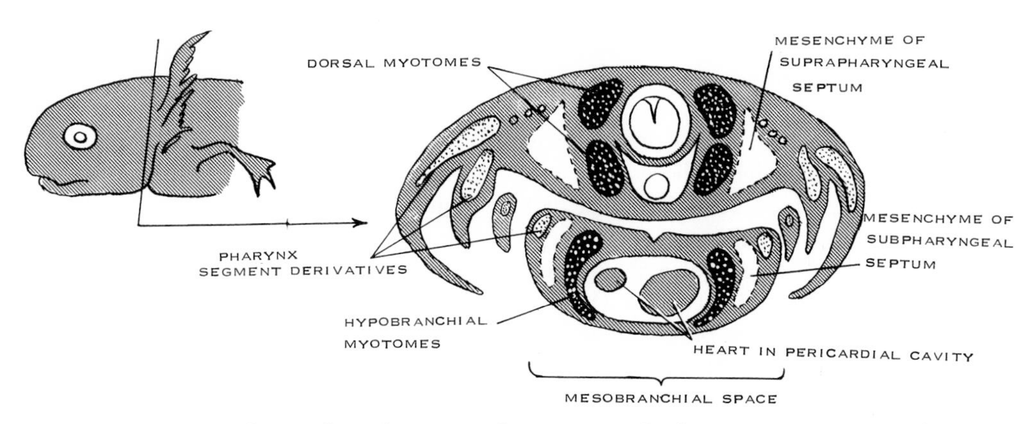

Fig. 17–2. Relationships between derivatives of pharynx segments and somites in the amblystoma larva.

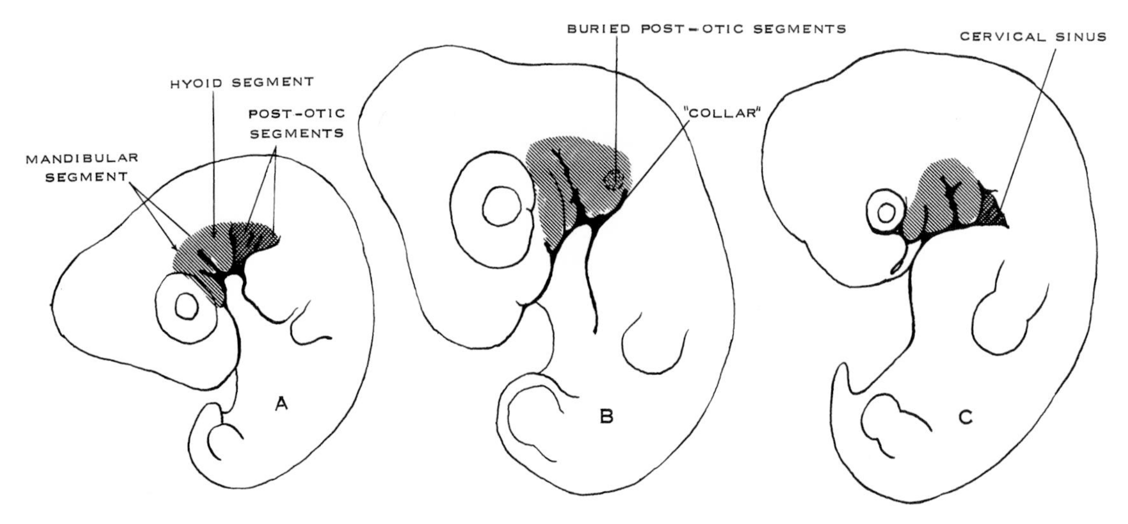

Fig. 17–3. Repression of post-otic pharynx segments in amniotes. A. 4½-day chick, stage 24. B. 5-day chick, stage 26. C. Human embryo, 10 millimeter, 6th week.

pharyngulas of mammals (Fig. 17–3 C), the surrounding ectoderm is rolled outward by the very abundant mesenchyme, producing a deep pocket on each side called the **cervical sinus,** at the bottom of which the last post-otic segments are hardly discernible as individuals, and in which they are eventually swallowed up. In the chick at the fifth day of incubation (Fig. 17–3 B), the post-otic segments are covered over by a "collar" or operculum of skin which extends back rapidly from the hyoid segment. The supra- and subpharyngeal septa are correspondingly reduced, and crowded up under the hindbrain.

D. Clefts

The post-otic pharyngeal clefts which are regularly formed in anamniotes, are less regular and conspicuous in the amniotes (Fig. 5–9). At the height of their development, lizard pharyngulas show three pairs of open clefts, those lying anterior to segments II, III, and IV. The next two pairs merely come close to the rupturing stage as closing plates. Chick pharyngulas show open clefts anterior to segments II, III, and IV, but the next two pairs of pouches barely reach the covering ectoderm. In mammals, one or two of the clefts may open briefly, but in general the anterior pouches and grooves do not go beyond the closing-plate stage and the posterior ones do not reach the ectoderm at all. Nevertheless the successive post-otic pouches can be made out in frontal sections (Fig. 5–5 B) or reconstructions (Fig. 17–19) of the embryos for some time. As rare anomalies, they may overdevelop and produce blind pouches or **cervical fistulas** in the adults (Fig. 17–4).

This marked repression of the post-otic segments in amniotes makes it a little difficult to determine how many of them there are. At early stages the pharyngeal pouches that come between them are clearly visible in frontal sections (Fig. 5–5), and aortic arches form at least temporarily in segments III–VI (Fig. 5–13). Rarely, indications of a fifth post-otic pair (VII) are seen. Skeleton formation does not take place in all of the segments, and muscles either may not be produced at all, or they may be transported to new and strange locations, with consequent disturbance of nerve patterns.

The *development of the neck* (Fig. 17–26), a uniquely amniote phenomenon, together with the allotment of many pharynx-segment derivatives either to the tongue or to the larynx apparatus, swiftly disguises the segmental nature of their embryonic pharynx wall pattern. Along with the transfer of the heart from the embryonic head into the thorax region, the surviving elements of the aortic arch system become dislocated from the skeletal and muscular derivatives of their segments. Muscles and skin, carrying their origi-

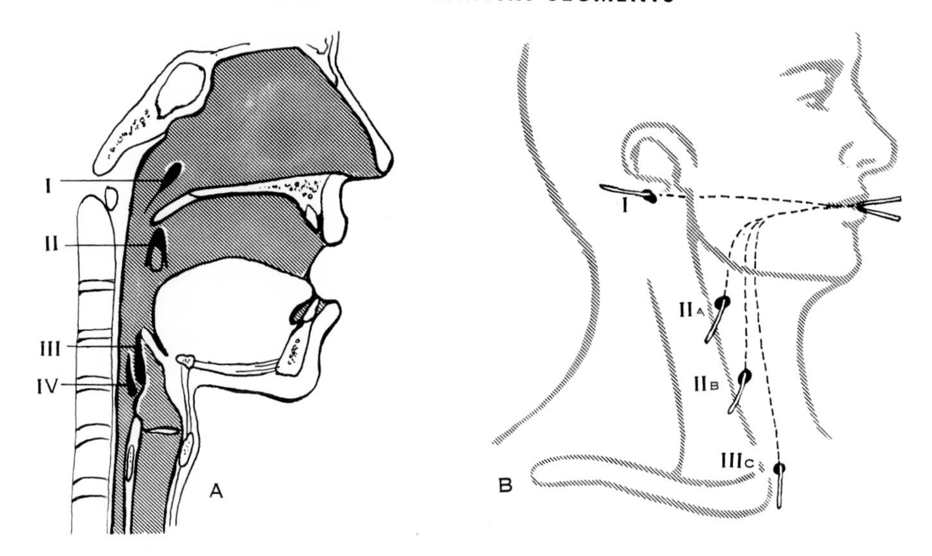

Fig. 17–4. Anomalous persistence of pharyngeal pouches and clefts in man. A. Internal openings of pouches. B. Various possible openings of cervical fistulas from persistent clefts I and II.

(After H. K. Corning, Lehrbuch der Entwicklungsgeschichte des Menschen, 2d edition, 1925, by permission of J. F. Bergmann Verlagsbuchhandlung.)

nal nerves with them, are shifted past each other to new locations. As a result, the anatomy of the amniote neck becomes quite complex, but the key to it is found in the simpler segmental arrangements of the pharyngula (see Part VIII below).

In the sections which follow, the tissues characteristically differentiated in the post-otic pharynx segments of all gnathostomes will be taken up in the following order: **skeleton, muscle, nerves, blood vessels and gills,** and **endocrine glands.** Thereafter, the **pharyngeal mills,** which occur only in bony fishes, and **muscular tongues,** which occur only in tetrapods, but both created out of pharynx-wall materials, will be examined. Later sections will discuss the transformation of the pharynx region in **amphibian metamorphosis,** and mention the conditions in agnathous fishes, which are too aberrant for detailed description in an elementary text.

II. POST-OTIC VISCERAL SKELETON

A. Fishes

The tongues of neural crest cells that move down into each of the post-otic pharynx segments (Fig. 9–8) differentiate at first into simple curved rods of cartilage, which then break up into smaller elements. In some fishes (Fig. 12–6), they line up in more or less vertical series, but usually the segments are so compressed ventrally that the bars are nearly horizontal from the first, their "ventral" ends swung forward and medially.

The number of cartilage elements formed from each bar is constant per segment and per species, and each is given a name according to its position (Fig. 17–5). The more posterior segments have a smaller number of elements, even in primitive fishes. The ceratobranchial elements, which are principal gill supporters in fishes, are the strongest and most persistent members of the series.

In elasmobranchs (Fig. 17–5), the visceral skeleton extends far posterior to the skull, and each arch, instead of being a flattened half-hoop as in teleostomes, is a zigzag bow. In the teleostomes (Fig. 17–6), the whole apparatus is crowded under the skull between the jaws and hyoid arches (Fig. 12–6) and presently replaced by a faithful bony copy. The pharyngeal surfaces of various elements become studded with tiny **teeth** which project through the mucous membrane. Tooth patches may be aggregated in small

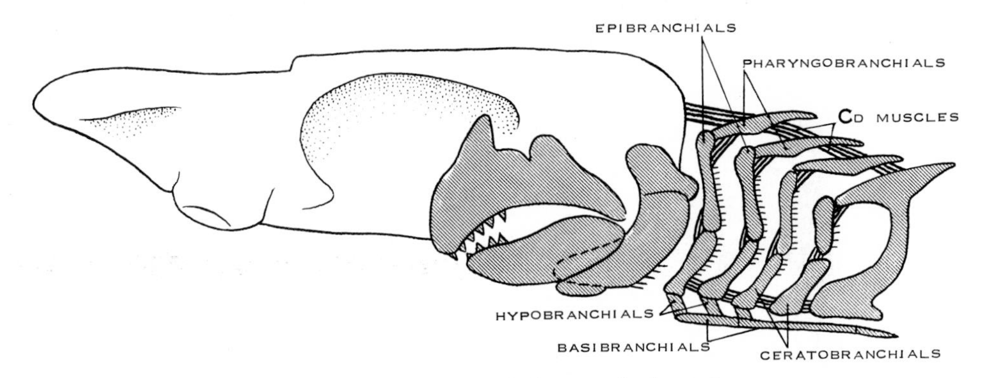

Fig. 17–5. Visceral skeleton of dogfish.

bristly mounds or strongly developed into broad crushing plates, so that their function may be merely to tighten the grasp on the prey, or to mash it up for swallowing.

B. Amphibia

The pattern of visceral skeleton elements developed in the amphibia is considerably reduced from that of fishes, but is not fundamentally different (Fig. 12–6 C). The largest element in each arch (or, in the more posterior segments, the only one) is customarily called a ceratobranchial, but it does not develop any rays (cerati) like those that support the internal gills of teleosts, and it could just as well be homologized with the whole chain of elements in a fish as with the ceratobranchial element alone. A pair of tiny lateral cartilages that form at the sides of the **glottis,** a midventral opening from the pharynx toward the lungs, can be interpreted as a pair of post-branchial elements belonging to a repressed VII segment on each side.

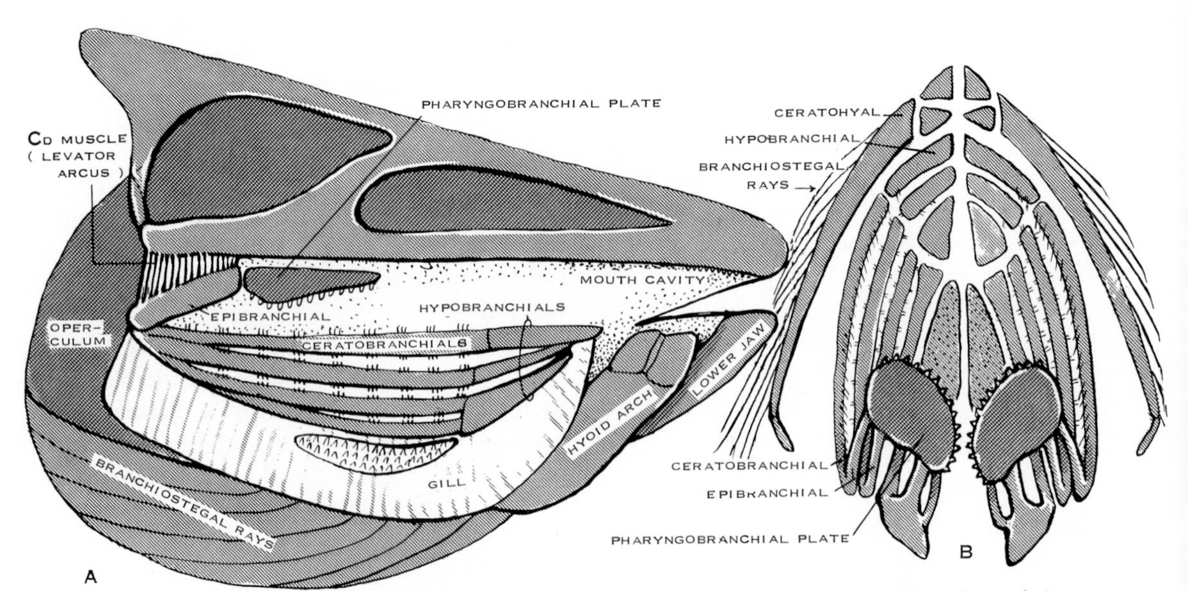

Fig. 17–6. Visceral skeleton of codfish. A. Head bisected in sagittal plane, left side seen from the midline. B. Dorsal view of hyobranchial skeleton.

C. Amniotes

In amniotes, the cartilages formed in the anterior two or three of the post-otic pharynx segments (and their replacement bones) regularly join with the lower hyoideum part of the II arch skeleton, to form a tongue support. In some sauropsida this may be quite like the equivalent apparatus in amphibian larvae or fishes, but it can also become highly specialized.

The typical pattern in sauropsida (Fig. 17–7) consists of a median **hyoid body** comparable to a basihyal or copula element, with a forward-directed **lingual process** to support the tongue and a series of posterolaterally directed and paired **horns** representing the rest of the hyoideum and skeletal elements of post-otic segments III and IV. Those derived from segment III are usually the longest, the other pairs being variously reduced. In fact, only stubs remain to represent segment IV in various lizards, turtles, and the sphenodon, and even these are lacking in other turtles, crocodilia, and birds. Of all the amniotes, the snakes show the poorest tongue skeleton development, though they have an extremely active tongue.

In mammals (Fig. 16–22), there is also a "body of the hyoid" in the midline, but it does not have a lingual process and is not always derived entirely from the hyoid segment. Sometimes it contains material from arch III as well as arch II. There are usually two pairs of horns, the first pair reaching toward the otic capsules of the skull and the second reaching posterodorsally to make a connection with the larynx skeleton. The first pair of hyoid horns either may be short and rudimentary (hence called the "lesser horns" in human anatomy), or may consist of a long chain of ossicles (sometimes interspersed with ligament) reaching all the way to the crista parotica of the ear capsule, like a nearly complete hyoid arch. The second pair represent the III pharynx segment skeleton. Monotremes achieve a closer resemblance to the fishlike hyobranchial apparatus of larval amphibia than any of the surviving sauropsida, for their "hyoid" has four pairs of horns, representing pharynx segments II–V.

In all the amniotes, cartilage-forming cells from the more posterior pharynx segments are also diverted ventrally to take part in building a more or less elaborate **larynx,** associated with the glottis. This will be described later in conjunction with their respiratory tract (Chapter 23). In sauropsida, the larynx usually lies cradled in an expansion of the body of the hyoid, but not jointed to it. In mammals, on the other hand, it is more posteriorly located, and the posterior

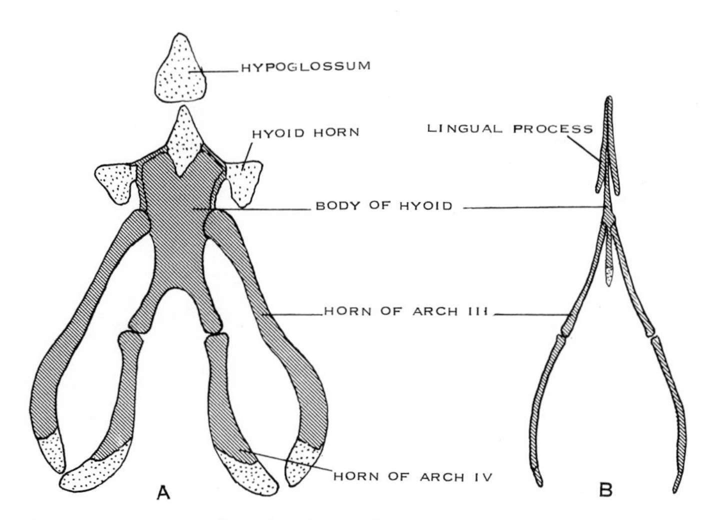

Fig. 17–7. Sauropsidan hyobranchial skeletons. A. Turtle. B. Bird.
(After Siebenroth, 1898, and Leiber, 1907.)

horns of the hyoid, i.e., the elements of skeletal arch III (or arch V in monotremes) reach down and make joints with it.

Evidence that the laryngeal cartilages are derived from the post-otic pharynx segments is not obtained by direct observation in amniotes, since the segments concerned lose their identity at an early stage and the cartilages differentiate later. Rather, the evidence is from anatomical relations: the close association of the larynx with the hyobranchial skeleton, whose origin is clear, and the fact that the laryngeal muscles are innervated by the vagus, the nerve of the pharynx segments posterior to III.

III. VISCERAL MUSCLES

A. Anamniotes

In the gnathostome fishes and amphibia, a muscle plate forms in every post-otic pharynx segment (Fig. 5–10), and this is supplied from its earliest appearance by its own motor nerve. The **glossopharyngeal nerve IX** supplies the III, or first branchial, segment. Successive **branchial trunks** of the **vagus nerve X** supply the rest [1].

These muscle plates divide into dorsal and ventral portions, which become completely separated in most species. Only in elasmobranchs, by virtue of an unusual construction of the gill septa does any intergradation or overlap occur between the Cd and Cv muscles produced from them.

1. Dorsal Series. The Cd muscles can be classified in extrinsic and intrinsic series. The extrinsic muscles are attached at one end to the skeletal arch of the segment of origin, but reach out with the other end to the skull or the shoulder girdle or some other relatively firm point of attachment. The intrinsic muscles on the other hand (Fig. 17–5) have both their ends attached within their segment of origin, working across joints between the successive skeletal elements.

As for *extrinsic muscles,* the bony fishes (Fig. 17–6) and larval amphibia (Fig. 17–8) usually produce a **levator arcus** (plural, **levatores arcuum**) in each post-otic segment, which commonly takes origin from the skull and inserts on the bony arch. These are variously modified as to strength, origin, and insertion, and they are often subdivided into external and internal derivatives. The last pharynx segment in the series projects a member of the levator arcus series posteriorly, to an insertion on the shoulder girdle. This is the **trapezius muscle** (Figs. 17–8, 17–11).

Information on the trapezius of teleosts is scanty, its development and nerve supply being known for only a few species. It lies in an area which is complicated by the firm attachment of the shoulder girdle to the skull through a chain of bones, as well as by the intrusion of myotomic muscles. In dipnoi, the trapezius is simply an extension of the last branchial constrictor muscle toward the shoulder girdle.

In rays, the shoulder girdle becomes immovably fused with the vertebral column, and the trapezius, though formed in the embryo, disappears. (This is the usual fate of a muscle when the parts between which it runs become im-

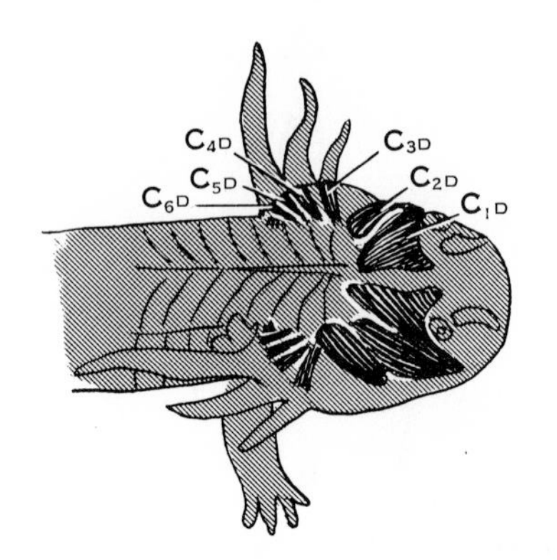

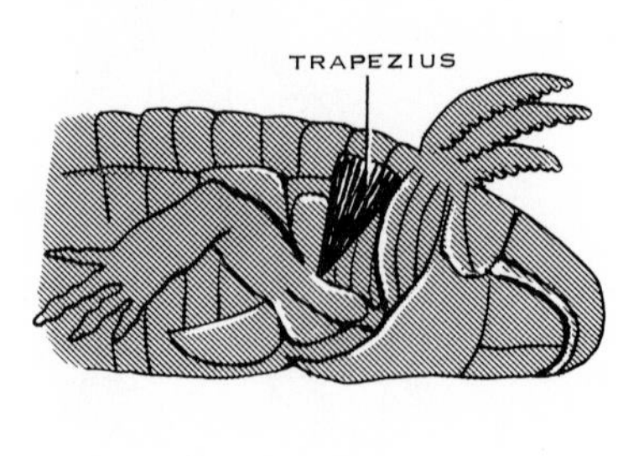

Fig. 17–8. Cd muscles of the amblystoma larva.

movable; for instance it has been seen that muscles do not normally occur between braincase and upper jaw when these parts are immovably fused together.)

In sharks (Fig. 17–11), there is a long pyramidal trapezius muscle dorsal to the gill mass, inserting its base on the scapular process of the shoulder girdle. Since in these animals the gill skeleton lies too far back for practical development of the usual attachment of levatores arcuum to the skull (Fig. 17–5), such muscles do not develop, but instead all of the post-otic segments —not just the last one—contribute to the formation of the trapezius.

Members of the *intrinsic series* of Cd muscles straddle the joints between the upper elements of the skeletal arches. Elasmobranchs for instance (Fig. 17–5) produce a series of small **arcuales dorsales** each of which runs from the pharyngobranchial to the epibranchial cartilage of its own arch, and also a series of stronger **adductores** which run in similar fashion from epi- to ceratobranchials. The teleosts produce several similar series of arcuals and adductors.

2. *Ventral Series.* Serially homologous sets of Cv muscles are also produced from the ventral muscle plates of the post-otic segments in fishes and amphibia, by the repetition of a similar pattern of differentiation in each. For instance **subarcual muscles** (Fig. 17–9 B) may arise, one in each segment, extending from the ceratobranchial cartilage forward to the similar element in the next arch forward. **Transversus** or **oblique** muscles may reach across the ventral midline to join their antimeres, like weak imitations of the intermandibular and interhyoid sheets of the pre-otic segments, or failing this they may tie each ceratobranchial element to the hypobranchial of its own arch. In many fishes, **coracobranchial muscles** run from the ventral ends of the skeletal gill arches posteriorly, to insertions on the ventral (coracoid) part of the pectoral girdle.

While most of the ventral visceral muscles of gnathostome fishes can be referred to these series, some fish groups lack one series or another completely, and in given species one or more of the segmentally repeated members of a particular homologous series may be absent. Cartilage fishes and some others, for instance, completely lack the subarcual series and the post-otic transverse series. Members of the coracobranchial series are found in every post-otic segment in the elasmobranchs, but are lacking in the III segment in dipnoi and occur only in the last segment of teleosts. The coracobranchial muscles are rather delicate, and become deeply buried under the somatic muscles of the hypoglossal or hypobranchial group which migrate forward into the mesobranchial field from the more anterior myotomes (Fig. 17–1).

3. *Electric Organs.* In the family of electric rays, some of the cells of the muscle plates of

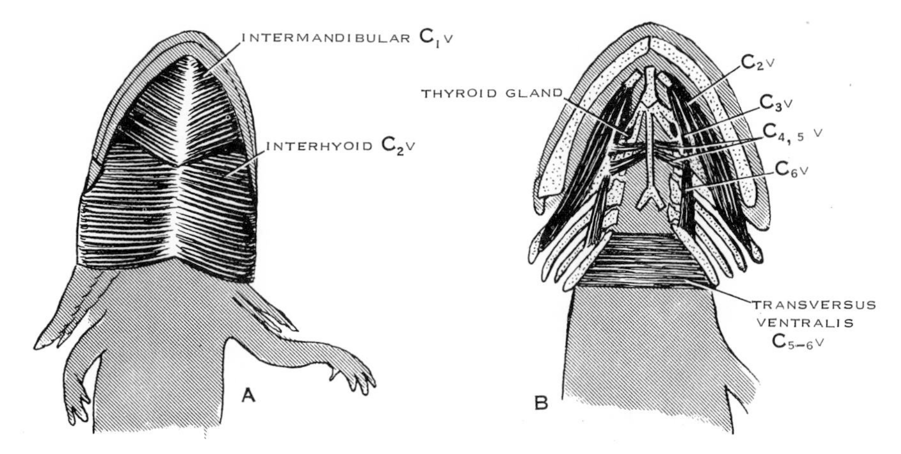

Fig. 17–9. Cv muscles of the amblystoma larva. A. Skinned head, ventral view. B. Same, after removal of superficial transverse muscles.

pharynx segments II through VI produce the usual patterns of Cd and Cv muscles attached to the visceral cartilages, but others multiply exceedingly and transform into units called **electroplaxes.** Under the control of proportionately enlarged motor divisions of cranial nerves VII, IX and X, these piles of electroplaxes can deliver an electric shock of high enough voltage to stun prey, or protect their owner from the largest predators.

Similar transformation of embryonic muscle cells into electroplaxes occurs in other fishes as independent evolutionary developments. The electric organs of these rays are from visceral musculature. In the South American electric eels they come from somatic myotomes of the tail. A little electric organ is produced by the star-gazer *Astroscopus,* a teleost, from its somatic eyeball musculature. In the electric catfish from the Nile, the organ is subcutaneous and its derivation is not known. In some cases these organs give off continuous rhythmic discharges which may be used for direction-finding, or recognition of others [2].

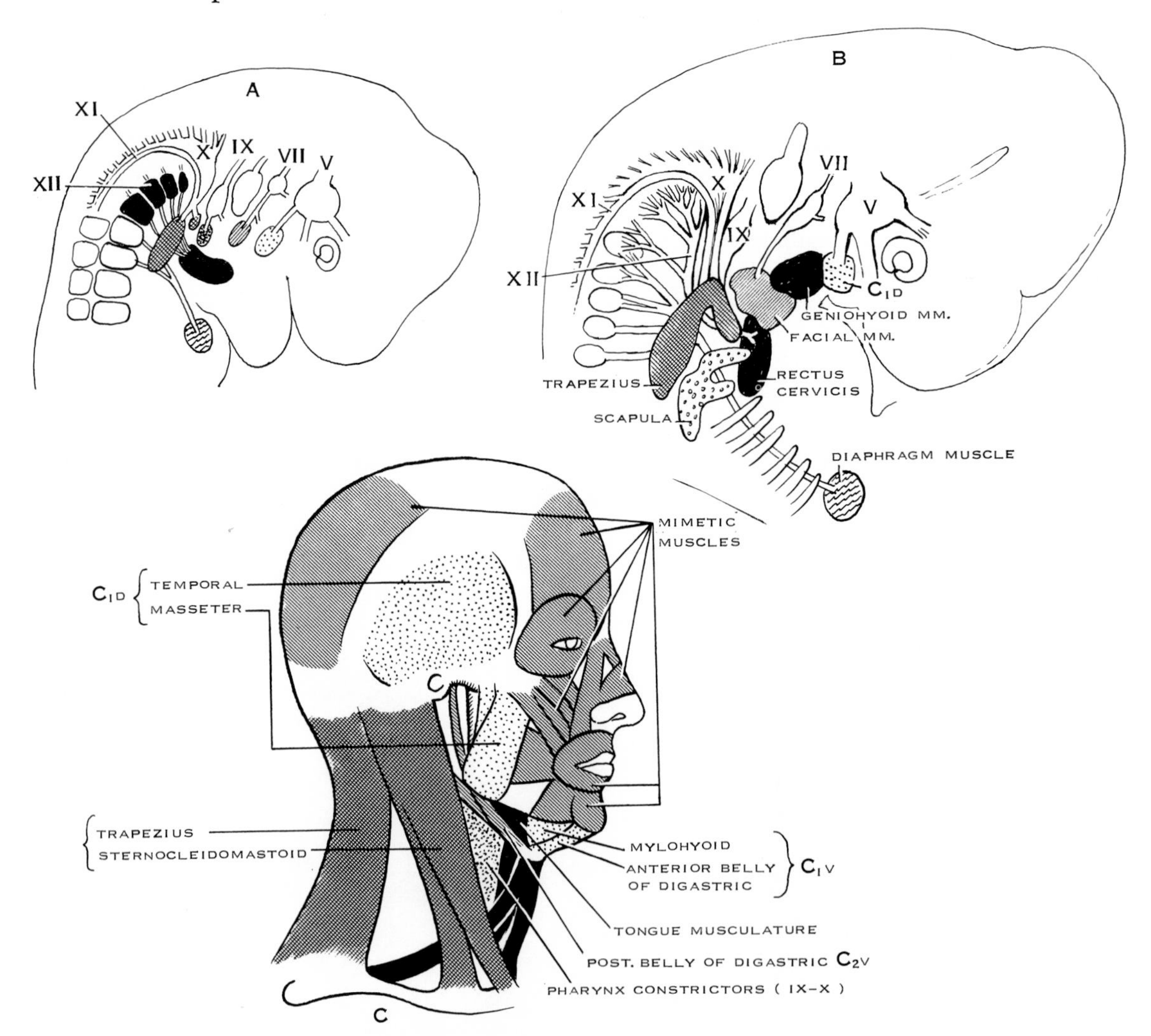

Fig. 17–10. Visceral and hypoglossal muscles of man. A. 7-millimeter embryo. B. 11-millimeter embryo. C. Adult.

(After H. K. Corning, Lehrbuch der Entwicklungsgeschichte des Menschen, 2d edition, 1925, by permission of J. F. Bergmann Verlagsbuchhandlung.)

B. Amniotes

Quite in contrast to the anamniotes, which produce visceral muscles of several series in every segment and only have an insignificant overflow of muscle-forming cells into the trapezius, the amniotes generally show powerful trapezius developments (Fig. 17–10) and almost a lack of muscles in the post-otic segmental series. Muscle plates are never formed in more than three of the four post-otic segments, and sometimes only in two or even one. Whichever is the last in the series produces the trapezius. This becomes shaped into a family of muscles, all of them retaining their original vagus innervation (X or XI, see below).

The hyobranchial apparatus, to which the main series of Cd and Cv muscles of amniotes would apply themselves, remains only as a support for the tongue, which is a rather simple affair except in mammals. And when the tongue becomes prominent it usually calls up muscles from an entirely different source: the hypoglossal group from post-otic myotomes. The trapezius on the other hand acquires great new importance. It is only absent in limbless lizards and snakes, and reaches its maximum development in mammals. In climbing, flying, or swift-running mammals a half dozen or more muscles may differentiate from the embryonic trapezius mass on each side, spreading all over the shoulder region and down the vertebral column. The posterior dorsal part of this expansion receives supplementary innervation from several spinal nerves.

The trapezius is the only post-otic Cd muscle formed in the sauropsida, but C_3d regularly appears in mammals, as the **stylopharyngeus muscle,** with the expected IX nerve supply. Like most levatores arcuum, it has an origin on the skull, but since the visceral bar on which it might be expected to insert has been directed toward the larynx as the posterior horn of the hyoid, it inserts its fibers over the soft pharynx. The rest of the post-otic Cd muscle cells, uniquely in mammals, but always in them, spread themselves over the pharynx as a sphincter sheet of striated muscle called **constrictor pharyngeus** (Fig. 17–10 C), which functions in swallowing. In different degrees in different species, this overflows anteriorly into the soft palate, posteriorly onto the esophagus and ventrally into the larynx. Since no pharynx pouches remain to separate the segmental nerves, it is innervated by a plexus of motor fibers derived from IX and X.

A representative of C_3v appears regularly in sauropsida as a **branchiohyoideus** muscle, or by extension to the lower jaw as a **branchiomandibularis.** This is represented by a family of muscles in crocodilia, and especially in birds, serving in the latter for protrusion of the tongue (Fig. 17–24). A similar branchiohyoideus muscle is found in many groups of mammals also, running between the anterior and posterior horns of the hyoid (i.e., between arches II and III) and innervated by the glossopharyngeal nerve as a result of its origin from the III segment. It happens to be lacking in man. C_4v never develops, but curiously enough the monotreme mammals produce a subarcual C_5v muscle, which comes closer to the amphibian pattern than anything of the sort in any living bird or reptile.

IV. GLOSSOPHARYNGEAL AND VAGUS NERVES

A. Triplet Patterns, and Segmental Branches

1. In fishes which have an open spiracle, the facial nerve VII has a triplet pattern (Fig. 16-17). This is repeated, with some minor modifications, in the nerve supply to every one of the post-otic pharynx segments. Each of the triplets arises from a **branchial trunk** in the suprapharyngeal septum. The first is the glossopharyngeal, nerve IX, and the others are given off in succession by the vagus. The last member of the series is usualy somewhat defective. Normally the pretrematic branch and the one that extends forward in the roof of the pharynx carry only visceral sensory components for mucous membrane, while the post-trematic branch carries, in addition to these, some visceral motor fibers to the Cd and Cv muscles formed in its own segment.

Presence of visceral clefts seems important in keeping the visceral branches of the cranial nerves within the territory suggested by this pattern. In the bony fishes, the gills and their skeletal bars are usually pressed backward, tight against each other (Fig. 17–6), so that the post-trematic branch of one segment is lateral, not anterior, to that of the next. Nevertheless, these branches remain separated by the intervening cleft.

If however the clefts disappear, the adjacent nerve branches may be bound together by connective tissue, with consequent loss of the segmental pattern. A similar thing happens normally within a segment. It is common, for instance, in segment IV to find that the post-trematic branch of that segment, and the pretrematic branch of the segment V nerve which travels a parallel course with it, are bound together. In like manner, in bony fishes, the pharynx-roof branches of VII and IX tend to fuse, or as it is usually described, a commissure is formed between the IX nerve root and the palatine branch of VII. This becomes a constant feature in the bony fishes and tetrapods.

2. *In amphibia,* as a minor modification, a "recurrent branch" of the vagus passes down from the suprapharyngeal septum posterior to the last pharyngeal cleft, and as it runs forward through the subpharyngeal septum it supplies not only the mucous membrane of the posterior floor of the pharynx, but also the Cv muscles of all four post-otic segments, thus usurping part of the usual function of the several post-trematic branches.

3. *In amniotes,* the early obliteration of post-otic visceral clefts, and even of pharyngeal pouches, encourages plexus-formation between neighboring nerves. Therefore the orderly distribution of the IX nerve to derivatives of segment III, and of separate trunks of X to the remaining segments IV–VI, is no more than suggested at the pharyngula stage, and becomes progressively more difficult to make out during later development. Although nerves IX and X continue to carry the same visceral components and to supply the same mucous membrane and visceral muscles, the triplet pattern does not appear.

The name **glossopharyngeal,** an unfortunate heritage from early human anatomy, then becomes appropriate in many amniotes. The usually small sensory component to the floor of the pharynx is enlarged when it becomes involved in the tongue (**glossus**) and most of the rest of the nerve is allotted to mucous membrane of the **pharynx,** and to its constrictor sheet of muscle in mammals.

The vagus nerve X of amniotes gives off two or three visceral motor branches to the pharynx and the larynx, but their relation to the embryonic post-otic pharyngeal segments is difficult to determine. (Cf. discussion of the amniote neck, page 333.)

B. Non-Segmental Branches

The glossopharyngeal and vagus nerves can give off as many as five other systems of branches, each illustrating in its own way how little of the anatomy of the vertebrate head is segmental in nature.

1. A visceral-motor **ramus accessorius** (Fig. 17–11) is given off at the posterior end of the segmental zone of the vagus (appearing as a twig of the last branchial trunk in many fishes). It supplies nothing but trapezius musculature. In amniotes, its fibers arise from the posterior part of the hindbrain and the anterior part of the spinal cord, and many of these have to pass forward through the foramen magnum to join with the rest of the vagus before leaving the skull (Fig. 17–10 A). It remains a part of the vagus in many sauropsida, but rather late in the development of mammals and a few reptiles the connective tissue binds its fibers up separately so that it is then defined as a cranial nerve in its own right, the XI or **accessory nerve.**

2. In fishes and amphibia, the vagus projects a **ramus intestinalis** (Fig. 17–11) beyond the last branchial trunk, which distributes fibers to the heart and the esophagus, and to the lungs when these are present. It carries visceral sensory components, but in amniotes it may acquire autonomic (visceral motor) fibers which exercise certain controls over the rate of heart beat. In the higher mammals these autonomic components greatly increase in it, acquiring control over the action of many glands (liver, pancreas, adrenals, kidneys, and secretory tubules of the intestine) and over the peristaltic muscles of the

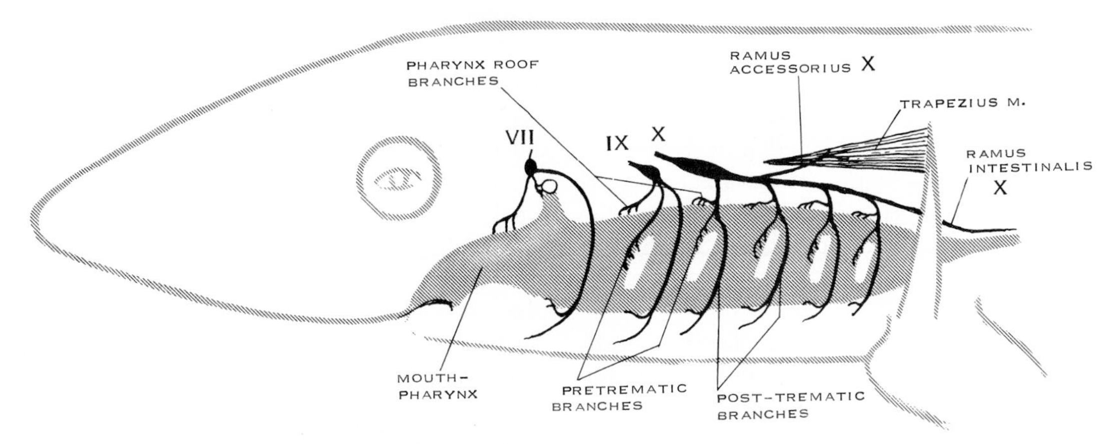

Fig. 17–11. Branchial trunks and triplet branches in the dogfish.

upper intestine, as far as the beginning of the duodenum (Fig. 17–17). (Cf. Chapter 30.) This is why the name vagus ("wanderer") was assigned to nerve X in human anatomy.

3. **Ramus dorsalis** is a somatic sensory branch given off from the vagus in many bony fishes. It distributes dorsally to the skin just posterior to the skull.

4. **Ramus lateralis accessorius** is also found in most bony fishes. It was mentioned previously as a branch of the facial nerve VII (Fig. 16–18 A, codfish), but it usually receives some somatic sensory and taste fibers by one path or another from the vagus, and in some species it is actually dominated by vagus fibers.

5. The post-otic dorsolateral placode, (Fig. 15–1) gives rise to both the neuromasts and the nerves and ganglia of the post-otic part of the lateral-line system. There is usually a short **ramus supratemporalis** which attends a line of neuromasts spread across the top of the head; its ganglion may be associated with either the IX or the X nerve (Fig. 15–2). The principal **ramus lateralis** and its large ganglion are invariably joined with the vagus, though the ramus itself takes a separate course almost as soon as it leaves the skull, following its line of neuromasts. These nerves, in correlation with their sense organs, are variously elaborated or repressed in different species of anamniotes, but are absent only rarely. They never form in any amniotes.

V. AORTIC ARCHES AND THEIR DERIVATIVES

The first aortic arches take shape in the embryo before the blood begins to flow, and successively more posterior ones are prepared and cut into the circuit after the first ones are functioning. How the delicate new arteries can introduce themselves into a system which already includes briskly flowing blood and a rhythmic pulse from the nearby heart, without the pressure of the blood causing ruptures and hemorrhage into surrounding tissues, is a problem that may engage the imagination of the reader. Little is known about it.

The time of formation of the full series of aortic arches, and the time of their subsequent regression or transformation, varies in different kinds of vertebrates. The number of arches that are formed varies with the numbers of pharynx segments (page 307). Those that form in the mandibular segments of the two sides are always obliterated soon after the more posterior ones begin to function. Except in a few fishes, this is also true of the ones in the hyoid segments.

A. Stem Conditions

Always at the pharyngula stage, the aortic arches of at least the more posterior pharynx segments are still found arising from the ventral aorta in the mesobranchial space, crossing to their own segments through the subpharyngeal septum of their own side, following their own segments dorsad, and then joining the dorsal aorta by passing through the suprapharyngeal septum, past the descending visceral branches of their cranial nerves. The blood flow is not interrupted by any capillaries. These uninterrupted arteries will be called **primary circuits** to distinguish them from later specialized conditions.

B. Divergent Trends

After the pharyngula stage, this fairly uniform arrangement is transformed in one way in the anamniotes, and in quite another way in the amniotes. Neither "recapitulates" any aspect of the other's transformation. In amphibia there is a two-stage transformation with features in part comparable, first to those of fishes, and then those of amniotes.

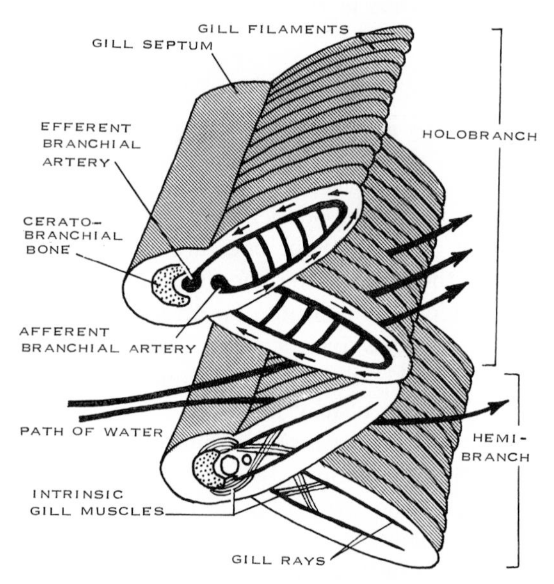

Fig. 17–12. Structure of teleost gills.
(After J. H. Bijtel, 1949.)

In the anamniotes, the primary circuits of the aortic arches are complicated by the interposition of gill capillaries between their ventral or afferent parts and their dorsal or efferent parts. In the amniotes, there is no such specialization of gill tissues, but instead some of the primary circuits are completely obliterated, and others are broken, their blood flow being diverted completely from the dorsal aorta, either into the head, or toward the lungs. In addition, some parts of the aortic arch system are markedly affected by the elongation of a neck. Details of the transformation of the aortic arches will be described first for fishes, then for amphibia, and finally for the amniotes.

1. Fishes. The post-otic pharyngeal pouches and clefts appear in regular sequence at the pharyngula stage of fishes, and in subsequent development they are enlarged and specialized, in contrast to the obliteration of their homologs in amniotes. Not only are **gills** formed from their opposed surfaces, but **gill rakers** usually develop at their inner margins (Fig. 17–13). The rakers are absent in a few species and generally remain small and simple in carnivorous fishes which swallow large pieces of meat, but in many mud- or plankton-eating species they become greatly elongated and even branched, serving as filtering devices.

(a) *Structure of Gills.* In the larvae of amphibia and some of the "living fossil" fishes, (*Polypterus,* dipnoi), external gills sprout from fleshy stalks at the tops of the pharynx clefts. In all adult fishes, however, the gills are internal. A single gill, defined as a **holobranch,** is the product of a single pharynx segment, but usually consists of two **hemibranchs** or half-gills which project respectively into the clefts anterior and posterior to the segment that produces them (Fig. 17–12). The supporting part of the pharynx segment is defined as the **gill septum,** through which the cartilaginous or bony **gill arch** and the principal parts of the aortic arch run. Also included in the gill septum are intrinsic muscles and pre- and post-trematic nerves.

The structure of gills is superficially quite different in elasmobranchs and teleosts (Fig. 17–13). Each hemibranch is subdivided into a considerable number of gill filaments, but the gill septum of elasmobranchs reaches all the way to the skin and is supported by gill rays of cartilage that lie between the hemibranchs, whereas the gill septum of teleosts is highly restricted in cross section (Fig. 17–13 B) and the very tiny gill rays lie in each filament of each hemibranch (Fig. 17–12). The gill filaments of elasmobranchs

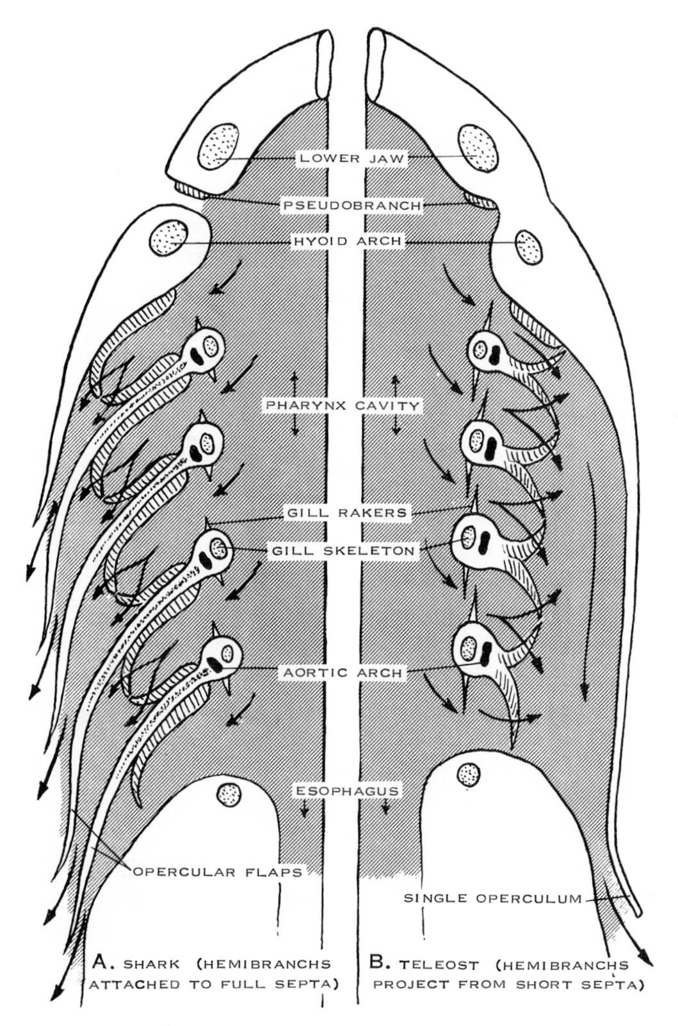

Fig. 17–13. Breathing mechanism in elasmobranch and teleost (described in text).

are attached along their lengths, projecting their narrow widths into the branchial chambers, but in teleosts they are attached at their bases to a rudimentary septum and project their full lengths into a common chamber. A fish-louse could step from one hemibranch to the other of a single teleost gill, but to do this in a shark it would have to make a journey either through the pharynx cavity or around the skin strip between the two gill slits on the outside of the head.

However, in both cases, the filaments of opposed hemibranchs of two adjacent gills interlock with each other externally (Fig. 17–12), and the water which filters through to the outside has to pass through extremely thin spaces between them, where it is separated from the blood stream by the thinnest of cell membranes. Special intrinsic gill muscles keep the gill filaments interlocked in this way at all times, except when the fish coughs, which it does periodically in order to clean its gill surfaces [3].

Blood always flows through capillaries within the gill filaments in such a direction that it is first brought close to the water that is about to leave the gill surface, and last to the water which is just reaching the gill surface (Fig. 17–12).

This is a **counter-current arrangement** which creates the most efficient circumstance for maximum extraction of oxygen from the water, or for liberation of carbon dioxide into it [4].

The gills are not only used for respiration, but also for the excretion of nitrogenous wastes and of excess salt [5].

Some pelagic fishes apparently irrigate their gills simply by swimming forward with their mouths open. Usually however, ventral throat muscles that run from the pectoral girdle to the forward ends of the gill arches are used to open the mouth, filling the pharynx cavity with water by a suction-pump action. This suction would simultaneously close the soft opercular flaps that cover over each of the successive gill chambers in an elasmobranch (Fig. 17–13 A1). Or in a teleost (Fig. 17–13 B1), backflow would be similarly prevented by closure of the large single operculum and branchiostegal membrane which are formed by the spread of the hyoid segment backward over all the gill segments.

Next, the mouth is closed, and the gill arches are constricted like a force-pump, and the water is pushed out through the opercular flaps (Fig. 17–13 A2) or the operculum (B2).

Not all the walls of the gill septa form gills. Usually the posterior wall of the last cleft fails to do so, and in bony fishes it is uncommon for the anterior wall of the hyobranchial cleft to produce its own hemibranch, though a pseudobranch may arrive there secondarily (Fig. 17–13 B). Teleosts often have four holobranchs, borne on segments III–VI, but there are species in which the number of gills is reduced to 3½, or 3, or even 2½. This does not mean that the surface available for gill respiration is correspondingly diminished, for the gills themselves may independently vary in different species, both as to their size and richness of their capillary nets. They are also supplemented by other respiratory devices in some species [6]. The mechanisms for ventilating the gills have also been adapted in various ways, in some cases by building up the efficiency of the force-pump ahead of them, or in others by improving the suction-pump of the operculum and branchiostegal membrane behind them. Many ways have been found to compensate for the wide variation in total gill surface per body weight which exists among teleosts.

(b) *Alteration of Aortic Arches by Gills.* Gill lamellae cannot be supplied with blood without an interruption of the primary circuits of the post-otic aortic arches. This occurs in different ways in different fishes (Fig. 17–14). During the time the first lamellae are being formed after the pharyngula stage, the fish embryo is using the capillaries over its entire body surface, including its extensive yolk-sac circulation, for absorption of oxygen. A number of loops are subsequently formed from the primary circuit of each gill septum, one for each filament, and this alows a distinction between gill capillaries, and **afferent branchial arteries** that lead to them (the ventral parts of the original aortic arches), and **efferent branchial arteries** that lead away from them (the dorsal parts of the arches). Soon however, the afferent and efferent arteries grow past each other through the base of the gill. This happens in slightly different ways in different fishes. In elasmobranchs (Fig. 17–14 C) the efferent branchial vessels are regrouped during development so that each drains the two hemibranchs associated with a single **gill chamber,** rather

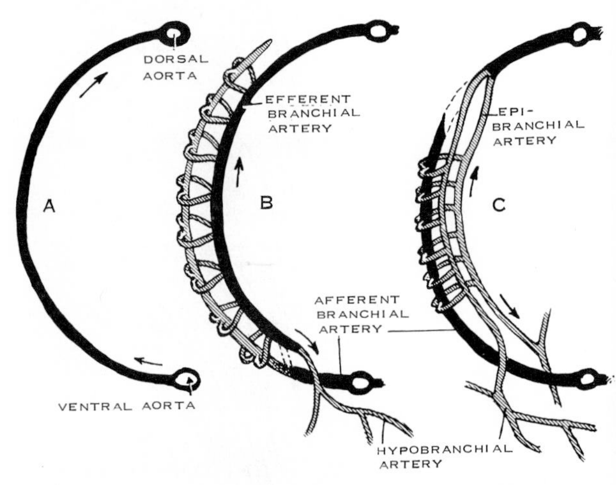

Fig. 17–14. Specialization of aortic arches in teleosts and elasmobranchs. A. Embryonic primary circuit. B. Teleost adult. C. Elasmobranch adult.

(After E. S. Goodrich, Studies on the Structure and Development of Vertebrates, 1930, by permission of Macmillan & Co., Ltd., London.)

than the two borne on a single **gill septum**, as in teleosts (Fig. 17–14 B). This has no effect on the function of the gill circulation.

The fresh (oxygenated) blood that is carried away from the gills is mostly delivered to the dorsal aorta through the confluence of all the efferent branchial (or epibranchial) arteries in the dorsal midline, under the skull or the first vertebrae. However, some of it is tapped off and delivered to important structures both (1) ventral and (2) anterodorsal to the gill region.

(1) The ventral or hypobranchial structures, which include the Cv and hypobranchial (hypoglossal) muscles and the pericardial cavity itself, receive a variable number of paired **hypobranchial arteries** (Figs. 17–14 B, C; 17–15) which extend down to them from the efferent branchials. It would be interesting to know the mechanics of how and why these tissues select (or are awarded) a supply of *fresh* (oxygenated) blood. The afferent branchials, which carry *stale* (de-oxygenated) blood and do *not* supply them, are actually nearer, and have a higher blood pressure.

(2) *Pre-otic blood supply*. Structures anterodorsal to the gill region are supplied with a variable network of arteries carrying fresh blood (Fig. 17–15). These are partly derived from surviving elements of the hyoidean aortic arch in species which develop a pseudobranch or spiracular gill—called a hyoidean efferent or **ophthalmic artery**—and partly from a group of dorsal vessels that can be defined either as branches of the most anterior aortic arches or as anterior continuations of the roots of the dorsal aorta. One of the latter, called the **orbital artery** in fishes, runs forward across the hyomandibular cartilage and so into the orbit, corresponding rather well with a **stapedial artery** which is commonly formed in tetrapods. It supplies the face through branches that follow the main divisions of the trigeminal nerve. Other branches of the dorsal group enter the cranial cavity to supply the brain.

2. *Amphibia*. Most amphibia develop four pairs of post-otic pharynx segments. In some species, clefts are maintained anterior to each of these during the larval stage, but in others the number of clefts is reduced to 3, 2, or even 1 pair. Normally they are all closed up later, during a period of metamorphosis. However, there are aquatic species which maintain them through life, just as there are unusual people with cervical fistulas. The deciding factors are poorly understood.

Larval **external gills** are usually developed

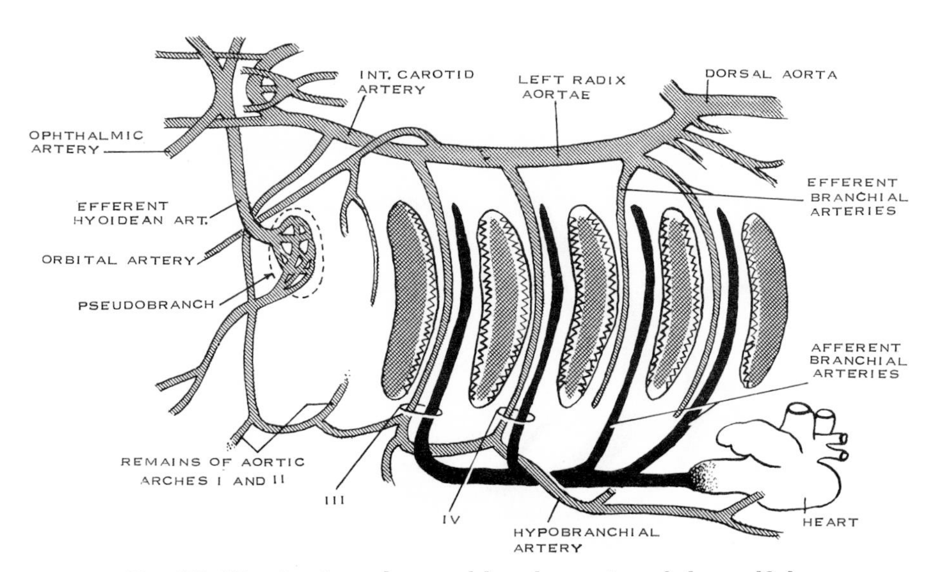

Fig. 17–15. Aortic arches and head arteries of the codfish.
(After Allis, 1912.)

from the skin dorsal to several of the pharynx clefts. They are augmented and then replaced in anuran tadpoles, by **internal gills** that grow out from the pharynx segments themselves, but even these are quite different in their structure from the orderly demibranchs of bony fishes.

In urodele larvae, a broad ventral *operculum* is developed from the hyoid arches, containing the C_2v interhyoideus muscle sheet (Fig. 16–15 A), but it does not cover the external gills, and is not used in breathing movements. When it is removed, nothing is revealed but the postotic pharyngeal bars themselves, each bearing a thin translucent flap of tissue which can be compared either to a non-functional gill or to a little operculum of its own. In anuran larvae, the operculum quickly develops to great size, engulfing the external gills. Its posterior border fuses with the belly skin all except for a single small opening called a spiracle (but not to be confused with a hyomandibular pharyngeal cleft). After water has been pumped through the mouth and past the gill slits, it can escape from the opercular cavity by way of this spiracle. In anura, not only the larval gills and their supporting skeletal arches but also the developing forelimbs are hidden inside the opercular cavity.

Aortic arches are formed in all the branchial

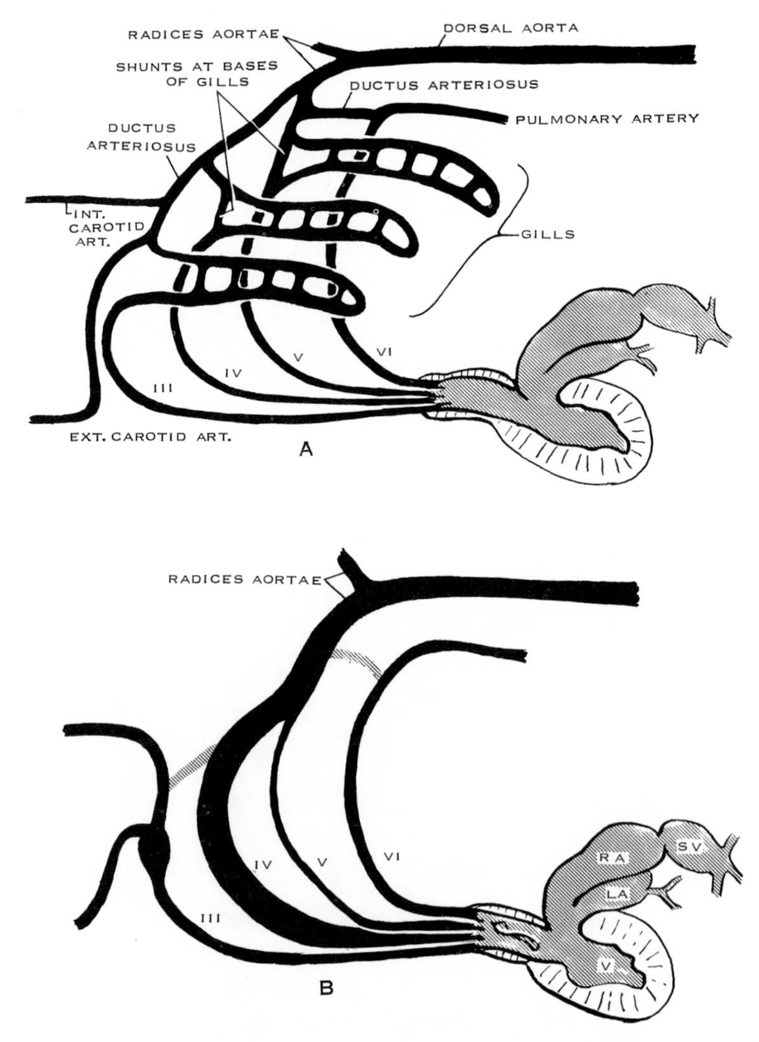

Fig. 17–16. Aortic arches of the amblystoma. A. Aquatic larva. B. Terrestrial adult.

pairs of embryonic pharynx segments, each connecting the ventral aorta with the dorsal aorta. Those in the mandibular segment arise but are obliterated, and it is the rule in the urodeles that none are ever formed in the hyoid segments. The last pharynx segment on each side regularly omits to form a gill, and its aortic arch develops a **pulmonary artery** (except in lungless salamanders). In the other pharynx segments, the embryonic aortic arches are pulled out into loops within the external gills, and the loops are elaborated into capillary nets serving the gill filaments. This divides the embryonic arches into afferent and efferent branchial arteries (Fig. 17-16 A). Later on, in the amblystoma, shunts may be developed across the bases of the gills, so that when oxygen is abundant the blood may be bypassed directly toward the dorsal aorta without being all forced through the gill capillaries. On the other hand in foul water or an accumulation of carbon dioxide the shunts can be closed off by reflex vasconstriction, requiring all the blood to run through gill filaments.

The embryonic radix aortae of each side of the embryo extends into the head, and remains in larva and adult as the **internal carotid artery.** After disappearance of the aortic arches in the mandibular and hyoid segments, the brain, ear, and eye receive blood through this vessel by way of the III aortic arch. From the dorsal or efferent branchial part of this same III arch, an **external carotid artery** grows ventrad and forward, to deliver fresh blood to the lower jaw region.

In the larval amphibian, blood from the III arch may be delivered either to the carotid arteries, and so to the head, or else to the dorsal aorta, through a short connecting vessel which may be called the **ductus caroticus** (Fig. 17–16 A). Likewise, blood from the VI arch may be delivered either to the lungs through the pulmonary artery, or else to the dorsal aorta, through a connection called the **ductus arteriosus.**

After some months of aquatic life, the larval amphibian undergoes a metamorphosis which involves, among many bodily changes, the transformation of its aortic arches. The gills are completely resorbed, and direct circuits are established across their bases, rather like the primary aortic arches of the embryo (Fig. 17–16 B). The aortic arch of the V pharynx segment, which had been getting relatively smaller during late larval life, shrivels and later disappears without a trace. The efferent branchial paths to the dorsal aorta from both the III and the VI arches (ductus caroticus, ductus arteriosus) also disappear. At the end of this time all the blood delivered into the remaining ventral stem of the III arch on each side is sent to the head through the external and internal carotid arteries. All the blood that enters the VI arch goes to the lung of that side. The dorsal aorta receives blood only through the right and left IV arches, which converge upon it dorsally as the **radices aortae,** the roots of the aorta.

These events, and comparable ones about to be described in amniotes, provide a convenient set of names for the aortic arches, as well as their pharynx segments:

Arch	*Name*	*Nerve*
I	Mandibular	Trigeminal
II	Hyoid	Facial
III	Carotid	Glossopharyngeal
IV	Systemic	Vagus X Br_1
V	Vanishing	Vagus X Br_2
VI	Pulmonary	Vagus X Br_3

3. Amniotes. Traces of six pairs of aortic arches regularly appear in the embryos of amniotes. Usually, even before the VI pair have been formed, the I or mandibular pair have been lost in a bed of capillaries, though their dorsal and ventral ends usually remain as forward continuations of dorsal and ventral aortae. The persistent dorsal parts distribute medially to the brain and laterally along the branches of the trigeminal nerve, as the **internal carotid artery** systems. When the hyoid aortic arch in its turn disperses in capillaries, its dorsal part remains, with its flow of blood reversed, as a branch of the internal carotid artery. It is called the **stapedial artery** because in mammalian embryos it is usually found piercing the stapes. In some reptiles and amphibia the same artery pierces the columella (Figs. 16–12, 16–20).

The capillaries formed by the mandibular and

hyoid aortic arches in their respective segments usually continue to be supplied by the ventral aortae, or (as in the chick) they may come later to be supplied by a new stem which grows into them from the internal carotid artery at the level of the IX nerve. Thus arise the **external carotid arteries.** As in fishes (Fig. 17–15) and amphibia (Fig. 17–16), the III arch of each side becomes the source of blood for the entire internal and external carotid artery system after the loss of the mandibular and hyoid aortic loops (Figs. 17–17, 17–18). During the early post-pharyngula stages, blood from this III arch can flow either to the carotid system, or to the dorsal aorta through a **ductus caroticus,** as in tadpoles. Whereas this ductus does not cease function and disappear until the time of metamorphosis in amphibia, it is lost in early fetal development in all mammals, all birds and most reptiles. It survives insignificantly in the sphenodon and a few lizards. After the loss of the ductus caroticus, all the blood of the III aortic arch must go to the carotid arteries and the head.

The aortic arches of the V pharynx segments, which are robustly developed in amphibian larvae but usually obliterated at metamorphosis, are repressed much more promptly in amniotes. At best, they have only a brief existence at the pharyngula stage, and often (Fig. 17–17 C) they only appear as rather casual bridges between arches IV and VI or separate twigs at the base of arch VI, rather than as direct connections between the ventral and dorsal aortae. No trace of them ever remains in adult amniotes.

In all amniote embryos, the point of origin of the lung is very close to the VI pharynx segment, and the VI aortic arch, as soon as it appears, or even before it completes its connection to the dorsal aorta, gives off a **pulmonary artery** posteriorly (Figs. 17–17 C, 17–18). This also happens in lungfishes and all the amphibia except the lungless salamanders. Thereupon, blood can flow from the VI arch *either* to the pulmonary system *or* to the dorsal aorta through the **ductus arteriosus.** This ductus persists until hatching or birth, but then promptly atrophies. The only modern amniote in which the ductus arteriosus persists as a normal adult structure is the sphenodon. However, in some mammals, a trace of it remains in the form of a connective tissue strip called the **ligamentum arteriosum** (PNA). As an occasional anomaly it may continue to carry

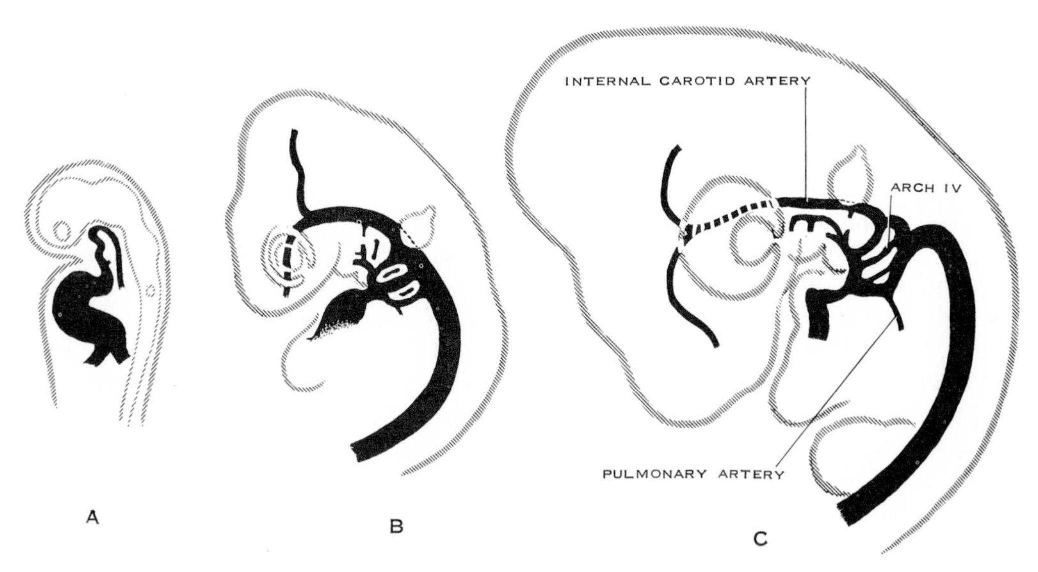

Fig. 17–17. Development of aortic arches in the chick. A. Stage 14, 48 hours. Arch I and beginnings of Arch II. B. Stage 17, 56 hours. Arch I broken, arches II, III, and IV functional. C. Stage 21, 3½ days. Arches I and II broken, arches III–VI functional.
(After A. F. W. Hughes, 1934.)

blood after birth. Usually not even a ligamentum can be found in adult birds and reptiles.

In adult reptiles, even after aortic arches I, II, and V have disappeared and both ductus caroticus and ductus arteriosus have ceased to carry blood, the heart is still delivering blood to the dorsal aorta through the IV arch paths of both right and left sides. Only one further reduction in the embryonic aortic arch system is possible without destroying the circulation, and this would be the elimination of one or the other of these two paths. In all normal individuals of the modern mammalian groups, the *right* IV arch path is discarded during the mid-fetal period of development (Fig. 17–18 D). In practically all birds, the *left* IV arch path is discarded, though there are a few species that either retain the reptilian symmetry or develop the mammalian type of asymmetry. Experiments clearly show that the enlargement or the obliteration of this or that aortic arch is a function of local pressures of the blood stream [8].

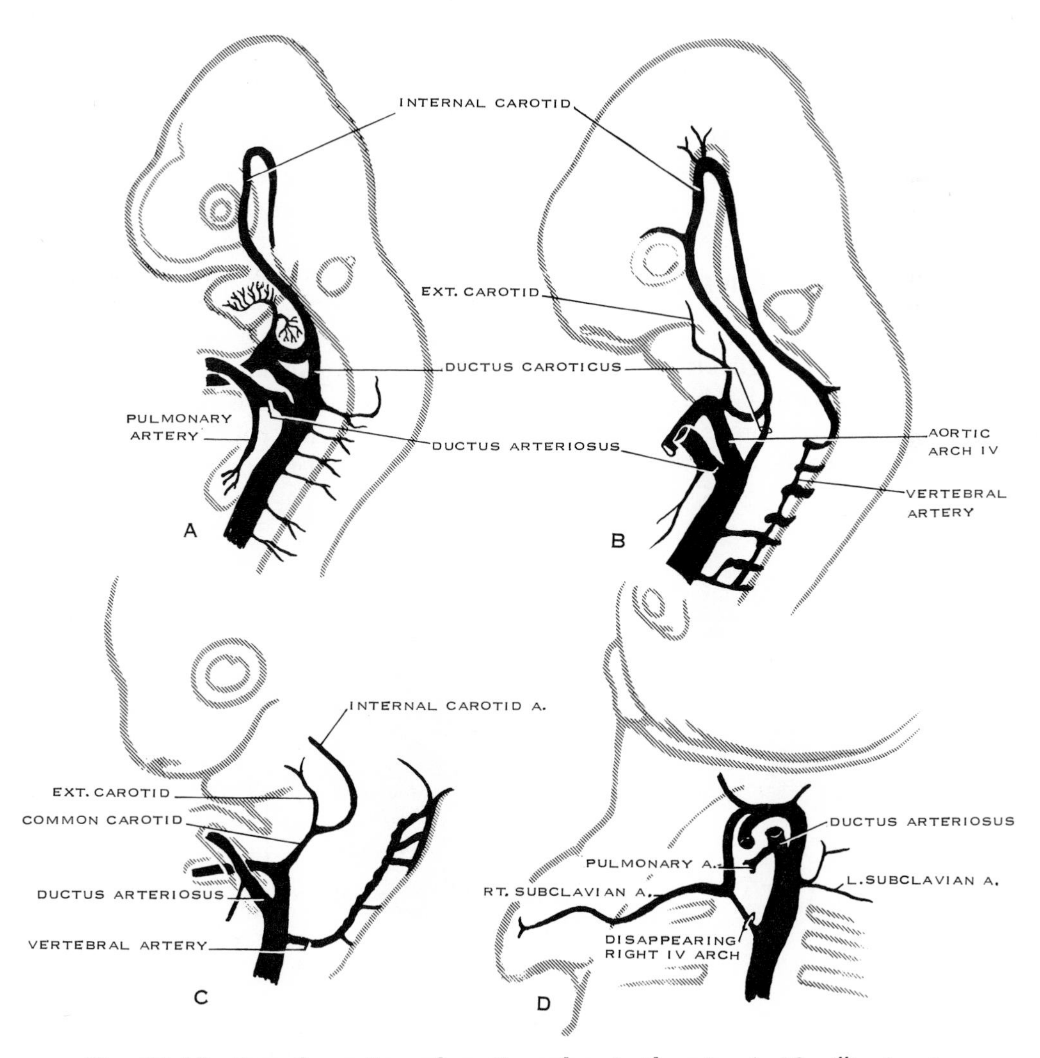

Fig. 17–18. Transformation of aortic arches in the pig. A. 12-millimeter stage. B. 14-millimeter stage. C. 19-millimeter stage, side view. D. 19-millimeter stage, ventral view.

(After C. H. Heuser, 1923.)

Coincident with these reductions in the aortic arch system of amniotes, there develop partitions in the heart and ventral aorta. Detailed consideration of these must be postponed to Chapter 25, but it may be mentioned that their result is to divide the blood stream either partially or completely into two alternating circuits, the pulmonary and the systemic. The **pulmonary circuit** takes stale blood to the lungs, and returns it fresh to the heart. The **systemic circuit** then takes the fresh blood to the rest of the body and returns it stale to the heart, whence it makes a new circuit through the lungs, and so on. In all amniotes, this separation, whether it is completed or not, is successful enough that the brain and major sense organs always receive fresh blood through the carotid arch III, and the lungs receive most, if not all, of the stale blood that returns to the heart.

VI. GLANDULAR DERIVATIVES OF THE PHARYNX

Thymus and parathyroid glands are formed from the dorsal and ventral borders of various pharyngeal pouches in vertebrate embryos, and thyroid glands from the floor of the pharynx. They vary considerably in their sites of origin, the importance of their functions, and their locations in adult anatomy.

A. Thymus

The **thymus glands** of gnathostome fishes always develop out of the *dorsal* margins of pharynx pouches. This is also true in all the amphibia and sauropsida, but in mammals they form at *ventral* margins. In all tetrapods except mammals, **parathyroid glands,** or epithelial bodies that represent them, are formed at the *ventral* margins of pharynx pouches, but in mammals (Fig. 17–19) they are formed *dorsally.* No explanation has been offered for this puzzling switch. Another frequently confirmed irregularity is in the germ layer from which the mammalian thymus buds arise. Usually it is the *endoderm* which forms them (e.g., in man, rabbit, rat, dog, sheep, Echidna), but sometimes it is the adjacent *ectoderm* (mole, fieldmouse), and in still other species *both* germ layers participate (marsupials, pig, guineapig, *Tarsius*). In other vertebrates the source is presumably always *endoderm,* but in the chick it has been reported that experimental removal of the adjacent *ecto-*

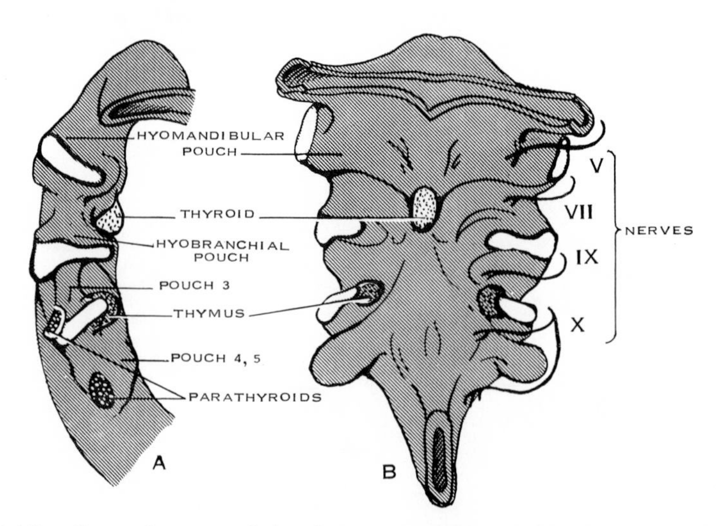

Fig. 17–19. Sites of origin of the thymus, parathyroid and thyroid glands in a 4-millimeter human embryo (areas of ectoderm-endoderm contact cross-hatched). A. Lateral view of pharynx. B. Ventral view.
(After G. L. Weller, 1933.)

derm cuts down thymus formation by 95 per cent [9].

A few sharks (Fig. 17–20 A) develop a thymus bud from the dorsal rim of every pharynx pouch, but in most species of fishes the first and last members of the series are lacking. In amphibia, they only form in vagus territory (Fig. 17–20 B). In some amniotes they form from the hyobranchial or the final branchial pouches, but usually only from the pouches that lie at the anterior faces of segments IV and V.

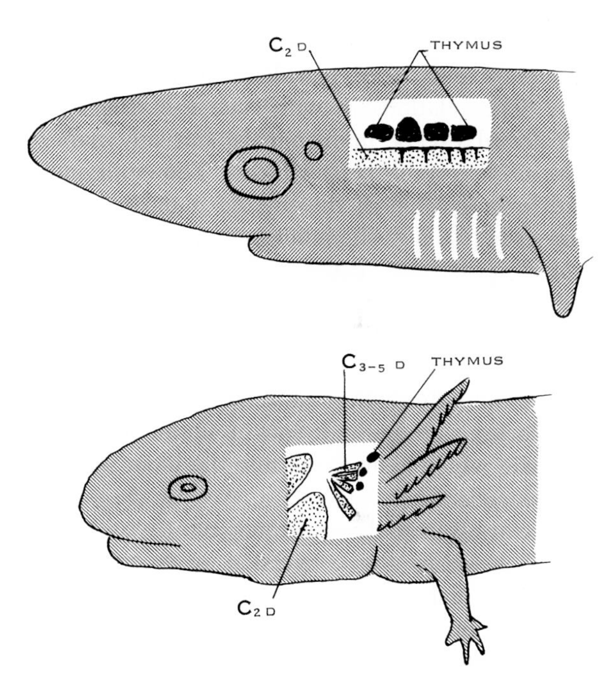

Fig. 17–20. Location of thymus in dogfish pup and larval amblystoma.

The segmental masses of thymus tissue may remain in the dorsal walls of the branchial chambers of anamniotes, or they may sever from them and extend posteriorly, losing their segmental appearance and placing themselves along the head veins or the efferent branchial arteries in the suprapharyngeal septum. They tend to shrink with age, but do not disappear.

In the amniotes, the thymus has at first the structure of a ductless gland, but it becomes packed with lymphoid tissue and regresses sharply after sexual maturity. There is much variation in its final location. It is generally associated with the vagus nerve and its accompanying jugular vein, but it may be found near the ear, or in the thorax, or extending in a thin ribbon or a train of isolated lobules the length of the neck. In many mammals, including man (Fig. 17–21), it grows very rapidly during fetal stages and packs almost entirely into the thorax, where it is applied irregularly over the surface of the pericardium. Such erratic distribution is presumably the result of the stretching and sliding of tissues past each other as the neck is elongating.

There is clear evidence that in mammals and birds the embryonic thymus gives rise to lymphoid cells that colonize other tissues, for instance the spleen and lymph nodes, and serve to manufacture antibodies in the reactions of immunity. The thymus, like these other tissues, loses such lymphoid cells in great numbers during infections (cf. page 529).

B. Parathyroid

The **epithelial bodies** or **parathyroid glands** of mammals differ in their site of origin from those of amphibia and sauropsida (page 326). In frogs and the amniotes they become such critically important endocrine glands, that their removal is quickly followed in most species by convulsions and death. Their hormones control the levels of calcium and phosphate in the blood, and exert a general control over bone formation.

In mammals, these glands often (but not always) become buried within or pressed against the lateral masses of the thyroid gland (Fig. 17-21 B, C), thus acquiring the name of **parathyroids.** Such a relationship is not found in the other tetrapods, and even among mammals it is common for accessory "parathyroid" fragments to be found scattered anywhere in the neck, or in the partitions of the thorax as far back as the diaphragm.

In amphibia the epithelial bodies remain in the head, at their segments of origin close by the thymus nodules. In sauropsida they are carried into the neck but always in close association with the main jugular veins and the vagus, and they

B. Tongues

In all the gnathostome fishes and in larval amphibia, the tongue consists only of an elevation in the floor of the mouth, produced by the union of the two halves of the hyoid arch and covered with gelatinous connective tissue and mucous membrane, with no special glands or intrinsic musculature. This elementary structure may be designated the **primary tongue** (Fig. 17–22 A). It is actually no tongue at all, and serves only to ram food against the teeth of the palate and hold it there temporarily. The mucous membrane which covers it is innervated by the internal mandibular branches of the right and left facial VII nerves. The site of origin of the thyroid gland is in the midline just anterior to the primary tongue.

During amphibian metamorphosis, the hyoid skeleton becomes much transformed in the service of a new **secondary tongue** (Fig. 17–22 B, C), and the most anterior members of the ventral series of somite muscles, i.e., the **hypoglossal group,** differentiate so as to give it a considerable mobility. As a much enlarged pad of mucous membrane and connective tissue, the secondary tongue is raised prominently off the floor of the mouth, either broadly attached at its whole base, or supported on a pedicle. Its thick blunt anterior border is filled with special glands and underlaid with lymphoid tissue that is sometimes called the sublingual tonsil. The animal still lunges at its prey, but now it has a sticky secondary tongue which it can flip out to catch food on.

The primary tongue of early amniote embryos likewise lies over the hyoid and more posterior visceral skeletal arches in the floor of the mouth. The point of origin of the thyroid gland is just anterior to it, and remains marked for a while in mammals by a shallow pit called the **foramen caecum.** Secondary tongue developments take place both anterior and posterior to this point, and either the hyobranchial skeleton or an invasion of hypoglossal muscles, or both, cause the floor of the mouth to be conspicuously elevated. The result is an organ of great diversity. The secondary tongue is used in this or that species for the capture of prey, the rasping or manipulation of food, for drinking, for taste and smell, for swallowing, coat-care, voice control, etc.

In fishes, the tongue region is supplied with visceral sensory components by the internal mandibular branch of the VII nerve (Fig. 16–18 A). As the chorda tympani VII, this branch of the *facial* nerve remains visceral sensory in the mammalian tongue (Fig. 16–18 B), but two anterior mounds and a third more medial mound of tissue are regularly contributed to the secondary tongue from *trigeminal* territory, not to speak of more posterior masses. The mucous membrane of the finished organ is therefore innervated in zones by the V, VII, IX, and sometimes even the X nerves, the relative prominence of these several lingual branches varying in different species. In amphibia, those of VII and IX are predom-

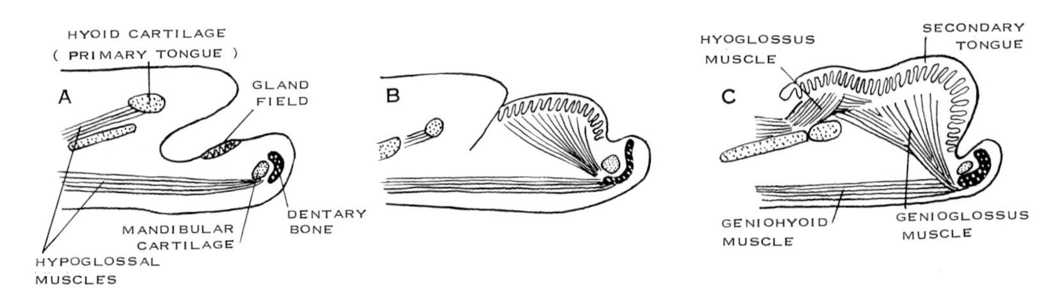

Fig. 17–22. Primary and secondary tongues in a urodele, *Salamandra*, seen in sagittal sections of the floor of the mouth. A. Larval stage. B. During metamorphosis. C. Adult stage.

(After Kallius, 1901.)

inant. In birds, nearly the whole lining of the secondary tongue is supplied by IX. In man (Fig. 17–23 B), as evidence of the importance of the more anterior embryonic tongue mounds, the general sense of touch in the anterior two-thirds of the tongue is carried by the lingual branch of the mandibular (V_3) nerve and the chorda tympani VII, and the posterior one-third by the lingual branch of IX, slightly overlapped by X at the posterior root. The taste buds are supplied partly by the chorda tympani but chiefly by IX.

The musculature of the tongue may be produced predominantly from the Cv visceral series, and consequently innervated by the IX and X nerves, or principally from the hypoglossal group, or from both groups in some specific proportion.

The **hypoglossal muscles** are derived from ventral parts of post-otic or anterior cervical myotomes of the somatic series, and bring their hypoglossal nerve supply with them [12]. The ventral-and-anterior arc of this nerve in the adult (Figs. 17–23, 17–29) is a reminder of the path through which its muscle-cell anlage migrated in the embryo.

In modern amphibia this hypoglossal nerve is made up from parts of several of the first spinal nerves, as is the equivalent hypobranchial nerve of fishes. If the posterior limit of the skull is moved back, as in amniotes and some fossil amphibia, this nerve automatically becomes de-

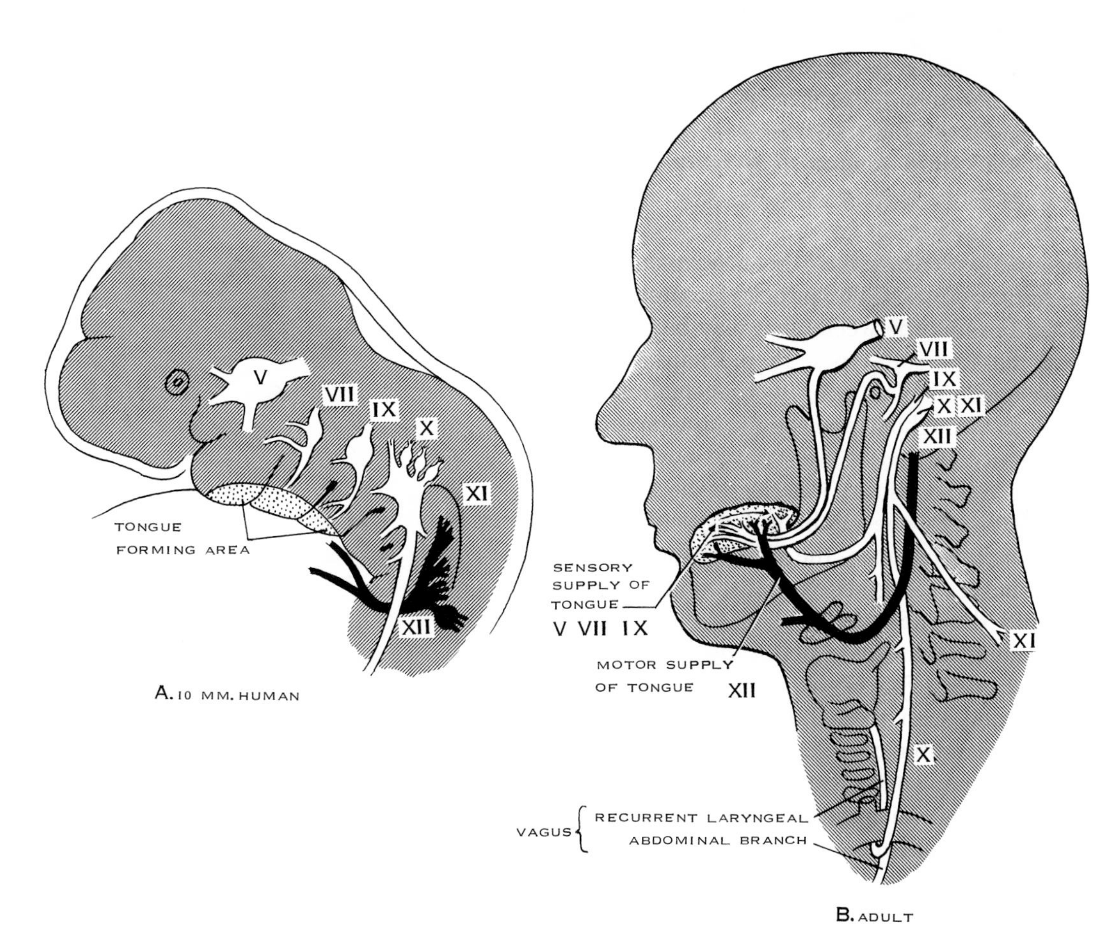

Fig. 17–23. Source and nerve supply of the mammalian tongue.
(After H. K. Corning, Lehrbuch der Entwicklungsgeschichte des Menschen, 2d edition, 1925, by permission of J. F. Bergmann Verlagsbuchhandlung.)

a leg-propelled lunge and a quick eversion of a sticky tongue pad, the retraction of which drags the prey into the mouth cavity. The tongue itself is a product of metamorphosis.

The tadpole's blood is aerated in the gills, which are borne on cartilage arches between gill slits. The whole gill apparatus disappears during metamorphosis, and as the animal crawls out on land it begins to use the remains of its hyobranchial skeleton and musculature as a force-pump to circulate air from the closed mouth cavity to the lungs and back again rhythmically, pausing occasionally to renew its air supply through the nostrils. The skin supplants the lungs as the principal respiratory organ of frogs under water, and aids them on land, being supplied by extensive branches from the pulmonary arteries, among others.

After the visceral clefts are closed, the opercular chamber is obliterated. The skeletal visceral arches are so changed in pattern that it would be difficult to homologize the separate parts of larva and adult without watching the actual steps of transformation. The post-otic arches lose their connection with the skull, much of their substance disappears and the rest is subordinated to a greatly enlarged midline copula which supports the newly developed secondary tongue. Those of the post-otic Cv muscles which do not entirely disappear are brought into association with the fused post-otic Cd muscles in a complex throat band whose originally segmental nature is quite obliterated.

The general appearance of segmented groups of visceral cranial nerves is preserved in the adult, though when the pharynx clefts are closed the adjoining pre- and post-trematic branches of the branchial trunks are brought so close together as to be distinguishable with greatest difficulty. Lateral line branches tend to disappear.

The changed method of respiration is naturally reflected in drastic alterations of the aortic arches (Fig. 17–16). All secondary circuits are lost with the gills, completely. In all but gymnophiona and a few urodeles, the ductus caroticus is obliterated, so that arch III no longer connects with the dorsal aorta. All its blood is then delivered through the external and internal carotid arteries to the head. The ductus arteriosus of arch VI is reduced, and actually disappears in anura and most urodeles, so that all the VI arch blood must go to the lung and to the skin through the pulmonary artery. Simultaneously the V aortic arch is at least sharply reduced and commonly obliterated altogether, leaving the IV arch of each side as the principal or the only remaining path to the dorsal aorta; the IV arch enlarges commensurately. Meanwhile, the whole region that the aortic arches occupy collapses with the resorption of its skeletal arch supports, and the remaining blood vessels shorten and smooth out their curving paths.

The net effect of this transformation is to change the amphibian aortic arch system from something rather like that of a fish to something rather like that of a reptile.

These metamorphic changes are very well known in the morphological sense, but almost completely unexplained physiologically. The thyroid hormones are principal agents in starting them off, but there are only tentative theories as to what these molecules do at the surface of cells, or inside them. Each organ and tissue responds specifically to the general stimulus. Of two tissues lying side by side in the larva, one may be destroyed and the other spurred to vigorous growth and differentiation. Even certain neurons within the brain regress while others near them take on new growth. The multitudes of specific changes are regulated on a perfectly adjusted timetable in the intact animal, but they can be produced ahead of time, and manipulated individually and locally, by the implantation of thyroxin pellets.

X. PECULIARITIES OF CYCLOSTOMES

Like many of the fossil agnathous fishes from the Silurian and Devonian periods, the surviving lampreys and hagfishes have an excessive number of post-otic pharynx segments. Lampreys regularly show seven functional pairs of branchial pouches in the adult, but two additional pairs are reported to appear posteriorly and then disappear in the embryo. Hagfishes go even farther. One species whose members regularly show

10 pairs of functional gill pouches contains some individuals with as many as 13. Some more anterior pairs of pharynx segments are aborted during development.

The pharynx clefts which develop gills become sharply constricted at both their pharyngeal and external openings, leaving the gill lamellae crowded into drum-shaped **branchial sacs.** These drift posteriorly in hagfishes, and lose their contact with the few wisps of cartilage provisionally identified as visceral skeleton. Also their external openings are prolonged and narrowed into **water ducts** whose openings through the skin are displaced far back, and may even be collected into a common pore. Since water can be both inhaled and exhaled through this hole, the hagfish can crawl a good way inside another fish to mine its soft tissues with the piston-and-rasper device that is called a "tongue," while still breathing ocean water. Lampreys are also able to inhale as well as exhale through their gill pores, and regularly must do so while their heads are being used as anchors, since the mouth lies in the center of the sucker.

Lampreys do form regular segmental bars of cartilage in their pharynx segments, but these gradually become knit together in one lacy structure, the **branchial basket,** quite unlike the visceral skeleton of gnathostomes. Though this is said to be formed from neural crest cells as in higher vertebrates [13], it lies *outside* the principal branchial muscles, the post-trematic nerves, and the aortic arches, whereas the visceral skeleton of gnathostomes lies *inside* them.

Muscle plates are formed in each of the post-otic pharynx segments in lampreys and hagfishes, but do not subdivide into Cd and Cv groups, and none of the special sets of muscles they produce can be homologized with any in gnathostomes.

Lampreys have a glossopharyngeal IX nerve with a triplet pattern of branches around the first functional gill slit, as in gnathostomes. There is no IX nerve in hagfishes, since the pharynx pouch and segment which it would supply are obliterated early in embryonic development. In both these kinds of fishes, the long vagus nerves subdivide into enough branchial trunks and triplets to take care of all the rest of the branchial pouches and segments. In lampreys, the intestinal ramus of the vagus is very short, but in hagfishes the two of them fuse into a single trunk that follows the intestine all the way to the anus.

No pharynx-segment derivatives corresponding to the thymus or parathyroid are formed in either lampreys or hagfishes. Both have thyroid glands during adult life; but in both there are outstanding developmental peculiarities. In hagfishes a thyroid gland arises from a midventral strip of solid epithelium extending the whole length of the enormous pharynx, later breaking up into beads scattered between the ventral aorta and the intestine.

In adult lampreys the thyroid survives as a series of twisted endocrine tubules lying ventral to the second, third, and fourth branchial sacs, but during the several years of larval existence it is one of the cellular constituents of a complicated organ called the **hypobranchial sac.** This arises as a midventral evagination, which is first pinched off from the embryonic pharynx, and then later sends a small communicating duct back to it. The sac itself develops elaborate median and paired chambers which contain glandular strips wrapped in ciliated epithelium. Besides secreting a rope of mucous material that passes down the intestine (thus resembling a food-trapping apparatus known as the endostyle, found in tunicates and the amphioxus), it functions even in the larval stage as an agent for trapping and binding iodine, which is the first step in synthesis of a thyroid hormone.

At the time the ammocoetes larva metamorphoses into the adult lamprey, a break appears in the alimentary canal between pharynx and esophagus, which leaves the gill-bearing zone as a **water sac** with a blind posterior end, still leading to the gill sacs but useless for swallowing. The gap in the alimentary canal is repaired in most species, through the agency of a solid strand of pharynx tissue that forms in the dorsal midline of the water sac, separates off, and excavates itself as a new esophagus. In some species this repair is not completed, so that the adults can never feed after metamorphosis, but live on their stored reserves only only enough to produce one crop of fertilized eggs, and then die.

REFERENCES

As a summary of known anatomy of the post-otic *visceral skeleton* and associated *muscles* and *nerves,* nothing has supplanted (or is likely to supplant) the monographs by Haller von Hallerstein in vol. 2, 1934, by Martinelli, Stadtmüller, and Versluys in vol. 4, 1936, and by Luther and Lubosch in vol. 5, 1938, of the great *Handbuch der vergleichenden Anatomie der Wirbeltiere.* Comparable works in English are few. There is Edgeworth [1] for the *muscles.* Goodrich [7] is still the best single reference for *aortic arches* and *head arteries;* also, he discusses *gills* comprehensively, though some of his widely copied diagrams were rendered obsolete by the work of Bijtel [3]. There is a new compendium of information on the much-neglected cyclostomes in Tome 13 of Grassé's *Traité de zoologie,* 1958.

1. EDGEWORTH, F. H., 1935. *The cranial muscles of vertebrates.* Cambridge University Press, London.
2. KEYNES, R. D., 1957. Electric organs. *In* M. E. Brown (ed.), *The physiology of fishes,* Vol. 2. Academic Press, Inc., New York.
3. BIJTEL, J. H., 1949. *Arch. Néerl. Zool.* 8: 1.
4. FRY, F. E. J., 1957. Aquatic Respiration of Fish. *In* M. E. BROWN (ed.), *The physiology of fishes,* Vol. 1. Academic Press, Inc., New York.
5. BLACK, V. S., 1957. In BROWN (ed.); see Ref. 4.
6. CARTER, G. S., 1957. In BROWN (ed.); see Ref. 4.
7. GOODRICH, E. S., 1930. *Studies on the structure and development of vertebrates.* Macmillan & Co., London.
8. RYCHTER, Z., 1962. *Advances in Morphogenesis* 2: 333.
9. HAMMOND, W. S., 1954. *J. Morphol.* 95: 501.
10. BAKER-COHEN, K. F., 1959. *In* A. GORBMAN (ed.), *Comparative endocrinology.* John Wiley & Sons, Inc., New York.
11. TURNER, C. D., 1960. *General endocrinology.* 3d ed. W. B. Saunders Co., Philadelphia. See also D. F. TAPLEY, 1962. *Am. Zoologist* 2: 373.
12. DEUCHAR, E. M., 1958. *J. Embryol. Exptl. Morphol.* 6: 527.
13. NEWTH, D. R., 1955. *Doklady Akad. Nauk.* S.S.S.R. 102: 653.

18

Further Developments in the Brain

The development of the central nervous system is a story of mitotic cell proliferation, cell growth, and cell differentiation.

Proliferation. Many kinds of cells continue their mitotic divisions throughout the lifetime of the individual, and their multiplication centers can be spotted in particular organs or tissues, for instance the germinal layer of the epidermis, the blood-forming tissues, the seminiferous tubules of the testis, etc. Not so the neuroblasts. Their proliferation slows down and stops before birth or hatching.

Growth. Nevertheless the neurons continue to increase in size as long as the animal itself grows, and in proper proportion. If this were not so, one of the consequences would be that the nerves which extend out from the brain and spinal cord would be pulled loose from their peripheral organs, or so attenuated that their function would be impaired. The gross form of the brain continues to be molded for some time by the total effect of the growth of hundreds of millions of its individual neurons, though most of its permanent structural features are established in early fetal periods, many of them being visible already at the pharyngula stage.

Differentiation. While the multiplication of neuroblasts is slowing down in the central nervous system, their differentiation has only begun, and this phase of development coincides with the later aspects of growth. The central nervous system becomes (1) an information-gathering mechanism, through its sensory neurons; (2) an analyzing and deciding mechanism; and (3) an executive mechanism through which behavior appropriate to the total situation is carried out. All this is produced by individual neuroblasts, which elaborate their axons and dendrites, develop their own individuality, and selectively establish contacts with particular other neurons in exquisitely precise patterns.

In the aggregate, this differentiation produces a histologic structure of nuclei, tracts, and neuropil (page 156) whose structure is more complex than that of any other tissue. It also produces a behavior pattern which is characteristic of the species but subtly and unpredictably modulated from instant to instant.

The development of behavior may be completed in a few days or weeks, or it may take years. For instance many fishes and reptiles break from their eggs or drop away from their mothers with a nearly perfected behavior. Others, such as amphibia, nidicolous birds, and many mammals, slowly evolve their adult behavior through active larval or juvenile phases, or undergo a long, rather passive maturation while under the care of their parents.

Both the anatomical complexity and the behavior arise from the development of neuroblasts. These are the cells that link the whole body into a functioning unit. For convenience, this chapter will take up first the motor apparatus of the central nervous system, then the sensory apparatus, leaving the more complex and mysterious associational areas of the brain to the last.

I. MOTOR NUCLEI OF ORIGIN, AND THEIR TRACTS

In cytology, a **nucleus** is a karyon, the chromatin-containing spheroid in the interior of a single cell. In neurology, a **nucleus** is a multicellular functional center, a group of the somata of neurons clustered together in the central nervous system, and associated in transmission along some particular pathway. As an example, during fetal stages, the cells from which the axons of the trochlear IV nerves arise tend to draw together in the gray substance of the somatic motor column (Fig. 9–5), becoming somewhat segregated from the rest of the neurons in the area. So do those of the III and the VI nerves. Each of these cell clusters may be identified as a **motor nucleus of origin.**

It is not known what causes these cells to clump together in a recognizable nucleus. In the chick, prior removal of the anlage of the superior oblique muscle in no way discourages the formation of a full-sized IV nerve nucleus, but if the axons from this nucleus do not locate and make contact with this muscle they subsequently degenerate [1].

The neurons of one of these motor nuclei send dendritic twigs branching widely through the lower part of the brainstem. The function of all these twigs is a matter of speculation. However, synaptic knobs of axons grow in from various parts of the brain and end close to the somata of the motor cells or close to the bases of their axons and main dendrites, and undoubtedly bring to these neurons the information that decides what combination of impulses to send out along their peripheral axons. Thus the motor nuclei in concert give the final orders which, for example, turn the eyeballs in a particular direction.

But what leads their axons to precisely the right eyeball muscles rather than to some other muscles, or to skin, or glands? How does it happen that, of all the possible billions of neurons in the central nervous system the few thousand which make synapse with the motor nucleus of origin of the IV nerve are just the ones which will bring it the proper information upon which an appropriate response can be based? There are no good answers for these questions yet, but certain hints from recent experiments will be considered below.

There are two principal classes of motor nuclei in the brain, and each lies in its own functional column in the floor of the brainstem (page 293). This is most clear-cut in the primitive fishes,

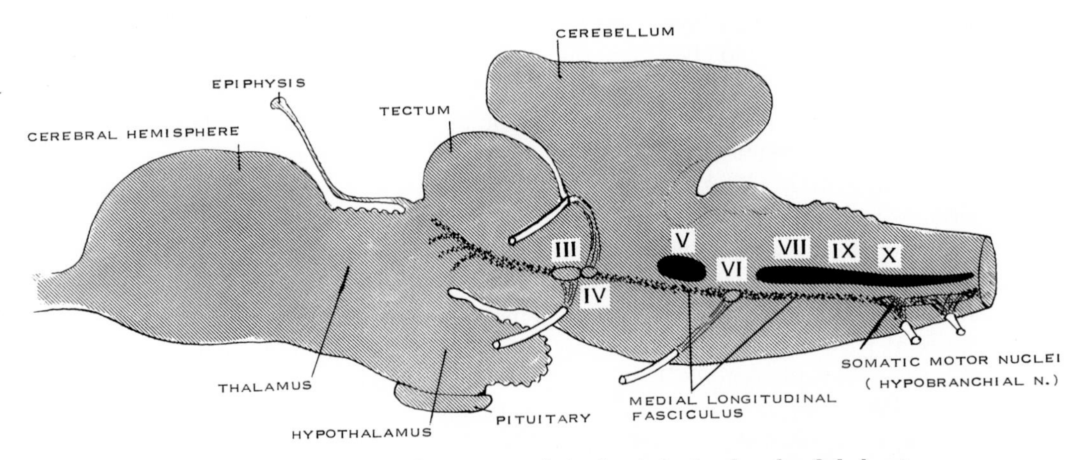

Fig. 18–1. Location of motor nuclei of origin in the dogfish brain.

which show a sharp segregation of **visceral motor** and **somatic motor columns** in the gray substance at the floor of the IV ventricle (Fig. 18–1).

A. Somatic Motor Nuclei

A somatic motor column of ventricular gray substance runs on each side of the sagittal plane, down the full length of the floor of the midbrain and hindbrain. It continues less conspicuously through the length of the spinal cord. In all vertebrates, the nuclei of origin of the III, IV, and VI cranial nerves lie in it, each on their own side. The roots of III and VI always emerge close to the midline on the ventral surface of the brainstem near their nuclei, providing there an external mark of the location of the somatic motor sector. In all vertebrates, however, this rule is flouted by the axons from the IV nuclei. For no known reason, each of the IV nerve roots skirts the gray substance and runs illogically dorsad, decussating across the top of the central canal and emerging on the dorsal surface of the opposite side of the brain, between tectum and cerebellum (Fig. 18–2). From there, each nerve passes out from the cranial cavity to the orbit and ends in contact with its own muscle (page 255).

The **nucleus of the hypoglossal nerve** also lies in the somatic motor column, and its roots follow the rule, emerging with those of III and VI (Figs. 18–1, 18–3). In some vertebrates the hypoglossal nucleus overlaps the boundary between brain and spinal cord, and in others it is entirely a spinal cord structure. This difference is the result of two variables. One is the location of the boundary between brain and spinal cord, which is defined by where the foramen magnum of the skull comes to be. This boundary has drifted backward and forward along the central nervous system in various evolutionary lines of vertebrates [2]. The other variable is the poorly understood, possibly nutritive, interrelation between nerves and their peripheral organs generally. Not only do organs eventually suffer when deprived of their nerves, but the size of the nerves is also developed in close correlation with their peripheral load. In many fishes and amphibia the hypoglossal (hypobranchial) muscles are rudimentary, and their hypoglossal (hypobranchial) nerves have few axons and spring from small nuclei. At the other extreme, the hypoglossal muscles of mammals are built into a large muscular tongue, and the nerves increase commensurately. Their nuclei then may spread far down the cervical part of the spinal cord, and as far forward as the roots of the vagus in the hindbrain. The mechanism by which extra cells are drafted into a nucleus until it is large enough to match the peripheral requirements is not understood. It is spoken of as an "assimilative induction" influence which travels in over pioneer fibers which have made their peripheral contacts [3].

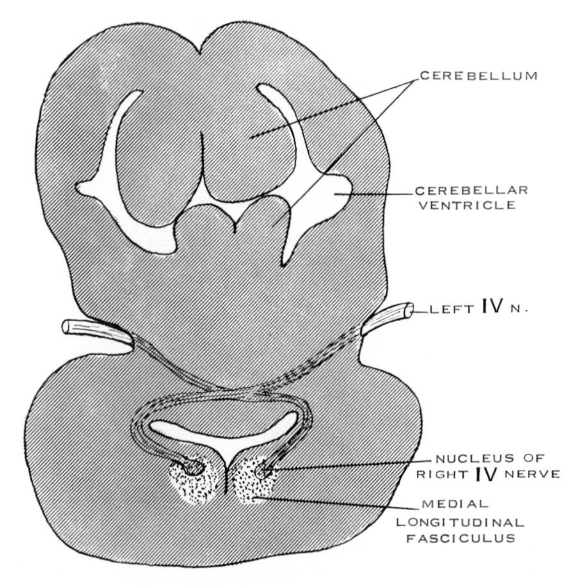

Fig. 18–2. Diagrammatic cross-section of the dogfish brain through the trochlear nucleus.

All these somatic motor nuclei lie embedded in, or in close functional relationship with a descending tract called the **medial longitudinal fasciculus** (Figs. 18–1, 18–2, 18–3). In the brains of all vertebrate embryos this is one of the first motor-coordinating systems to be established. Though it receives contributions from many sources, its principal cells of origin lie in the diencephalon and midbrain. The protrusion of the somatic motor column into the floor of the

IV ventricle is partly caused by the bulk of this tract. In serial sections, the axons of the medial longitudinal fasciculus can be traced down through the entire length of the spinal cord. They send synaptic processes into all somatic motor nuclei, which includes those of spinal nerves as well as III, IV, VI, and XII in the brain. One cannot say why these neurons behave in concert like this, selecting a path and connections which give them the function of a primitive somatic motor coordinating apparatus. Even the more general question of what decides the direction of outgrowth of an axon is still only partly explored (page 59).

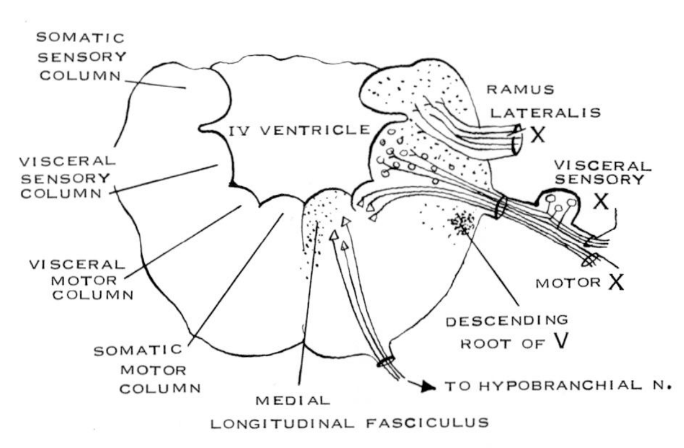

Fig. 18–3. Diagrammatic cross-section of the posterior part of the dogfish hindbrain.

In primitive brains like that of the amblystoma, the medial longitudinal fasciculus is not clearly segregated from visceral transmission systems. In more specialized brains it becomes quite separate, though much of its function may be subordinated to newer and more elaborate control centers arising in more anterior parts of the brain. And other more locally specialized motor projection systems are gradually developed, sending their axons caudad along other pathways through hindbrain and spinal cord.

In the anamniotes, the medial longitudinal fasciculus is involved in the rhythmic trunk-and-tail movements of swimming, and it is usually augmented by special **giant neurons.** Each hagfish or lamprey has a few dozen of these, which arise in the floor of the midbrain and send their axons down to the caudal end of the spinal cord. In the gnathostome fishes and amphibian larvae these are inconspicuous and functionally replaced by a single pair of gigantic neurons (commonly called Mauthner's cells), whose huge somata lie in the hindbrain at ear level, receiving many hundreds of synaptic knobs from neurons located in many parts of the brain. The axons of these two giant neurons decussate at once and follow the somatic motor gray substance to the tip of the tail, giving off collateral terminals at all levels. How these fibers, and the rest of the tracts that accompany them, coordinate the timing of contraction of the paired series of myotomes so as to produce a controlled rhythmic swimming action is unknown, but if they are destroyed or interrupted the effect on behavior and even on posture is disastrous.

The two giant neurons of Mauthner are almost unique in the central nervous system of vertebrates, since they are individually identifiable and capable of being extirpated or transplanted in embryos, or selectively stimulated or destroyed in adults. Therefore they have been the focus of some of the research on factors which control differentiation and function inside the central nervous system. The question as to what guides their growth caudad and the choice of neurons with which they form synapses is not yet answered. When transplanted to quite abnormal locations in the brain [4] they usually (but not always) thread their way through strange territory and apparently seek out the medial longitudinal fasciculus, down which they then distribute normally. Similar evidence has been found that other neuron bundles preferentially select their pathways through the central nervous system.

B. Visceral Motor Nuclei

In embryonic brains of all vertebrates, the visceral motor nuclei of the mixed pharynx-segment nerves V, VII, IX, and X differentiate in a linear series in the visceral motor column of gray substance of the hindbrain (Figs. 9–5, 18–1, 18–3). They achieve various degrees of discreteness. For instance in some very primitive brains they show little separation from one another, and even when they become discrete they may be displaced either anteriorly or posteriorly in the visceral motor sector. The motor VII nucleus of one species may be quite by itself, but in another it might be in contact either with the motor V nucleus, or (Fig. 18–1) with the motor IX. It is fairly common to find the motor nuclei of IX and X in one continuous strip [5].

In more advanced brains, there is a tendency for a separation of the primitive motor nuclei into special subgroups, some of which may migrate laterally, abandoning the original location close to the IV ventricle, though still remaining in the visceral motor sector. In sharks and many other fishes for instance, the whole motor VII nucleus lies at the ventricular surface, but in some of the more advanced bony fishes it is divided into two masses, one of which is displaced a considerable distance ventrolaterally into the reticular substance. This is frequently true in amniotes, in which there is a VII nucleus which supplies axons to salivary glands, and another which supplies hyoid-segment muscles. The former tends to remain near the original ventricular position, while the latter usually migrates outward, even so much as to lie on the ventrolateral surface of the hindbrain. The cause of these concerted migrations of groups of neurons is not known [1].

The size of particular visceral motor nuclei is correlated with the bulk of the tissues to which they send axons. For instance, increasing the amount of mandibular muscle experimentally on one side of the amblystoma head increases the motor V nucleus of that side. In weak-jawed anteaters the motor V nucleus is small, but it is exceptionally large in the carnivores and grazing mammals that have the most powerful jaws. There is a new development of hyoid-segment musculature in mammals consisting of mimetic muscle sheets that project all over the face (page 304). To serve this increased bulk of tissue, the motor VII nuclei of mammals are correspondingly enlarged. These same animals also have a powerful development of the trapezius musculature (page 315), which is innervated by the accessory nerve, a subdivision of the vagus. Correlated with this is a great increase in the motor X–XI nucleus, which may be subdivided into sections, and in some species extends as far back as the last cervical segment of the spinal cord.

In the electric rays, the transformation of pharynx-segment muscle cells into a huge electric organ on each side (page 313) is accompanied by such a development of the motor components of the VII, IX, and X nerves that the visceral motor column forms a mound on each side of the hindbrain larger than the cerebellum, practically obliterating the IV ventricle.

II. SENSORY NUCLEI OF TERMINATION, AND SECONDARY TRACTS

It will be necessary at once to distinguish between sensory nuclei of *origin* and of *termination,* and between *primary* and *secondary* sensory tracts.

Since a motor nucleus of origin has been defined as the cluster of cells which gives out the axons of a peripheral nerve, then it is logical to consider the ganglion of a peripheral nerve as a **sensory nucleus of origin,** for here lie the somata of the sensory axons of that nerve. These axons enter the central nervous system, and there they end in relation to other groups of cells which will be defined as their **sensory nuclei of termination** (Fig. 18–4).

The sensory roots of cranial nerves V, VII, and VIII all enter the hindbrain in a small area on each side. Among the fibers of these roots are axons of both somatic and visceral sensory neurons, some of each kind bringing in stimuli from free terminal twigs, others bringing stimuli derived from special sense organs. All these fibers, coming in from whatever nerve, sort themselves out inside the hindbrain according to their categories of sensation. All the **lateral line** fibers (from VII, IX, and X) for example, line up in one longitudinal bundle on each side. Other bundles are formed by the **general skin sense** fibers (from V, etc.), the **general** (mucous membrane) **visceral sense** fibers (from VII, IX, X), **taste, hearing,** etc. (Fig. 18–5).

Each of these discrete bundles is a **primary sensory tract** (Fig. 18–4). Characteristically it divides into an ascending and a descending arm, and its fibers can be distinguished in cross-sections throughout the entire length of the hindbrain, sometimes extending well down the spinal cord and up into the cerebellar region. In higher vertebrates, even the separate modalities of general somatic sense sort themselves out in this way. In man, for instance, the senses of touch, pain and temperature can be traced along separate tracts through the hindbrain. In quite mysterious ways, such extraordinarily specific differences

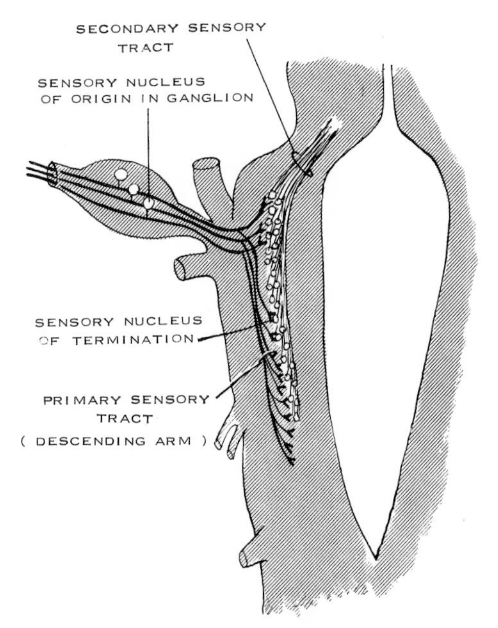

Fig. 18–4. Diagram of the connections of sensory neurons entering the hindbrain of a salamander.

between categories of neurons, and the affinities of similar ones for each other, seem to determine the functional organization of the central nervous system (see discussion of specificity, page 352).

These axonic bundles end in synaptic relation with streaks or elongated clusters of cells that gather around them from the gray substance through which they pass. Since these more or less well segregated groups of cells receive and relay impulses related to specific types of incoming sensory stimuli, they may be called **sensory nuclei of termination.** The axons which arise from the somata of a particular nucleus of termination are often collected together in an identifiable **secondary sensory tract,** which carries their specific information toward more central and more anterior coordinating or recording centers.

The development of certain sensory nuclei of termination associated with the VIII nerve has been studied experimentally in the chick [6]. In one case the nucleus failed to develop if the special primary sensory fibers were prevented from growing to it. In other cases, the nuclei formed normally in the absence of primary sensory fibers, but subsequently disappeared.

In the most primitive vertebrate brains, such as that of the amblystoma, all the primary incoming sensory fibers lose themselves in a general neuropil field. Nuclei of termination, and secondary tracts, though they must exist in a functional sense, are diffuse and unrecognizable in serial sections. In more complex brains, whether of fishes or of amniotes, the segregation of cells of the gray substance proceeds farther, so that secondary and even tertiary nuclei and tracts can be traced. In all cases however, the axons of the primary, the secondary and the later relaying neurons in the sensory transmission systems send collateral branches in many directions into the reticular substance or the general neuropil mat, serving functions far more elaborate than simple reflex action.

As with the motor nuclei of origin, the sensory nuclei of termination can be divided into somatic and visceral groups.

A. Visceral Sensory Nuclei of Termination

The visceral sensory sector of the hindbrain appears in some fishes as a beaded column of gray substance projecting into the IV ventricle dorsolateral to the visceral motor column, from which it is separated by the sulcus limitans (Fig. 18–3). Visceral sensory axons from cranial nerves VII, IX, and X make their way there, spread out anteriorly and posteriorly as primary tracts, and end within it in relation to their nuclei of termination.

The secondary sensory tracts contribute to a primitive visceral bundle called the **fasciculus solitarius** (Fig. 18–5), which contains not only general mucous membrane sense from the mouth and pharynx, but also taste sense. The ratio of these two components in the fasciculus vary according to the adaptation of their peripheral fields. A secondary nucleus of cells is segregated from the nearby gray substance in association with the fasciculus solitarius, and these two structures account for most of the ventricular bulge of the visceral sensory zone (Figs. 9–5, 18–3). Experiments with this area show its important involvement in respiratory reflexes of fishes. In terrestrial vertebrates it contributes to mechanisms for controlling the rhythms of the heart and lungs, and for vomiting, coughing, and other visceral reflexes.

The taste system is developed to its maximum in bony fishes such as carp and catfish. In these, taste buds may be scattered over the skin from head to tail, and the nuclei of termination of the enlarged incoming taste nerves may bulge the visceral sensory column of each side into a lobe that rides up out of the IV ventricle, rivaling the cerebellum in size. At the other extreme, the central nervous representation of the taste system in mammals is diffuse and vague.

B. General Somatic Nuclei of Termination

The two principal functional components in this category, so far as cranial nerves and the brain are concerned, are (1) the general skin sense reported through the four principal divisions of the trigeminal nerve, and (2) the proprioceptive sense from the jaw muscles and tendons, reported through the mandibular branch of the trigeminal.

1. General Skin Sense. In the head the principal nucleus of origin of this sense is in the trigeminal ganglion. The corresponding primary tract which enters the brain from this nerve associates itself with a quite typical nucleus of termination. The two together form a streak of recognizably segregated tissue that runs caudad in the somatic motor column, usually through the length of the hindbrain and often far down the spinal cord This **descending root of the trigeminal** (Figs. 18–3, 18–5) makes secondary connections with many if not all the motor centers; it is thus possible for the whole body, or any appropriate parts of it, to react swiftly to outside developments that are detected by the important face area of skin.

However, provision of these multitudes of rather simple reflex paths does not produce normal behavior. It must be remembered that

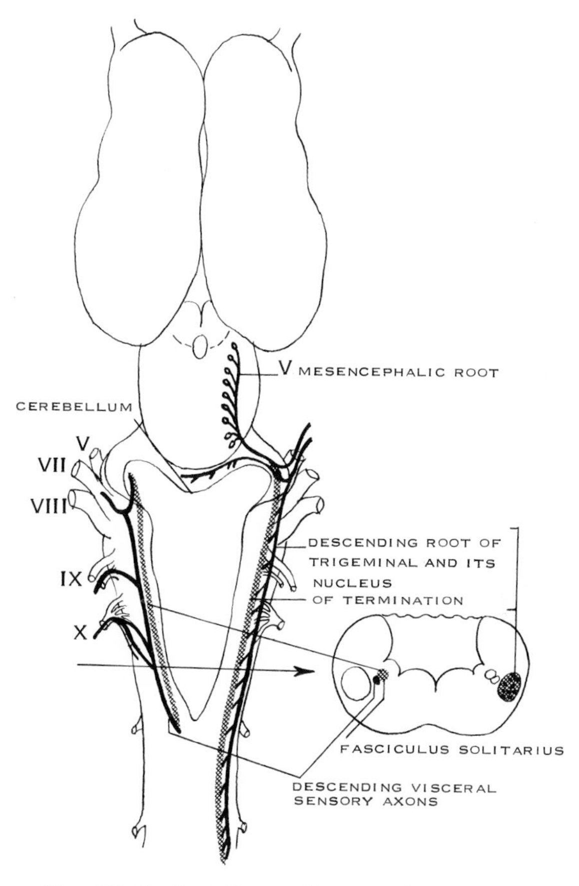

Fig. 18–5. Locations of two primary sensory tracts and their nuclei of termination in the amblystoma brain.

(After C. J. Herrick, 1948, The Brain of the Tiger Salamander, by permission of The University of Chicago Press.)

there must also be mechanisms for choosing and effecting the best response to each unique stimulus received on the face, and for inhibiting all the other possible responses (cf. Part III, page 355).

In most vertebrates, the trigeminal nerve is almost exclusively the agent for registering general skin sense over the whole head region. Vestiges of this somatic sensory function do remain in the IX and X nerves of gnathostomes, and sometimes even in the VII nerve, but such cutaneous-sense fibers as do occur in the VII, IX, or X roots join the descending root of the trigeminal as soon as they have entered the hindbrain. The same is true in the more simply segmental heads of the cyclostomes, whose branchial-segment nerves all still contain important cutaneous components.

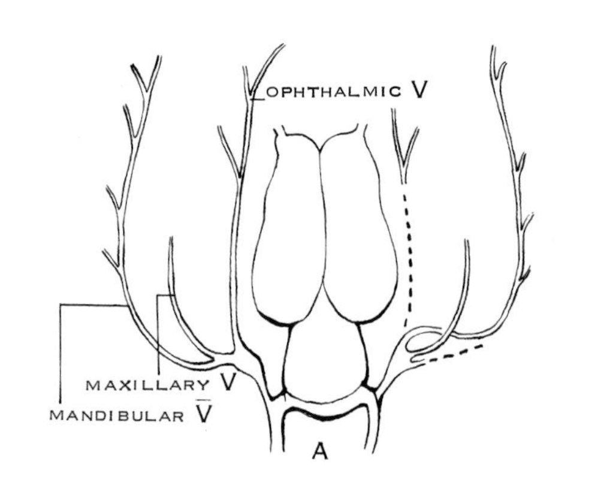

Fig. 18–6. Results of misdirecting the regeneration of sensory neurons in a salamander. A. Cross-union of ophthalmic with mandibular nerves on right side. B. Result of pinprick on jaw of normal left side, felt through normal mandibular nerve. C. Result of pinprick on jaw of right side supplied by misdirected regenerated ophthalmic nerve.

(After R. W. Sperry, 1951, in Handbook of Experimental Psychology, by permission of John Wiley & Sons, Inc.)

If all these sensory fibers enter the same primary tract, how does the animal know, when it feels a pin prick, which part of its head has been touched? If the ophthalmic and mandibular divisions of the V nerve of a salamander are cut just outside the ganglion, the regenerating sensory fibers that grow out from the ophthalmic stump can be directed into the territory of the mandibular division, and vice versa (Fig. 18–6). When these fibers have made functional contacts with the skin in their new territories, the animal will foolishly dodge its head upward instead of downward if pricked on the top of its snout, and dodge downward instead of upward if pricked on the chin. It acts as though the sensation comes from where the nerve ending *should have been,* rather than where it *is* [7].

If the V nerve root of this salamander is cut medial to the ganglion, the sensory ganglion cells belonging to all the divisions of the nerve will regenerate new axons, which have to grow back to the brain through a wound area disordered by clotted blood and degenerating cells. In so doing, they become so snarled and intermingled that it would seem hopeless to expect that each could re-establish its specific reflex connections in the hindbrain. Nevertheless in several weeks the animal will again dodge *away* from a pin prick in the normal way, whatever part of the trigeminal territory the pin touches. The same is true if the regenerating trigeminal fibers are caused to grow into the brain through the root of the facial nerve. Such experiments as these have a bearing on the question of how the central nervous system becomes so organized as to perform specific functions instead of becoming a chaotic snarl of fibers. We will return to such experiments and the questions which they illuminate, in the discussion on specificity (page 352).

2. *Proprioceptive Sense.* This sense, which comes from jaw muscles, is reported by sensory neurons of the mandibular V nerve, which break a rule obeyed by all other sensory nerves in the body. One would expect the somata of these neurons to lie in the trigeminal ganglion outside the brain. Instead, they occupy a streak of gray substance in the somatic sensory column throughout the length of the midbrain, called the **mesencephalic root of the trigeminal** (Fig. 18–5). This is the only known case of a well-organized *sensory nucleus of origin* inside the brain. It is found there in all vertebrates except the cyclostomes, which do not have jaws. The primitive "mouth sense" that the mesencephalic root is concerned with is a very important one to a hunting or feeding animal equipped with jaws. Its neurons

make wide and quite direct connections with the motor transmission systems of the brainstem.

Secondary nuclei and tracts establish associations with both the descending tract of the trigeminus (skin sense of the head) and somatic sensory components of the spinal nerves (skin sense of trunk and tail), and relay their information anteriorly to higher brain centers. These bundles of ascending fibers increase in number at more and more anterior levels, and appear in cross sections of the hindbrain as important elements of the white substance outside the sensory sectors on each side. They are collectively termed the **medial lemniscus system** (Fig. 18–7). In the brains of anamniotes the spinal components of the medial lemnisci are feebly developed, since more of the discriminating, deciding, and directing functions of the central nervous system seem to be handled at local levels of the spinal cord instead of being transferred to more anterior levels of the brain. (cf. comments on cephalization, below, page 351).

C. Special Somatic Sensory Nuclei

The segmental structure of the tail and trunk imposes a more or less segmental organization on the spinal cord and its nerves. The pharynx segments are similarly important in setting a pattern for the "bulb" or myelencephalon. In sharp contrast, the more anterior and dorsal parts of the brain, into which the special somatic sensory fibers of the lateral line, ears, eyes, and olfactory organs are projected, take on an altogether different external appearance. They used to be referred to as the **suprasegmental zone** of the central nervous system, as distinguished from the **segmental zone** of the hindbrain and spinal cord.

1. Lateral Line. In the anamniotes, the primary axons of this widespread sensory system stream into the anterodorsal parts of the hindbrain through a pre-otic VII root and a post-otic IX-X root (Figs. 18–3, 18–7). Their fibers divide into ascending and descending branches, and most of them end in large nuclei of termination which make easily recognizable excrescences in the somatic sensory sectors, called **acousticolateral lobes.** However some of the primary fibers go to the cerebellum, as a great many of the secondary ones do, and some form a descending bundle that may even reach into the spinal cord.

Masses of secondary fibers arise from these nuclei of termination, many of them decussate, and they form on each side an ascending bundle called the **lateral** (or acousticolateral) **lemniscus**

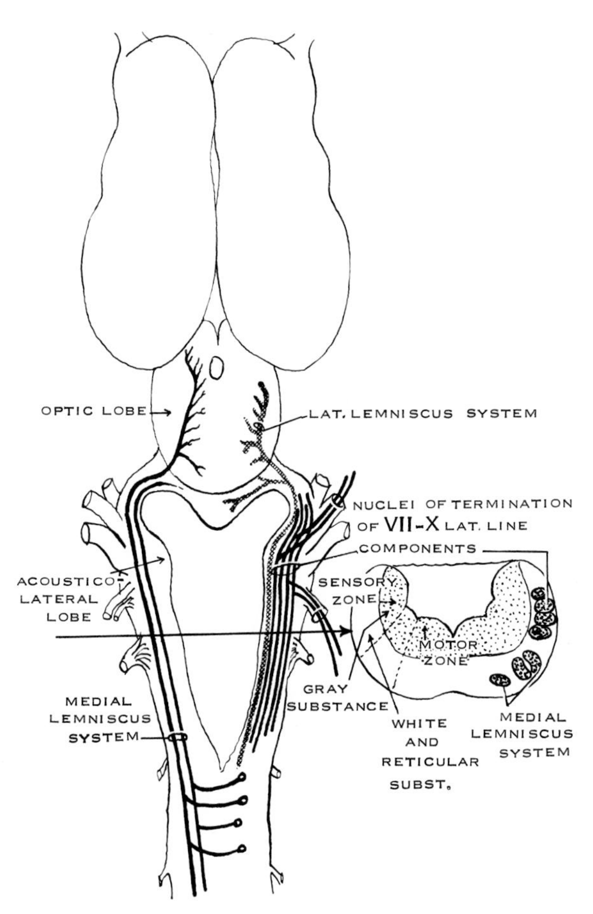

Fig. 18–7. Lemniscus systems of the amblystoma brain.

(After C. J. Herrick, 1948, The Brain of the Tiger Salamander, by permission of The University of Chicago Press.)

(Fig. 18–7), which ends in relay centers on the posterolateral surface of the optic lobe of the midbrain. In contrast with the medial lemnisci, which are well developed only in the amniotes, the lateral lemnisci are strongly developed in both these and the anamniotes. However, as will shortly be seen, their main component is not reach the tectum but are intercepted in thalamic nuclei, which then relay the sensation to levels of consciousness in the cerebral hemispheres. This is an example of cephalization.

Specificity of Neurons. If an optic nerve of an amphibian is cut, information from that eye stops going to the brain, and the animal of course no longer responds to such information. New optic fibers are soon regenerated from the ganglion cells of the isolated retina, but as they approach the brain they become snarled and randomly mixed in crossing the disordered zone where the cut had been made. Nevertheless, the contact of each quadrant of the retina with its own particular part of the tectum is somehow restored, and normal reflex connections through the midbrain to all the motor nuclei of the body thereupon reappear. This astonishing and experimentally repeatable result could hardly be achieved by chance. It seems more likely that each primary optic fiber has some sort of affinity for very particular secondary fibers, and can make functional synaptic connections only with these. Otherwise, light striking the regenerated eye would not set off an appropriate, coordinated response, but a disordered convulsion.

About the specificity of the primary fibers there is little question. It is possible to loosen the eyeball of a frog and turn it 180 degrees in the orbit without hurting the optic nerve. When the eye has healed in this position, the quadrant of the retina that once looked forward now looks backward, that which once looked downward now looks upward, etc. (Fig. 18–10 B). Each quadrant nevertheless still delivers information to the brain *as though it were in its original position.* The brain has no way of realizing that the information, while still valid, has been rendered false. Thus, when the frog sees food with one quadrant of its rotated eye, and lunges for it, the strike is made away from the food, not toward it. This mistake is repeated time and again, and no learning process ever corrects it. (The frog does not possess the cerebral apparatus with which such learning would be accomplished in man.)

If the twisted optic nerve is now cut and allowed to regenerate, the hundreds of optic fibers get badly snarled with each other as they thread their way through the scar tissue. Nevertheless, they find their way to the optic lobe and succeed in establishing the same sorts of reflex connections they had before. They do not form helter-skelter synapses, as might have been expected. As a result, the upside-down vision of the inverted eye is restored in all its absurdity, along with the completely useless business of snapping in the wrong direction [7].

Other errors of behavior result from cutting out the two eyes of a frog and exchanging them. If each eye is carried over the top of the head, keeping its cornea always outward, it may be installed in the other orbit with its anteroposterior axis normal, but its dorsoventral axis reversed (Fig. 18–10 C). After re-establishment of connections with the optic lobes, the frog now reacts as though what it sees below it is above it. If each extirpated eye is carried around the nose, cornea outward, it may be implanted with normal dorsoventral axis but a reversed anteroposterior axis (Fig. 18–10 D). With such eyes restored to function, the frog now behaves as though what it sees in front of it is behind it.

There is some evidence that the primary neurons derive such specificities as these from their peripheral contacts. (a) Thus, as noted above (page 348), trigeminal neurons which have originally taken the ophthalmic path to the skin become stamped with an upper-snout specificity such that any information they may later bring into the brain is identified as having come from that area, even though their dendritic zones may later have been transferred experimentally to the mandibular area (Fig. 18–6). This "cutaneous local sign" is never exchanged for another one, once it has been established in the developing neuron by its original contact with the skin of its own area [9].

(b) In the case of optic nerve fibers, the specificity of the different quadrants of the retina may be determined by the same mesodermal field which determines where the chorioid fissure will be (page 245). When the amphibian retina is caused to degenerate, a new one regenerates from the ciliary border, but its new optic fibers develop the same pattern of specificities as the original ones.

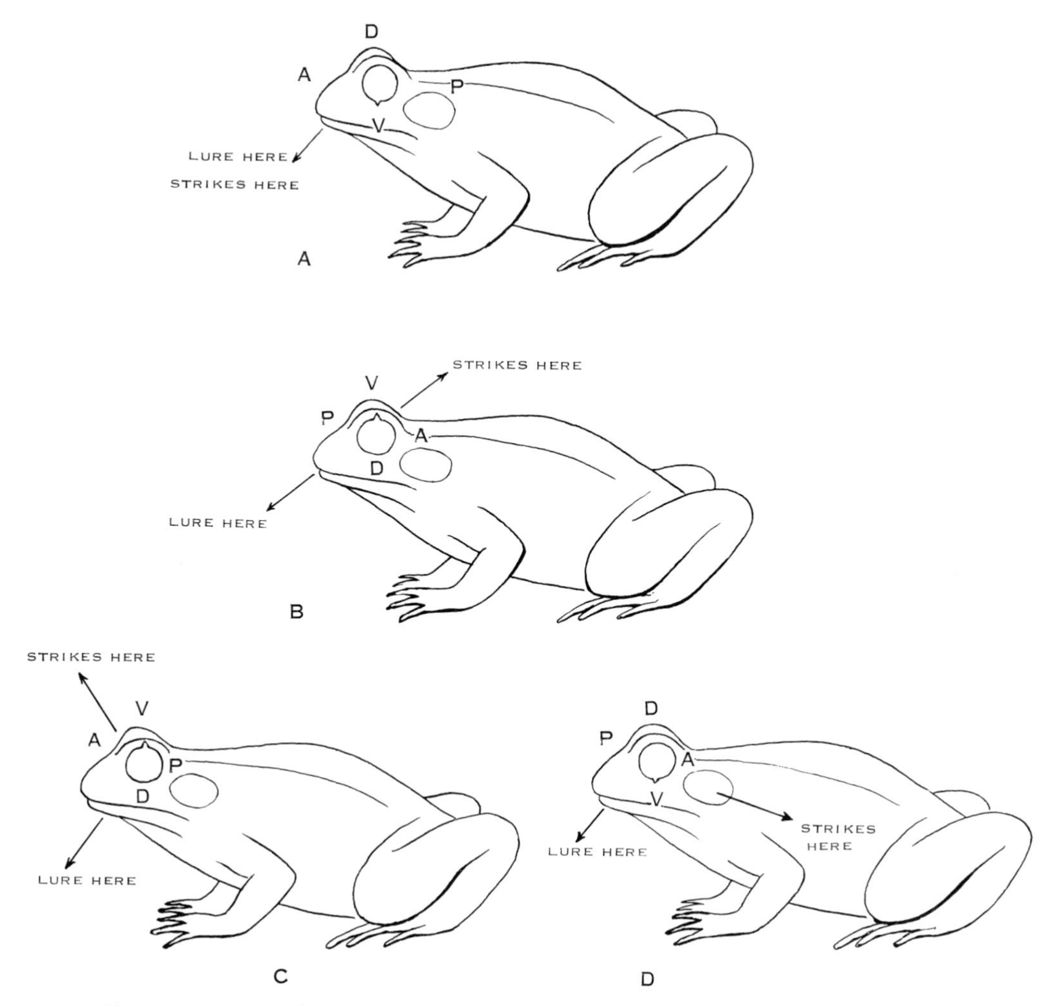

Fig. 18–10. Results of reversals of frog eye polarities by rotations and transplantations. A. Normal eyes. B. Eyes rotated 180°. C. Eyes inverted dorsoventrally. D. Eyes reversed anteroposteriorly.
(From data of R. W. Sperry, 1951.)

(c) Motor fibers also acquire specificities from their peripheral contacts. In the limbs of amphibian larvae this happens so slowly that the axons of incompletely specified nerves can be transplanted from one muscle to another and become specified in abnormal ways; nevertheless this provides evidence that each muscle imprints its own specificity on the nerve fibers that reach it, and this in turn limits and directs the kinds of functional connections that these nerves can make within the central nervous system.

The nature of this neuron specificity is in doubt, but its reality is not, nor can it be doubted that the neurons make specific, rather than random connections inside the central nervous system. Whether the primary sensory fibers pass their specificity on to the secondary fibers with which they happen to associate in the early embryo, or whether they seek out secondary fibers which already have matching specificities, is uncertain; both situations probably exist. Nevertheless, transplantation and regeneration experiments show that active selection of functional connections, based on neuronal specificities that they were, the animal would have to choose from among the total number of its possible automatic reflexes. Behavior of a vertebrate is not normally a selection of reflexes. It is analytical and discriminative, it involves the whole body, and it gives every sign of being purposeful. The endless variety of the behavior of a single individual from moment to moment, not to speak of the behavior of unrelated species, implies that there are interposed between the relatively standardized sensory and motor components some areas of far more elaborate structure and more subtly adjustable function. It is these areas which will now be considered.

In the amblystoma brain, one of the most primitive among vertebrates, the sensory components enter through the roots of the nerves and segregate by function into their own nuclei of termination. But the secondary neurons related to them are very widely branched, and their processes are lost in neuropil fields, in which several sensory systems are mixed [10] Very few sharply defined, automatic, and predictable reflexes can be elicited through the amblystoma brain. What the animal gives out is *total responses* to *total situations*. This is one of the best-known brains, but where in it the specifications for these responses are made, and how, is almost completely unknown.

If one searches for the parts of more elaborate brains in which integration of information, discrimination, choice, and coordination of appropriate responses occur, one also loses the trail, but not so promptly as in the amblystoma brain. The sensory nuclei of termination are more clearly segregated, and one can map secondary and even tertiary centers and tracts along which the incoming information of particular sorts is propagated. On the response side, one can also find nuclei and tracts once or twice removed from the final motor nuclei, along which the directives for peripheral action are brought.

But between these sensory and motor paths there lie one or more (usually several) great areas of such histologic complexity that the anatomist cannot point to one joining path across them which is more probable than any other, in reference to any specific stimulus–response activity. Nor can the physiologist thread the maze in the manner of an electrician looking for a live circuit through a tangle of wires, for there is a continually flickering rhythmical state of electrical activity intrinsic to each part of the central nervous system, against the background of which all but the most massive volleys of neuron discharges would be lost. In most cases the best present source of information about the function of particular areas of this sort is what happens to the animal's behavior when these areas are removed surgically, or stimulated in the unrestrained unanesthetized animal. Neither of these types of experiment tells anything about neuron pathways.

Some of the brain parts in question, which for want of a better name may be called **association areas,** are well marked and visible in dissection, for instance the cerebellum and the tectum, and in the mammals the thalamus and cerebral cortex. Or they may be buried and diffuse, like the reticular substance of the brainstem. Each one of them receives fiber tracts from a variety of sources, and has within it neuron arrangements (different for each area) for spreading, joining, and overlapping of stimuli from various sources. From each, fiber tracts project to many separate motor nuclei. Any one of them is interconnected with all the others by tracts and commissures. The great association areas, which have been named above, will be commented upon separately below. There are hosts of lesser areas. Indeed, each secondary and tertiary nucleus of the sensory input, and many other nuclei which might seem to be principally engaged in relaying impulses from one tract to another, participate also in the associational functions.

The early embryonic arrangement of a mantle of differentiating neuroblasts and a marginal layer of their axons and dendrites, is quickly obliterated over large areas of the brain. It is sometimes difficult to decide whether this happens because the longer tracts invade and break up the mantle layer like tree roots in a clay bed, or because cells of the mantle actually migrate into the marginal layer. Both processes certainly occur. In any case, many groups of functionally related somata become isolated from the mantle layer and lie as more or less well-defined nuclei of gray substance interspersed with white, the histologic pattern previously referred to (page 157) as reticular tissue. Even in the much studied human brain, the identification of smaller and smaller nuclei continues, by more and more refined techniques, like the mapping of the stars. Some of the larger nuclei can be safely homologized within whole classes of vertebrates.

The development of the reticular substance progressively disturbs the position of even the most constant nuclei, such as those that give rise to the motor cranial nerves. The embryonic picture of simple functional columns of gray substance is usually partly obliterated in adult brains, and particularly in birds and mammals.

In certain regions of the brain, whole layers of cells also migrate away from the mantle layer toward the outside. Thus, peripheral gray substance may be established which is well separated from the ventricular gray substance by intervening white or reticular substance, and may even lie on the surface as a **cortex** (Figs. 18–15, 18–20). All but the most primitive brains (cyclostomes and amphibia) show cortical developments in the cerebellum, and a piling up of special gray layers also occurs in the midbrain roof of amniotes, spectacularly in birds. The rudiments of a cerebral cortex can be detected in the brains of lungfishes, and suggestive preparations for one in amphibia, but the development of this organ never became an explosive and dominating element except in the placental mammals.

A. Reticular Substance

There are no sharp boundaries, or even precise definitions of this issue. Embedded in it are many identifiable nuclei and tracts to which, in some cases, rather precise functions have been ascribed. The fruitful exploration of this difficult material depends on quite new techniques.

A single neuron in this area (Fig. 4–11) may develop a very long axon that sends branches to a dozen or more parts of the brain, its terminal twigs forming a different pattern in each area [11]. Some reticular cells are known to be directly stimulated by certain hormones, or by simpler molecules such as CO_2, O_2, sugar, etc. Incoming tracts bring to the reticular pool *exteroceptive* sensation from stimuli outside the body, *proprioceptive* sensation from the tension of muscles and tendons, and *interoceptive* sensation from the viscera.

The implantation of microelectrodes has proved that a single neuron in this area may directly or indirectly be stimulated by impulses from half a dozen or more sensory sources, such as nose, eye, ear, skin of face, skin of hindleg, etc. [11]. If it is giving off a regular rhythmic pattern of nerve impulses, it will change to a new and characteristic pattern of impulses for each source, or combination of sources, of the stimuli it receives. In other words it is giving out information in a pulsed code which represents a moment-to-moment summary of the information it is getting. There is a possibility that this code produces a different effect in each of the areas where its many axon branches terminate. The explanation of the brain's mysterious and wonderful abilities for discrimination, and for choice and coordination of appropriate responses will presumably have to be found by studying the complex individual behavior and interrelations of such intricately specialized individual cells as these.

When stimuli are introduced into the reticular substance by microelectrodes, the responses are not specifically directed, like reflexes. Instead, qualities and intensities are added to the general behavior. Through one localized region, the stimuli may arouse the individual, through another they may relax him. In an area whose activity leads to arousal reactions, electrical stimuli can produce a mere awakening, or definite arousal, or general alerting of all the senses, or a specific alert response, or behavior marked by the signs of fear, or a paroxysm of terror, depending on how the rheostat is set.

Experiments have been designed in which rats, cats, monkeys or other animals can furnish circumstantial evidence of affective functions in the reticular substance. A plug is fixed in the skull, through which microelectrodes can be sunk into exactly determined regions of the brain. When sources. Their efferent tracts make massive connections with the cerebellum in fishes, but in amniotes they have more important connections with the thalamus, as well as with more ventrally located motor transmission systems in the tegmentum. Since these posterior tectal centers of amniotes receive an abundance of secondary auditory fibers, it is reasonable to suppose that they act to incorporate information from the hearing apparatus into the stream of impulses converging on the general motor-coordinating apparatus of the brainstem. However their function is not precisely known, and it seems likely that much of the importance they had in lower vertebrates has been lost in mammals.

D. General Remarks on Forebrain Structure

In the primitive forebrain of the adult amblystoma there is a layer of central gray substance, vaguely differentiated by regional variations in thickness, overlaid by an outer layer of neuropil, i.e., white substance. The neuropil exhibits slight gradations in texture, of unknown significance. This forebrain receives chiefly olfactory fibers, and there is little evidence that it is anything more than a region for coordination of olfactory impressions and the promulgation of behavior dominated by the sense of smell.

In bold contrast to this, the forebrain of a mammal is almost entirely a new development. The neurons which perform the olfactory coordination and reflex functions are still represented, but they are shoved into corners and vastly overshadowed by massive afferent tracts which have grown in from more posterior parts of the brain. These all end in special associational nuclei and extensive strata of gray substance, from which regulatory efferent tracts run to all other parts of the brain.

By establishment of homologies between regions and tracts of the brains of urodeles, reptiles, and mammals, a hypothetical evolutionary story has been put together to explain the tremendous development of the mammalian forebrain. But the everted forebrains of bony fishes (Fig. 18–13 B) have had another sort of evolution, and those of birds still another. This is a region which has been used, in various ways, for superimposing associations upon associations, and controls upon controls, through which the individual animal is able to work out more and more precisely calculated solutions to the ever-changing problems presented by the conditions of its body and of the external environment.

The principal centers to be discussed in such forebrain developments (Figs. 18–12, 18–16) are the *thalamus,* a cluster of nuclei on either side of the diencephalon; the *striatum,* a nuclear mass at the base of each cerebral hemisphere; the *cerebral cortex,* a layer of gray substance displaced to the outer surface of the cerebral hemisphere; and the *hypothalamus,* an area of nuclei and reticular substance in the ventral half of the diencephalon on each side. Thalamus, hypothalamus, and striatum can be found in the brains of all vertebrates, but there is no real cortical sheet of cells in the cerebral hemispheres of any living anamniotes except dipnoi, and little of it in reptiles and birds. The cerebral cortex is a device which has been seriously exploited only in mammals.

All these forebrain centers are paired, and all are extensively interconnected, not only by commissures across the midline, but also by unilateral tracts. Most of the information about their function comes from exploration of mammalian brains and little of this can be extended to the remarkably different forebrain patterns in birds and teleosts.

E. Thalamus

In fishes (Fig. 18–1), the nuclei of the thalamic region are not well developed and their functions are not known at all. Fibers project down into them from the elaborate olfactory centers in the cerebral hemispheres, and they receive a few collaterals or even primary axons from the optic tracts. They have extensive two-way contacts with the hypothalamic nuclei.

In amphibia (Fig. 18–12), superimposed upon this earlier fishlike pattern, many fibers enter the thalamus from the lateral lemniscus. These are primary and secondary axons, from the lateralis and statoacoustic systems, and from the sensory nuclei of termination of the trigeminus. In the

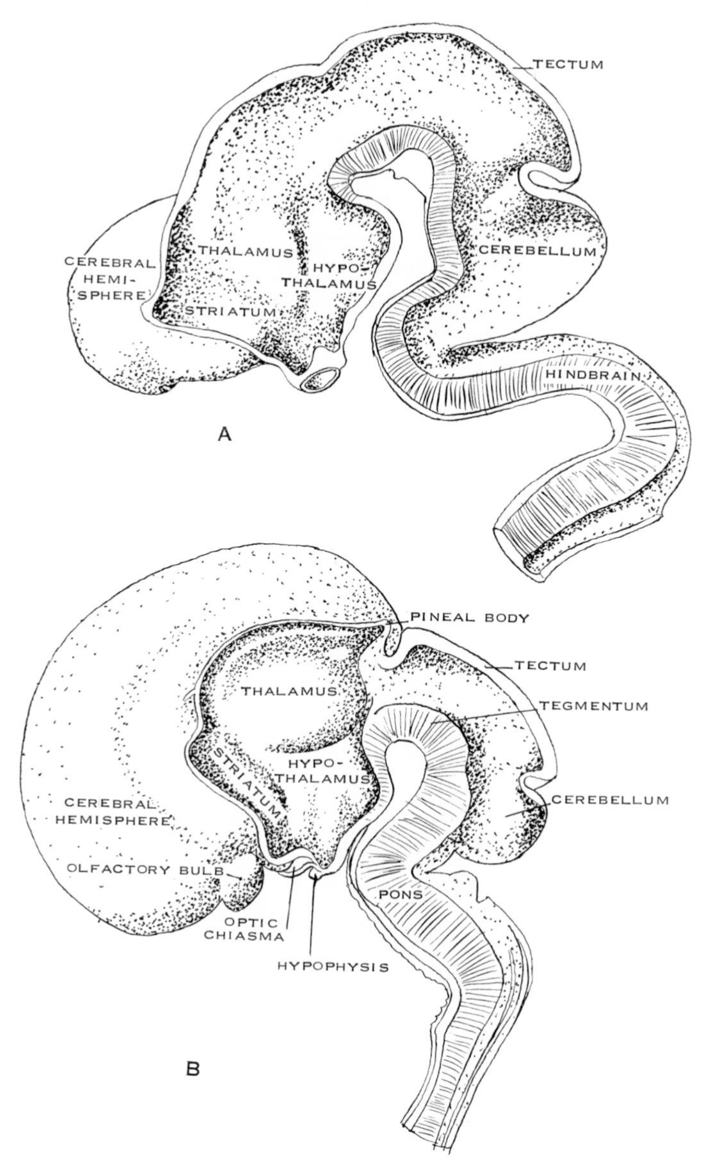

Fig. 18–16. Stages in development of the human brain. Right half seen from the sagittal plane. A. At 5 weeks. B. At 3 months.
(After the models of W. His.)

rich synaptic bed of thalamic neuropil there are abundant opportunities for the integration and interaction of these diverse stimuli, and some modestly developed tracts relay the resulting excitations into the striatal areas of the telencephalon. This new arrangement foreshadows the immense new forebrain developments in amniotes, though the amphibian thalamus, in terms of its size and the degree of segregation of nuclei within it, must be regarded as far more primitive and neurologically less important to the individual's life than the thalamus of teleosts.

In the amniotes (Figs. 18–16, 18–18), the thalamus becomes a massive collection of a score of recognizable nuclei. Into it flow tracts from various parts of the cerebral hemispheres, including the developing new cortex, and from the striatal areas, the hypothalamus, the tectum, and the cerebellum. Most conspicuous are the great bands of fibers it receives from both the lateral and the medial lemnisci, which represent the inflow of statoacoustic senses from the head, and the various categories of sensation from the spinal cord. Increasingly massive tracts stream from these thalamic nuclei into the striatal areas, so that the thalamus may be seen to have increased in importance not only as a center for sensory associations but also as a relay station, sending sensory information on toward even more cephalic levels.

This aspect of cephalization is especially clear in mammals. Sensations from particular parts of the body are reported to particular nuclei of the thalamus in orderly fashion, and from these they are projected, still in order, to localized spots in a postcentral band of the cerebral cortex. Here at last, in man, the sensations are consciously recognized.

This forward transfer of the sensory association functions, through ascending tracts to and beyond the thalamus (Fig. 18–17), is accompanied by the development of descending bundles of fibers from both the thalamus and from these higher centers, which go not only to the motor nuclei of the brainstem and spinal cord, but also to the areas which had ancestrally become centers of coordination and control over these same sensations and motor mechanisms in the anamniote brains. This capping of control centers by super-controls at more anterior levels of the brain, this **cephalization,** has occurred in different forms in mammals and birds.

In mammals, the secondary sensory fibers of the auditory pathway, instead of ending chiefly in the posterior parts of the tectum (inferior colliculi) as they do in reptiles, sweep onward in the lateral lemniscus and end in special nuclei of the thalamus called **medial geniculate bodies** (Fig. 18–17), from which they are relayed to conscious levels of hearing in the cerebral cortex. This leaves the inferior colliculi with little detectable function. Similarly the mammalian optic fibers, as they sweep dorsoposteriorly from the optic chiasma on each side of the dien-

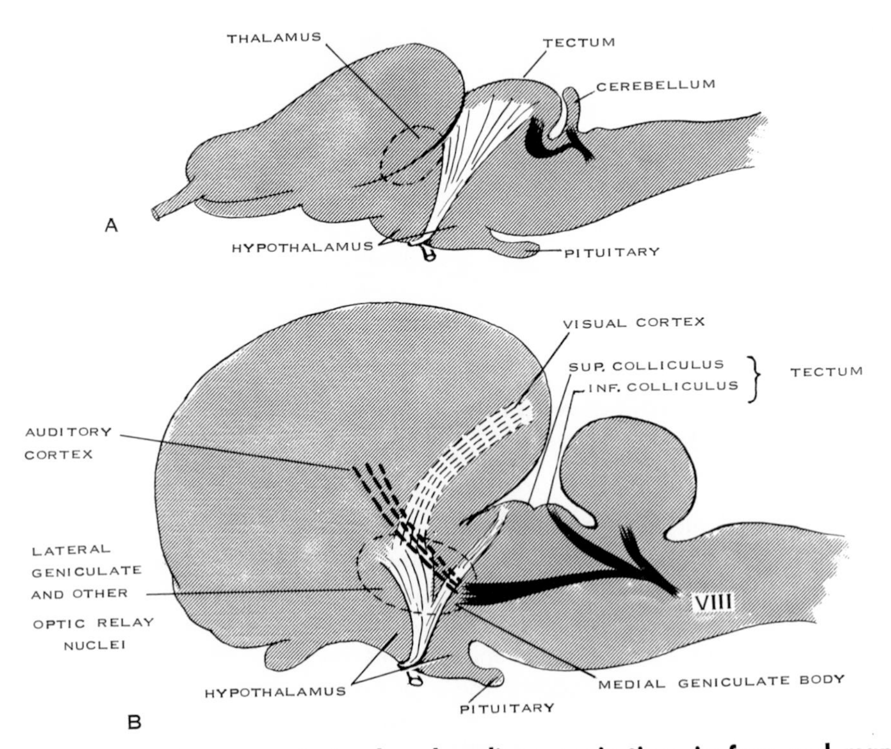

Fig. 18–17. Diagrams of visual and auditory projections in frog and mammalian brains. A. Frog. B. Mammal.

cephalon, end in far greater numbers in the mammalian thalamus than do those in lower vertebrates. This robs the superior colliculi of all the normal function of optic lobes except the mediation of optic reflexes.

In mammals furthermore, the II nerve fibers concerned with conscious vision are relayed from special thalamic nuclei (the **lateral geniculate bodies,** etc., Fig. 18–17) through special thalamocortical tracts to a zone of cortex in the occipital lobe of the cerebral hemisphere on each side, in which vision is recognized consciously. A mammal may be experimentally deprived of conscious vision by damage to any one of several levels of this optic projection system on the way from the thalamus to the occipital lobe, while still retaining optic reflexes through tectal pathways. In this condition, he may still jump at a sudden flash of light though he is blind in the ordinary sense of the word.

F. Striatum

On each side of the base of the mammalian telencephalon, interposed between the thalamus and the cerebral cortex, is a cluster of nuclei of gray substance, through and around which pass great bundles and bands of axons to and from the cortex (Figs. 18–16, 18–20). This area therefore appears in dissection as an alternation of gray and white stripes, which suggested the name *corpus striatum* to earlier anatomists. The comparable masses of nuclei which occur in the brains of other vertebrates have also been called *striatum,* but only to suggest a homology, not because they are striped.

In the extremely primitive amblystoma brain, the striatal area is merely one of the poorly differentiated areas of olfactory association tissue in the cerebral hemisphere, occupying the ventrolateral wall of its posterior half (Fig. 18–13). It receives a few axons from the rudimentary thalamus, but is dominated by secondary and tertiary olfactory fibers. Its efferent axons project in modest numbers into the thalamus, the hypothalamus, and the motor transmission centers of the tegmentum in the midbrain.

In the bony fishes, which lack a cerebral cortex, and in reptiles and birds, which have little of it, the striatal nuclei are very stoutly developed but in different patterns. The forebrain of the teleosts is everted, so that the ependyma which links the two hemispheres dorsomedially is pulled out to form an extensive epithelial capsule, inside which lie the enlarged parts of the primitive olfactory forebrain, including the striatal masses. It is not clear which of these complex nuclear mounds are homologous with the sectors of the primitive amblystoma hemispheres, and their functions in the living adjustments of the normal fish are almost unknown. There is, however, experimental evidence that teleosts deprived of their forebrains show impairment in certain qualities of their total behavior, characterized in such terms as initiative and caution, which would certainly have survival value in their native environment [12].

In reptiles and birds, the striatal nuclei form huge masses bulging into the ventricles of the cerebral hemispheres from their posteroventral quadrants, crowding the olfactory apparatus of the hemispheres into outlying areas (Fig. 18–18 A). In transverse sections (Fig. 18–18 B), one sees the thin lateral ventricle bent around a robust striatal mass in the floor, separating it from a thin roofing layer called the mantle or **pallium.** The two striatal mounds become the largest parts of the brain, and in birds their expansion even brings the hemispheres into contact with the cerebellum, forcing the optic lobes out of their embryonic dorsal location into ventrolateral positions (Fig. 18–18 A). In proportion to their size, these highly differentiated nuclei receive huge numbers of afferent fibers from the thalamus, and send massive tracts down to other association areas, and especially to the motor systems of the brainstem.

In mammals, as already mentioned, these striatal nuclei become subordinate to new and overwhelming cortical developments in the pallium (Figs. 18–19, 18–20). One finds them lying in the path of the thalamocortical tracts and of the equally important new connections from the cerebral cortex down to the brainstem and spinal cord. This intrusion of white substance divides them into nuclear masses which have been given descriptive names (caudate and lenticular

dering ridges called **gyri**, separated by fissures called **sulci**, which increase in complexity during early life. Whales and elephants carry this cortical wrinkling to its greatest extent. It is a device for increasing the proportion of cortical to interior volume.

A general pattern of localized function appears in the cortex of many kinds of mammals. A more or less transverse central sulcus usually divides an anterior motor gyrus from a posterior sensory one (Fig. 18–21). The giant pyramidal cells from which the pyramidal tract arises lie in the former, in such a precise pattern that a localized stimulation there will cause contraction of individual muscles of a particular region of the body. Maps of these point-for-point connections can be made by such experiments.

Projections from the thalamus into the postcentral gyrus are similarly sorted out. If you stimulate in succession a number of spots in the postcentral strip of the cortex of a person whose brain has been exposed under local anesthesia, he will report conscious sensations, and name the parts of his body he thinks the sensations are coming from.

When the precentral and postcentral gyri of the cortex are mapped by such experiments, the motor and sensory zones for each part of the body are found to be lined up opposite each other in the same order. The cortical space associated with any particular part of the body is proportional not so much to its size as to its functional importance. Thus, face areas may be as large as, or larger than, areas for the hindleg. In a pig, the snout is given expanded representation on the cortex; in man, the fingers are.

The forward transfer of these functions to the cerebral cortex from lower levels, as a new phase of cephalization, has not taken place equally in all the mammalian lineages. In rats, for instance, large areas of the neocortex can be removed without serious damage to visual recognition, learned behavior or other capacities, but these functions are completely and permanently destroyed by removal of similar areas in dogs or cats.

After the discovery that such long and rather direct connections could be sharply localized in the precentral and postcentral cortex, other areas were extensively explored. Special bands of thalamic fibers were found to project vision upon the occipital cortex (Figs. 18–17, 18–21), while others project auditory sensations to the lateral or temporal cortex. In man, special areas are known to be involved in the visual and auditory

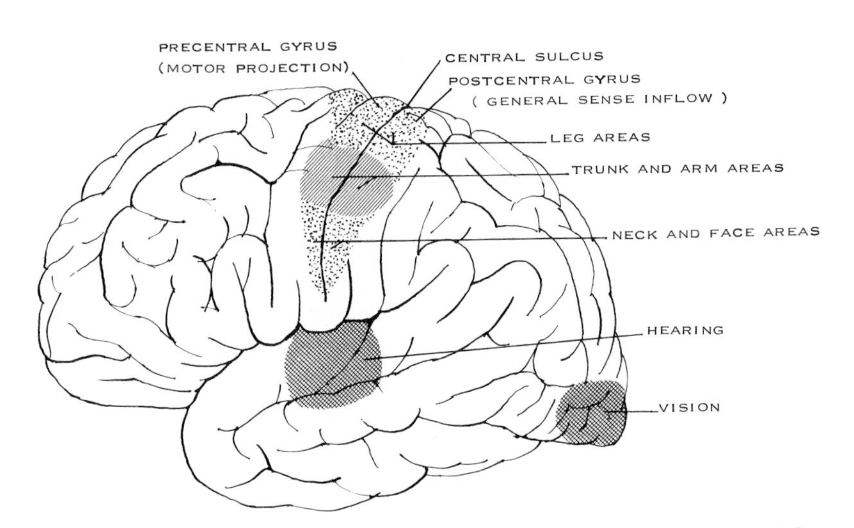

Fig. 18–21. Some areas of the human cerebral cortex concerned with reception of regional sensory signals and transmission to specific muscle groups.

recognition of words, and the composition and execution of speech. There is a bulky literature discussing the evidence for function in still other areas, derived from experimentation and from the results of localized injuries and disease.

Not long ago, various parts of the cortex, particularly in the frontal lobes, were called "silent areas," because there was little knowledge of their function. Improved concepts and more delicate techniques are eroding the very idea of "silent areas." For one reason, if a spot on the cortex operates to inhibit, or partially suppress, or release, or augment, an activity that is being directly operated through some lower center, or if it balances or modulates a combination of activities, each of which is separately controlled elsewhere, it would be a remarkably lucky accident if the experimenter discovered what this spot is doing by merely stimulating it locally, or by studying an individual after its subtle influence on total behavior had been removed by a local injury. Yet newer methods reveal these capacities.

The electroencephalograph gives another reason for setting aside the notion of "silent areas." It shows that every part of the cortex is ceaselessly pulsing with changeable patterns of electrical potentials, and that these patterns are exquisitely sensitive to stimuli coming into the brain from various sources. The brain waves cannot yet be decoded to provide direct information as to what is going on in the regions from which they are recorded, but they are direct evidence that something is indeed going on. Even many of the individual neurons have spontaneous and changeable rhythms of activity.

I. The Mammalian Rhinencephalon

It will be recalled that in the primitive amblystoma brain the hippocampal and pyriform areas lie in contact with each other in the mantle, respectively medially and laterally. Directly below, separated from them only by the ventricle, lies the striatal area (Figs. 18–13, 18–22 A, B). The hippocampal area is connected fairly directly with the hypothalamus (Fig. 18–12) by a projection tract, the **fornix** (path *d*, Fig. 18–22 B). In reptilian brains these relationships reappear, altered only by the marked bulging of the striatal nuclei and the formation of cortical layers in the hippocampus and the pyriform area, separated by a small zone of "general cortex." In all these brains, the hippocampus receives secondary olfactory fibers through a medial olfactory tract, the pyriform likewise through a lateral olfactory tract (respectively paths *a* and *b*, Fig. 18–22).

No sooner does this pattern re-appear in the mammalian fetus than the rapid interrelated proliferations of thalamus, striatum, and neocortex start to twist it into a new shape. In order to understand the result, it is necessary to remember three simultaneous processes:

1. The striatum bulges up from below not only because of its own growth, but because it is being split and widened by the fibers projecting through it, from thalamus to cortex, and from cortex down (Figs. 18–19 B; 18–22 B, and D). This not only thins the ventricle to a slitlike space, but also stretches the hippocampal area until it is wrapped into a tight arc over the striatum dorsally, and down around its posterior side (Fig. 18–22 D).

2. The neocortex proliferates upward above the ventricle (Fig. 18–19 B) in an area which is originally bracketed in olfactory tissue, i.e., the diverging medial and lateral olfactory tracts and the hippocampal and pyriform areas in which they end. This becomes a rhinencephalic circuit when tertiary fibers grow across from the pyriform cortex to the hippocampus (Fig. 18–22 A, and C, path *c*).

3. The corpus callosum, developed as a commissure between the neocortical areas of the two hemispheres above the ventricle, proceeds unavoidably to press upon and stretch the anterior part of the hippocampus until it becomes a mere thread (Fig. 18–22 C, D). Thereafter, these tertiary olfactory fibers from the pyriform area (path *c*) will be the principal influx to the hippocampus.

These relations having been established, the mammalian rhinencephalon takes on a variety of forms in later fetal growth determined by (a) the degree of development of the olfactory apparatus itself, which is feeble in microsmatic

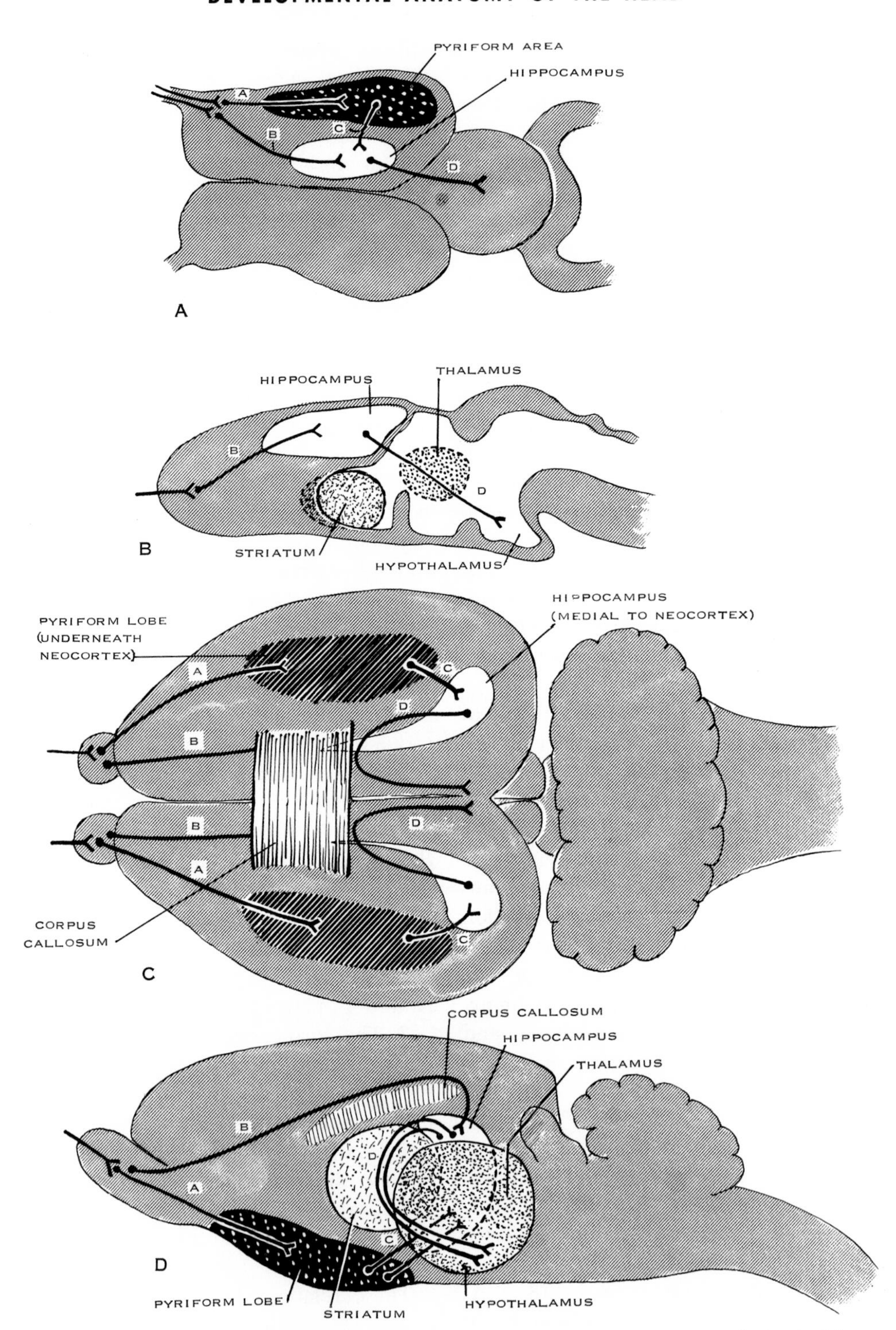

Fig. 18–22. Rhinencephalon of urodele and mammal compared. A. Amblystoma brain, top view. B. Same, sagittal section. C. Mammal brain (rodent), top view. D. Same, sagittal section.

animals like whales and man, but strong in macrosmatic ones like carnivores and ungulates; and (b) the degree of development of the neocortex, which is huge in whales and man, much less so in marsupials and rodents.

When the rhinencephalon is strongly developed and the neocortex is only moderately hypertrophied, one can still recognize a resemblance to the reptilian layout. Usually however, the following spectacular shifts take place.

1. The pyriform area is first shoved laterally (Fig. 18–22 C, D) and finally ventrally (Fig. 18–22 C) so that it finally lies on the floor of the brain. In man it is even partly concealed from sight by a rolling forward of the temporal lobe of neocortex.

2. The hippocampus, representing only the posterior part of the original mediodorsal hippocampal area, is wrapped so far around the striatal bulge (Fig. 18–22 D) that its main bulk comes to be on the ventral surface of the brain, lateral to the brainstem and optic chiasma. Furthermore, in the human brain, due to the rolling out of the temporal lobe of neocortex, it is completely concealed even from ventral view. It is still close to the pyriform area and receives rather direct fibers from it, but its projection fibers must take the long arched pathway up and over the striatal mass (from which it is still separated by a slitlike ventricular space), forward under the corpus striatum and then toward the midline and down to the hypothalamus. This curious pulled-out pathway, called the **fornix** (path *d*, Fig. 18–22 C, D), remains in the adult brain (Fig. 18–14) as a broad hint of what happened to the hippocampus because of the growth forces of the neocortex.

However much it is put upon by these forces the mammalian rhinencephalon retains most of its ancestral connections and functions. In fact these are augmented variously, being invaded by visceral afferent fibers from the hypothalamus and fibers from other parts of the neocortex. Through experimentation with laboratory animals and study of diseases and local injuries in humans, it is found to have acquired strong effects on a variety of emotional, sexual, and visceral behavior.

REFERENCES

1. Hamburger, V., and R. Levi-Montalcini, 1950. An essay on experimental neuroembryology, *in* P. Weiss (ed.), *Genetic neurology.* University of Chicago Press, Chicago.
2. de Beer, G. R., 1937. *The development of the vertebrate skull.* Oxford University Press, London.
3. Hamburger, V., 1952. *Ann. N. Y. Acad. Sci.* 55: 117.
4. Oppenheimer, J. M., 1942. *J. Comp. Neurol.* 77: 577. Also Piatt, J., 1950. *In* P. Weiss (ed.); see Ref. 1.
5. Ariens Kappers, C. U., G. C. Huber, and E. C. Crosby, 1936. *The comparative anatomy of the nervous system of vertebrates, including man.* Vol. I. Macmillan Co., N. Y.
6. Levi-Montalcini, R., 1949. *J. Comp. Neurol.* 91: 209.
7. Sperry, R. W., 1951. Mechanisms of neural maturation, *in* S. S. Stevens (ed.), *Handbook of Experimental Psychology.* John Wiley & Sons, Inc., New York.
8. Machin, K. E., and H. W. Lissmann, 1960. *J. Exptl. Biol.* 37: 801.
9. Sperry, R. W., 1955. Biochemical specification of neurons. *In* H. Waelsch (ed.), *Biochemistry of the developing nervous system.* Academic Press, Inc., New York.
10. Herrick, C. J., 1948. *The brain of the tiger salamander.* University of Chicago Press, Chicago.
11. Scheibel, M. E., and A. B. Scheibel, 1958; also Amassian, V. E., and H. J. Waller, 1958. *In* H. H. Jasper *et al.* (eds.), *Reticular formation of the brain.* Little, Brown & Co., Boston.
12. Healey, E. G., 1957. *In* M. E. Brown (ed.), *The physiology of fishes,* Vol. 2. Academic Press, Inc., New York.
13. Piatt, J., 1951. *J. Comp. Neurol.* 94: 105.

Part V

DEVELOPMENTAL ANATOMY OF THE TRUNK, TAIL, AND APPENDAGES

The chapters of Part IV illustrated the developments that take place in organs of the vertebrate head after the pharyngula stage. We turn now to the somatic parts of the rest of the body. The chapters of Part V consider the integumentary, nervous, muscular, and skeletal parts of the trunk, tail, and appendages, and how they reach their adapted structure in the adults of representative vertebrates, by development from the more easily comparable rudiments of the pharyngula.

Chapter 19, on the skin, falls in this section by defensible but arbitrary choice. It could just as well have been located in Part IV. The other chapters have a common concern with the locomotor adaptations of the individual. Digestive, excretory, reproductive, and regulative functions and apparatus are discussed in Part VI.

19

The Skin and Its Derivatives

I. INTRODUCTION

There are two main parts to the skin, which are normally bound together in an unbroken and unitary surface cover. The outer **epidermis** is principally of ectodermal origin, and is continuous through the body openings (mouth, cloaca, pharynx clefts, choanae) with the endodermal lining of the alimentary canal. The inner part or **dermis** is principally of mesodermal origin, though it contains pigment and other constituents which are derived from the neural crest. It is also penetrated by ectodermal peripheral nerves.

Skins of unending variety are developed in different animals by variation of the proportions and arrangements of the epidermis and dermis, and by the fabrication of skin derivatives from them. One thinks for instance of the sandpaper hide of a shark, the silky pelt of a seal, the reef fish's scales and rainbow stripes, the thick hairless blubber of a whale, the slimy greasiness of a lamprey, the armadillo's mosaic of bone and bristle, the metallic glitter of a snake newly emerged from his old husk, the very different shells of a turtle and a boxfish, the tender and fantastically ornamented skin of a bird-of-paradise. There are also great variations in the skin of different regions of a single animal.

For instance the skin of a man. His *epidermis* is thirty or forty times as thick on the soles of his feet as over the front of his eyeballs. At the latter site it achieves a glassy transparency, but elsewhere there is a locally variable pigmentation. The capacity of the skin to form hair varies sharply with regions, and with age. There are marked glandular specializations on the margins of his eyelids, in his ear openings and armpits, and around his breasts, genitals and anus. The epidermal sweat glands vary locally from a few dozen to nearly a thousand per square centimeter, but are absent at the tip of his penis and deep in his ear passages. The degree of cornification of the epidermis shows marked contrasts on palms, eyelids, knees, lips, soles, elbows.

As to his **dermis,** it is tightly applied over his nostrils and ears, but underlaid by loose fibrous tissue over his belly so that it can be picked up in great fat folds. It is extremely thick and tough on palms and soles, and thin in eyelids and scrotum. The boundary layer between epidermis and dermis may be smooth, or may be thrown into an elaborate pattern of papillae and ridges, as partly reflected externally in fingerprints, for instance. Tiny muscles develop in his dermis, either in relation to hair follicles, or independently, as in the nipple region, scrotum, and elsewhere.

Vertebrate skin is variable not only by regions but also in time. It adjusts to many outside stimuli, either directly as in wound healing and scar formation, sun-tanning, callus production, etc., or indirectly by reflex action through the nervous system, as in the production of slime or sweat, flushing or blanching of the skin capillaries, etc.

Other changes are more profound and alter the anatomy of the skin. The pigment pattern of amphibian larvae changes abruptly at the time of metamorphosis, and in many fishes and mammals there is a marked but gradual change from the juvenile to the adult appearance. Birds moult their old feathers and produce new ones with different color patterns, altering their appearance according to their stage of life, or with the seasons. The new hormone balances of sexual maturity or seasonal ripeness bring on "nuptial" skin patterns in a great many fishes, amphibia, reptiles, birds, and mammals. The seasonal coat changes of weasels are initiated by the shortening or lengthening of the day. The shedding of old skin, and the changes of skin and mammary glands during or after pregnancy, are cyclic but not seasonal. Those of puberty and metamorphosis occur only once and are irreversible. In all these multifarious changes the skin shows itself to be full of life, and its study is full of biological interest.

II. BASIC ANATOMY OF SKIN

At the pharyngula stage, few if any of the special integumentary derivatives are detectable, even as anlagen. Only a generalized epidermis and dermis are present. As these two parts differentiate, each produces several specialized layers.

A. Epidermis

The surface ectoderm, originally a simple epithelium one or two cells thick, proliferates from its basal layer until the sheet is three, four, or many cells thick, the newer cells pushing the older ones outward. In fishes, it usually remains rather thin and simple, but in land vertebrates a great many more cells accumulate, the older and outer ones transforming into a **stratum corneum.** Here the cells shrink and lose all recognizable cell structures, and their remaining cytoplasm is replaced by a relatively inert and amorphous protein husk called keratin. This cornification or keratinization process reaches its extremes in the formation of the horny scutes and scales of amniotes, and hair, feathers, digital tips, etc. The shed "skin" of snakes, lizards, and amphibia is the stratum corneum, which is periodically loosened and scratched off (Fig. 19–2).

The basal layer of the epidermis remains as a mitotic replacement zone, the **stratum germinativum,** and this is also a principal agent in wound healing and skin regeneration. It produces all the skin glands, which are usually unicellular in anamniotes, but may be tubular or alveolar, and simple or complex (Fig. 4–2). The sweat glands of mammals, for instance, are complex glands produced by sharply localized germinal zones (Fig. 19–14). They maintain openings through the stratum corneum and have long ducts which commonly extend into the underlying dermis, or even beyond it into the next layer of connective tissue, the superficial fascia.

B. Dermis

The watery mesenchyme that accumulates under the embryonic ectoderm gradually becomes strengthened and differentiated by the deposition of fibers in the intercellular substance. It comfortably fills the spaces between the surface layer and the deeper formed structures, and produces a considerable variety of tissues and layers. Skeleton-forming elements, muscle cells, pigment cells, and other structures differentiate in it.

In a skinning operation, the knife is worked through a vague zone of connective tissue called the **subcutis,** leaving other connective tissue firmly adherent to the epidermis. When the skin is tight, as in most lower vertebrates, the subcutis may be extremely thin and composed of strong elastic fibers. In the loose-skinned amniotes however, it becomes highly developed, and a distinction appears in it between a **superficial fascia** (Fig. 19–13) and a **deep fascia.**

The superficial fascia is richly vascularized with both blood and lymph channels, is delicately fibrous and often laced with fat. It even forms a blubber layer in whales and some others.

The deep fascia, on the other hand, is relatively inelastic, fat-free, and forms dense sheaths over the muscles and other formed organs that lie inside the skin. Though formed from the same mesenchyme that contributes the dermis layer to the skin, these fascia layers are excluded from the skin by definition, for convenience.

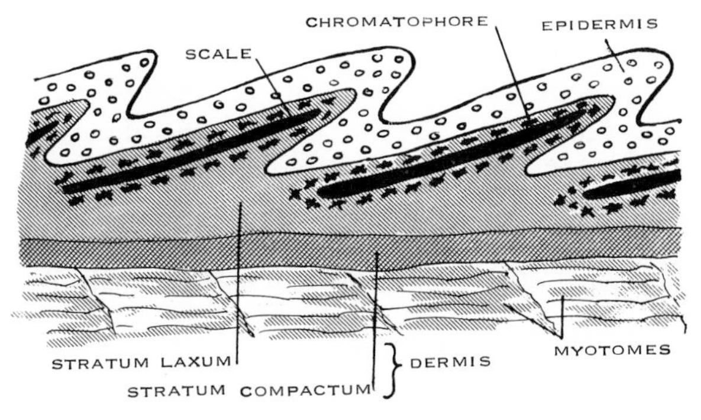

Fig. 19–1. Fish skin.

In frogs, the lymph spaces of the subcutis are inflated into enormous sinuses, with the result that the skin is attached to the deep fascia only along a few restricted lines (Fig. 26–10).

The dermis itself generally differentiates into two fibrous layers in most regions of most vertebrates. A relatively loose layer just below the epidermis, richly vascularized, is called **stratum laxum.** The **stratum compactum** is a deeper sheet of a denser and more fibrous texture. In fishes which show a mosaic of scales (Fig. 19–1), these are mostly in contact with, and are formed from, the stratum laxum, though they may be anchored deeply in pockets of stratum compactum. If they project outward and overlap one another, they push the epidermis outward rather than pierce it.

In amniotes, the scales are of an entirely different sort, produced by locally heavy keratinization of the epidermis (the layers marked A in Fig. 19–2), and not by the dermis at all. Nevertheless, in reptiles and birds an outer pigmented and vascularized stratum laxum is generally distinguishable from an inner stratum compactum. Regionally, however, this distinction may disappear, and this is generally the case in mammalian skin. In such cases, the whole dermis consists of a single tough and histologically complex layer which is usually given the older name **corium** (Fig. 19–2). Leather is made from stratum compactum or corium.

The epidermis of actively growing snakes and lizards is formed as a succession of unlike layers. An outer **stratum corneum** (Fig. 19–2) becomes keratinized and dry, and is shed when a special layer of large cells inside it (marked A in the figure) breaks down. Before this happens, other layers of similar destiny are being proliferated by the still more internal **stratum germinativum.**

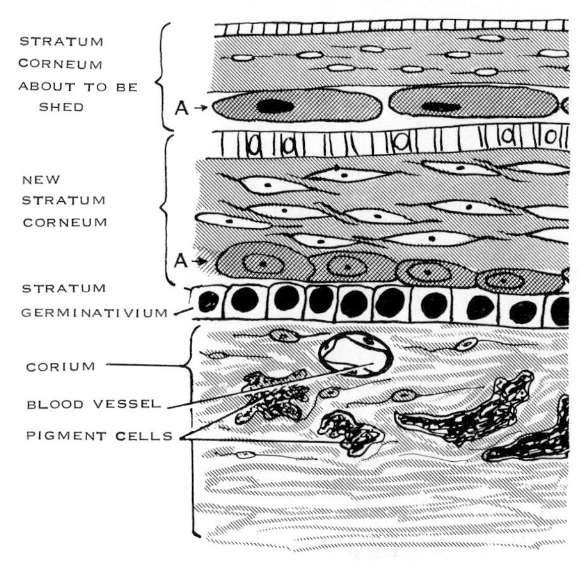

Fig. 19–2. Lizard skin before shedding.
(After Maurer, 1895.)

III. EMBRYOLOGY OF SKIN

A. Sources

Observation of serial sections originally produced the idea that all the dermis was derived from cells migrating away from the outer border of the mesodermal somites, i.e., the so-called **dermatome** (Fig. 8–14). It is not easy to prove this. Perhaps any mesoderm can furnish cells for the purpose. Experiments have shown that mesoderm of the lateral plate, or of the limb bud, can form normal-appearing dermis when cultured with epidermis in the complete absence of somites.

It has also been proved in many ways that the neural crest contributes general mesenchyme and pigment cells (**chromatophores,** Figs. 19–1, 19–3), to the dermis layer of the skin. It seems likely that all of the mesenchyme of the larval amphibian dorsal fin and much of the mesenchyme of the head skin is derived from this source. Before the pharyngula stage and considerably before the first appearance of pigment itself in most vertebrates, prospective chromatophores of neural-crest origin have distributed themselves into all parts of the body. Although their pigment-forming capacities are genetically determined, their actual fate, i.e., the realization of some one of their various potentialities, is determined in relation to the location they find themselves in.

B. Ectoderm–Mesoderm Interactions

Before the establishment of the germ layers, the prospective mesoderm resists fusion with the ectoderm and takes up a preferred position inside it, by invagination or ingression. Then, by some ripening of new properties in the cells, the mesoderm and ectoderm develop a positive affinity for one another. The prospective epidermis and dermis layers not only apply themselves tightly together, they form a cementing membrane at their common boundary. The prospective chromatophores from the neural crest seem also to have a special affinity for this basement membrane, for as soon as they have become individually visible through production of pigment it is seen that they have applied themselves to it in great numbers.

The surface ectoderm has innate potentialities for differentiation into epidermis of a generalized sort, which can be realized in isolated pieces grown in tissue culture. If it is not allowed to have a free external surface, however, it will not remain in an epithelium. Furthermore, unless it is underlaid by mesoderm it does not form hair, feathers, glands or any of its other special derivatives.

The epidermis acquires polarity, which becomes visible in many fishes, in birds, and mammals at late stages in development through the characteristic slants and overlappings of scales (Fig. 19–1), feathers (Fig. 19–11), or hair (Fig. 19–13). In amphibia the polarity is detectable at a much earlier stage, because cilia are developed all over it, beating in predictable directions in coordination with each other. The time of establishment of this polarity has been discovered. If a piece of the young unciliated ectoderm is rotated 180 degrees before this time, it will later produce cilia which beat in conformity with its new position in the body; if transplanted after this time, the cilia will beat in the direction which has already been determined, though this is discordant with the new surroundings. If the ectoderm is cultured under circumstances which deprive it of an underlying endomesodermal substrate, it develops a chaotic ciliation.

C. Regional Specificities

Anatomical demonstration of the regional specificities within a coat of skin has already been submitted for the human. All other vertebrates present similar contrasts in different parts of their bodies. Some areas of a bird's skin produce scales, some feathers, some neither. In specific locations the feathers may take the form of plumes, or coverts, or bristles, eyelashes, down, flight feathers, etc. The pigment pattern is scarcely the same for any two of the feathers in many species [1].

The skin of different regions may react in very different ways to sex hormones, forming richly vascularized areas, callosities, pigment patterns, beards and manes, etc., as local responses. Some startling examples of regional specificities are seen in amphibian metamorphosis. While most of the skin of the frog is becoming greatly thickened and strengthened, the skin of the gills and the tail is being destroyed, and a window appears in the operculum through which the foreleg ruptures to the outside. Degenerating tissues underneath contribute local factors to these events, but local areas of skin do clearly differ in their sensitivity not only to these but also to thyroxine, the triggering agent of general metamorphosis. Skin transplanted from the back of a tadpole to the tail is not resorbed during metamorphosis. Opercular skin, similarly placed, is resorbed [2].

The local specificity of the skin is in some way transmitted to sensory nerves. In a duck's bill, certain sensory endings acquire a unique histologic pattern that is found nowhere else in the body. If some of the skin of the bill is transplanted to the leg, the twigs of leg nerves that invade it adopt this pattern. On the contrary, if the leg skin is transplanted to the bill the nerves that normally show the pattern fail to develop it after they have penetrated the graft.

Another example of transferred specificity is seen when cornea tissue is transplanted to the ear or nose region in the newt, and invaded by nerves of the graft site. Normally, stimulation of the cornea brings about an eyelid-closing reflex. Unexpectedly, the stimulation of the *transplanted* cornea causes the lid of the normal eye to close [3]. The suggested explanation is that the nerves that have grown into it have received some sort of cornea-specification which causes them to hook up with the normal lid-closing reflex centers of the brain. The exchanging of territories between ophthalmic and mandibular nerves, cited in Chapter 18, page 348, indicates that once this specification of neurons has been established through their peripheral contacts it cannot be changed. The specification may be so strong that when these nerve fibers are cut, and later regenerate out toward their former territories, they will reject opportunities to make functional contact with any but the type of tissue with which they were formerly associated. Thus, cutaneous nerves misdirected into deeper tissues will not maintain terminals there, but withdraw them and send out new ones, which prosper and become functional only if they reach the skin [4]. Sensory neurons cannot take part in formation of motor end plates on muscle fibers. Only lateral-line nerves can make functional contacts with lateral-line neuromasts. The specification of the neurons, once established, seems to determine what reflex connections they can make within the central nervous system. Experiments on feather development (described below, page 390) suggest that the regional specificity of the epidermis, from which the cutaneous nerves develop their "local sign," may have been previously impressed upon it in very early development by the underlying mesoderm.

IV. SPECIAL SKIN STRUCTURES

Neuromasts, lateral-line canals and related structures have already been discussed in Chapter 15, pages 259, 262. Taste buds, which appear on the outer skin of many fishes, are mentioned in Chapter 16, pages 293, 296.

A. Dermal Pigment

The color of the skin of the so-called races of man is mostly due to pigment discharged into the epidermis, but in vertebrates generally the color patterns of the skin are caused by aggregations of huge numbers of pigment-producing **chromatophores** in special areas of the dermis. As already mentioned, these are generally derived from the neural crest, they distribute to all regions of the body at an early stage, and wait in readiness for the stimulus to form pigment. The stimulus may be the supply of a needed molecular component from a nearby tissue (Chapter 10, page 177). If a piece of skin which has been prevented experimentally from acquiring neural crest cells is later transplanted into an area that contains chromatophores, these quickly move in from the sides and colonize it, multiplying until the whole area reaches the normal state of saturation with them. If the transplant already has its share of chromatophores, no such inward migration takes place.

Chromatophores also move by the millions into the developing feather germs and hair papillae of birds and mammals. There they die and deposit their pigment granules in the keratinizing epidermal layers, as these are being converted into the finished feathers and hairs.

Some fishes, amphibia, and lizards can alter their pigment patterns or colors so as to camouflage themselves against the background of their environment. The pigment granules of the chromatophores can spread out so as to provide a maximum display, or to form a continuous sheet of color which masks the color of deeper layers (Fig. 19–3 A, C). Alternately, the granules can be clumped at the centers of the individual chromatophores, which has the opposite effect (Fig. 19–3 B, D).

In some fishes, cutting a single cutaneous nerve destroys the ability to change color only in the territory of that nerve. In other fishes, and generally in tetrapods, the nerves are of less immediate importance, and the whole skin changes its color at once through the influence of blood-borne hormones. Different hormones are involved in different cases, and one hormone may have opposite effects in two different species [5].

The nervous and hormonal mechanisms for pigment migration seem very different, but only in an anatomical sense. Physiologists recognize an intergrading series of **neurohumoral mechanisms,** which use both nerves and hormones in different proportions. At one end of the series is the medulla of the suprarenal gland, which responds to the stimulus of visceral nerves by releasing the hormone epinephrine into the blood stream, and thus produces its effects on tissues all over the body. At the other end of the series is an ordinary motor neuron which serves only one specific end-organ by producing an effective

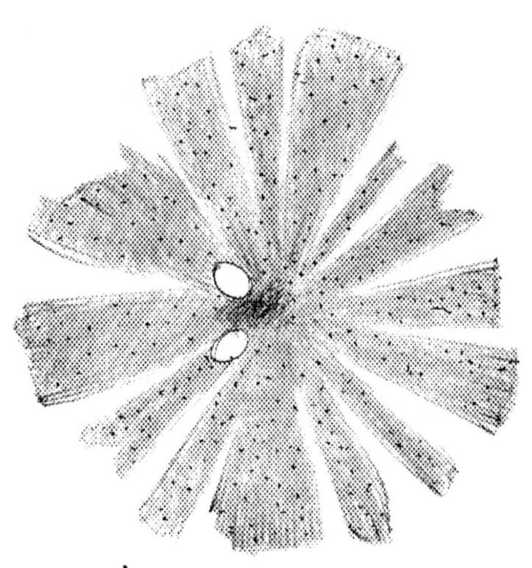

A. SINGLE CHROMATOPHORE WITH PIGMENT DISPERSED

B. SAME, PIGMENT AGGREGATED

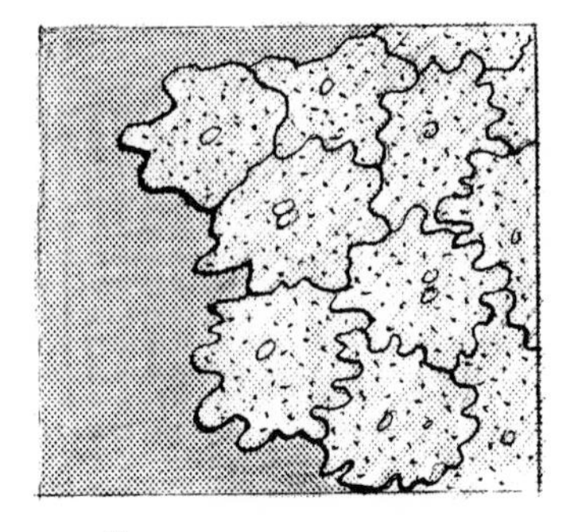

C. PIGMENT DISPERSED, BACKGROUND MASKED

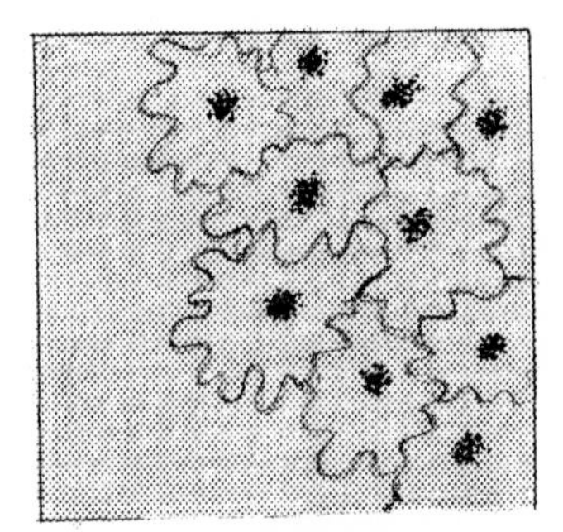

D. PIGMENT AGGREGATED, BACKGROUND REVEALED

Fig. 19–3. Chromatophores with migratory pigment granules.
(A and B after Ballowitz, 1914.)

concentration of a hormone-like chemical practically in contact with the responding tissue, with a highly localized effect. There are intermediate conditions. For instance, certain neurosecretory cells in the diencephalon produce a material which is carried by a short network of veins down a narrow path to the nearby hypophysis, where it causes the secretion of special pituitary hormones from this one target organ (cf. Chapter 30).

B. Dermal Skeleton, and Fish Scales

Many examples of the bone-forming potential of the dermis have already been seen, in the shape of dermal or membrane bones in the skull (page 218). Various groups of the early Paleozoic fishes developed a massive armor in the skin of their heads and trunks. Beside these, the armor of the modern turtles, garpikes, and boxfishes is thin indeed. Armadillos, alligators, and many teleosts produce mosaics of isolated bony plates scattered over the whole dermis. The modern boneless elasmobranchs show a feeble variant of this, in the shape of multitudes of little **dermal denticles,** sometimes called placoid scales, all over their skin. Other dermal bones form in the fins of the teleostome fishes and in the pectoral girdles of tetrapods.

While there are scaleless species in many orders and families of the bony fishes, most of them develop patterns of scales in the dermis [6].

The more ancient groups often had large bony plates, or flat tilelike scales (Fig. 19–4 A) of the **ganoid** or **cosmoid** varieties. These are distinguished from each other both in the microscopic structure of their underlying bone and in the chemical nature of the shiny enamel-like outer covering of ganoine or cosmine. Cosmoid scales are no longer found in living fishes, and the ganoid type are rare, though good examples survive in garpikes and *Polypterus.* The common types now are **cycloid** (rounded) or **ctenoid** (toothed), and they overlap like shingles (Fig. 19–4 B, C). They are relatively feeble structures, bonelike but containing few or no specialized bone cells.

C. Dermal Denticles, and Teeth

The whole skin of the common dogfish, and the pharynx as well, is studied with little isolated **dermal denticles,** each consisting of a broadened anchoring plate in the dermis and a sharp projecting thorn. Instead of these, close-set rows of knifelike **teeth** develop at the mouth opening, where the embryonic skin is stretched over the jaw cartilages. In the summer skate, a smooth transition is found within the rows of teeth on the jaw, from specimens shaped exactly like placoid scales marked with tiny ridges, to specimens which are flat tooth plates specialized for

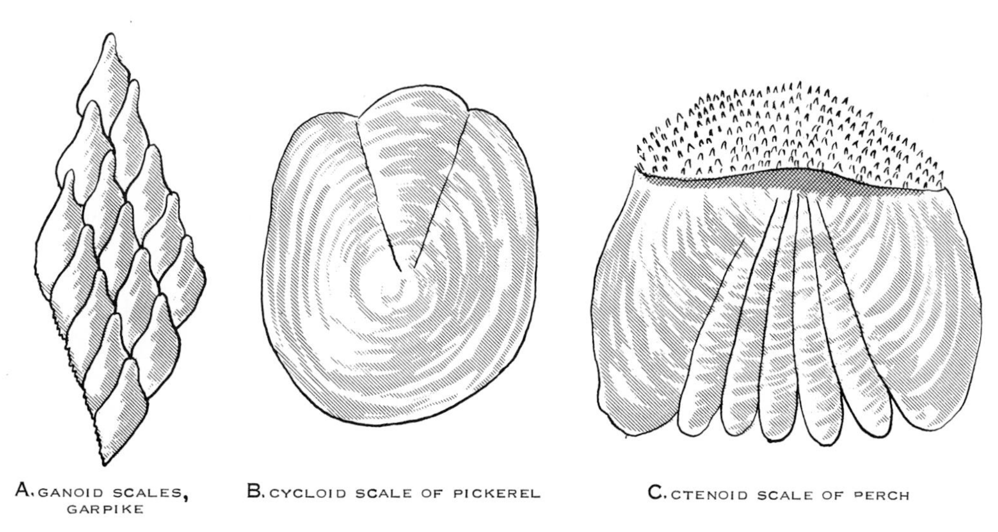

Fig. 19–4. Types of fish scales.

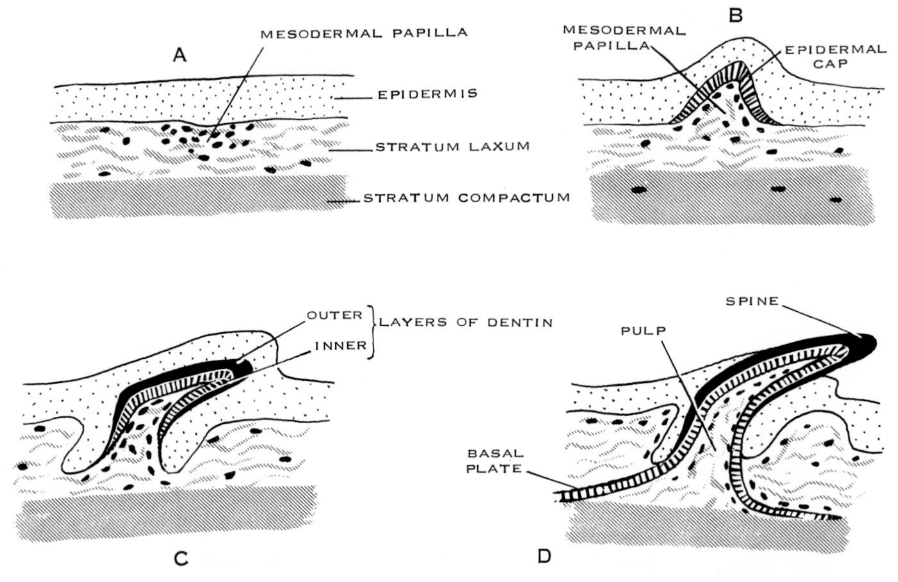

Fig. 19–5. Formation of a dermal denticle.
(After H. Klaatsch, 1890.)

crushing mollusc shells. The dermal denticles and the teeth are formed by essentially identical processes, and this is the reason teeth are considered here rather than in the sections on pharynx segments or the intestine.

1. Development of a Dermal Denticle. The first sign of differentiation of one of these structures is a mesodermal papilla, which arises as a condensation in the dermis, covered by a thickening of the epidermis (Fig. 19–5). The papilla proceeds to form a shell of special bonelike tissue called **dentin** around itself, which is thickened by newer deposits on the inside so that the cavity containing the soft mesodermal **pulp** shrinks correspondingly. In the case of the dermal denticle, the dentin first forms an outward-projecting spine and then extends inward along a fibrous anchoring plate. In the case of the tooth, the shape may be knobbed, serrate, leaflike, or platelike. The outer surface in either case becomes covered with a hard glossy material called vitrodentrin, similar but not identical to the enamel of mammalian teeth, which is the product of a handsomely developed epidermal cap. The rest of the elasmobranch denticle or tooth is mesodermal in origin.

2. Development of Teeth. The teeth of higher vertebrates always also develop from an epidermis-coated (or perhaps sometimes endoderm-coated) **dermal papilla.** Experiments with amphibian embryos indicate that the papilla is actually derived from neural-crest cells, and that the presence of both mouth ectoderm and pharyngeal endoderm may be necessary for the differentiation to proceed. In the simplest cases the tooth anlage remains at the surface while it develops, but complex teeth such as those of mammals sink into deep pits, differentiate and grow there, and erupt at a later stage.

Dentin is laid down at the outer boundary of the dermal papilla, growing by accretion from the inside and at the expense of the pulp cavity. In addition, the epidermal cap, which makes its appearance before the papilla takes shape (compare Figs. 19–5 and 19–6), becomes active as an **enamel organ,** laying down a sheet of true enamel on the outer surface of the oldest dentin. As the tooth erupts, the enamel organ is pierced (Fig. 19–6 E) and remains behind as a collar at the base. Since the dermal papilla remains also as the inner **pulp,** with its own blood vessels and nerves, the tooth can continue to grow from below for some time. The incisor teeth of rodents grow throughout life.

3. Tooth Location and Anchorage. Teeth of vertebrates are by no means confined to the jaws. In many reptiles and anamniotes they also commonly occur on various palate bones, and in bony fishes on the hyobranchial skeleton.

Dermal denticles are fastened to the stratum compactum by connective tissue fibers. Even some teeth have an anchorage as casual as that, but usually the fibers tie them directly to bone, or the growing bone actually encases their roots (Fig. 19–6 D–F). Teeth that are borne on jaws are described according to their arrangement, as **acrodont** when they are perched on the rim of the bone, or **pleurodont** when lashed to its inner surface, or **thecodont** if set in sockets of bone. Teleosts show all three types, and so do reptiles. By the formation of a special bonelike substance called **cement** or the continuing expansion of bone, any of these types may become fused to the jaws. In such cases, the blood and nerve supply to the persistent pulp is also embedded in the bone, but it is not obliterated, for teeth normally remain alive.

4. Function, Shape and Succession. The modifications of vertebrate teeth to the type of diet are so clearly adaptive that a glance at the dentition of a fossil usually tells something specific about its former way of life. Multitudinous "grab and gulp" teeth are used merely for holding onto the prey until it can be torn to pieces or crushed or swallowed entire. A large catfish may carry nearly ten thousand of these tiny teeth in its mouth, massed on various bones. Animals that live on shellfish are apt to have heavy flat crushing plates for teeth. Bloodsucking animals develop sharp elongated teeth for piercing the skin. Insectivores usually show poorly developed or degenerate conelike or knobby teeth.

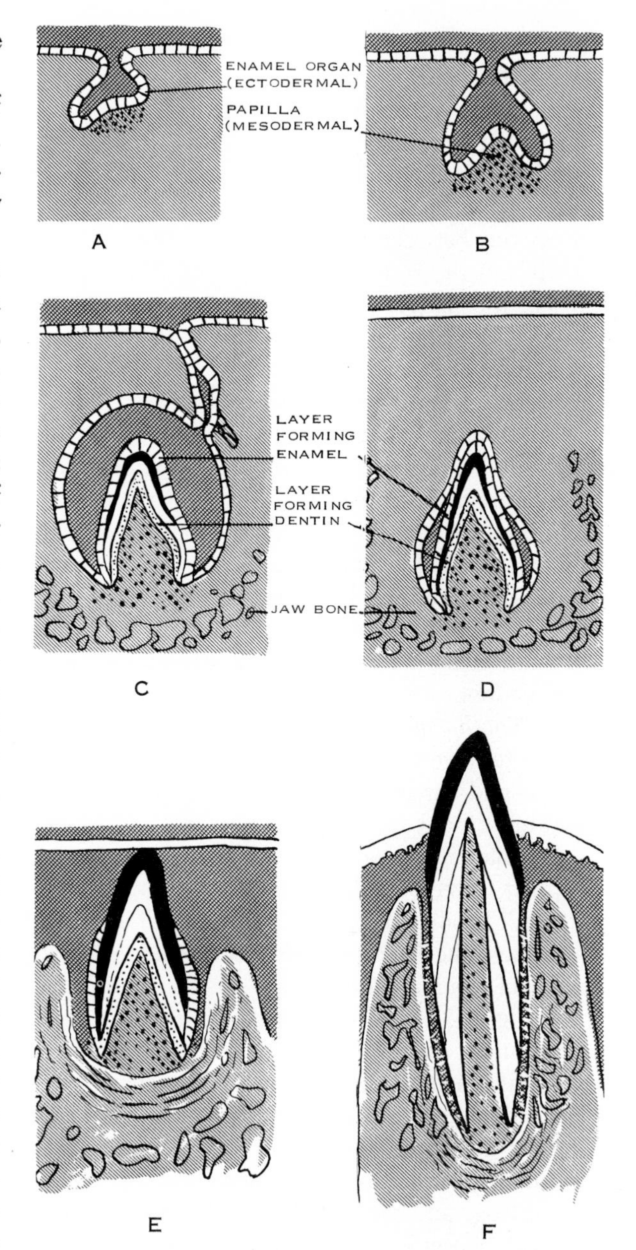

Fig. 19–6. Formation of a human tooth.
(After Schour and Poncher, 1937.)

In most fishes, amphibia, and reptiles, all the teeth of an individual are alike; i.e., the dentition is **homodont;** nevertheless **heterodont** dentitions, with different sets of teeth for different functions, are developed in surprising variety in some groups of teleosts and reptiles. This latter condition has survived and been much elaborated in mammals. Carnivores have special teeth for tearing and others for cutting. Animals that browse on plant food often have nibbling teeth in front and flat grinders or molars inside. Rodent incisors are similarly combined with elaborate molars. The tooth structure has been endlessly varied in different stocks by the formation of patterns of cones or cusps, or by the application of enamel only on particular surfaces, or by the formation of pleated folds of enamel.

In many vertebrates, teeth are being broken, discarded and replaced by new growths throughout life. The replacement teeth may be formed directly underneath the old ones, or behind them, or between them. The currently active teeth and the reserve teeth may be lined up in rows, the latter being moved into place as needed. This is certainly the case with the fangs of rattlesnakes and the molars of elephants, and may be so in some sharks also.

When an animal has a succession of teeth like this, the condition is described as **polyphyodont.** A dentition that develops all at the same time and lasts for life is said to be **monophyodont.** In many mammals there is an early "milk dentition," replaced later by a permanent set of teeth; this is the **diphyodont** condition. The dentition of man is normally heterodont, thecodont, and diphyodont.

5. *Tooth Substitutes.* None of the agnatha seems to have formed dentin teeth. Modern hagfishes and lampreys both have a rasping apparatus of a very complex nature, worked by their unique visceral cartilages and muscles, and capped externally by several fearsome horny "teeth," produced by the *epidermis.* Lampreys also have the inside of the sucker studded with rows of conical horny teeth of the same sort (cf. Fig. 2–3). The underlying parent epidermis forms new replacements in rhythmic sequence, so that each tooth has several replacements stacked underneath it. Examples of similar epidermal developments are rare, but not unknown in other anamniotes, for instance the "claws" of some frogs and salamanders, and the temporary conical "horns" of the breeding males of the horned dace.

Birds and turtles, perhaps independently, have evolved epidermal **bills** or **horny beaks** which are specialized for almost as many functions as teeth are, and serve as a substitute for them. In both groups, extinct species are known which did have teeth, but none of the living species shows any signs of them even as embryonic vestiges. Similar substitution of a horny bill for teeth is known also in the egg-laying mammalian platypus, and in some extinct groups of reptiles.

There are two suborders of modern whales, one characterized by teeth and the other by whalebone. The great whalebone whales develop embryonic teeth but lose them, and frayed horny plates later grow down from their upper jaws, acting as food strainers. The toothed whales are peculiar in another way, having a homodont dentition of simple conical teeth. This condition is secondary, for many of their extinct carnivorous ancestors are known to have been heterodont.

During the tadpole stage of frogs and toads, the nibbling teeth are formed as horny products of the lip epidermis. They are replaced functionally at the time of metamorphosis by a full set of "grab and gulp" teeth, complete with enamel and dentin, in the upper jaw, unmatched by any teeth in the lower jaw.

D. Scales of Amniotes

The scales of fishes are formed by the *dermis,* but the scales of reptiles, while they may be underlaid by bony plates, are formed from localized thickenings of the stratum corneum of the *epidermis.* These may be only slightly raised from the surface, or they may be folded so as to overlap one another. Similar horny scales are exuberantly developed in such unusual mammals as the pangolins and armadillos, but are common also on the feet of birds, and on both feet and tail in rodents and some other mammals.

The shell of a turtle consists of a continuous horny layer from the epidermis, grooved into a pattern of **scutes,** and a sheet of bony **plates,** formed underneath, from the dermis. The stratum germinativum lies beneath them, continually adding more horn to the undersides of the scutes. The bony plates are sutured together and united with parts of the pectoral girdle, ribs, and vertebrae.

Snakes have discovered ways of using their belly skin for locomotion on land. Broad transverse scales extend in a series from the neck to the cloaca, each overlapping the one posterior to it. Complicated groups of integumental and belly muscles attach to the inner surfaces of these scales, which can be erected so that their protruding posterior edges will catch on the ground, acting as anchors. When such a scale is anchored, the coiled body in front of it can be pushed forward by straightening, and the straight body behind it can be pulled forward by coiling. Rhythmic erections and relaxations of the scales, complexly coordinated with rhythms of coiling and straightening of different levels of the trunk, enable the snake to progress over rough ground. Even without the coiling and straightening, some snakes move along by pulling forward and anchoring local belts of their belly skin and then drawing themselves forward through the belts of anchored skin. On a flat plate of clean glass however, a snake can go through its entire repertoire of motions without making any progress at all, for the scales find nothing to anchor themselves in [7].

E. Digital Tips, Horns, and Antlers

The tips of the digits of amniotes are usually outfitted with **claws,** which are horny derivatives of the epidermis. The claws of many turtles are simple conical caps, each being underlaid by a stratum germinativum which is contributing to the formation of all its parts at once. In more elaborate claws of other reptiles there is an upper dense scale called the **unguis,** and a lower sole of **subunguis** whose horny structure is much looser (Fig. 19–7 A). The differences between claws of mammals, and the **hoofs** or **nails** (Fig. 19–7 B, and C) which replace them in some orders, are reducible to variations of this pattern of unguis and subunguis, together with their relation to a pad or "frog" of thickened integument just proximal to them. Also, both in advanced reptile types and in mammals, only a restricted proximal region of the underlying epidermis, called the **germinal matrix,** produces horn, and the rest of it is quite sterile. In this case, the claw (or nail or hoof) is being produced only at its base, and is forced slowly outward over the **sterile matrix** to which it is tightly adherent.

The horns and antlers of mammals form an intergrading series of variants on a pattern, involving both a bony outgrowth from the skull and the formation of horn by the skin that covers it. In the male elk or moose, an annual outburst of bone growth from each side of the top of the skull produces an antler, which is first covered with hairy skin and then stripped

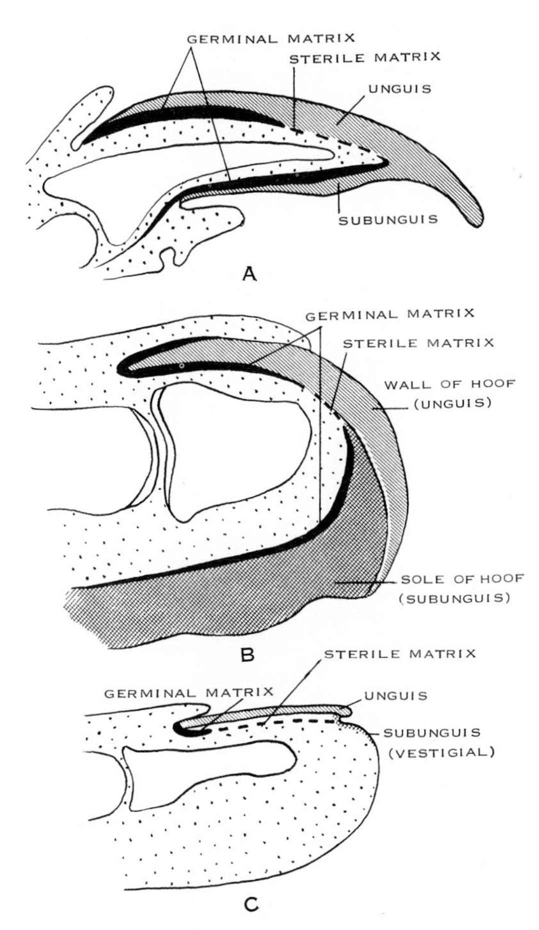

Fig. 19–7. Digital tips. A. Claw of sphenodon. B. Hoof of camel. C. Human fingernail.

(A and B from J. Boas, 1931, in Handbuch der Vergleichenden Anatomie der Wirbeltiere, by permission of Urban u. Schwarzenberg.)

bare. After the breeding season the bare bone is dropped off at a special breaking zone, leaving a skin-covered stub from which next year's larger antler will grow.

Intermediate forms exist in which the furry base is elongated and the shed antler reduced in size. The tiny knob of exposed bone is not

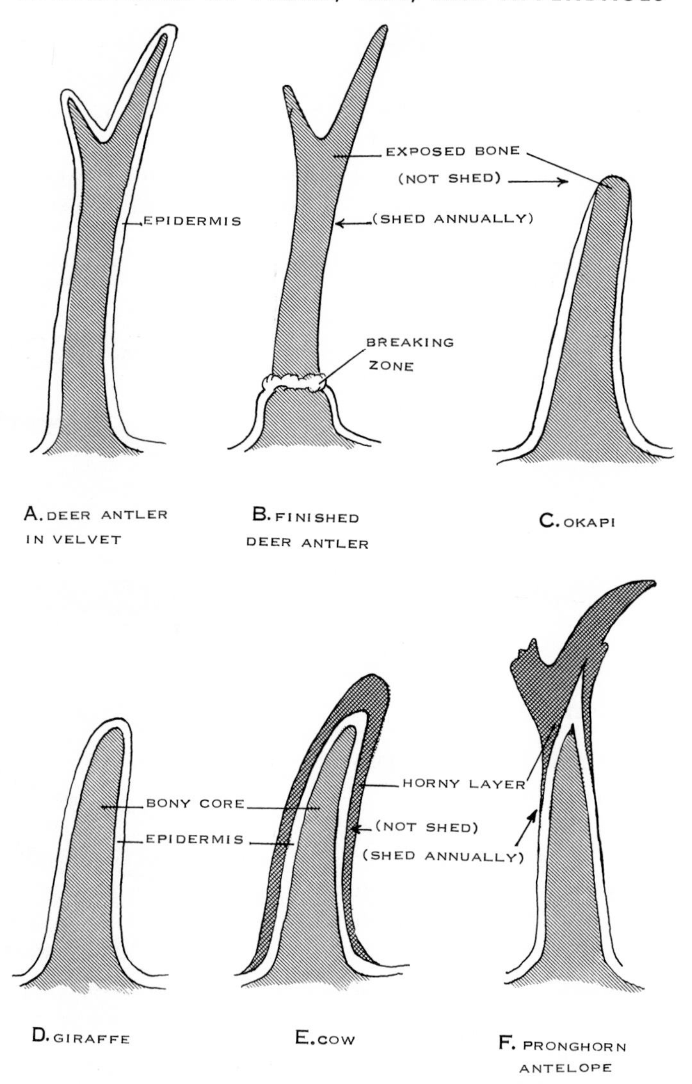

Fig. 19–8. Mammalian horns and antlers.

shed in the okapi, and the bony core is not exposed at all in the giraffe. The American pronghorn has similar protruding bones covered with persistent skin, but the hair of this skin grows outward with, and embedded in, a thickening layer of horn which is shed annually (Fig. 19–8 F). African antelopes and various horned sheep and ruminant mammals vary this sequence merely by retaining the horny layer permanently, to the exclusion of the hair (Fig. 19–8 E). In a new horn just beginning to form on a heifer, some hair can be found embedded in the keratin, but it is later lost sight of. Between the bony core and the permanent horn lies an unbroken and continuously active stratum germinativum and an elementary dermis layer.

F. Feathers

Fully developed feathers were present on the essentially reptilian Jurassic creature, Archaeopteryx (Fig. 2–17). They presumably evolved from modifications of the reptilian scale pattern but there is no record of how it happened, and only the birds now produce them.

The specialized types of feathers are usually restricted to certain skin tracts called feather

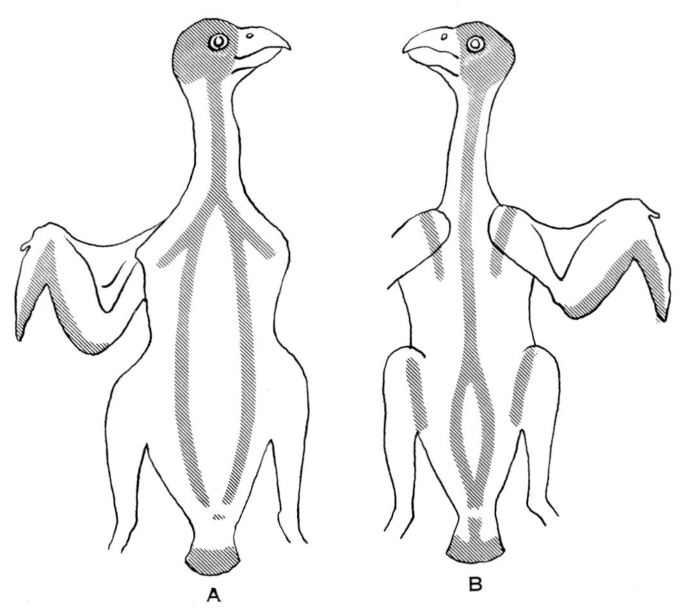

Fig. 19–9. Feather fields. A. Ventral side. B. Dorsal side.
(After Nitzsch, 1840.)

fields, which are asymmetric in themselves, but grouped in symmetrical pairs (Fig. 19–9). The intervening and relatively naked areas are normally covered by the overlapping vanes of feathers reaching out from the fields. The feather tracts vary somewhat with the species, and may expand at the expense of the naked areas, even to the condition in penguins, nearly all of whose skin produces feathers.

1. Types. There are three main types of feathers on most birds.

(a) Those with a long quill and an intricately dissected vane are the **contour feathers.** They include the long stout **flight feathers** of wings and tail, and the general outer shingling of **coverts.**

(b) Inside the contour feathers and arising with them from the same feather tracts, and sometimes also from the relatively naked skin areas, are other feathers which have the same hollow tubular quill for a base but carry a soft mass of fluff instead of a flat vane. These **down feathers** or **plumules** are retained in the adults of some orders of birds, but lost in others. They are characteristic of juvenile or nestling birds.

(c) **Filoplumes** are sparsely distributed among the contour feathers, generally do not show at the surface, and consist of a rather long delicate quill and a tiny tuft at the tip.

2. Structure. The **quill** of a well-developed contour feather (Fig. 19–10 A) has a proximal section called the **calamus** which is hollow, tubular, and open at each end, and a distal **shaft** which supports the working surface or **vane.** The vane can easily be fragmented into scores of obliquely placed rays or **barbs,** and under magnification each barb is found to be dissected similarly into scores of barbules (Fig. 19–10 B). The barbs of a well-preened feather adhere to each other by tiny sets of **hooklets** developed on each distal series of barbules. The fluffy plume of an ostrich has shaft, barbs, and barbules but no hooklets. The fluffy down feather has barbs and barbules but no hooklets and little or no shaft.

The advantage of down feathers for insulation is obvious. In birds which lose most of their down feathers as they mature, the contour feathers have proximal barbules lacking in hooklets and distal barbules which have them (Fig. 19–10 A). This combines the advantages of a down blanket inside and a smooth waterproof cover

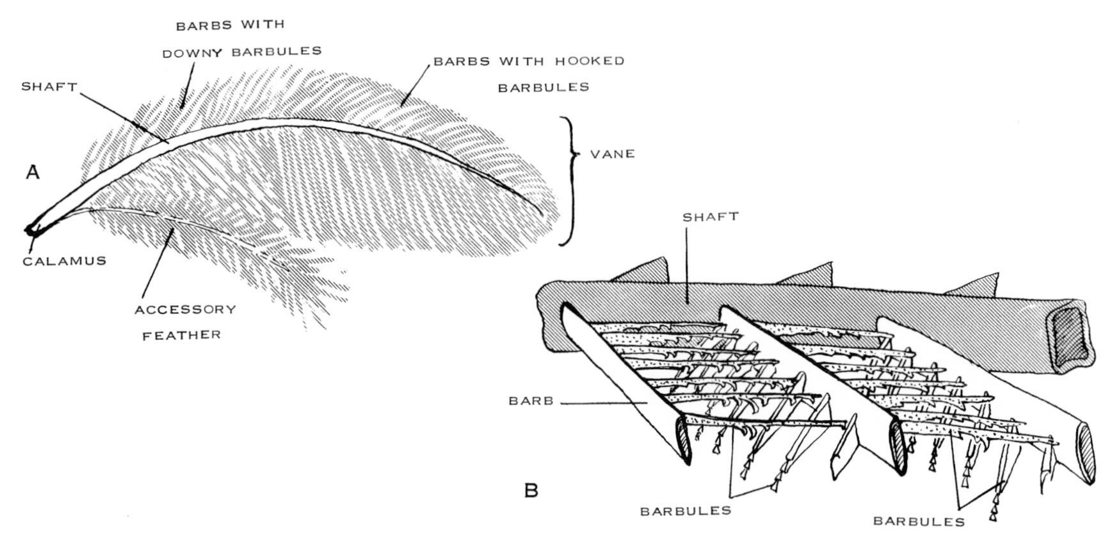

Fig. 19–10. Feather structure. A. Parts of a contour feather. B. Relationships of barbs and barbules in the vane.
(After Storer and Usinger, Elements of Zoology, 1961, by permission of McGraw-Hill Book Co., Inc.)

outside, since each contour feather is then fluffy where it is overlapped, and hooked up in a flat vane where it is exposed to the outside.

The aerodynamic requirements of flight at different speeds and with different degrees of maneuverability, and for hovering, soaring, diving and swimming, and many other uses, are found quite admirably matched by special adaptations in the design of individual feathers and their different regional combinations in different birds. It is by feather design that the owl flies silently and the nighthawk performs his loud courtship boomings. Woodpeckers help themselves climb trees by specially shaped tail feathers. Chimney swifts have special feather bristles around the mouth, that help them catch insects on the wing. Feather pigment patterns help to conceal birds against their favorite backgrounds and make the breeding males of many species elegant and flashy. Who is not moved by the sight of strutting peacocks and lyre birds?

3. *Development.* The first indication of a feather anlage is a very slight concentration in the dermis, with no visible change in the simple two-layered epidermis that covers it (Fig. 19–11 A). As the dermis thickens, it forms a cone that pushes the epidermis outward, looking at this stage like the beginning of a conical reptilian scale. At a later stage, its base sinks in, forming an ectoderm-lined follicle. As it grows longer, its apex projects from the mouth of the follicle. For each of the feather tracts, a lengthening first line of such feather germs is established, followed by other parallel lines of them to the sides [8].

Experiments have shown that the mesodermal core of the feather germ cannot form a feather, or even a follicle, by itself. The epidermis, which normally gives rise to the entire finished feather (except for its pigment), cannot do so in the absence of the dermal papilla. What is necessary is a combination of the action and reaction tissues, the dermis being the inductor and the epidermis the competent epithelium which produces the specific response (page 179).

Many ingenious experiments have contributed to this conclusion. Mesoderm from the early leg bud of the chick, introduced into the skin of the under side of the wing (which is normally a featherless area), can induce the formation of feather germs there. In an adult hen, if the mesodermal core of a regenerating feather papilla is transplanted, together with its own epidermal covering, from a follicle on the rump to a follicle on the breast, it will develop there as a conspicuous *rump* feather. On the other hand, if only the mesodermal papilla, free of ectoderm, is transplanted from a rump follicle to a wing follicle, it becomes covered by wing epidermis, and induces this to form a feather. But in such a case a *wing* feather is formed. The mesoderm provides the inductive stimulus and determines the symmetry and the orientation of the feather, but the ectoderm, besides actually forming the feather out of its own substance, gives it its specific local character [1, 9].

Oddly enough, the local specificity of the ectoderm, as revealed by these feather-regeneration experiments in adult hens, seems to have been derived from contact with mesoderm in embryonic stages. If mesenchyme from the thigh is substituted for shoulder mesenchyme in early wing-bud stages, the ectoderm which overlies it becomes specified as though it were thigh skin. The result is that the hatched chick forms a patch of thigh feathers on its shoulder [10]. Further evidence of the specific inductor role of the mesoderm is obtained by transplanting apical leg-bud mesoderm to the wing bud, where it induces the wing ectoderm to form typical toe claws [11].

As in the case of most claws and all hairs, the completed feather is far longer than the follicle in which it is produced, for there is exceedingly

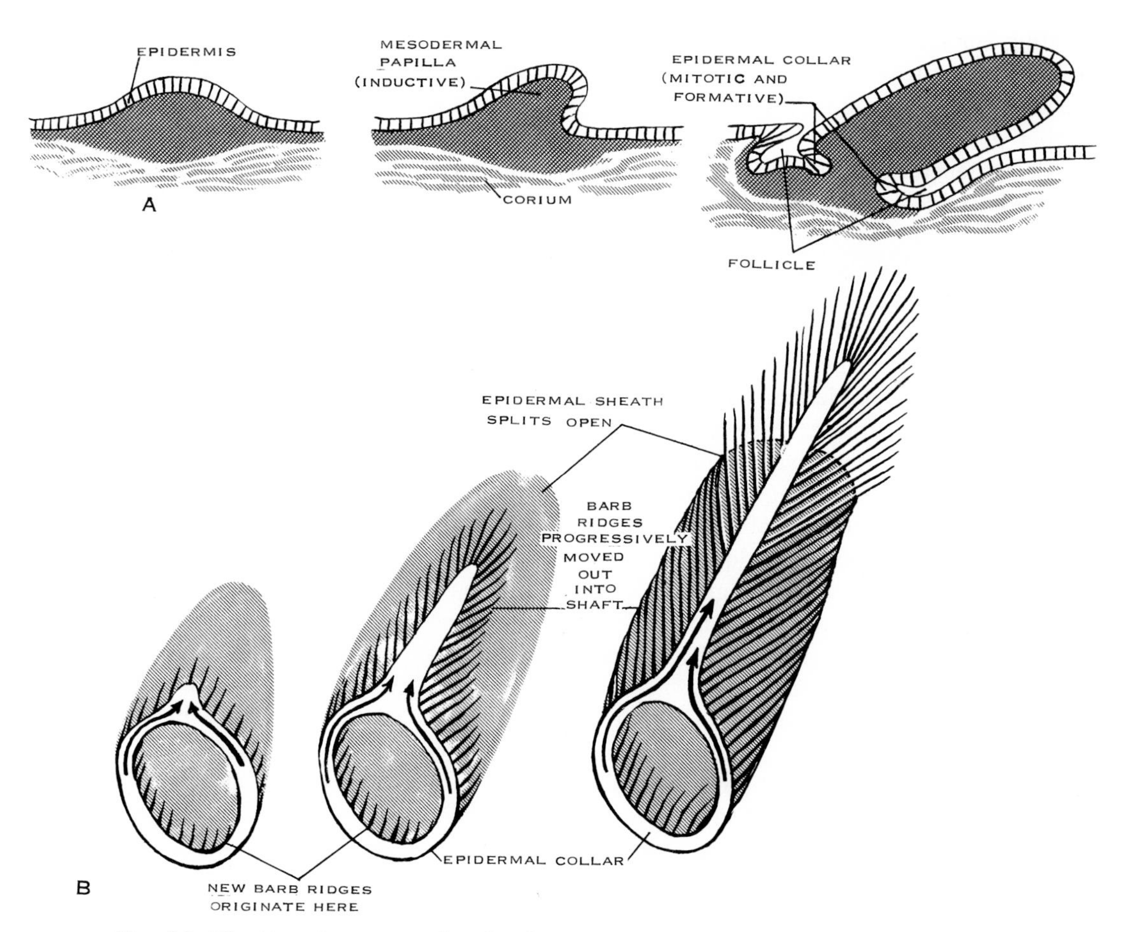

Fig. 19–11. Development of a feather. A. Formation of feather follicle and papilla. B. Formation of barb ridges and shaft from epidermal collar.
(B is after Lillie and Juhn, 1938.)

rapid proliferation of horn-forming tissue from the epidermal collar at the vase (Fig. 19–11 A), while the dead, drying, and opening part is slipping outward (Fig. 19–11 B). Three successive layers of horny material are differentiated by the epidermal covering of the feather germ. The first or outer layer is a thin husk that peels off and blows away when the feather unfurls. The last or inner layer remains in disintegrated form inside the hollow calamus of the finished quill. The feather itself is almost wholy formed from the middle layer. During its production, the mesodermal core recedes from the cone, its place being taken by air. There is no core left in the quill of a finished feather, but after it has moulted or been plucked, the pulp again rises in the follicle, becomes coated by a collar of regenerating epidermis, and initiates the formation of a replacement feather from it.

Melanoblasts of neural-crest origin swarm into a feather germ when it is first forming, or toward the regenerating collar of epidermis in a follicle from which the feather has moulted or been plucked. Ranging themselves uniformly, they differentiate their pigment either uniformly or in spots or in bands according to locally determined requirements. They die and their pigment granules are incorporated into the epidermal feather as the mesodermal core recedes. In experimental combinations, these melanophores may be introduced from any part of the body, for instance the coelomic lining, but they always produce the kind and pattern of pigment which is appropriate to their new region; i.e., breast pigment in breast feathers, wing pigment in wing feathers, etc. But of course robin melanoblasts will produce *robin* breast pigment if introduced into chick breast feathers (page 180).

For some time after the feather material has begun to be extruded from the follicle, it exists as a hollow cone of keratinized epidermis. Then it begins to split open (Fig. 19–11 B). The splitting is determined by the arrangement of the cells and the molecular structure of the keratin, and may be compared with a much simpler event, the popping open of a ripened seed pod. The part that splits and unfolds forms the barbules and barbs, the part that dries without splitting forms the shaft and the basal calamus part of the quill.

In the simplest known feathers there is no shaft but the outer part of the horny cone is split into barbs which spring in a circlet from the end of the calamus. In more typical contour feathers, while the horny cone is being very rapidly proliferated at the base, the splitting proceeds in such a pattern that a strip along one side is retained as a shaft. During development, most of the columns of cells that form the barbs (barb ridges, Fig. 19–11 B) have been moved out along this shaft. Only the last few to be formed remain attached to the calamus of the finished feather. The shaft has two series of barbs attached to it in the same plane but approximately at right angles to each other. Each of these barbs in turn consists of a miniature shaft and a little vane of barbules, these likewise in the same plane and in two series at right angles to each other. Furthermore the barbules are hooked and overlapping, so that they hold the vane together (Fig. 19–10 B). The hooks, however, like the barbules, barbs, shaft, and all the rest, are elastic, so that the vane can bend and spring back, or it can be torn into ribbons like a banana leaf in a hurricane, but quickly stroked together again, good as new.

Very commonly a mirror-twin of the shaft is found developing from the calamus, 180 degrees away from the base of the shaft. This "aftershaft" (Fig. 19–10 A) bears barbs and barbules likewise, constituting an **accessory feather,** which in some orders of birds may be half as long as the main one, or more. In different regions of the same bird, long or short accessory feathers, or none at all, may be found. Since the barbules of accessory feathers lack hooklets, they are fluffy, and improve the insulating qualities of the plumage.

4. Feather muscles. During development there is a rich capillary circulation in the mesodermal core of a feather papilla, but after retraction of the core and the splitting open of its vane, the feather has no further metabolism and may be considered dead. Contour feathers, however, may be moved about by muscles which operate upon the follicles in which they remain anchored. The quills of these feathers are embedded in the dermis at an angle, most of them sloping posteriorly or laterally. Smooth muscle fibers which stretch from the neck of each follicle to the base of the nearest overhanging follicle constitute a system of **erector muscles** which ruffle the feathers, spectacularly in a strutting cock or a menacing owl. Another set run from the neck of each follicle to the base of the follicle which it overhangs, constituting **depressor muscles.** Other sets interconnect the necks of the follicles. All these unstriated muscles are formed in the dermis itself.

Deeper-lying striated muscles, which are derived from the myotomic skeletal musculature, insert in the skin of the feather tracts. They are not skin derivatives; nor are the ligaments which envelop the deep-lying follicles of the great wing feathers. These structures accomplish the all-important split-second adjustments of the whole wing to air conditions or to the bird's wishes, in soaring and flight. Striated muscles from the tail myotomes also grasp the bases of the tail feathers so as to manipulate them in braking and steering actions.

G. Hair

No vertebrates but mammals have true hair, and all mammals, except for a few species of whales, grow hair at least in some region of the body, or in fetal or juvenile life. Undoubtedly hair, like feathers, came from variations of reptilian scales, but all record of its evolution has been lost. As with other skin derivatives, a hair starts as an epidermis-coated dermal papilla. In some special cases, such as the spines of the European hedgehog or the vibrissae ("whiskers") of a cat, the mesodermal concentration shows first and pushes up a slight epidermal mound, quite like that seen in the earliest development of a down feather. But then the epidermis grows inward as a tongue of cells which wraps around the tiny mesodermal papilla lying at its deep end, forming a **follicle.** Ordinary body hairs do not show the papilla until the epidermal ingrowth is well advanced (Fig. 19–12).

The inner end of the ingrowing epidermal strand forms a tight cap over the dermal papilla, and the entire solid hair shaft and its sheath are formed from this cap, called the **germinal matrix.** If the papilla becomes separated from the matrix, no hair is formed. Matrix and papilla form an enlarged **bulb** at the base of the follicle, and this is enclosed in a basket of blood capillaries in the surrounding connective tissue. The innermost cells of the germinal matrix form a zone of exceedingly rapid mitosis, from which

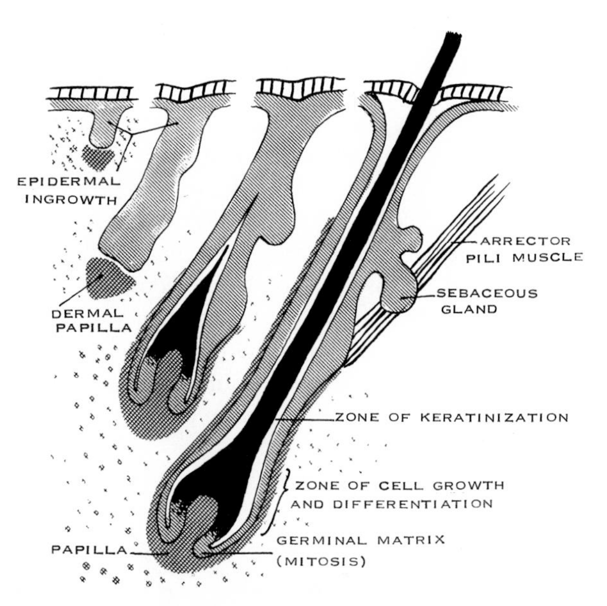

Fig. 19–12. Development of embryonic hair follicle.

(After W. Montagna, The Structure and Function of Skin, 1956, by permission of Acadamic Press, Inc.)

the new hair-forming and sheath-forming cells move outward. The hair-forming cells line up in three layers, which form respectively the outer thin **cuticle,** the (usually) pigmented **cortex** and the innermost **medulla** of the hair shaft. These parts are all produced by the extreme growth and then the complete keratinization of the cells as they move outward from the follicle. While the germinal matrix is adding to the length of the hair shaft from the inside, the older outer part is boring its way to the exterior along the strand of ingrown epidermis. Although cortex and medulla may contain tiny air bubbles in addition to, or in place of, the pigment, the hair shaft itself is essentially solid, and it is quite dead.

Each hair follicle has its own cyclic periods of active hair production and quiescence (Fig. 19–13), though in some mammals all the follicles in whole belts of skin are in phase together and in others there is seasonal replacement of the entire coat [12]. At the completion of growth of an individual hair, the germinal matrix collapses away from the dermal papilla, but retains a tenuous connection with it, as both hair and the remains of the follicle withdraw toward the main sheet of epidermis. Now, if the hair is plucked, the germinal matrix promptly enevlopes the papilla so as to form a new follicle, which extends deep into the dermis and starts to form a new hair. If the hair is not plucked, there is a period of quiescence, and then the follicle becomes reconstituted automatically and goes into production again. The old hair presently falls out.

What establishes the rhythm of hair formation and quiescence in an individual follicle is unknown. Some follicles form quite different kinds of hair seasonally, or in response to sex hormones, etc., producing winter and summer, or juvenile and mature, coats. These responses may be locally different, forming manes, beards, crests, fetlocks, genital hair, etc. The baldness which overtakes many men is not a loss of hair, but a replacement of the regular mature head coat by a delicate short fuzz like the hair which is formed by fetal skin. Aristotle, who was no doubt bald, considered this a sign of virility. There is better evidence that it is gene-controlled, like many other aspects of hair production.

The barbed quills of the porcupine are unusually stout hairs, which are interspersed with more usual sorts. Similar quills have been developed independently in three orders of mammals: monotremes, rodents and insectivores. The interspersing of coarse with fine hairs is common. The soft fur of carnivores, beavers, etc., is interspersed with, and covered by, long coarse hairs, much as the down of birds is protected by coverts.

The sheath of epidermis, through which the hair emerges, normally proliferates a **sebaceous gland** (Fig. 19–12), whose waxy secretion makes

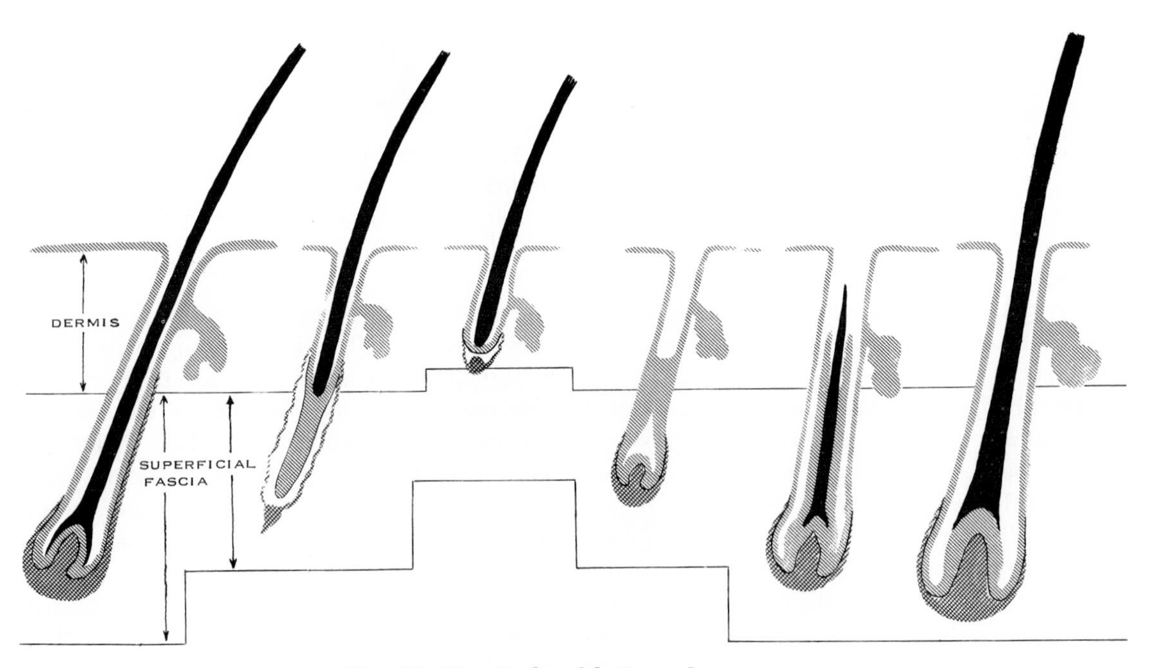

Fig. 19–13. Cycle of hair replacement.

(After W. Montagna, The Structure and Function of Skin, 1956, by permission of Academic Press, Inc.)

its way out through the same pore, keeping the skin pliable and the fur in good condition. Regeneration experiments indicate that all the cells of the hair follicle are essentially alike in their potencies and can substitute for one another in altered conditions. It is not known what sets some of them to manufacturing the keratin of the hair shaft, and others to the synthesis of sebum, a species-specific mixture of cholesterol, fatty acids, and other substances.

Smooth muscle strands differentiate from the dermis in relation to hair follicles. Each of these little **arrector pili** muscles (Fig. 19–12) is attached at one end to the inside of the general epidermis, and at the other to the middle of its own hair sheath. When it contracts, it pulls the root of the sloping hair in such a way as to make it stand up straighter, and at its other end it may roughen the surface of the skin, forming a "goose pimple." As with the process of sweating, this may be either a heat-controlling mechanism, managed through the hypothalamus, or an emotional sign, managed through the cerebral cortex.

H. Skin Glands

Many skin glands are **holocrine;** i.e., they extrude whole cells. For instance, in the sebaceous glands which were mentioned above, the gland cells become loaded with their fatty products as they mature, and then disintegrate, so that the sebum which reaches the follicle is a mixture of these molecules with cellular debris. There is little to separate this process from the way in which the cells of the follicular bulb become loaded with keratin and are pushed out into the hair shaft while other cells take their place and repeat the process. In the same general sense, horny scales, claws, and feathers are the product of keratin-forming holocrine glands.

Merocrine glands are quite different from holocrine glands, for in these the cells which do the secreting remain intact, while the secretions are passed through their cell boundaries. Nevertheless, the gap between holocrine and merocrine glands is bridged by many known grades of **apocrine glands,** whose cells slough off their outer surfaces to make their secretions, and then repair themselves. The slime glands of amphibian skin, and the milk glands of mammals are apocrine. Sweat glands may be either merocrine or apocrine. Those of the human skin (Fig. 19–14) are mostly merocrine, but the apocrine type are met in the axilla, genitals, eyelids, etc. Apocrine sweat glands are the commoner type in hoofed animals.

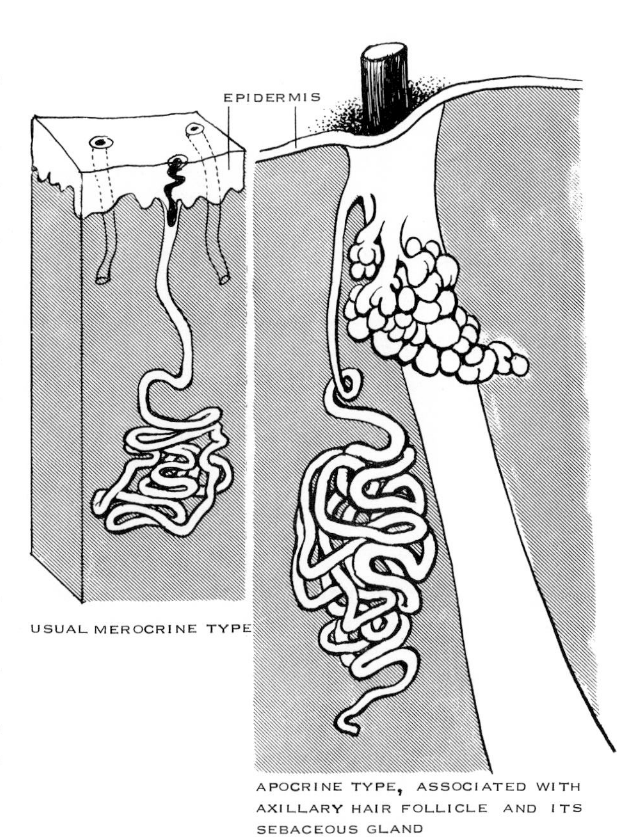

Fig. 19–14. Human sweat glands.
(After W. Montagna, The Structure and Function of Skin, 1956, by permission of Academic Press, Inc.)

Sweat glands intergrade with glands producing slime or lather or earwax, and sometimes secrete pigmented material or substances which quickly become degraded and volatilized as strong scents. They are absent in fully aquatic mammals and a few others. They may be distributed generally and in huge numbers in the skin, or as in many rodents and other furry mammals they may be restricted to the relatively bare areas like palms and soles. Typical merocrine sweat glands occur in the hippopotamus only on the ears, which stick up out of the water. In the rest of the skin they are replaced by apocrine slime glands.

Mammary glands occur in all mammals and in both sexes, always remaining rudimentary in normal males and responding in marked ways to endocrine and reproductive rhythms in females (cf. Chapter 30). In their manner of development, their compound tubular structure, and their apocrine method of secretion, they resemble certain sweat glands. No other known vertebrates besides mammals have either sweat glands or mammary glands.

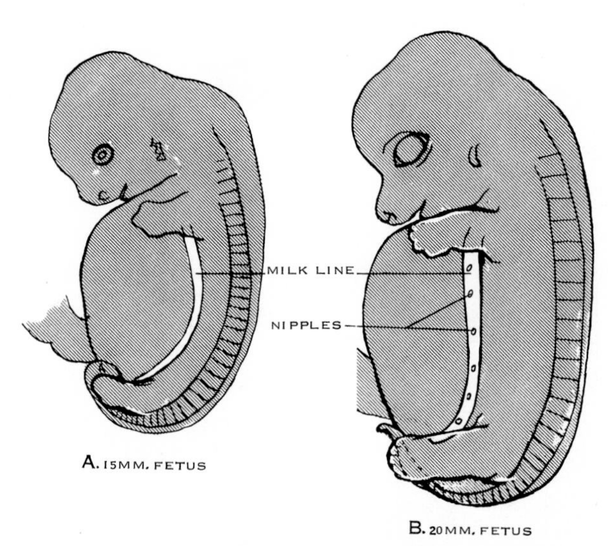

Fig. 19–15. Mammary development in the pig. A. 15-millimeter fetus. B. 20-millimeter fetus.

(Redrawn from B. M. Patten, Embryology of the Pig, 3d edition, 1948, by permission of McGraw-Hill Book Co., Inc.)

The mammary glands of monotremes differ considerably from those of higher mammals. They arise in two groups of lobules which comprise a right and a left abdominal glandular field, each group emptying its watery secretion in a restricted hair-covered area which is not elevated into a nipple or set apart in any way. It is presumed that the newly hatched young ones lap the liquid off the wet hair.

Marsupial and placental mammals all show a **milk line** on each side of the ventral trunk in early fetal stages (Fig. 19–15). Epidermal invaginations take place at certain intervals along these skin ridges to form the nipples and milk glands. This happens only in the axillary level of bats, the pectoral level in sea cows, elephants, and many primates, and chiefly from the lumbar and pelvic region in rodents, carnivores, and many ungulates. In some mice the middle of the milk line is suppressed, and both pectoral and inguinal glands develop. In other mammals, mammary glands are formed along the whole line. These variations, and the frequent anomalous development in certain individuals of more glands than are normal for the species (Fig. 19–16), suggest the selective evocation of potencies which exist at first in the entire milk line. The number of mammary glands developed in a species approximates the number of young born in a normal litter.

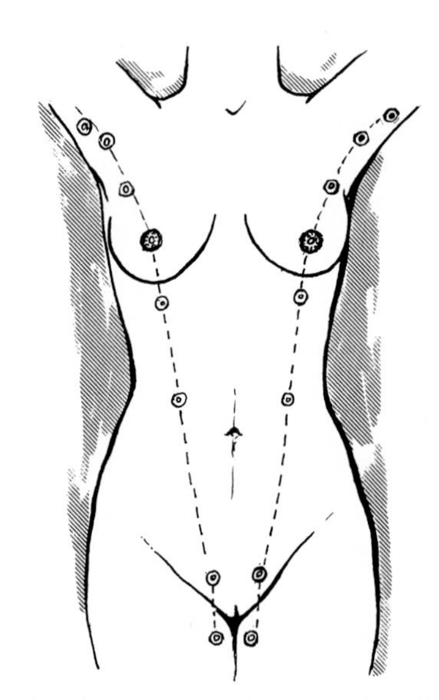

Fig. 19–16. Commonest sites for occurrence of accessory nipples in the human.

(After H. K. Corning, Lehrbuch der Entwicklungsgeschichte des Menschen, 2d edition, 1925, by permission of J. F. Bergmann Verlagsbuchhandlung.)

The invaginating epidermal plug may form only one duct system and one gland, or may form a small chamber from which as many as 15 or 20 glands arise, according to the species. The suckling area or nipple may be formed by the elevation of surrounding skin, or by the excavation of the invaginated plug and its subsequent eversion. The nipple may be nothing more than a rough hairless spot, or a warty excrescence, or a dangling teat.

The milk discharged by the special apocrine cells in the terminal alveoli of the mammary gland remains in the alveoli until it is forced out into the duct system by a network of contractile cells that wrap around the alveoli. This milk-ejecting action is set in motion by a hormone from the posterior pituitary, which has been discharged reflexly in response to the sensory stimulus produced by the young one at the nipple [13]. The duct system may be enlarged into a milk cistern, as in the udder of a cow. After the neuroendocrine milk-ejection response, the milk in the cistern is under some pressure, and the suckling young one need only overcome the resistance of the sphincter muscle at the external opening of the teat.

Besides their characteristic sebaceous, sweat, and milk glands, mammals produce a great array of special glands which cannot be reduced to ordered groups or homologous series, since they occur in special body regions in only certain orders, families, or genera. The same is true of all the other classes and orders of vertebrates. Some such glands can obviously be classified as producers of slime, or poison, or scents for recognition or repulsion. The functions of many others are unknown.

V. FUNCTIONS OF THE WHOLE SKIN

A. Sensory

The skin is a giant sense organ. Cutaneous branches from all the spinal nerves and certain cranial nerves pierce the deep fascia at regularly spaced intervals and ramify through the subcutis and the dermis, their terminal twigs ending either in these layers or at the basement membrane of the epidermis. Some of the nerves of the skin are motor, supplying glands, integumental muscles and blood vessels. The rest of them are specified both as to regions and as to modalities of sensation. A few of them have their dendritic zones in relation to special ectodermal sensory cells, for instance the cutaneous taste buds and lateral-line organs of the anamniotes. Others become ensheathed in special connective tissue capsules and acquire highly individualized histologic patterns. Many types of these have been described in localized skin areas of various vertebrates. However, most of the sensory nerve endings are naked and unornamented. The nerve impulses which they bring into the central nervous system are registered in the human consciousness as pain, temperature, pressure, or other exteroceptive modalities, each of which travels by its own tracts to higher centers. In the trunk and tail, the territories of the individual sensory nerves can be mapped, and reveal the somewhat distorted remains of segmental distribution, with slight areas of overlap between them (Fig. 19–17).

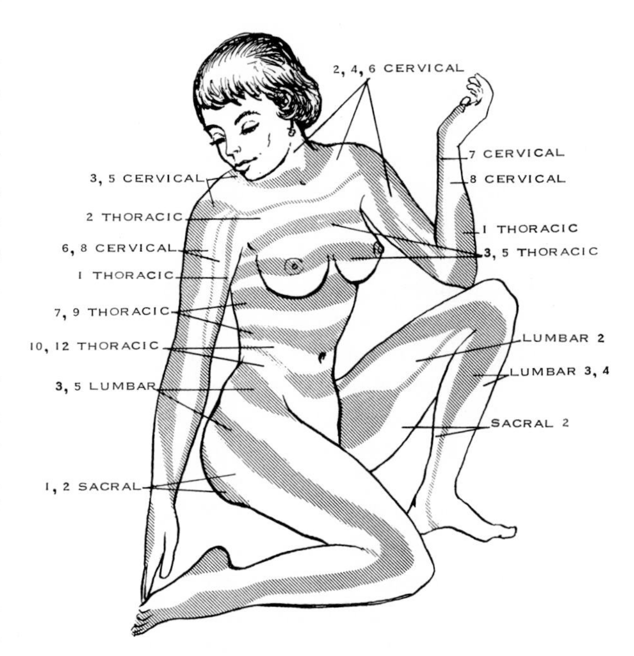

Fig. 19–17. Territories of cutaneous branches of human spinal nerves.

(After W. S. J. Krieg, Brain Mechanisms in Diachrome, 2d edition, 1957, with his permission.)

B. Defense

The *first line of defense* is the maintenance of an unbroken epidermis which can prevent invasions or infections, as well as blunting or parrying blows. The superficial strength of the fish skin lies in the dermal armor of scales, but once the delicate epidermis is broken there is danger of infection. Certain advantages accrue to the amniotes from their tough epidermal stratum corneum, especially when there is elaborated from it a practically non-living scaly layer or a covering of insensitive and completely dead hair or feathers. If the epidermis has been broken by a blow, the clotting mechanism of the blood is useful in making a temporary closure, and the clot itself is a favorable medium on which the cellular movements involved in wound healing can operate.

The *second line of defense* is mobilized if an infection is actually introduced through a break in the skin. Specialized migratory mesodermal cells move quickly to the site of infection, and there they make a business of ingesting and destroying bacteria and other foreign bodies. Others set up a wall of connective tissue around the site, which tends to prevent the spread of infection. In the higher vertebrates, a natural wall exists in the strongly developed deep fascia, so that even if an established infection spreads laterally in the superficial fascia it cannot find ready access to more internal structures.

In addition to the elaborate networks of blood capillaries, there are lymph channels profusely and delicately woven through the subcutis and the dermis, which converge upon particular subcutaneous veins in the lower vertebrates but drain into lymph nodes in mammals The lymphatic fluid comes from the blood by leakage through the capillaries, and by these lymph channels is returned to the blood The mammalian lymph nodes form a *third line of defense,* acting as straining devices to capture and remove bacteria or foreign particles that may have breached the skin and gotten into lymph spaces. Even in the absence of these lymph nodes, all vertebrates have a final line of defense, namely the production of antibodies and immunities, but the skin is not specifically involved in this.

C. Insulation

Subcutaneous blubber, and superficial hairs or feathers, and other structures in other ways, protect the individual from heat, cold, or physical bruises. The skin capillaries generally, and in mammals the sweat glands also, help get rid of unwanted heat. Both the epidermal pigment and the dermal chromatophores guard against sunburn. Land animals are protected from excessive drying through the skin by virtue of the relatively impervious stratum corneum, while the fishes and aquatic amphibia are protected from hydration and maceration by the mucous secretions of innumerable microscopic epidermal glands.

D. Other Functions

When the skin produces teeth, claws, horns, poison, or stink glands, it may be classed as an organ of offense.

Carbon dioxide and oxygen are probably exchanged to a slight degree in the capillaries of the thinnest skin areas in all vertebrates. In certain eels, one-third of the total gaseous exchange with the outside takes place through the skin. In adult amphibia generally, the lungs are very primitive, and the skin constitutes an essential and principal respiratory organ with a very active capillary net applied to the base of the epidermis. In frogs, a major proportion of the blood in the pulmonary arteries is diverted into cutaneous branches. During larval life the skin flaps of the tail fin act as a respiratory organ.

The natural histories are full of startling and unusual examples of other functions performed by the skin in special groups. Whole volumes have been written on the protective value of pigment patterns in vertebrates, which, to the human observer at least, camouflage their owners by imitating the background or confusing the eye with disrupting blotches or streaks of contrasting color. There are even a few species of harmless vertebrates which "mimic" or at least closely resemble poisonous species, and so may benefit by the avoidance reactions of their natural enemies. The camouflage devices are not all contrived of pigment. Drooping tufts of skin sprout from some of the fishes that live in seaweed.

The male obstetrical toad fashions a brood pouch out of the skin of his back, on which the female lays her eggs. Similar but more elaborate pouches are produced in the males of some pipefish and in the sea horses from the skin of the base of the tail. Still another but quite different brood pouch is produced on the abdomen of the female in marsupial mammals.

There are deep-sea fishes which develop phosphorescent spots like rows of illuminated portholes from the skin of their flanks. Some river minnows hear low sounds through the lateral line organs of their skins. Pit vipers develop a heat-sensitive organ in the skin of their face. Bats fly with a webbing of skin that grows between their fingers, and dragon lizards volplane on a skin membrane stretched between their protruding ribs. The rattlesnake's rattle is a chain of unsuccessfully shed scales. The tail flukes of whales, and the flat tail of a beaver, are principally skin developments. With these few random examples, the discussion of the functions of the skin may be interrupted. The subject is too vast, not to say too diverting, for the present volume.

REFERENCES

1. RAWLES, M. E., 1955. *In* B. H. WILLIER, P. A. WEISS, and V. HAMBURGER (eds.), *Analysis of development.* W. B. Saunders Co., Philadelphia. Developmental relationships between skin components, particularly in birds.
2. ETKIN, W., 1955. *In* WILLIER *et al.* (eds.); see Ref. 1. Factors and events in the metamorphosis of amphibia and insects.
3. KOLLROS, J. J., 1943. *J. Exptl. Zool.* 92: 121.
4. SPEIDEL, C. C., 1950. *In* P. WEISS (ed.), *Genetic neurology.* University of Chicago Press, Chicago. Establishment and maintenance of the relationships of nerves to peripheral structures.
5. ODIORNE, J. M., 1957. *In* M. E. BROWN (ed.), *Physiology of fishes,* Vol. 2. Academic Press, Inc., New York. Color changes.
6. VAN OOSTEN, J., 1957. *In* BROWN (ed.), Vol. 1; see Ref. 5. Skin and scales.
7. KLAUBER, L. M., 1956. *Rattlesnakes.* University of California Press, Berkeley.
8. HAMILTON, H. L., 1952. *Lillie's Development of the chick.* 3d ed. Holt, Rinehart & Winston, Inc., New York.
9. WANG, H., 1943. *Physiol. Zoöl.* 16: 325.
10. CAIRNS, J. M., and J. W. SAUNDERS, 1954. *J. Exptl. Zool.* 127: 221.
11. SAUNDERS, J. W., 1958. *In* W. D. MCELROY and B. GLASS (eds.), *The chemical basis of development.* Johns Hopkins University Press, Baltimore. Induction and other determining factors in the limb buds of the chick.
12. MONTAGNA, W., 1956. *The structure and function of skin.* Academic Press, Inc., New York. Mostly mammalian skin.
13. FOLLEY, S. J., 1956. *The physiology and biochemistry of lactation.* Oliver and Boyd, Edinburgh.

20

Locomotor Apparatus: I
Trunk and Tail

I. INTRODUCTION

This chapter brings together the axial skeleton, and its muscles and their nerve supply, for the reason that all these are functionally a unit both in development and in adult behavior. The paired appendages have a little more independence, and are separated for this reason as well as for convenience of description, becoming the subject of Chapter 21.

The functional unity of the adult locomotor apparatus is obvious. The skeleton cannot move without muscles, there can be no meaningful pattern of muscular action without nerves, and the nervous system is powerless by itself. It is less obvious, but demonstrable by experiment, that the somites and the neural tube, from which these structures arise, are mutually interdependent in development. Their sizes, specializations, and interconnections become exquisitely correlated in endless adaptations to different methods of locomotion.

The mesoderm sheet is no sooner well-established as a middle germ layer than it differentiates into an axial strand of notochord, a right and left flanking strip of epimeric segments or **somites,** and a lateral plate or **hypomere.** The somites nearly all divide their substance into **sclerotome** and **myotome** parts (Fig. 5–8.) From the former come the axial skeleton and various other tissues, and from the latter, the trunk muscles. The neural tube sends out a series of spinal nerves, one to each myotome. There is strong evidence of reciprocal developmental relationships among these parts.

The *spinal cord* makes important adjustments to the muscle-forming tissues around it. To begin with, the very shape of the neural tube, as seen in cross sections of salamander embryos, is determined by the arrangement of the muscle, notochord, mesenchyme, and general ectoderm around it (Fig. 9–4). Later, if somites have been completely removed from part of the flank, the number of spinal ganglia that develop in that area is reduced, and they are quite erratically distributed. The remaining unsegmented hypomere mesoderm is incapable of marshalling them into segmental order [1]. When somites are present, the ganglia do become segmental, and if the number of somites is experimentally increased or decreased the number of ganglia is adjusted accordingly [2]. Furthermore the number of nerve fibers in each spinal nerve becomes adjusted in correlation with the amount of tissue there is to be innervated in the periphery. Since the evidence for this comes largely from transplantation of limb buds, it will be considered in the next chapter.

Even more, the differentiation of *somite material* is dependent on some influence from the spinal cord [3]. In teleost, salamander, chick, and mouse, somites will not form normal vertebral cartilages unless a normal spinal cord is present. Defects in the cord lead to correlated defects in the vertebral arches (rhachischisis, page 131). If the spinal cord is reduced in size, reduced vertebrae are formed to fit it. In tissue cultures, somite material will not form cartilage at all unless some neural tissue accompanies it.

The power to induce the formation of cartilage from somites resides only in the ventral half of the spinal cord. This is a case of an inductive influence which travels through thin membrane filters or agar plates without the necessity of cell-to-cell contact. Oddly, neither in normal nor in experimental conditions does cartilage ever form in direct contact with neural tissue, but rather at a little distance. The intervening space is normally occupied by watery mesenchyme which later gives rise to the meningeal membranes.

Although the lateral somite material normally forms muscle and the medial part forms vertebral cartilage, each part can substitute for the other in experimentally altered situations. The somites of salamanders, even after having taken shape, will adjust to the intrusion of a length of spinal cord, transplanted at whatever angle. They reorganize themselves so as to line up on both sides of it, enclosing it in vertebral arches flanked by segmental masses of muscle fibers. This suggests that the spinal cord may be primarily responsible for the gathering of the flank mesoderm into a linear series of segmented masses along the body axis, in bilateral symmetry.

It is not known what decides the normal number of segments. The number is fairly constant for each species, but can be altered slightly in some teleosts by temperature [4]. Within the phylum, on the other hand, there is extreme variability. Some pythons have as many as 435 segments in the spinal column, but *Ostracion*, one of the trunk fishes, has only 14. In frogs, after the tadpole tail has disappeared, the number of free vertebrae may be reduced as low as 5.

The segmentation may be preserved with great clarity in both the adult vertebral column and the myotomic musculature in some species, but in others some of the vertebrae may fuse together, and the original division of the muscles into myotomes may be almost totally obliterated. How this is determined is also unknown.

II. THE VERTEBRAL COLUMN

A. Types of Vertebrae

1. Basic Pattern. A representative modern vertebra consists of a hefty **centrum** (corpus, PNA) which surrounds the notochord, and **neural arches** and a **neural spine** that enclose a **neural canal** in which the spinal cord lies completely protected (Fig. 20–1). It also usually shows various processes jutting from the centrum or the neural arches. Some of these receive the attachments of muscles, and others form joints, either with ribs or with the adjacent vertebrae. There is an enormous range of variation on this pattern.

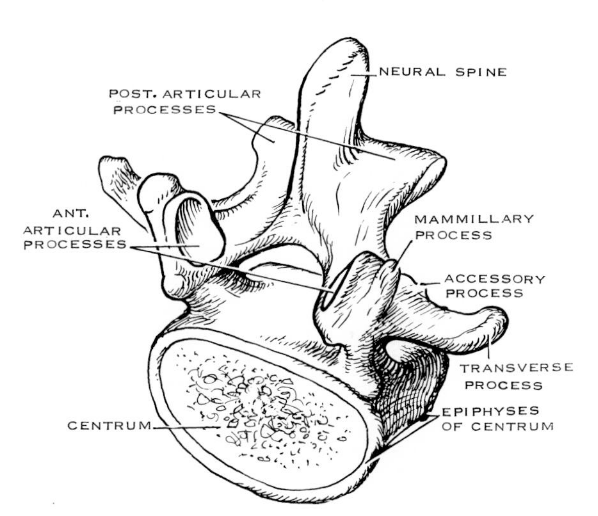

Fig. 20–1. Human lumbar vertebra from above and behind.

2. Aspondyly and Acentrous Vertebrae. Hagfishes and lampreys have a vertebral column without any real vertebrae at all. The condition is called **aspondyly.** The hagfish has a huge, toughly sheathed, elastic notochord, enclosed together with the spinal cord in a fibrous casing. To this the lampreys add only an irregular scattering of cartilage nodules which arch up at the sides of the spinal cord without providing it any important protection.

In the modern chondrosts (see sturgeon, Fig. 20–2 A) and lungfishes, and in the surviving coelacanth, *Latimeria,* the spinal cord runs on top of the huge notochord and is encased in regular neural arches made up of cartilaginous or partly ossified pieces. The caudal artery and vein, running below the notochord throughout the tail, are similarly encased. Thus there are segmentally repeated structures which can be called vertebrae, but they have no centra.

3. Hemispondyly and Holospondyly. Fragmented vertebrae, consisting of from two to eight or ten pieces of cartilage or bone per segment, are found among a number of adult vertebrates and in almost all of them during development. This condition is called **hemispondyly.** The most complete array of separate pieces is found in sturgeons (without a centrum) and in elasmobranchs (with a centrum), but many fossil vertebrates (Fig. 20–2 B), most of the groups of fishes except teleosts, and some modern reptiles and mammals show hemispondylous conditions, in a wealth of variations.

If the number of these pieces is reduced by disappearance or fusion subsequent to their formation in the embryo, until just one vertebra is left per segment, in one piece, the condition is known as **holospondyly.** Usually the result of such fusions is just one vertebra per segment (**monospondyly**) but clear-cut doubling of some, or all, of the parts of vertebrae may take place in this or that group of vertebrates. A centrum may bear two sets of neural arches, or an archless centrum may occur between each two arch-bearing ones. Or an embryonic somite segment may produce two complete vertebrae, arches and all, which is the condition of **diplospondyly.** Cases of **polyspondyly,** more than two centra per segment, are known in holocephals and dipnoi. Further knowledge of induction relations might make some sense out of this variability.

B. Formation of Vertebrae

1. Components. Inductive influences aside, there are only two components to be considered in the formation of the vertebral column, namely the notochord and the sclerotomes. Both are universally present, but may be involved in remarkably different ways, and different formations of maneuver are seen in the process of assembling vertebrae from these components in

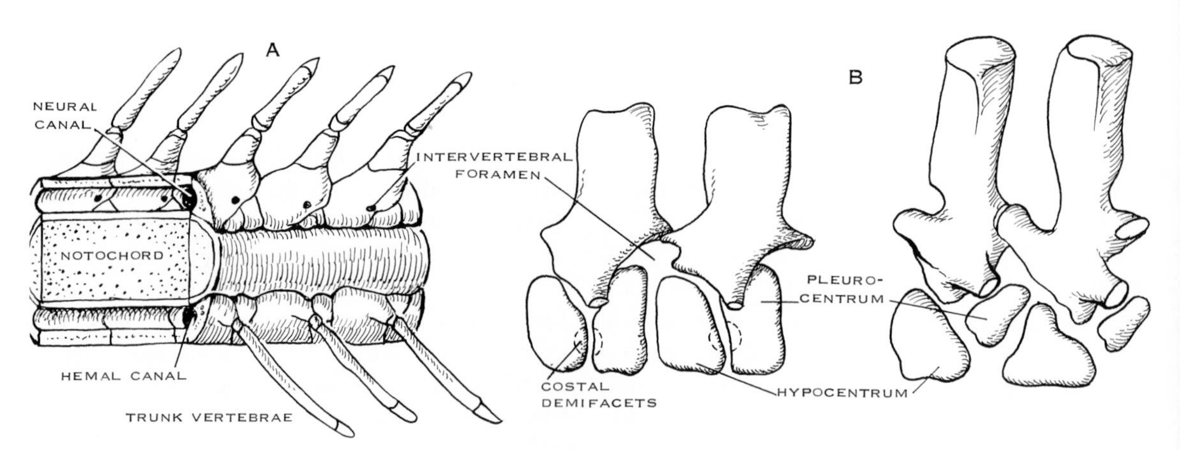

Fig. 20–2. Hemispondylous vertebrae. A. Dissection of sturgeon trunk vertebrae. B. Pairs of vertebrae from two extinct amphibia (*Archeria* and *Eryops,* Permian).

(A after E. S. Goodrich, Vertebrata Craniata, Vol. IX of Lankester's Treatise on Zoology, 1909, by permission of A. & C. Black Ltd. B after A. S. Romer, Vertebrate Paleontology, 2d edition, 1945, The University of Chicago Press, by permission of Dr. Romer.)

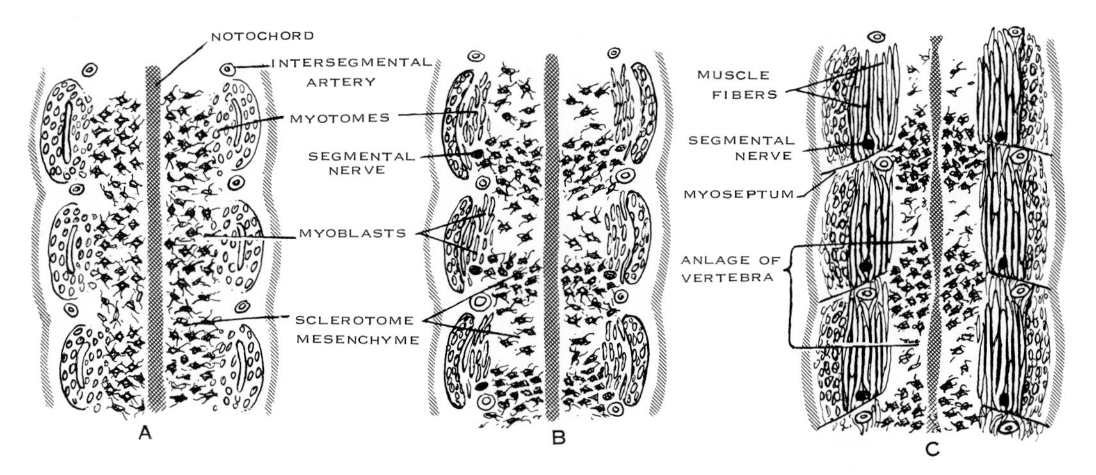

Fig. 20–3. Emergence of vertebral rudiments from sclerotomes (diagrammatic). (Original drawings suggested by B. M. Patten's figures in Human Embryology, 1946, by permission of McGraw-Hill Book Co., Inc.)

different classes of the phylum. The descriptive stages do not fit well into a simply evolutionary scheme [5].

The **notochord** is relatively huge in embryonic fishes, and may remain so, dominating the formation of the vertebral column, other components being functionally insignificant (Fig. 20–2 A). Or it may be tiny, as in the embryos of birds and mammals. It may be hemmed in and pinched off to any degree, even to the point of almost total obliteration in a heavily ossified column.

The **sclerotomes** are invariably produced by conversion of the inner parts of the mesodermal somites into loose mesenchyme, differing in texture and staining facilities from the more lateral mytome–dermatome parts (Figs. 5–8, 5–19, 8–14). In bony fishes they are sparse, and in amniotes they are very thick. Sclerotomes, as seen in frontal sections at early stages, are separated from each other by thin sheets of relatively cell-free material in transverse planes. The sclerotome cells assemble and differentiate into vertebrae through formations of maneuver which are not strictly comparable in the different classes of the phylum [5].

In elasmobranchs and amniotes, the sclerotomes are handsomely developed, and at an early stage they become visibly differentiated into anterior halves with scattered cells, and more densely packed posterior halves (Fig. 20–3). The roots and ganglia of the spinal nerves, and segmental arteries that run dorsad from the aorta, lie within the anterior halves. The sclerotome cells condense out of the mesenchyme in a sort of tissue tube around the notochord and spinal cord. During the condensation the appearance of light and dense halves fades, but not before it can be made out that the definitive vertebrae are formed, not segmentally in series with myotomes, but *intersegmentally* (Fig. 20–3 C). This happens because each vertebra is formed from cells of the dense posterior half of one sclerotome and the anterior half of the next sclerotome farther caudad. The first muscle fibers to be formed from the myotomes are thus enabled to straddle two vertebrae and work upon the joint between them.

2. *Processes.* In most vertebrates, but not in all, the vertebrae are formed in cartilage before ossifying, and a number of pairs of cartilages form per segment. Elasmobranchs and some bony fishes show a schematic arrangement of four pairs of these cartilages, called **arcualia,** arranged about the notochord (Fig. 20–4), producing a temporary, or sometimes permanent, condition of hemispondyly. The neural arches and haemal arches may be directly derived from these arcualia. In the amniotes, the separate cartilages of the hemispondylous stages do not seem

to be the simple equivalents of the arcualia of fish embryos [5].

Three different processes have been seen in the establishment of the vertebral centra, and almost all the possible combinations of these processes occur in particular species:

(a) Arcualia, perched above and below the notochord, may extend around it to form a centrum. Cases have been described in which one, two, or four arcualia on each side may contribute to the centrum.

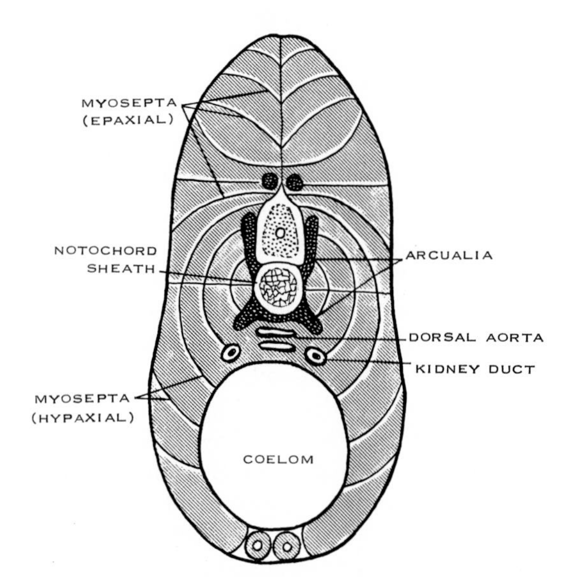

Fig. 20–4. Cross-section of trunk of trout fingerling.

(b) The centra may condense directly from the mesenchymal tube that has been deposited about the notochord by the sclerotome cells, either with or without contributions from arcualia or other cartilages. The latter is the method of centrum formation in amniotes.

(c) Sclerotome cells may penetrate the fibrous sheath of the notochord and give rise there to a considerable portion of the vertebral centrum. This process may be augmented by either or both processes (a) and (b), but is itself well represented only in the elasmobranchs and a few other fishes.

3. *Achievement of Monospondyly.* The fossil record suggests that the diplospondylous condition, with two vertebral centra per segment, is the primitive arrangement in the phylum, but it seems to be a rather second-rate one. Monospondyly has been achieved by most of the modern vertebrates, but in five different ways.

Some of the early amphibia had two equally massive disc-shaped centra per segment, and others had wedge-shaped ones, broad above, alternating with others that were broad below. All degrees can be found, in well-known lineages of reptiles, from the interlocked wedges (**pleurocentra** above, **hypocentra** below) (Fig. 20–2 B) to a monospondylous condition through elimination of the hypocentrum and enlargement of the pleurocentrum to a massive disc. In nearly all modern amniotes the hypocentra have been quite lost from most segments, only vestiges of them remaining in tail segments and those next to the skull.

A well-documented lineage of ancient amphibia shows equal diplospondyly giving way through interlocking-wedge diplospondyly to monospondyly in the opposite way, namely through wastage and elimination of the pleurocentrum, the hypocentrum becoming a massive disc.

Monospondyly has also been achieved by fusion, and in two ways. Usually in bony fishes, the arch-bearing hypocentrum fuses during development with the pleurocentrum *posterior* to it, i.e., of the next segment, producing an intersegmental single centrum. In the trunk of the holostean *Amia,* each arch-bearing hypocentrum fuses with the pleurocentrum *anterior* to it, i.e., the one formed in its own segment. (In this same fish, most of the tail vertebrae remain diplospondylous because this fusion does not take place.)

Monspondyly may arise not only in these four indirect ways, it may also arise directly through the complete development of the centrum from one center. In the strictest sense, then, one centrum may not necessarily be homologous with another.

4. *Shapes of Centra.* In practically all fishes that have vertebral centra these are hollow at each end (**amphicoelous**) (Fig. 20–6 A). The spaces thus left between adjacent vertebrae of fishes are filled by expansions of the continuous notochord, or by isolated sections of the noto-

chord if centrum-production is vigorous enough to pinch it into a series of intervertebral pieces. The notochordal tissue usually becomes extensively vacuolated (Fig. 20–6 A). In tetrapods, an intervertebral cartilage is formed in each of these spaces, which crowds the notochord almost or quite out of existence. Such cartilages may remain separate from the vertebrae, in which case the centra are still amphicoelous, as in most urodeles. On the other hand, it is common for the cartilage to split into either equal or quite unequal parts which then fuse with the adjacent centra. When the major fragments in each intervertebral space are the anterior ones, and they fuse with the vertebrae just anterior to themselves, each centrum then shows an anterior indentation and a posterior bulge, the condition being designated **procoelous.** Much more commonly, the major fragments are the posterior ones, and their fusion to the vertebra back of them results in centra with an anterior bulge and a posterior indentation, described as **opisthocoelous.**

If the intervertebral mass is divided equally between the two adjacent vertebrae, centra may be produced which are **acoelous** or nearly flat-ended. In birds, the division of intervertebral material is made in such a way that the centra are saddle-shaped, or **heterocoelous.** A similar condition occurs sporadically elsewhere, as in the cervical vertebrae of cows.

Not all these centrum-end shapes are developed in the same way, for they can be produced by growth of the original centrum, as well as by the allocation of parts of the intercentrum. In nearly all mammals, the prevailing acentrous condition arises in a novel way. When the cartilage stage has passed its prime and ossification centers begin to appear in the late fetal period, the centrum develops flat anterior and posterior caps of bone called **epiphyses** (Fig. 20–6 B). Very much reduced flat discs of intervertebral cartilage and nodes of notochord tissue (**nucleus pulposus**) remain sandwiched between the epiphyses of adjacent vertebrae (Fig. 20–6 B, C).

While the amphicoelous type of centrum is unquestionably primitive, being found in practically all fishes and presumably therefore in the ancestry of all the land vertebrates, it may either precede the final form in the development of the more advanced tetrapod centra, or it may be completely bypassed in a direct differentiation of the vertebra from mesenchyme. The acoelous vertebrae of mammals are not developed through any amphicoelous, pro- or opisthocoelous stages, although the ancestors of mammals certainly had such centra.

The vertebral centra of an individual may or may not be all of one type. A single turtle neck may have amphicoelous, procoelous and opisthocoelous centra, plus one or even two transitional centra that are **biconvex,** i.e., having both ends bulging (Fig. 20–5). Other types are also known that show doubled protuberances or concavities or even more complex arrangements.

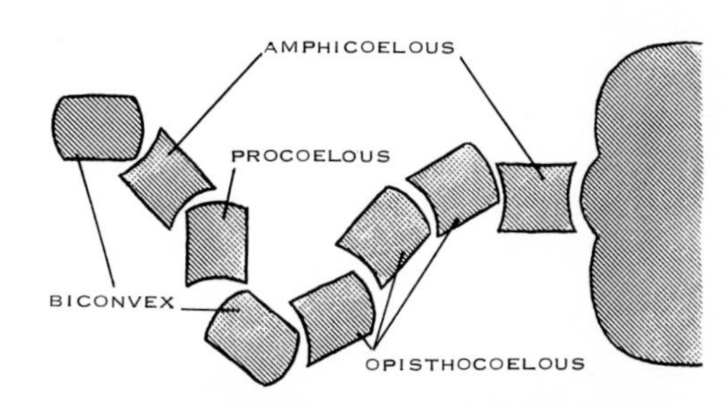

Fig. 20–5. Shapes of vertebral centra in the neck of an Australian side-necked turtle, *Chelodyna*.

(After data of Vaillante, 1879.)

C. Regional Specializations of Vertebrae

In some sharks which have one centrum per segment in the trunk and two per segment in the tail, a transition zone of a few segments occurs in which the relations between spinal nerves, centra, and arches become nothing less than chaotic. One might guess that regional specificities in the inductive influences from the spinal cord are competing for effect there.

Another such area of morphological confusion occurs at the anterior end of the vertebral column in tetrapods. Amphibia have a single peculiar first vertebra, the **atlas,** which forms a specialized joint with the skull. In urodeles this is the only trunk vertebra which bears no ribs.

In amniotes there are two elements, called **atlas** and **axis** (PNA), which surround the spinal cord, and sometimes one called the **proatlas** which perches above the cord between skull and atlas. These structures are built in a great variety of ways, out of originally separate segmental hypocentrum, pleurocentrum, and neural arch components, without much respect for proper segment boundaries. In terms of these elements, there seem to be at least five types of atlas and six of axis among amniotes, not counting additional subtypes according to the manner and degree of fusion of the parts, for hemispondyly is particularly common in this transitional zone [6].

The homology questions that have been debated for so long about these anterior vertebrae did not lead to simple answers, but to the realization of new complexities. The boundary between head and trunk has been moving fitfully back and forth in vertebrate evolution, as though a morphogenetic cranium-field and a trunk-field were competing for the materials in that region in every embryo, with the greater strength now in one, and now in the other.

D. Joints and Joint Processes

When growing cartilages or bones extend toward each other and meet they may either fuse together, or form a joint. In a given case, one can safely predict what will happen in one individual, from knowledge of what has happened in older individuals of the same species; but there is little information on what factors make the decision in any particular case [7]. There is, for instance, no adequate theory as to what leads vertebral structures in one segment to holospondyly while keeping them in a hemispondylous condition in another. One does not understand why the pleurocentrum of the proatlas segment fuses with the skull in birds and many reptiles, but fuses (along with the pleurocentrum of the atlas) to the centrum of the axis in other reptiles and mammals.

There are various ways of classifying joints, some emphasizing the degree of mobility in

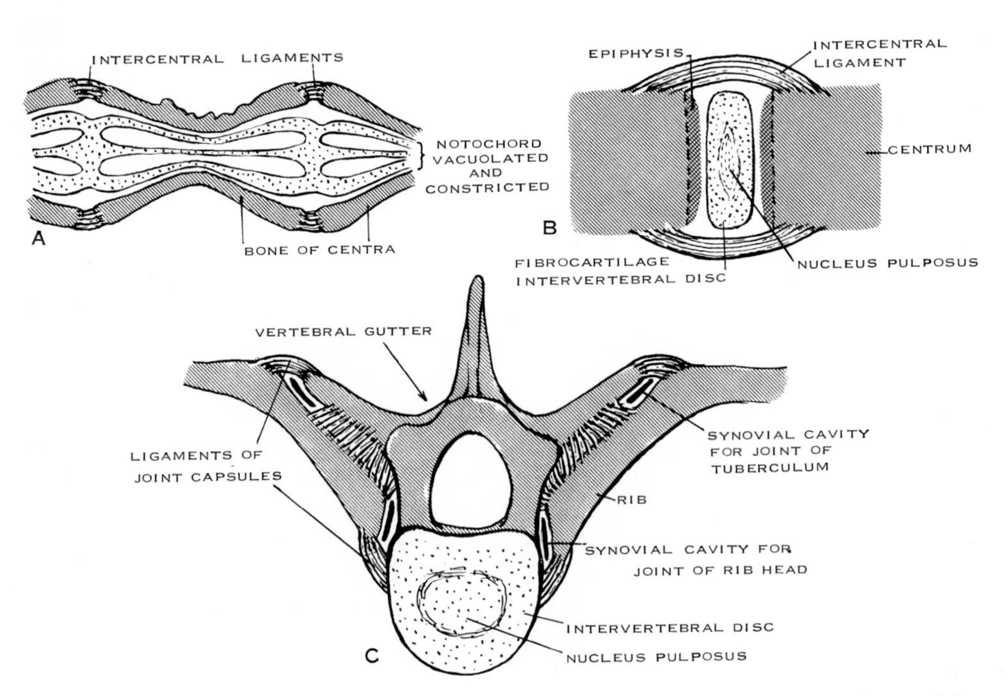

Fig. 20–6. Types of joints. A. Joint between amphicoelous centra of two fish vertebrae. B. Joint between acoelous centra of two mammalian vertebrae. C. Joints between a mammalian vertebra and its ribs.

them, others the types of tissues and structures which differentiate in them. **Synarthroses** are relatively simple joints which do not contain lubricated cavities (Fig. 20–6 B). **Diarthroses** are those which have, interposed between the surfaces of the associated bones or cartilages, a special **synovial sac** lined by membrane which secretes a slippery fluid (Fig. 20–6 C). Commonly, synarthroses are said to be rigid or slightly movable, but they are highly variable, including not only the almost immobile sutures between some skull bones but also joints of almost maximum freedom in the appendages of some cartilaginous fishes, which are held together by loose fibrous tissue. Similarly, diarthroses are spoken of as freely movable, but some are quite tight. Structurally, each joint is to a degree unique.

The relatively immobile vertebral centra of fishes are held together merely by ligaments that run from bone to bone (Fig. 20–6 A), the more or less vacuolated notochord tissue providing for adjustments in bending. In tetrapods (Fig. 20–6 B), the joints between centra are more complicated sorts of cartilages (later, often ossified) which crowd out the notochord. This material may either be added to the centrum anterior or posterior to it, or kept independent of both (Fig. 20–6 B). The joints are formed by secondary cleavage of originally continuous tissue. In urodeles, no such cleavage takes place if the spinal cord has been removed [8]. Such joints are completed by a capsule of stout ligamentous tissue running from vertebra to vertebra. Strong ligaments are also formed between adjacent neural spines or haemal spines.

Most vertebrates achieve a stronger binding of the backbone by means of projections or processes from one vertebra toward another. In the larger teleosts, these take the form of bony spurs from the bases of the neural (and sometimes also the haemal) arches, and they give a firmer anchorage to the intervertebral ligaments. They do not form special joints with each other.

In most of the tetrapods, however, similar extensions expand into real joint processes (Fig. 20–1). Their usual position is on the bases of neural arches, though they are built out from the centrum of mammalian tail vertebrae in the absence of arches. Characteristically there are a pair of **articular processes** (PNA) projecting anteriorly, and another pair projecting posteriorly over the dorsal surfaces of the anterior ones of the next vertebra (Figs. 20–1, 20–2 B). Thus they overlap like shingles down the back of an erect animal like man. Diarthrodial joints containing synovial cavities are formed between opposed anterior and posterior articular processes. In the trunks of mammals that have strongly backward-sloping neural spines in the thoracic region, similar joint surfaces may be formed on the neural arches without being built out into jutting processes.

These articular processes perform the important function of limiting the amount of twist that can be imposed on the backbone and the spinal cord. Additionally, twisting has been much more severely limited in several small groups of tetrapods by the development of accessory articular processes and various other dovetailed or wedge-and-socket processes for locking the vertebrae together. Snakes, for all their mobility in the frontal and sagittal planes, are carefully protected from shearing in transverse planes by the uniquely augmented articular devices on their vertebrae. One order of mammals has been named Xenarthra ("strange joints") because of the extreme complexity of these processes.

III. THE RIBS AND STERNUM

A. Ribs

In the great majority of vertebrates, ribs are attached to some, if not most, of the trunk vertebrae. The series of them may even be continued a few segments into the tail. Ribs are absent however, in cyclostomes, holocephals, a few elasmobranchs, and most anura.

In the amniotes, the regional differences of the axial skeleton between cervical, thoracic, lumbar, and sacral zones are mostly defined by what happens to the ribs. The hindlimb girdles of tetrapods usually attach to one or more *sacral* vertebrae by way of skeletal bridges that appear embryonically as ribs, and may remain so in more ancient types, but show a tendency to fuse with the sacral vertebrae in more advanced species (Fig. 20–7 C). *Cervical* ribs may remain as backward-projecting two-jointed spines in some reptiles but in others, and in birds and mammals, usually become solidly attached to their associated vertebrae. In such cases an outer part of the definitive transverse process of the adult cervical vertebra is actually the remains of an embryonic rib. Whether fused or jointed to the vertebrae, cervical ribs have no connections with a sternum, and this is their principal contrast with the thoracic ribs. However, in man, the seventh cervical rib, which normally fuses (Fig. 20–7 A), not uncommonly remains free, and may rarely achieve its own direct joint with the sternum.

In mammals and many reptiles, an apparently ribless set of vertebrae between the thorax and the sacrum is defined as the *lumbar* zone. Here too, study of embryos shows that ribs form, but subsequently lose their identity by fusing with their vertebrae (Fig. 20–7 B). In occasional human individuals the normal fusion of the first lumbar rib may fail to take place on either or both sides, and an extra free rib or a pair of them results. The anomalous structure is called a gorilla rib, since the number of thoracic and lumbar vertebrae, normally twelve and five respectively in man, is thirteen and four in the gorilla.

Ribs are formed deep in the connective tissue between the embryonic myotomes, which clearly distinguishes them from the sometimes riblike **gastralia** formed in some tetrapods, both recent and fossil. Gastralia arise in the dermis layer of the skin, and therefore belong with the dermal skeleton, whether or not they subsequently become embedded in the belly musculature, as they do in alligators.

The spinal cord is implicated in the induction of rib formation in urodeles, as well as in the induction of vertebra formation [8]. A quantitative influence spreading out from the spinal cord is suggested by the fact that neither vertebrae nor ribs form when neural tissue is totally removed, but vertebrae form without ribs when the spinal cord is merely reduced a certain amount. Although the ribs normally appear separately from the vertebrae when cartilage formation starts, they never develop in the absence of vertebrae.

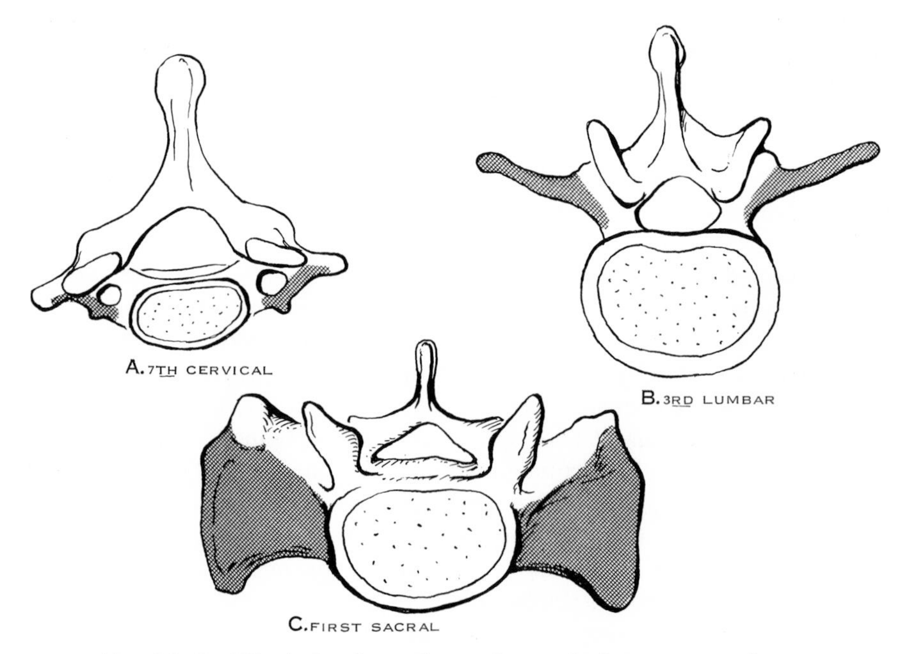

Fig. 20–7. Rib-derived portions of certain human vertebrae.

Many kinds of bony fishes produce two sets of ribs. One set is strongly developed internally in the flanks, against the peritoneum, and the series of the two sides approach each other toward the level of the anus, intergrading smoothly with the haemal arches of the tail vertebrae. They are called **peritoneal** or **haemal ribs** (Fig. 20–8). The other set is formed dorsally, in the myosepta at their intersection with a connective tissue plane that more or less horizontally divides the myotomic muscles into dorsal and ventral series along the flank. These are **dorsal** or **intermuscular ribs.** Commonly they are found only in the anterior part of the trunk.

Many kinds of teleosts also develop one or more sets of **fishbones,** which are a well-known nuisance at the dinner table. They turn up at the intersections of myosepta with various other connective-tissue planes, either in place of, or alongside the dorsal ribs. They may be tied by ligament to the vertebrae or to the ribs, or may float in the connective tissue. Extra upper and lower sets of them are not uncommonly Y- or T-shaped (Fig. 20–8). It is difficult to distinguish them from ribs on morphologic grounds, though they are generally ossified directly, while ribs are usually preformed in cartilage.

Since not only the tetrapods but also many groups of fishes possess only one set of ribs, the question has been argued at length which of the two teleost sets is homologous with the single set of this or that group. The evidence is often conflicting; probably the real difficulty is with the concept of homology itself.

The typical tetrapod rib makes two joints with its vertebra, an upper one by means of a **tuberculum** and a lower one by means of its **head** (PNA). After the fusion of a mammalian or avian cervical rib with its vertebra, the space bounded by the rib, the vertebra, and these two joints (Fig. 20–6 C) remains as a foramen in the transverse process (Fig. 20–7 A) and is often occupied by a longitudinal vertebral artery (Fig. 26–7).

Thoracic vertebrae often produce special rib-bearing processes from either the centrum or the neural arch, and these are marked by the facets for the rib joints. The joint for the head of the rib commonly straddles two vertebral centra, each of which contributes a demifacet (marked by dotted lines, Fig. 20–2 B). Since the capitular joint is apt to be on the end of the transverse process of the more posterior of these two vertebrae, the rib is given a backward slant and its motion is to a large degree restricted to a hingelike swing, either forward–outward or backward–inward. Such coordinated and alternating movements of the whole set of ribs would expand and contract the chest, as required in breathing.

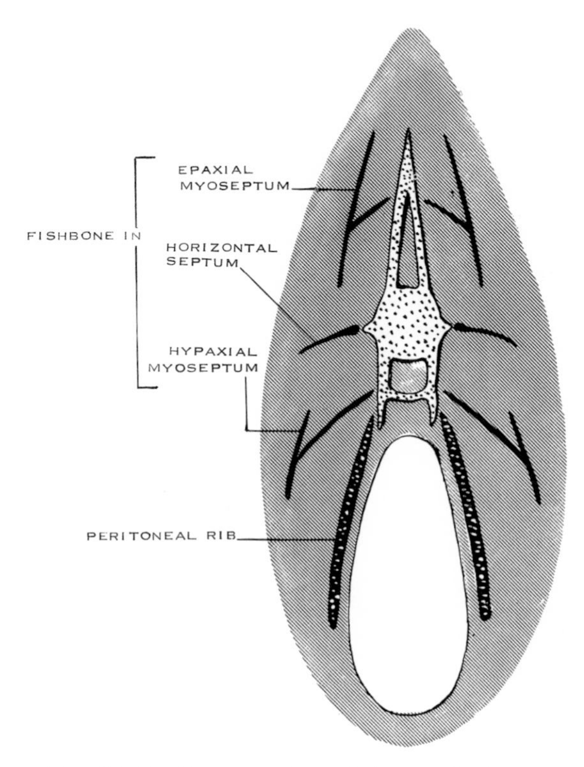

Fig. 20–8. Cross-section of the trunk of a herring, to show ribs and fishbones.
(After Bütschli, 1921.)

However, it should not be assumed that all tetrapod ribs have this manner of attachment to the vertebrae. The tubercles and their joints are missing in various reptiles, presumably by reduction, and disappear at the end of the thoracic series in many other amniotes, including man. And all fish ribs are single-jointed.

B. Sternum

The **sternum** is a structure found only in tetrapods, in correlation with the strength of development of the pectoral appendages. It is absent in snakes and the gymnophiona, and extremely weak and unossified in the urodeles. Turtles also lack a sternum, but their shell provides an adequate substitute. The greatest sternum development is found in birds (Fig. 20–9). Here it is immensely broadened and provided with a sharp keel-like projection in the midventral sagittal plane, for the attachment of a great thickness of pectoral flight muscles. A similar development of a keel has taken place quite independently in flying groups among both mammals (bats) and reptiles (the Jurassic pterosaurs). In flightless birds such as the ostrich, emu, kiwi, etc., the keel has been lost.

There are important variations in both development and anatomical pattern of the sternum. In urodeles and anura the sternal anlagen are unpaired and midventral (Fig. 20–14). In all but a few of the more primitive frogs, the two halves of the pectoral girdle meet firmly in the ventral midline, separating an anterior from a posterior midline sternal piece. This does not happen in other tetrapods. In the amniotes, whose embryos are at first spread out flat on a huge yolk sac, paired right and left sternal elements are formed, and only secondarily brought together in the ventral midline when the belly wall is finally gathered in. Adults show either multiple paired sternal elements, or a general fusion into a single midline element, or a series of them. The separate elements are called **sternebrae.** In

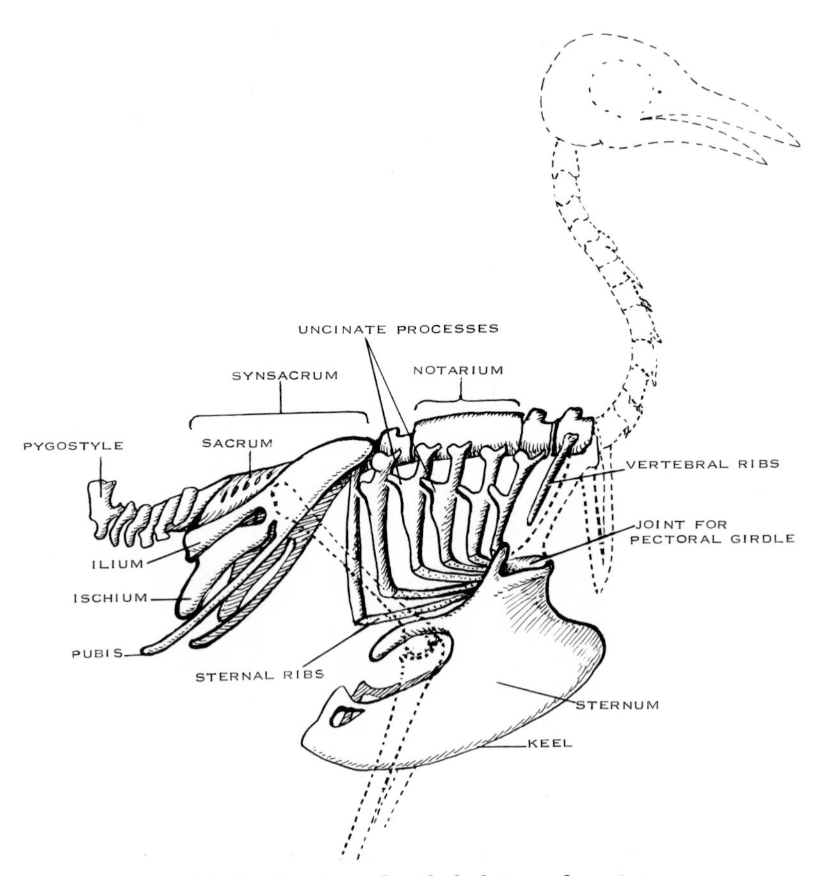

Fig. 20–9. Trunk and tail skeleton of a pigeon.

mammals, birds, and those of the reptiles that scamper on well-developed legs, ribs reach all the way down to the sternum, jointing with it between successive sternebrae.

This articulation of the ribs with the sternum is accomplished by separate sections called **sternal ribs,** which are smoothly continuous with the dorsal parts or **vertebral ribs** (Figs. 20–9, 20–10) but often do not ossify. Vertebral and sternal ribs may be interconnected in lizards by an intermediate section called the **intercostal piece.** In the chick, sternal ribs and sternum are formed from lateral-plate mesoderm, whereas the vertebral ribs arise from somites [9]. **Uncinate processes** develop from the vertebral ribs in most birds (Fig. 20–9), a few mammals, and various reptiles, extending backward to overlap the next ribs in the series and helping to bind the thoracic basket together.

The relations of the ribs to the sternum vary in other ways. In many reptiles and most mammals (including man), a distinction is made between **true ribs,** which make direct joints with the sternum individually, **false ribs,** which make indirect contact with it by tying their ventral ends to those of the nearest true ribs, and **floating ribs,** which end free in the flank muscles. There are a few lizards with a reduced sternum, in which some of the false ribs meet their antimeres in the midventral line. In animals which have free ribs in the neck, the first "true ribs" mark the anterior limit of the thorax. In snakes, which have no sternum, there cannot by definition be any "true ribs" and no regional differences in ribs exist for distinguishing cervical, thoracic, lumbar, or sacral trunk zones.

IV. REGIONAL SPECIALIZATIONS OF WHOLE AXIAL SKELETON

A. Necks

In most amniotes, the specialization of anterior trunk vertebrae and the associated segmental muscles, together with the shifting of heart, liver, and other viscera farther caudad, has produced a highly mobile neck, which greatly improves the feeding and fighting mechanisms. On the other hand, fishes do not have necks. Their swiftly directed swimming movements seem to require relative rigidity at the anterior end of the axis. It is appropriate then to find that usually the first few vertebrae of teleosts are fastened firmly to the back of the skull. The modern whales, which must have had terrestrial ancestors with long supple necks, develop cervical vertebrae in the usual mammalian pattern but at least in a functional sense they obliterate their necks in the late fetal stages. The cervical vertebrae cease to grow in length and become thin platelike affairs which may subsequently fuse together, making a **syncervix.** Some burrowing mammals show similar fusions and shortenings of cervical vertebrae.

B. Flight Adaptations

In skates and long-snouted rays, which do not drive themselves through the water with their tailfins but swim by dorsoventral undulations of the body and pectoral wings, a very good joint occurs between the skull and the vertebral column, but a considerable number of cartilaginous vertebrae back of the foramen magnum fuse into a single piece, providing a more rigid attachment for the "flight" muscles. The word **notarium** is used for such a structure, denoting a united backbone (or back-cartilage in this case). In the skates and rays the skeletal girdle of the pectoral wings makes a broad firm attachment to the notarium and in many species even fuses with it on both sides so that most of the trunk skeleton is of one piece.

In the thorax of many birds, the rigid frame required for flight is provided in part by fusion of from three to five thoracic vertebrae to form a notarium (Fig. 20–9). In certain bats, a similar fusion of two or three vertebrae and their ribs has been found. The extinct reptile *Pteranodon* (Fig. 20–10) had a notarium in which eight vertebrae and their ribs were fused together. These fishes, reptiles, birds, and bats acquired their flying habits in evolutionary ventures which were quite independent of each other, in time and lineage, and their separate inventions of the notarium in the interest of a rigid flight frame are examples of **convergent evolution.**

C. Sacrum

If it can be said that the requirements of efficient flight set such a premium on rigidity in the thoracic part of the axial skeleton that chance variations in this direction were encouraged by natural selection, it can also be said that weight-carrying hindlimbs in tetrapods encourage evolution in the direction of rigidity at the sacral level. In fishes, the hindlimbs do not carry any weight and their girdles do not attach to the vertebral column. In amphibia and primitive reptiles, there is apt to be just one sacral vertebra, and its attachment to the hindlimb girdle is by way of a pair of sacral ribs, which are extra heavy and shortened, but often movable. Such creatures do not spend much time with the weight of their trunks lifted off the ground. On the other hand, adult lizards, birds, and mammals show one (and usually more than one) sacral vertebra, and the sacral ribs that are found in the embryo lose their identity during growth, by fusion (Fig. 20–7 C). The multiplication of sacral vertebrae is commonly also followed by their joining into one piece, called the **sacrum,** as in all birds and most mammals.

Other neighboring vertebrae which cannot be called sacral because they make no direct contact with the pelvic girdle, may also join in this fusion. This creates a **synsacrum.** Some dinosaurs and the flying reptile *Pteranodon* (Fig. 20–10) had as many as ten synsacral vertebrae. Among mammals, only the synsacrum of certain armadillos reaches this degree of fusion, but here additionally it may be tightly jointed to the armor plates formed in the skin. The modern birds have a gigantic synsacrum of from 10 to 22 vertebrae, including even thoracic vertebrae bearing movable ribs, and the pelvic girdle is fused to it for nearly its full length (Fig. 20–9). It is always found that where a notarium and a synsacrum occur in the same animal (birds, *Pteranodon,* etc.) at least one free vertebra is retained between them.

D. Tails

Just as the caudal region of vertebrates can be spun out to include literally hundreds of ver-

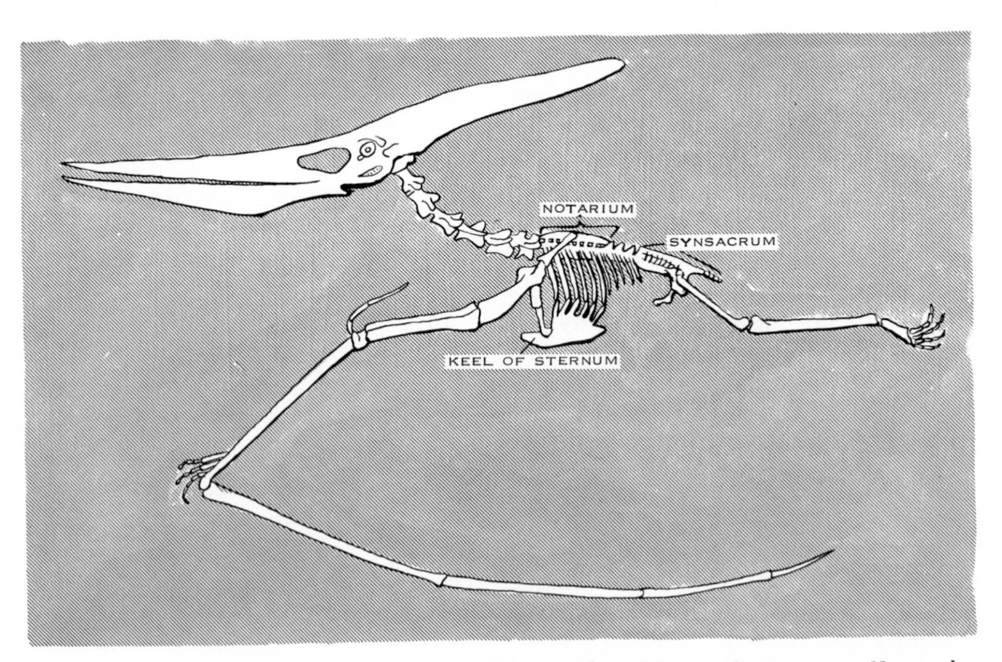

Fig. 20–10. Skeleton of a pterosaur, *Pteranodon* (Upper Cretaceous, Kansas).
(After G. F. Eaton, 1910.)

tebrae, so it can be abbreviated and degenerate. The fusion of postsacral vertebrae, or their failure to develop segmentally, sometimes occurs, as in the **coccyx** of man and pig, and also in the thin upturned **pygostyle** blade (Fig. 20–9) which supports the caudal flight feathers of nearly all birds. The fusion may take place in late fetal life or in youth. Segmental development of vertebrae does not occur in the tails of anuran tadpoles, and at metamorphosis a single bone, the **urostyle,** appears in their place (Fig. 20–20).

V. DEVELOPMENT OF THE MYOTOMES

A. Histogenesis

The prospective muscle cells in the outer part of the somites (the **myoblasts**) are at first indistinguishable from the sclerotome cells. In fact, transplantations and sandwich cultures at the primordial embryo stage and earlier show that any of the mesoderm cells over the roof of the amphibian archenteron—prospective notochord, cartilage, muscle, kidney, etc.—can be manipulated so that they will differentiate in any of these directions (page 168).

As the myoblast cells differentiate, they elongate in particular directions in parallel clusters, and apparently fuse together, transforming from mononucleate cells into multinucleate **muscle fibers** [10]. Long **myofibrils** accumulate in the cytoplasm of the fibers. They are arranged parallel to each other and to the long axis of the fibers, and are banded (page 55), the bands being lined up in the appearance of cross-striations. The property of contractility derives from a highly oriented protein system called actomyosin, synthesized in these myofibrils. The cells may contract in tissue culture either before (amphibia) or after they become multinucleate, and either before (chick, mouse) or after the cross-striations become visible with the ordinary microscope. There are special techniques, however, for demonstrating that the oriented protein has already been set in all contracting muscle fibers [3].

The conditions under which this highly specialized protein synthesis will take place, producing real muscle, have not yet become clear. As is the case with the differentiation of vertebral cartilage, presence of the notochord is not necessary. Sandwich explants of large masses of myotome material will differentiate into muscle in the absence of recognizable spinal-cord cells [11], though presence of neural tissue may be necessary for its subsequent maintenance and seems also to favor its growth [12, 13, 3].

B. Subdivisions

In normal development of the amblystoma, the dorsal part of each trunk myotome differentiates into the anteroposteriorly oriented fibers of the dorsal or **epaxial musculature.** From the ventral borders of these myotomes, segmental tongues of cells then spread downward toward the midventral line, or in amniotes outward over the lateral plates of mesoderm, insinuating themselves between the embryonic skin and the lining of the body cavity. From these **muscle processes** arise at least the main part of the ventrolateral trunk musculature, which becomes separated in more or less clear-cut fashion from the epaxial masses by a **horizontal septum** of connective tissue which runs lengthwise of the flank from the level of the cloaca to the pharynx-segment zone (Fig. 20–11). It is the **hypaxial division** of the myotomic musculature.

In the amblystoma, early removal of the somites greatly reduces or entirely eliminates the hypaxial musculature, and the same is true if the somites are merely removed and replanted upside down, so that the prospective muscle-process cells are trapped dorsally [14]. In the chick, however [9], hypaxial musculature is produced from the lateral plate or hypomere mesoderm if the somites have been removed. New light will no doubt be thrown on this contradiction when it is discovered what materials must be furnished to mesoderm cells to convert them into muscle, and where these materials can come from [10].

The hypaxial muscle zone of the amblystoma, and of all tetrapods, becomes gradually divided into inner and outer layers, and in other ways by region. A parent layer is differentiated whose fibers are laid out in parallel lines from anteroventral to posterodorsal. What determines this

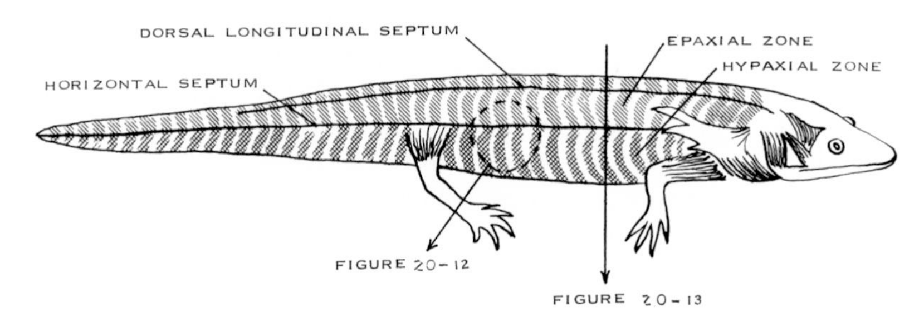

Fig. 20–11. Trunk and tail muscles of a larval amblystoma.

angle is unknown. Subsequently, deeper and more superficial layers of fibers are organized whose fibers are also arranged in parallel series, but at marked angles to the first ones, and separated from each other by connective tissue. There thus arise four superimposed layers of muscle in the flank of the amblystoma, like the layers of plywood (Figs. 20–12, 20–13). The parent layer is called the **internal oblique.** Inside it lies the **transverse** and outside it the **external oblique** layer, upon the dorsal limit of which is superimposed, in mid-larval life, a short series of slips called the **superficial external oblique** layer. All these sheets are interrupted at intersegmental intervals by the **myosepta,** the connective tissue planes that mark the boundaries between the derivatives of adjacent myotomes.

The muscle fibers of the oblique layers do not extend all the way to the midventral line but in strongly developed tetrapods the layers are continued in that direction by sheetlike tendons. On either side of the midventral line, other muscle fibers are differentiated in an anteroposterior direction, forming the **rectus** subdivision of the

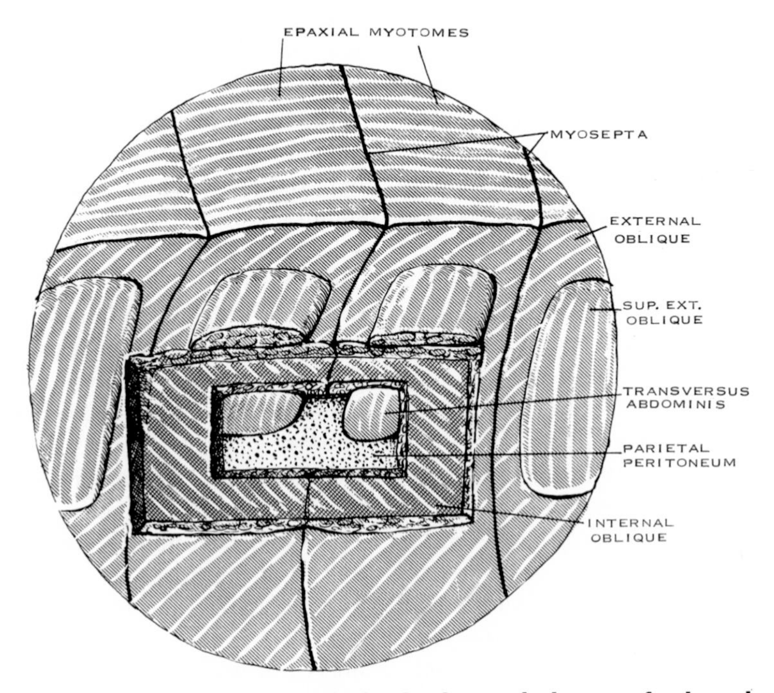

Fig. 20–12. Windows cut through the flank muscle layers of a larval amblystoma.

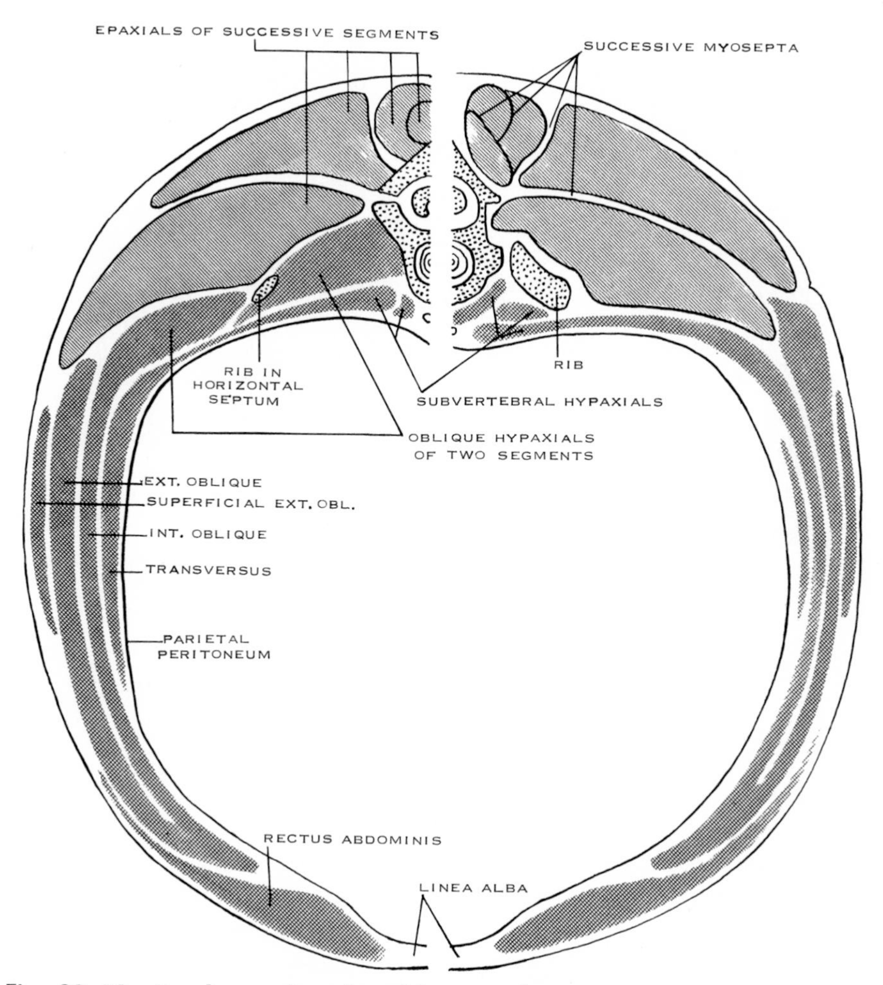

Fig. 20–13. Trunk muscles of amblystoma larva in transverse sections. Left side of section is cut half a segment posterior to the right side. Asymmetry of the muscle masses is caused by the zigzag and slant of myotomes.

hypaxial musculature (Fig. 20–13). The rectus strips may be enclosed by the sheet tendons of the oblique muscles. A strip of connective tissue in the sagittal plane separates the rectus strips of the two sides. This is the **ventral longitudinal septum** (linea alba, PNA), which lies in the same plane with the **dorsal longitudinal septum** that divides the epaxial muscles of the two sides.

In most amniotes, the ribs reach farther down through the myosepta of the somatopleure than they do in the amphibia, so that in their territory they interrupt the oblique sheets, which then appear as segmental strips of **internal and external intercostal** muscles. Further subdivision into tangential sheets occurs regionally in various tetrapods. In some lizards for instance, as many as eight different layers of hypaxial muscle are found, not all of them being superimposed at any one level.

Although the rectus muscles extend on each side of the midventral line of the amblystoma in an unbroken myotomic series from the pelvic girdle to the tip of the lower jaw (Fig. 20–14 A), various skeletal elements may break into them in other tetrapods. Strongly developed sternal ribs and sternum, for instance, may interrupt the rectus group, isolating a **rectus abdominis** series from a **rectus cervicis** series. The hyoid arch may

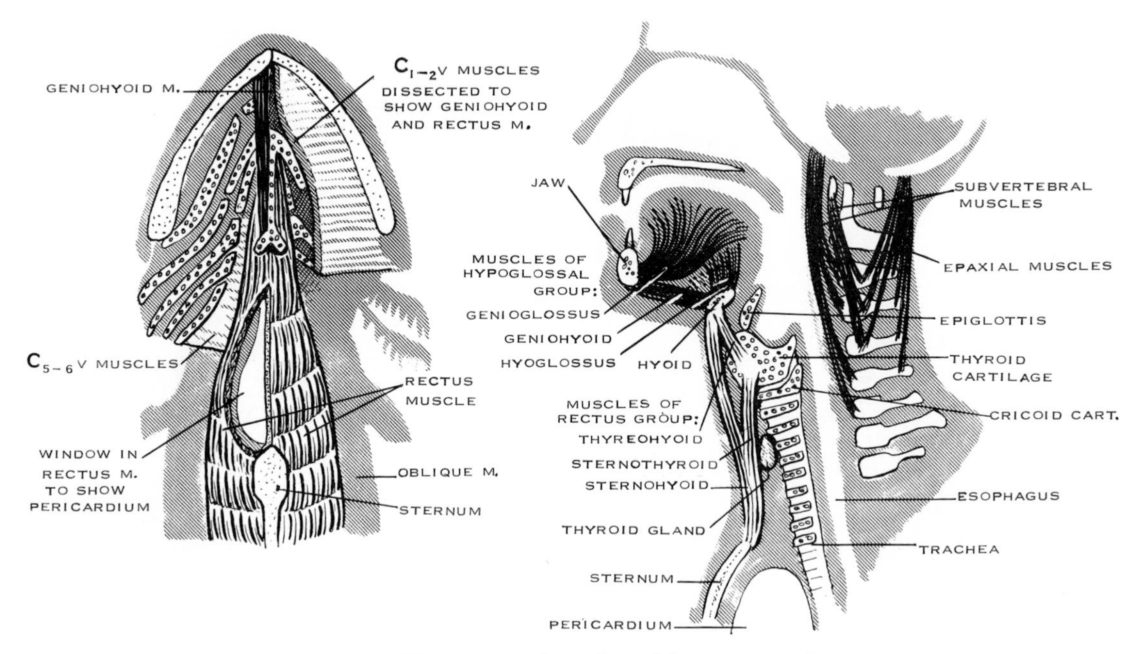

Fig. 20–14. Throat muscles of amblystoma and man.

be interposed between an anterior **geniohyoid** and a posterior **sternohyoid** part of the rectus cervicis, and in mammals the thyroid cartilage of the larynx may be interposed between a **sternothyroid** and a **thyrohyoid** subdivision (Fig. 20–14 B).

The most anterior part of the rectus series is distinguished as the **hypoglossal** group of muscles (the geniohyoid and its offshoots in the secondary tongue; compare Figs. 17–22 and 20–14). In the amblystoma they are formed by the muscle processes of the first three permanent trunk myotomes. These are crowded together in their downward growth by the posterior expansion of the pharynx segments. Nevertheless, they are able to migrate to a position near the ventral midline in the chin region, medial to the subpharyngeal septum, widely separated from their epaxial relatives. The ventral rami of their spinal nerves, which were in contact with the muscle processes almost before the bold shift in position started, are pulled out in a long arc and crowded together into a nerve trunk which is named the **hypoglossal nerve.** Its sweeping curve (Fig. 17–23) preserves in the adult the record of the source and migration of its muscles. The embryology of the hypoglossal muscles is less easy to trace in the amniotes but there is experimental evidence of a similar history for them in birds [15].

Still another subdivison of the hypaxial musculature tends to be developed against the centra of the trunk vertebrae and ventral to their transverse processes. These **subvertebral muscles** are feebly developed and poorly separated from the oblique group in the amblystoma (Fig. 20–13), but become much stronger and regionally specialized in amniotes with supple backbones (Figs. 20–14, 20–17). They work in concert with the epaxial musculature to produce the sinuous movements of snakes and the necks of birds, and reach their most massive development in the extraordinarily powerful necks of snapping turtles. In mammals, they are well developed only in the neck.

C. Specializations of Myotomes in Fishes

Trunk muscles of all the fishes and the amniotes develop from myotomes and their muscle processes, along lines generally comparable to those described for the amblystoma, but with remarkable contrasts in the end products. There are many variations and aberrant lines of evolution among the classes and orders, but in general the fishes retain and specialize the segmental aspects of their musculature, while amniotes disguise the segmental origins by reorganizing the muscle tissues into new functional groupings. The principal contrast here is in the fates of the myosepta.

In most fishes, myosepta are strongly developed in strictly metameric fashion, forming what might be called a fibrous skeleton to which practically all the myotomic muscle fibers attach. Only exceptionally do muscle fibers span a greater distance than that from one myoseptum to the next.

To observe the skinned amblystoma larva (Fig. 20–11), one might suppose that myosepta are simple transverse planes of connective tissue. Even here, however, serial sections or dissections from which all muscle fibers are plucked out show that the myosepta are complexly disposed in three dimensions (Fig. 20–13). A myoseptum which is attached medially along one vertebra slopes irregularly posterolaterad so that it reaches the skin at the transverse level of the first, second, or third vertebra behind the one it belongs with. Also it forms shallow pockets whose points are anterior and whose mouths open posteriorly. Nothing is known about the factors which establish these distortions as the myosepta develop.

In sharks and bony fishes, the similar dissection of a typical myoseptum reveals that it is broken into a number of crazily tilted planes forming several deep pointed pockets, some with their tips toward the head, alternating with others that point toward the tail (Fig. 20–15). The pockets occurring in successive myotomes at equivalent dorsoventral levels are stacked or nested together in horizontal series, so that a true transverse section will cut through several members of each series. This accounts for the roughly concentric circles of myotome muscle to be seen in a fish steak at the dinner table (Fig. 20–4). The embryonic myoseptum arises in contact with only one vertebra, but with the development of these zigzag extensions it comes to overlap three, five or more vertebrae in the adult.

Within each myotome, multitudes of short parallel muscle fibers run from the one myoseptum boundary to the other in roughly anteroposterior direction. When stimulated by their own spinal nerve, they can exert a rapid and powerful pull on the myosepta, which distribute the force in a smooth gradient over several vertebrae.

Though there are many exceptional cases, in most fishes the trunk itself is the principal locomotor agent, the fins serving more generally as brakes, rudders, or stabilizers. The spinal cord fires off timed patterns of impulses through the successive spinal nerves of the two sides so as to produce alternating bends to left and right, and these flow caudad rapidly enough so that the fish wriggles its way forward through the relatively inert water [16].

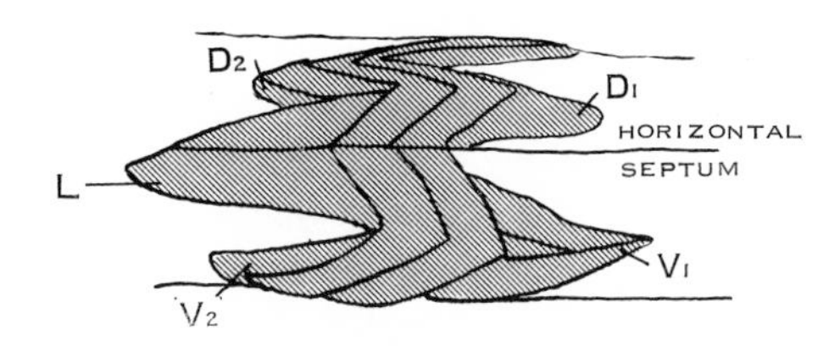

Fig. 20–15. Fish myotomes.

The myotomes in the tails of dipnoi and sturgeons remain relatively simpler than in most bony fishes. Each one shows one hypaxial pocket and two epaxial ones. The hypaxial and the dorsal epaxial pockets point caudad, the intervening lower epaxial one craniad. The myotomic walls of these three pockets are customarily labeled as D, L, and V in diagrams, from dorsal to ventral. The muscle tissue is uninterrupted.

The more common pattern, seen in sharks (Fig. 20–15), holosts and teleosts, shows five pockets per myotome: D_2 (most dorsal, epaxial, directed craniad), D_1, L, V_1 (upper hypaxial, directed caudad), and V_2. In some fishes other pockets are added, and a myotome may have to be described in parts D_3, D_2, D_1, L_d, L_v, V_1, V_2, and V_3.

In addition to this multiplication of reversing stacked pockets, the myotomes are further complicated by being cut across by longitudinal planes of connective tissue. A **horizontal septum** is usually found (though not in cyclostomes), dividing the myotomes into epaxial and hypaxial parts. A **sublateral septum** may also occur, dividing the hypaxial musculature of each successive segment from the pectoral fin level as far back as the cloaca or anus, into **dorsal oblique** and **ventral oblique** masses, in which the muscle fibers may be slanted at slightly different angles. The obliquity of the muscle fibers, if there is any, tends to be corrected toward the horizontal as their distance from the ventral midline decreases, but there is seldom a clear segregation of a rectus abdominis, and the homology of the oblique subdivision with those in tetrapods cannot be insisted on. Many bony fishes have a longitudinal strip of red oily muscle under the skin along the flank external to the lateral septum. There is nothing like it in tetrapods. On dinner plates it is commonly left untouched.

Hypoglossal muscles arise in all the fish groups except the hagfishes, in the manner described for the amblystoma, carrying their spinal nerves with them in their migration. In the gnathostome fishes, the muscles divide up to insert on the anterior ends of the lower jaws and the skeletal bars of the pharynx segments. Since they can pull these arches backward, they constitute a primitive mouth-opening apparatus, which has been replaced in tetrapods by C_2d depressor mandibulae muscles or (in mammals) by C_{1-2}v digastrics (page 304). Because the jaw-openers of fishes lie chiefly below gills rather than tongue, the name **hypobranchial** is preferred for them, rather than hypoglossal, and this name is also applied to their nerve (Fig. 17–29).

Reversing the general trend for elaboration of myosepta, several groups of fishes have eliminated them, in whole or in part. These are groups which depend less on trunk and tail than on fins for locomotion: skates and rays among the elasmobranchs, and sea horses and a few other highly unusual teleosts. Hypaxial muscles of the tail are transformed into electric organs in a few rays and several small groups of teleosts. In spite of these specializations, the segmental innervation by spinal nerves remains as a record of the generalized embryonic pattern.

D. Fate of Myotomes in Amniotes

1. Epaxial Zone. Crocodilia and the sphenodon retain V-shaped myosepta in the epaxial zone, as in the amphibia, and there may also be pocket-like distortions of them, as in fishes. Some families of lizards retain a myotomic arrangement of the epaxial zone, others lose it entirely, and there are all grades in between. On the other hand, snakes, birds, and the placental mammals give up all traces of myosepta in the epaxial region. What happens is that the muscle cells not only amalgamate into long fibers, but these in turn aggregate into bundles and attach by special tendons to particular parts of the bony skeleton, with no reference to segmental partitions. The fibers closest to the vertebrae may continue to bridge the gap between two adjacent centra, or transverse processes, or neural or haemal spines, but the more superficial ones may span three, four, or more vertebrae or even ribs. These, further, may be bound up by sheets of connective tissue into large new functional bundles. From one region of the trunk to another, such bundles will vary in correlation with specializations of ribs or the bony processes of the vertebrae. The degree of this development is a measure of the suppleness of the vertebral column. Naturally it is reduced to practically nothing inside the shell of a turtle, and remains feeble over the thorax of a bird when a notarium is achieved.

Nearly all the amniotes show a column of fiber bundles set off medially from the rest of the epaxial musculature, in specific relation to the neural arches and spines (**spinalis dorsi,** Fig. 20–16, and others). The deepest fibers are only one segment long, but outer bundles span a number of vertebrae.

A much broader column called the **longissimus** is developed lateral to these, running the full length of trunk and tail. In general its long bundles make tendinous attachments from one transverse process to another, or to myoseptal remains that tie to the transverse processes. In some mammals, feebly in man (Fig. 20–1) but spectacularly in armadillos, the vertebrae develop anteriorly directed **mammillary processes** and posteriorly directed **accessory processes** for the attachment of longissimus tendons and of deeper columns of shorter muscles that are laid on in bundles between the transverse processes and the neural spines, i.e., lying in the "vertebral gutter." These include the **semispinalis** and **multifidus** groups (Fig. 20–16). To bear the weight of the head, there is a special **splenius** mass on each side of the neck, covered by the trapezius but covering the semispinalis and longissimus muscles. It takes origin from the neural spines of cervical and thoracic vertebrae and from a stout checkrein ligament that interconnects these in the midline. Splenius muscles are exceedingly strong in the big heavy-headed hoofed mammals.

The most lateral of the epaxial columns, occurring in the trunk but not in the tail, is the **iliocostalis** muscle. As its name implies, it starts with the ilium or the sacral rib at the pelvic level, and it either attaches segmentally to myosepta that are fastened to ribs, or else it develops its own tendons that insert on ribs. Iliocostalis muscles are absent inside the shells of turtles, and weak in birds because of the extent of the synsacrum and the relative rigidity of the thoracic basket; they are enormously specialized in snakes, though in these there is no ilium to anchor to. It is iliocostalis and longissimus dorsi muscles that become sirloin steak at the butcher's.

The complex, interwoven, tendinous masses of specialized epaxial musculature make very difficult dissection in the higher amniotes. They can be analyzed most easily by first cooking them, which weakens the connective tissues that bind them and loosens the grip of the tendons on the skeleton.

In amphibia and some reptiles the **horizontal septum** of connective tissue makes a clear-cut separation between the hypaxial musculature and the iliocostalis part of the epaxial mass. In more advanced amniotes, the spread and specialization of subvertebral and oblique divisions of the hypaxial muscles in relation to the movable joints between ribs and vertebrae tends to obscure this septum. Also in birds and mammals the extensive development of appendicular muscles nearly covers the line where it would have reached the skin (see next chapter). In mammals, the epaxial mass is encased in an extremely tough shiny **lumbodorsal fascia**, which ties to the neural spines in the dorsal midline and to the bases of the ribs laterally. The hypaxial muscles advance somewhat over the surface of this sheet, taking origin from it. Part of the lumbo-

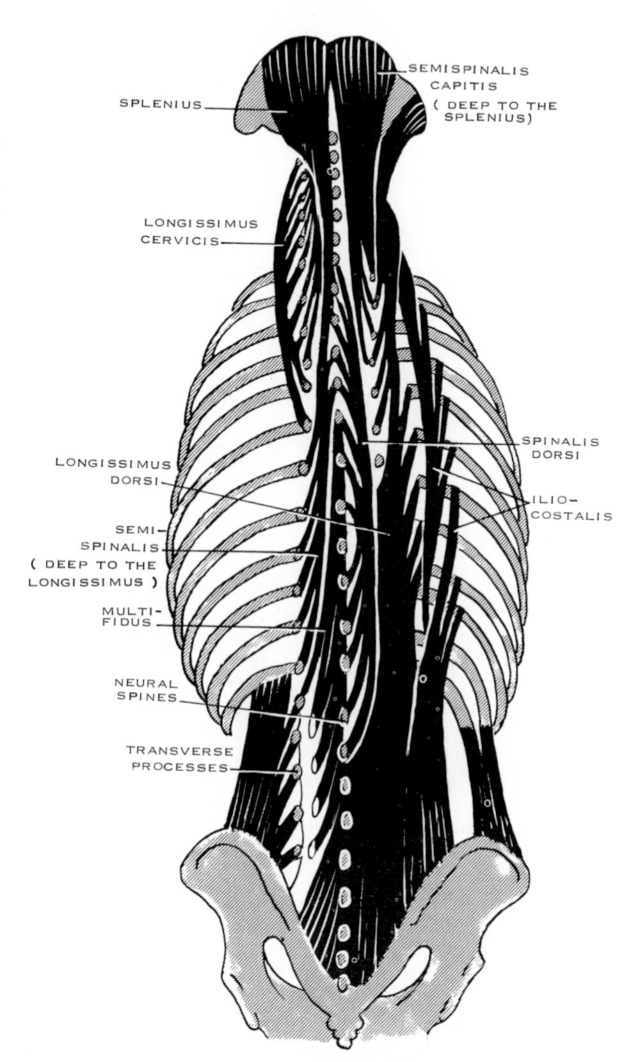

Fig. 20–16. Epaxial muscles of man.
(After Gray's Anatomy, 27th edition, 1959, with permission of Lea & Febiger, Publishers.)

dorsal fascia may represent the old horizontal septum.

2. *Hypaxial Zone.* Amniotes tend to lose myosepta also in the hypaxial territories, though not as completely as in the epaxial zone, and there are more variations. Long muscles with tendons, adapted for special regional functions, are assembled from the materials of many myotomes.

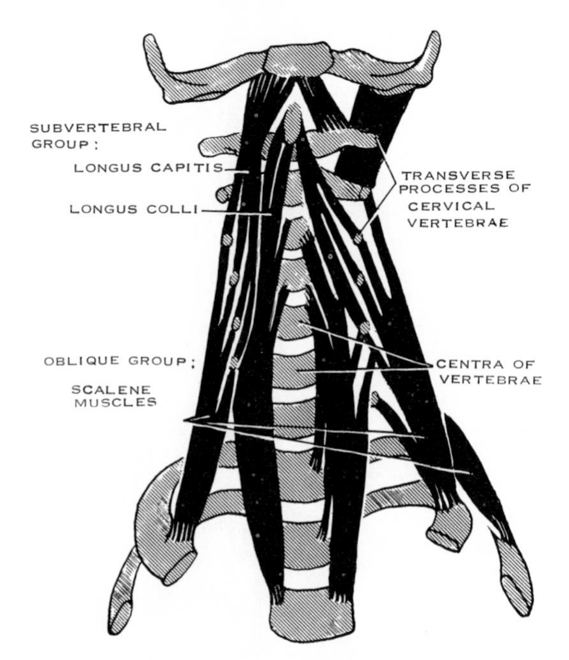

Fig. 20–17. Deep hypaxial neck muscles of man.

(After Gray's Anatomy, 27th edition, 1959, with permission of Lea and Febiger, Publishers.)

In the neck, for instance, special hypaxial muscles arise from the subvertebral group to work in concert with similar deep epaxial muscles in the region of the atlas and axis, for lowering and turning the head. Others spread into long groups interconnecting the centra of the cervical vertebrae (**longus colli,** Fig. 20–17), cooperating with similar epaxials to make the neck a supple organ for feeding or fighting (compare Figs. 20–16 and 20–17 with 20–14 B).

In mammals with long tails, most of the caudal myotomes degenerate and the more proximal ones develop stout muscle masses which operate the distal part of the tail through long tendons. In the abbreviated tails of birds, both the hypaxial and epaxial myotomes differentiate special slips of muscle that attach by individual tendons to each of the flight feathers of the tail so as to control their steering and braking functions. At the other extreme however, there still exist reptiles with tail musculature consisting of highly developed epaxial and hypaxial myotomes, more fishlike than those of the amblystoma, with as many as three pockets in each myoseptum below the horizontal septum.

Certain multisegmental units are synthesized from the oblique divisions of neck myotomes in amniotes, which take origin from cervical ribs (or transverse processes, if these ribs fuse to their vertebrae during fetal development), and insert on the free-moving ribs of the thoracic basket. These are the **scalene muscles** of human anatomy (Fig. 20–17). The thoracic ribs normally slope posteroventrad, but can be dragged toward the transverse plane by these muscles, which automatically swings the sternum ventrad (if there is one) and enlarges the volume of the thorax. This is how lizards and alligators normally suck air into their lungs, and this is how a mammal will do it if his diaphragm cannot function adequately (page 490).

Among tetrapods generally, though weakly in the amphibia, some segmental slips from the local oblique hypaxial musculature reach out and insert on the inside of the scapula, which is the upper end of the pectoral girdle skeleton. They thus form a sort of muscular sling by which the weight of the body may be hung on the forelimbs. This is a prerequisite to walking, as contrasted with crawling. The **rhomboid** and **serratus** muscles, described in the next chapter, arise in this way.

The strongest remaining indication of segmentation in the hypaxial territory of tetrapods is naturally in the thorax, where the oblique muscles of the original myotomes continue to be separated from each other by ribs. This, however, does not prevent the specialization of external and internal layers which work in functional groups. The ultimate in such developments occurs in snakes. Their superficial external oblique and rectus muscles become multilayered and fragmented into slips which insert on the scales of the sides and belly, and are very effectively used in the sort of locomotion called **rectilinear progression,** in which the snake seems to flow forward without the help of any bending from side to side. Close inspection shows that successive bands of the belly skin are being pulled forward, and their broad ventral belly scales tipped so as to anchor themselves against the ground, ratchet-like, while the muscles of the intervening bands cause the whole trunk to slip forward through the anchored bands of skin [17].

The more usual types of snake locomotion are even more complexly contrived, and are matched by adaptations in limbless lizards of several families as well as those of limbless gymnophionid amphibians. Terrestrial locomotion without limbs requires most remarkable transformations in the skeleton and muscles of the entire trunk and tail [18].

In man and other amniotes, after the breakdown of myosepta in the rectus musculature, a few more or less definite streaks of connective tissue may be found crossing the belly muscles transversely. These are called **tendinous inscriptions.** In some cases they are actually vestiges of the myosepta, but in other cases they have been found to arise after the complete disappearance of the original partitions. In fact, tendinous inscriptions sometimes arise in limb muscles which have a non-metameric origin.

VI. SOMATIC NERVES OF THE TRUNK AND TAIL

The locomotor apparatus includes not only the skeleton, and the muscles which move it, but also the nerves which supply the muscles. The nerves in turn are anatomically and functionally inseparable from the central nervous system, in which practically all of their constituent neurons have endings. This chapter will consider only the peripheral nerves which have somatic functions relating to epaxial and hypaxial zones, leaving the nerves of the limbs to Chapter 21, and the integrative functions and visceral components of all to Part VI.

A. Development of Spinal Nerves

The broad aspects of the formation of the spinal cord and its nerves were considered earlier (pages 130, 153). The motor neurons that distribute through most of the trunk and tail arise in the ventral half of the spinal cord (Figs. 4–10, 4–15), from large pyramidal cell-bodies. Their dendrites remain inside the cord but their axons stream outward, to be gathered segmentally into the ventral roots of spinal nerves. The ventral roots are motor in function.

Dorsal roots of the spinal nerves are practically all composed of processes from migrant neural crest cells which move out and locate in each segment as the spinal ganglia. These cells differentiate into both somatic sensory and visceral sensory neurons, from which the axons extend both medially to end in the dorsal half of the spinal cord, and laterally toward their dendritic zones in the peripheral tissues (Fig. 20-18 A, B). The dorsal roots are predominantly sensory in function, though some visceral motor fibers may emerge through them in non-mammalian vertebrates, particularly in primitive fishes (*not* shown in Fig. 20–18 B).

This exodus of sensory cells from the spinal cord continues for some time in the embryos of most vertebrates, and does not complete itself until after the larval stage in urodeles. It is never finished in some teleosts, or in the cyclostomes, adults of which still show primitive sensory elements called Rohon-Beard cells, whose axons distribute outward through the dorsal roots but whose somata lie within the gray substance of the spinal cord. In many bony fishes, other sensory cells just manage to leave the spinal cord but remain perched on its dorsal surface, inside the leptomeninx envelope.

In all the gnathostomes, each dorsal root meets its ventral root in a restricted **intervertebral foramen** (Fig. 20–2 B), and a common connective tissue sheath binds them together as one nerve in each segment. This nerve then divides into **dorsal** and **ventral rami** (PNA) as it distributes to the periphery (Fig. 20–18 A). The dorsal rami (usually one per segment but sometimes more) distribute to the myotome derivatives (epaxial muscles) and the skin above the horizontal septum; and the ventral rami similarly to the hypaxial muscles and skin below it. A visceral ramus or **ramus communicans** (PNA) separates promptly from the ventral ramus in most

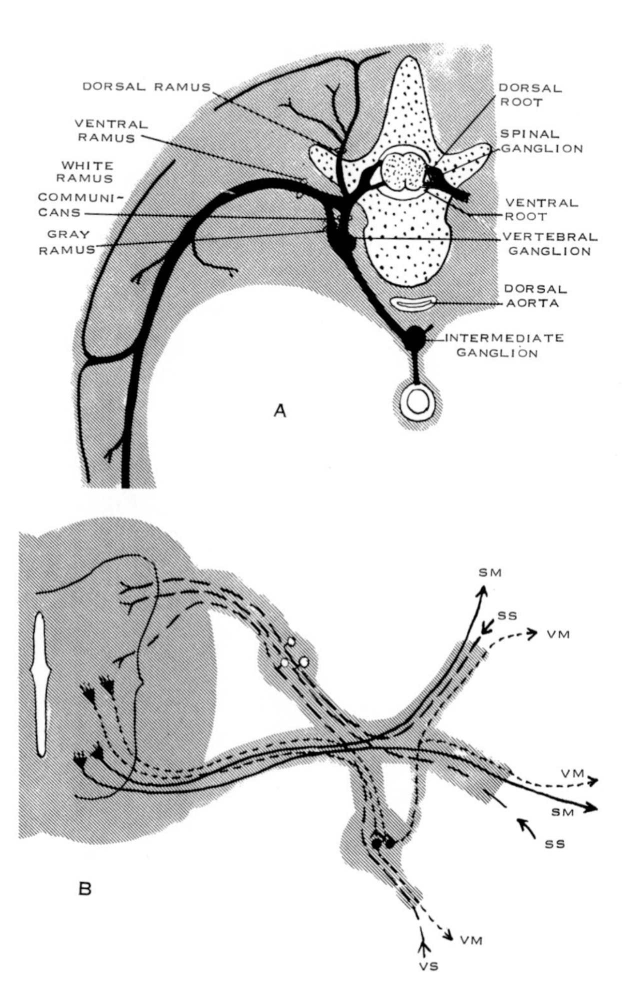

Fig. 20–18. Typical mammalian spinal nerve. A. General plan of roots and rami. B. Distribution of functional components.

of the trunk segments, but details of this, and exceptions, will be considered later.

In the modern cyclostomes the dorsal and ventral roots of the spinal nerves emerge in staggered series, the dorsal roots somewhat anterior to the ventral ones of their own segments. Furthermore, they distribute to the periphery separately, each dividing by itself into dorsal and ventral rami, though the myotomes are not themselves divided into epaxial and hypaxial parts. The failure of dorsal and ventral roots to join together in each segment may be a result of the sketchy development of the vertebral column in these animals; in other vertebrates the roots are crowded together in small intervertebral foramina by the formation of strong neural arches. From another point of view it may also be a case of survival of very ancient ancestral features: the amphioxus shows a similar arrangement of nerve roots.

B. Hypoglossal and Occipital Nerves

Attention has already been called to a transition zone in the skeletal patterns at the junction of the head and the trunk. Nerves share in this also. The roots and tracts of the visceral cranial nerves IX, X, and XI (or the ramus accessorius of X) overlap into the cervical segments of the spinal cord, grading off posteriorly. In the same area, the characteristic series of spinal nerves projects forward into the hindbrain region grading off anteriorly (Fig. 20–19). The boundary between the skull and the first free vertebra is laid down at a later stage across this zone of overlap in a way which seems to be fixed for a given species but is certainly highly variable within the phylum [6].

The series of spinal-nerve–like structures is continued within the definitive skull at embryonic stages by from one to fourteen pairs of nerves, depending on the species, the number being variable even within a single class of vertebrates. In this series, the nerves become progressively more defective in the craniad direction, losing first their dorsal-root ganglia and then their dorsal roots. In some cases these nervelets start out well enough in the embryo but then degenerate or disappear. For instance, the intracranial ganglion A in the human embryo of Figure 20–19 regularly disappears, and the normal first spinal ganglion (ganglion B) sometimes does.

The **hypoglossal nerve** arises from the ventral roots of this transition-zone series of defective somatic nerves. It is defined as a cranial nerve in amniotes because the skull has spread posteriorly so as to enclose it in a foramen, but in fishes and amphibia it comes from the spinal cord through intervertebral foramina. It remains a motor nerve, towed into a sweeping curve by the migration of the hypoglossal or hypobranchial muscles with which it makes an early contact.

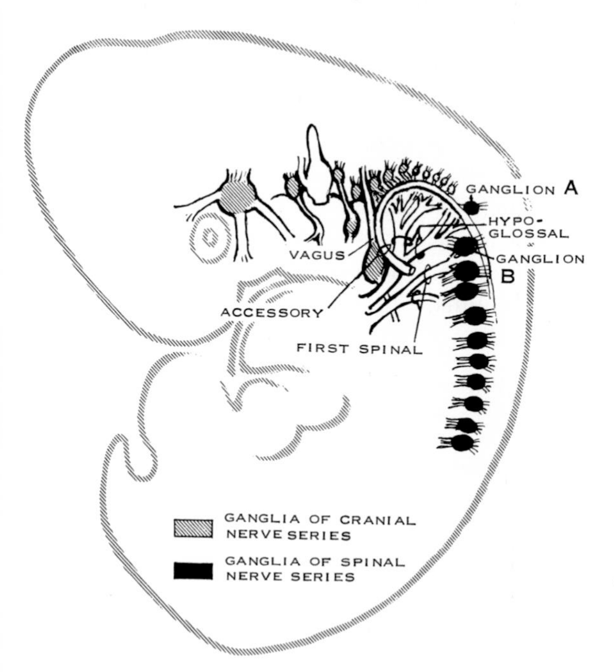

Fig. 20–19. Human embryo 10 millimeters long to show transition in nerve pattern at the head-neck boundary.

(Based on Streeter's reconstruction.)

C. Segmental Relationships

Not only the hypoglossal nerves, but all the spinal nerves make very early contact with their definitive territories, and their ventral rami are towed along with their hypaxial muscles. Thus they are laid down in essentially segmental territories, and the main features of their anatomy retain this arrangement in spite of widespread later obliteration of the myotome boundaries. This has been illustrated for the cutaneous branches of the spinal nerves already (Fig. 19–17). Although there is a narrow zone of territorial overlap of two adjacent spinal nerves in the supply of continuous sheets of oblique or rectus muscle, the nerves do not capture territory from each other with anything like the freedom of competing blood vessels. Muscles that are already supplied with nerves simply do not accept invading neurons from other sources.

If, however, the myocommata and other connective tissue planes of the early embryo make favorable pathways for the pioneering fibers of the spinal nerves, it might be expected that where these planes intersect there would be possibilities for the meeting and exchanging of fibers between adjacent nerves, tending to obscure segmental relationships. In fact, ventral rami of the spinal nerves do very frequently form interconnecting loops or arcades (called *ansae*) with their series neighbors where they are crowded together, or where the horizontal septum intersects with myosepta. For instance, the anterior spinal nerves form interconnections with themselves and with the hypoglossal nerve in amniotes (**ansa cervicalis** PNA). Conspicuous examples of such branched interconnections also occur in the mesenchyme just internal to each embryonic limb bud, where the nerves destined for the limbs collaborate in forming the **brachial plexus** and the **crural plexus** (lumbosacral plexus, PNA), as will be shown in the next chapter. Out in the limbs, each of the muscles receives axons derived from the ventral roots of two or more spinal nerves, and all appearance of segmentation in their nerve supply is thereby lost. In fishes and amphibia the pectoral appendages are placed so close to the skull that there is at least one spinal nerve that supplies fibers both to the hypoglossal trunk and to the limb on each side. This creates a continuous cervicobranchial plexus.

VII. CORRELATIONS OF SPINAL CORD AND VERTEBRAL COLUMN

In most vertebrates the spinal cord extends practically the full length of the neural canal of the vertebral column, and nearly fills it. In others, however, the growth of the vertebrae outstrips the cord so that the neural canal may have several, rarely even ten or twelve times the diameter of the contained cord.

If the vertebral column has a faster relative growth rate than the spinal cord, this means that the two structures will tend to slip past each other as they get larger, since the cord is anchored to the brain. But the spinal nerves were previously enveloped in their own intervertebral foramina and had established their permanent connections in the periphery. Roots and rami must be elongated to suit the changing proportions (Fig. 20–20). As a result, in adult mammals including man, the spinal cord

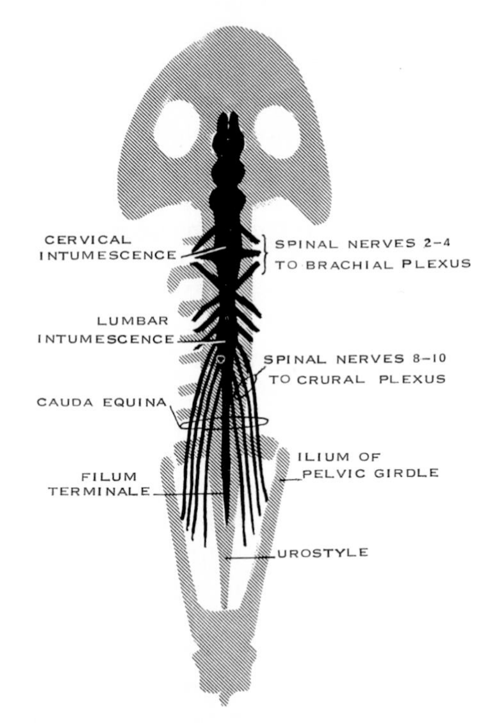

Fig. 20–20. Spinal cord and nerve roots of a frog.
(After Gaupp, 1896.)

may end in the lumbar region of the neural canal, and the parts of the cervical, thoracic, and lumbar spinal nerves that lie inside the canal are successively longer and more oblique. The last of them form a loose bundle called the **cauda equina** ("horse tail"), which extends back of the functional end of the spinal cord, reaching for the intervertebral foramina of the pelvic and sacral levels.

Even in mammals with long tails, all but the first few caudal myotomes degenerate. Perhaps because of this, but clearly in correlation with it, the posterior end of the spinal cord narrows into a useless string-like remnant called the **filum terminale,** lying amongst the roots of the cauda equina.

A cauda equina and filum terminale are also found in the anura (Fig. 20–20), as a consequence of the utter destruction of the tail at metamorphosis, and subsequent growth of the vertebral column at a rate faster than that of the cord. The ocean sunfish, *Orthagoriscus,* has been described as an enormous swimming head with a short trunk and no tail. It may weigh as much as a ton. The spinal cord is shorter than the brain and bears less than two dozen pairs of spinal nerves. There is a filum terminale but no cauda equina.

VIII. CORRELATIONS OF NERVES AND MUSCLE GROUPS

For convenience, the muscles of the vertebrate body may here be classified according to their nerve supply. A few minor categories, such as muscles wholly concerned with the skin or the external genitalia of amniotes, are omitted. Certain categories on this list have not yet been considered.

1. The **oculomotor muscles** (Figs. 14–11, 14–12) are in many cases clearly derived from preotic members of the somite series, and are innervated by the somatic motor cranial nerves III, IV, and VI.

2. The **pharynx segment group** (Figs. 17–2, 17–8, 17–9) are visceral muscles, being derived from the hypomeric mesoderm of the pharynx zone. They are innervated by cranial nerves V, VII, IX, and X, including the accessory ramus of the vagus, which may be separated during development as the accessory nerve XI.

3. **Cardiac muscle** (see Chapter 25).

4. **Smooth muscle** of the alimentary canal and the urogenital system and other viscera: Categories 3 and 4 are both derived from coelomic hypomere mesoderm (splanchnopleure), and both are innervated by the autonomic nervous system, as will be explained in Chapter 30.

5. **Appendicular muscles,** with certain exceptions, have their origin in the paired limb buds, as described in Chapter 21. They are innervated by plurisegmental branches from brachial or pelvic plexuses that are formed by ventral rami of a number of spinal nerves, medial to the shoulder or hip joints.

All the rest of the categories of muscles in this list arise from segmental myotomes and are supplied by rami of individual spinal nerves from their segments of origin (with qualifications respecting the last or hypoglossal category).

6. **Epaxial muscles** (Figs. 20–11, 20–12, 20–13, 20–16) are innervated by dorsal rami of spinal nerves.

7. **Unspecialized hypaxial muscles** of the tail (Fig. 20–11) receive ventral rami.

8. **Subvertebral muscles** of the trunk (Figs. 20–13, 20–14, 20–17).

9. **Oblique muscles** of the thorax and flanks (Figs. 20–11 through 14).

10. **Rectus muscles** bordering the ventral midline of the trunk (Figs. 20–13, 20–14).

Categories 8–10 are innervated by ventral rami of spinal nerves in their own segments of origin.

11. **Hypoglossal muscles** (Fig. 20–14) are innervated on each side by a hypoglossal nerve, which is a combination of ventral rami of several anterior members of the spinal nerve series (whose origin becomes partly enveloped in the skull in amniotes, making it cranial nerve XII).

REFERENCES

1. Detwiler, S. R., 1937. *J. Exptl. Zool.* 76: 36.
2. Detwiler, S. R., 1934. *J. Exptl. Zool.* 67: 395.
3. Holtzer, H., 1959. *In* C. S. Thornton (ed.), *Symposium on regeneration in vertebrates.* University of Chicago Press, Chicago.
4. Taning, A. V., 1952. *Biol. Revs.* 27: 169.
5. Williams, E. E., 1959. *Quart. Rev. Biol.* 34: 1.
6. de Beer, G. R., 1937. *The development of the vertebrate skull.* Oxford University Press, London.
7. Chiakulas, J. J., 1957. *J. Exptl. Zool.* 136: 287.
8. Holtzer, H., 1952. *J. Exptl. Zool.* 121: 121.
9. Straus, W., and M. E. Rawles, 1953. *Am. J. Anat.* 92: 471.
10. Wilde, C. E., 1959. *In* D. Rudnick (ed.), *Cell, Organism, and Milieu* (17th Growth Symposium). Ronald Press Co., New York.
11. Muchmore, W. B., 1957. *Proc. Nat. Acad. Sci.* 43: 435.
12. Holtzer, H., and S. R. Detwiler, 1954. *Anat. Record* 118: 390.
13. Muchmore, W. B., 1958. *J. Exptl. Zool.* 139:181.
14. Detwiler, S. R., 1955. *J. Exptl. Zool.* 129: 45.
15. Deuchar, E. M., 1958. *J. Embryol. Exptl. Morphol.* 6: 527.
16. Nursall, J. R., 1962. *Am. Zoologist* 2: 127.
17. Klauber, L. M., 1956. *Rattlesnakes.* University of California Press, Berkeley.
18. Gans, C., 1962. *Am. Zoologist* 2: 167.

21

Locomotor Apparatus: II Fins and Limbs

I. GENERAL CONSIDERATION OF PAIRED APPENDAGES

A. History

Most vertebrates have a pair of pectoral appendages back of the head or at the base of the neck, and a pair of pelvic appendages whose normal location is just anterior to the cloaca. But some species do not have them. Fossils of the earliest fishes, such as ostracoderms and placoderms (Fig. 2–5) show either very peculiar appendages unlike anything now swimming about, or none at all. The anatomists of the last century speculated ingeniously as to how the appendages of the modern vertebrates could have arisen from precursor organs and tissues, but in fact one does not know [1].

There are two very distinct types of paired appendages in vertebrates, the **fins** of fishes and the **limbs** of tetrapods. Each has its basic developmental pattern, though both have been adapted for a variety of uses in different groups. The fishes that fly and those that walk on land do so with only slightly modified fins. The flippers of whales, sea cows, seals and sea turtles are obviously only modified tetrapod limbs. As will be seen, fins and limbs are radically different in their finished anatomical detail, but they share certain fundamental features of development. Since vertebrates with fins preceded the earliest vertebrates with limbs by many millions of years, it is natural to assume that there was an evolution from fins to limbs, and fossil evidence of the transitional stages, though still quite incomplete, is slowly accumulating. The conversion apparently took place in stocks of crossopterygian fishes during Devonian times. No recapitulation of this transition is seen in the embryonic development of limbs in modern species: fins and limbs diverge in character from their earliest stages of tissue differentiation.

The modern cyclostomes do not have paired appendages, and probably none of their ancestors ever did. All other modern vertebrates which lack fins or limbs have presumably lost them secondarily, for either they have near relatives possessing such appendages, or fossils of their presumed ancestors are known to have had them. Mutations which suppress limb development in whole or in part have turned up in various vertebrate stocks, including human families; theoretically, similar mutations could have been exploited by natural selection in the evolution of snakes and limbless lizards. Phenocopies of such anomalies were produced in shocking numbers in 1960–1962 by the unsuspected action of the drug thalidomide during early human pregnancy.

B. Early Development of Paired Fins and Limbs

Up to the time of differentiation of their main tissues, the development of fins and limbs can be described in common terms. They arise as ectoderm-lined mesodermal buds. The source of their mesoderm has been discussed before (pages 148–149).

In fishes (Fig. 5–19 A) the fin bud is first seen as a thin ridge, its plane horizontal (sharks) or vertical (teleosts) depending on the shape of the embryo, but its length always parallel with the embryonic axis. The ridge develops characteristically into a projecting disc or thin flange, whose outer border is almost entirely integumentary, the mesoderm being packed at its base. The limb bud of a tetrapod, on the other hand, quickly forms a stout paddle-like or finger-like protuberance, packed with mesenchyme throughout (Fig. 5–19 B). There is a thin ectodermal rim on the periphery of the amniote limb bud, which (in birds at least) is essential to the later differentiation of most of the free appendage, though not of the anchoring parts. This **apical ridge** (Figs. 5–19 B, 21–5) thus acts as an inductor. The lack of an effective apical ridge has been shown to be responsible for a hereditary "wingless" defect in domestic fowl. The inhibiting action of thalidomide may have been localized at the apical ridge of the human embryonic limb bud.

By reciprocal combinations of ectodermal and mesodermal components of the wing and leg buds of chick embryos, it has been shown that the apical ridge of a *leg* bud can induce the mesoderm of a wing bud to develop, but the latter nevertheless produces *wing* structures. As in so many other cases (page 179) the action tissue gives a general cue and the reaction tissue a specific response of its own kind. Experiments with the bird embryos [2] show a continuing two-way interaction and interdependence of the mesodermal and ectodermal limb-bud components, reminiscent of that which exists between developing spinal cord and nearby somites. Careful experiments show that the ectoderm plays no inducting or controlling part in the early stages of differentiation of the amphibian limb, but an equivalent of the amniote apical ridge has been described in the frog *Xenopus*. It seems to play an important role in late distal limb differentiation.

As described earlier (page 182), the limb field can be located experimentally even before the district is marked out as a fin bud or limb bud. The field is always larger than necessary, only part of its cells in the center of the disc being actually called into the eventual appendage.

There is some variation in the location of the appendage district in vertebrates. The pectoral appendages of fishes are usually close behind the head, and with some exceptions (elasmobranchs, holocephals, *Latimeria*) they become united to the skull by joints. In tetrapods, several, and sometimes many, segments lie between the skull and the forelimb. The hindlimbs of tetrapods develop, if at all, just anterior to the cloaca, and the same is true of the pelvic fin buds of many fishes, but in a number of orders of teleosts they arise farther forward. For instance the pectoral fin nerves of the whiting (*Gadus merlangus*) arise from spinal-cord segments 1–4, the pelvic fin nerves arise from segments 5–7, and the vent is at segment 9. The "pelvic" fins reach their permanent location in the throat by only a slight migration during development, though this is sufficient to tow their nerves across those of the ones to the pectoral fins.

The factors which establish limb fields in their normal locations have so far proved elusive. In some amphibia, it is possible to induce the formation of extra limbs at mid-flank levels by the implantation of materials that do not normally have anything to do with limb formation, but this merely shows that competence exists in areas where determination does not take place. It has been suggested that perhaps the basement membrane of the skin prevents induction of limb formation at all except the normal sites [3].

The first sign of differentiation in the fin bud or limb bud is usually the condensation of a central core of recognizable procartilage from the mesenchyme where the future shoulder or hip joint will be. From here it spreads both externally into what becomes the **free append-**

age and internally between the skin and the flank mesoderm, where it prepares to form the anchoring part or **girdle.**

Development of the appendage may be arrested at or before this time. Some whales have no pelvic appendages as adults, and among living amphibia the Gymnophiona have no appendages at all, yet these animals have good-looking limb buds as embryos. The teleostean symbranchs, some lizards, a few snakes, and certain other whales have appendage buds that form girdle elements but not free appendages (exactly as in the "wingless fowl" mutants). Most snakes do not even form limb buds at all.

While a pattern of cartilage-forming centers emerges from the procartilage a mat of muscle-forming mesoderm condenses from the mesenchyme dorsal to it, and another ventral to it (Fig. 21–1). From each of the segments of the trunk covered by the bud, ventral rami of spinal nerves grow out. Meeting each other inside the future shoulder or hip joint, they form a plexus from which regrouped nerves enter the bud and make permanent connections with all its tissues. A capillary network is established in the bud, later to differentiate into arteries and veins. From this time on, fin buds and limb buds develop in contrasting ways. There are, however, two overall processes which affect them both: the establishment of polarities, and the occurrence of rotations.

C. Polarity

Most of the information on this subject has come from experiments with amphibian embryos. Each amblystoma forelimb is differentiated along three polarized axes: (1) It has a mediolateral axis (M-L), along which the different parts become shoulder, elbow, wrist, and digits. (2) It has a short dorsoventral axis (D-V), with palm on one end, back of the hand on the other. (3) Also there is the anteroposterior axis (A-P), with ulna and last finger on the posterior end, and radius and thumb on the anterior. The normal right and left forelimbs have D-V and A-P axes respectively parallel, but the M-L axis of one is the opposite of the other; i.e., the digits extend out from the body in opposite directions. Any two objects which have three such axes, two coinciding and the third reversed, are mirror images of each other. They cannot be oriented in any way that causes the reversed axes to coincide without simultaneous reversal of one of the other sets of axes.

This may be seen in Figure 21–2. The normal *right* limb is indicated by A in the lower drawing. If the normal *left* limb is cut loose and brought in an orbital path over the top of the animal and implanted on the right flank with its A-P and its M-L axes parallel to those of the normal right limb, its D-V axis turns out to have been reversed. This may be seen in limb B, by

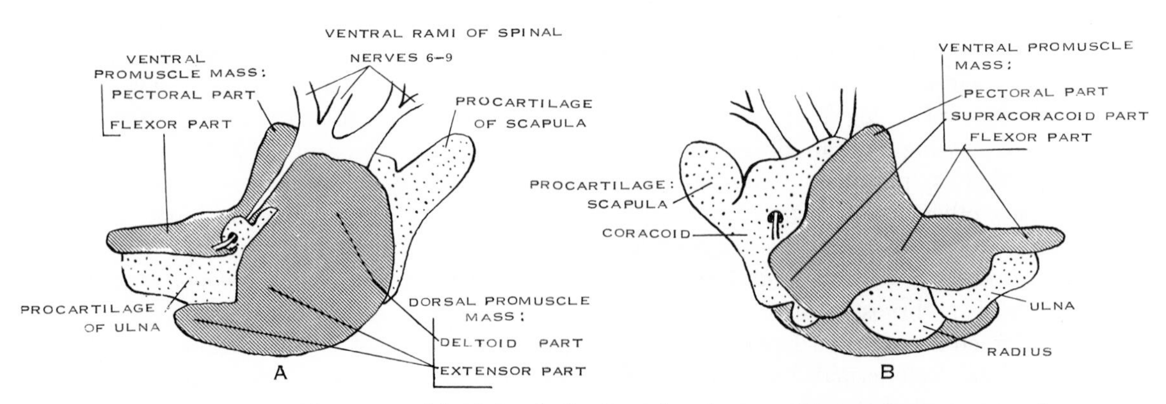

Fig. 21–1. Right pectoral limb bud of a lizard embryo, with ectoderm removed to show anlagen of skeleton and muscles. A. Dorsal view. B. Ventral view. (After A. S. Romer, 1944.)

comparing the elbow and the digits with those of limb A. On the other hand, if the normal left limb is transplanted through an orbital path around the front of the head, its M-L and D-V axes now coincide with those of the normal right limb (compare C with A), but the A-P axis is reversed.

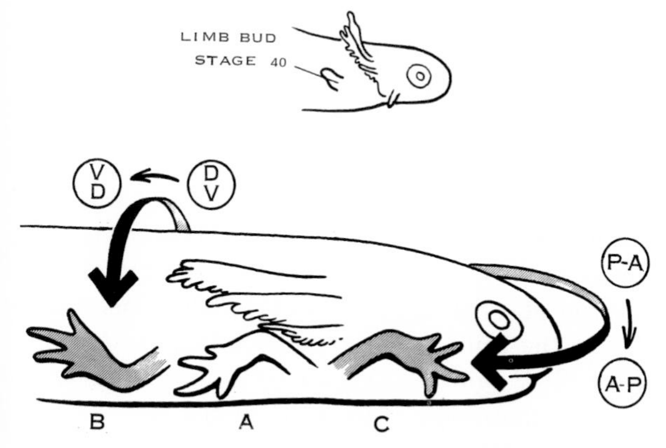

Fig. 21–2. Mirror imagery of limbs (explanation in text).
(Data from R. G. Harrison, 1921.)

These are precisely the results obtained if the limb bud is transplanted through either of these paths at stage 40, when it has grown outward but not yet undergone histodifferentiation. The transplanted bud, when it differentiates, becomes a mirror image of the normal limb of the other side. This indicates that its cells though not yet visibly differentiated have already become polarized, and do not reverse their axes to be in harmony with their surroundings. In spite of their now growing on the right side of the body, they only know how to form a left limb.

It can be shown that the limb-field district, even if transplanted at the slit-blastopore stage, has its anteroposterior axis irrevocably determined, so that if it is cut out, rotated through 180 degrees, and healed in again at the same spot, the ulna will develop anterior to the radius instead of posterior to it, and the elbow will point anteriorly when bent (Fig. 21–3). This operation also reverses the dorsoventral axis of the original limb-field district so that one might expect the palm of the developing hand to face upward instead of downward, but it doesn't. The polarity of the D-V axis, not being irrevocably determined at the time of operation, is reversed, or regulated, by some influence of the whole region in which it lies, preventing the appearance of the expected D-V disharmony.

Now, since two of the three axes of polarity of the limb-field district have *not* been reversed by the operation (A-P irrevocably fixed within the district though turned upside down on the animal, and M-L not affected by the operation at all), and one axis (D-V) *has* been reversed, the limb which develops is a mirror image of what it should have been. It is as though a solution which would normally give left-handed crystals has been forced to make right-handed ones of the same molecular formula. Assuming that the operation was done on the left side, the left

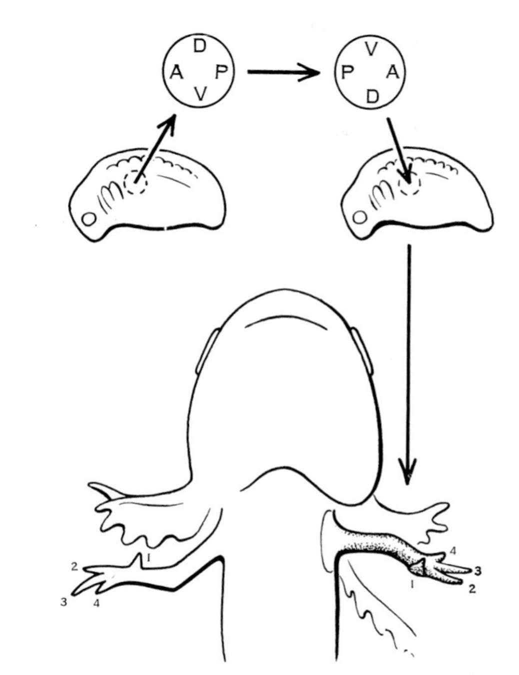

Fig. 21–3. Results of 180° rotation of early limb bud (explanation in text).
(Data from R. G. Harrison, 1921.)

limb-field district has been forced to produce a right limb. (The result, as shown in Fig. 21–3, is a little more confusing, because the A-P axis, though fixed with respect to the limb-field dis-

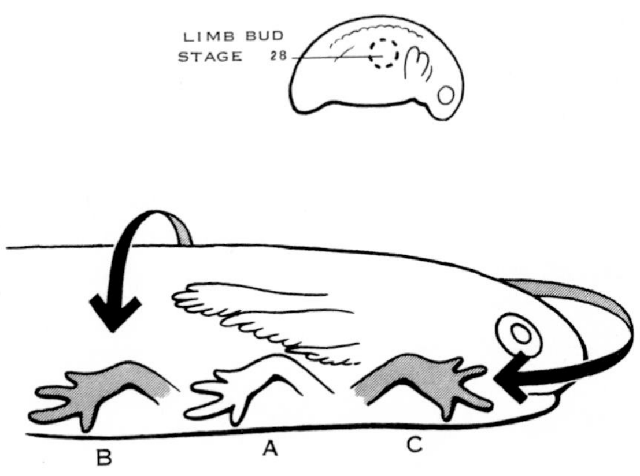

Fig. 21–4. Results of transplanting early limb bud (explanation in text).

trict, has been given a 180-degree turn with respect to the animal: what actually develops on the left side is a right limb installed backward.)

If the same limb-field district is cut out and rotated in the same way as indicated in Figure 21–3, but transplanted to other locations on the flank, the D-V axis may *or may not* be reversed. One concludes that the field is tentatively polarized at this early stage, and either these internal determining forces or new external ones may win out in case of a competition. Since the external forces do win out and cause reversal of the D-V axis at the normal site in early stages, an operation like that shown for limb B at stage 40 in Figure 21–2 will not produce the same result if performed at stage 28 (Fig. 21–4). In this case, experimental reversal of only one axis, the D-V, makes the transplanted left limb into a mirror image of what it would have been, and it becomes anatomically a right limb, in harmony with its new location (Fig. 21–4 B). On the other hand, the A-P axis is fixed within the limb-field district at stage 28, and the results of operation C are the same as at stage 40 (compare C's of Figs. 21–2 and 21–4), namely a misplaced left limb, disharmonic with its location.

During the time when axis determination is tentative, reorienting the limb-field district may often throw the field out of order so that mirror-image twin limbs or other monstrous limblike growths are produced from it.

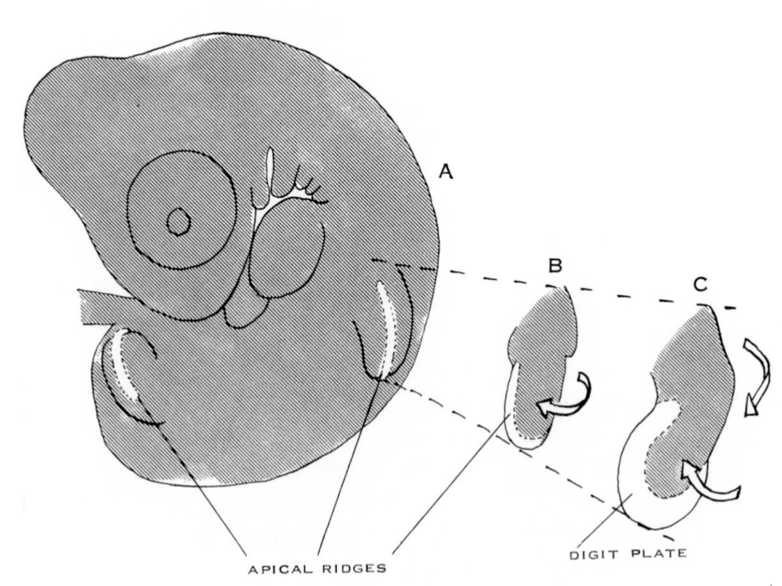

Fig. 21–5. Normal rotation of lizard pectoral limb bud. A. Crown-rump length 4 millimeters. B. 5 millimeters. C. 6 millimeters.
(After K. Peter, 1904.)

Studies on axis determination in other fields (hindlimb, ear, eye, lens, etc.) have yielded similar information on the progressive establishment of the several polarities, at separate times, by the continuing interaction of the field with its environment.

In amniote limb buds, the axial determination of distal parts is taken over as a continuing operation by the apical ridge of ectoderm. It is possible to reverse the symmetry of the wing from the elbow out by rotating the ridge 180 degrees, leaving the mesodermal core *in situ*.

D. Rotations

The ridge which first represents the fish fin is directed parallel to the embryonic axis. Fins of sharks, being chiefly useful as stabilizers rather than as organs of locomotion, retain this arrangement, but in most higher fishes the line of attachment of the pectoral fin shifts during development, wrapping down around the back of the pharynx-segment zone in an oblique or even a dorsoventral line. In the salmon, whose pectoral fin rotates 45 degrees, the original dorsal part of the line of attachment becomes posterior, and the fin is folded back against the flank, converting its original dorsal surface to a medial one. Both pectoral fins can be suddenly swung outward and spread out fanlike, bringing the forward motion of the fish to a quick stop. A shark cannot do this. The pelvic fins of the salmon undergo a rotation of 60 degrees, their attachment shifting from an anteroposterior line to a mediolateral oblique one.

More complex rotations take place in tetrapod limb buds, involving shifts not only at the line of attachment but in the distal or free parts of the appendage (Fig. 21–5), and producing quite different effects in the pectoral and pelvic limbs. Minor variations in the rotation produce important characteristic postural differences of great functional importance in the different orders and families. These are difficult to describe in words, but may be sensed by comparing the disposition of the adult limb skeleton in various animals.

The usual and outstanding results include a 45-degree twist (Fig. 21–5 B) within the upper arm (not present in the thigh) and angular joints at elbow, knee, wrist, and ankle, unlike anything known in fins. All these combine to bring the tetrapod appendage toward the ground or into a position suitable for flying, swimming, digging, climbing, etc. A final twist (Fig. 21–5 C) usually brings the elbow backward (Fig. 21–6 B) (except in turtles) and the knee forward (except in bats, Fig. 21–6 C).

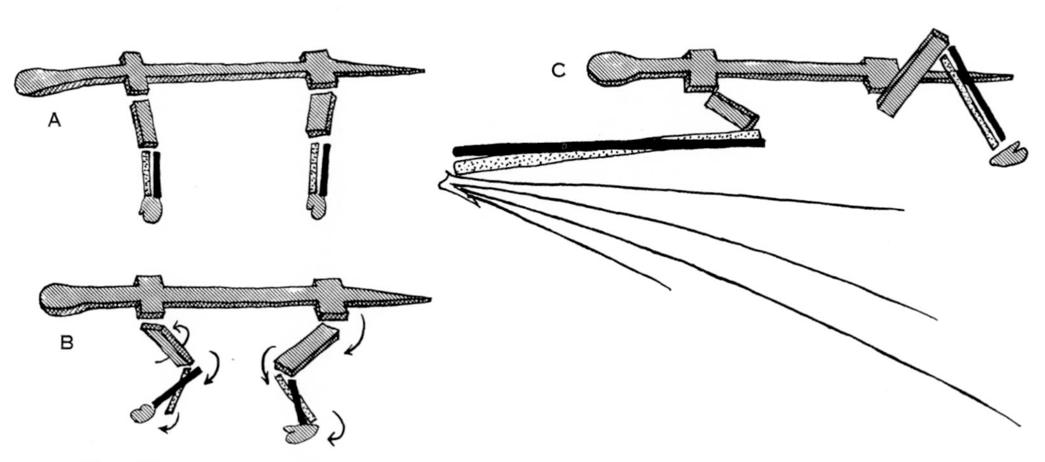

Fig. 21–6. Postures accomplished by various degrees of limb-bud rotation in tetrapods. A. Primitive tetrapod. B. Cat. C. Bat.

(Patterned after Nauck, 1938, in Handbuch der Vergleichenden Anatomie der Wirbeltiere, by permission of Urban u. Schwarzenberg.)

II. DIFFERENTIATION OF PAIRED FINS, CONTRASTED WITH LIMBS

A. Pectoral Fins

1. Skeleton. While skeletal anchoring elements form in both right and left pectoral fin buds, they generally join together in the midventral line. Other anchoring elements spread dorsally. In practically all bony fishes, these parts make firm joints with the skull back of the ears, so that the whole throat is encircled with a hoop of bone, and movable parts of the fins are tied to this. In sharks, the dorsal end of the girdle on each side ends freely, anchored only by muscles. In the rays, the tail has become nothing but a whip, and the great pectoral wings are the chief organs of locomotion. They are correspondingly supported by very stout girdles which either fuse with each other across the dorsal midline, or with a sort of notarium of fused vertebrae. In most other fishes, the tail is the principal organ of locomotion, and the pectoral fins are rather simple affairs, used for treading water, for steering and balance, or as brakes.

In all of these fishes, and in tetrapods as well, part or all of the pectoral girdle is preformed in cartilage, and except in the permanently cartilaginous fishes, much or all of it is later replaced by bone. The parts preformed in cartilage (there may be from one to three or four such elements on each side depending on the class or order) constitute the **primary girdle** (Fig. 21–7). The shoulder joint is always formed either on one of these elements, called the **scapula,** which extends dorsad from that point, or else between it and another element called the **coracoid,** which extends toward its fellow at the ventral midline. Homologies of the separate bones are in doubt.

In all the bony fishes, and in tetrapods that have limbs, with the exception of the urodeles, a **secondary girdle** is added to the primary one, from which it is distinguished by being ossified

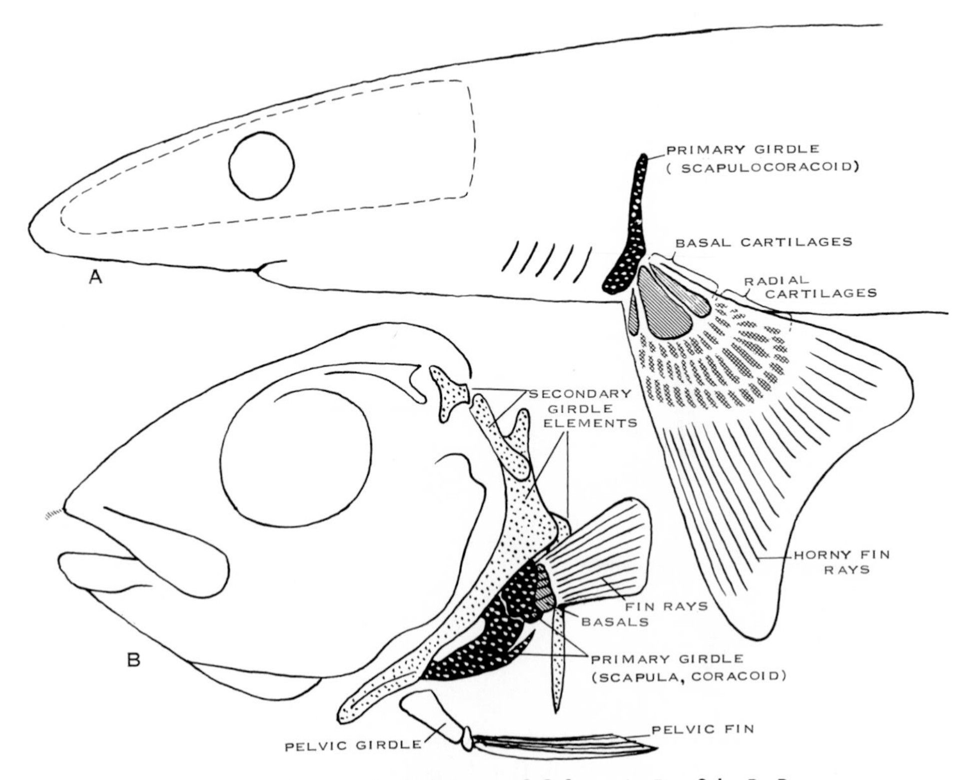

Fig. 21–7. Pectoral skeletons of fishes. A. Dogfish. B. Bass.
(B after W. K. Gregory, 1933.)

directly in membrane. This may consist of as many as five large bones on each side in bony fishes, though simpler arrangements occur in a few orders. The result is an extremely rigid ring of bone where a neck might be, reaching forward and helping to protect the heart and gills ventrally (Fig. 21–7 B).

Such excessively heavy multipartite pectoral girdles were inherited by the very ancient amphibians and reptiles of Paleozoic times, but modern tetrapods have in every instance reduced the number of elements. Each of several tetrapod lineages has accomplished this in its own way. The scapula is always easily identified, but as to the elements that remain in the ventral part of the girdle, one cannot decide their homologies, and hence their correct names, just by looking at them. One must know their paleontological history and whether or not they are preformed in cartilage or fused with other elements during their development.

Having been freed from the skull and simplified, the pectoral girdles of tetrapods became variously modified for maneuverability. Whereas in nearly all fishes the joints between the elements of the pectoral girdle are rather stiff synarthroses, simply constructed out of fibrous tissues, there is always a ball-and-socket diarthrosis at the shoulder in the tetrapods.

The skeleton of the free fin itself, the part distal to the shoulder joint, is made up of three groups of elements, in various proportions: (a) **basal cartilages,** defined as those parts of the fin endoskeleton that take part in the shoulder joint, lead laterally to (b) **radial cartilages,** which lead to the (c) **dermal elements,** which extend to the free edge of the fin (Fig. 21–7). There is much variety in the proportions and in the numbers of these elements.

The huge flying wing of a ray is very broadly based, with at least three huge basal cartilages that spread all the way from the rostrum to the pelvis, to which are jointed a great fan of ranks and files of radial cartilages that reach almost to the free edge. Dermal elements are at a minimum. The pectoral fin of a shark (Fig. 21–7 A) is less broadly based, but still contains three flattened basal cartilages and a large number of radials. However, the files of radials reach only perhaps halfway to the free edge of the fin, the outer membrane being stiffened by multitudes of elastic horny fibers produced in the dermis layer of the skin of both surfaces.

Bony fishes, and particularly the teleosts (Fig. 21–7 B), tend to reduce the basal and radial cartilages (as well as replacing them with bone), and rely almost exclusively on skin products for stiffening the movable fin. Horny fibers like those of elasmobranchs are formed at embryonic stages, but are pushed outward and more or less completely supplanted during later growth by rays of a different chemical composition, more like bone. These are assembled from strings of tiny scalelike elements that are produced in the dermis on both sides of the fin membrane, each string being paired with one in the skin of the opposite surface. The little elements of each string tend to fuse together forming a flexible fiber, and each such fiber becomes tied by ligament to its mate on the opposite side, or the two grow together and produce a single more rigid fin ray. Muscles, which in elasmobranch fins insert on the basal and radial cartilages, pass across these reduced elements in the fins of teleosts, and insert on the bases of the dermal fin rays. Often the rays at the leading edges of the fins are developed into heavy rods or sharp thorns and become fused with their supporting basal elements. Anyone who has taken a catfish off the hook knows these can be formidable.

Although the basal elements in the pectoral fins of elasmobranchs and teleosts are generally multiple, a number of unrelated groups of fishes (some Paleozoic sharks, the dipnoi, the crossopterygii) have experimented with a reduction of the fin base. This kind of fin may contain only one basal element and one file of radials down its axis, with the other supports, whether endoskeletal or dermal, fanning out on one or both sides of the axis (*Latimeria,* Fig. 21–8 A). Fins of certain fossil rhipidistia (Fig. 21–8 B), with one basal bone and reduced radials, seem good candidates for transitional stages to the pattern which has become standardized in the tetrapod limbs.

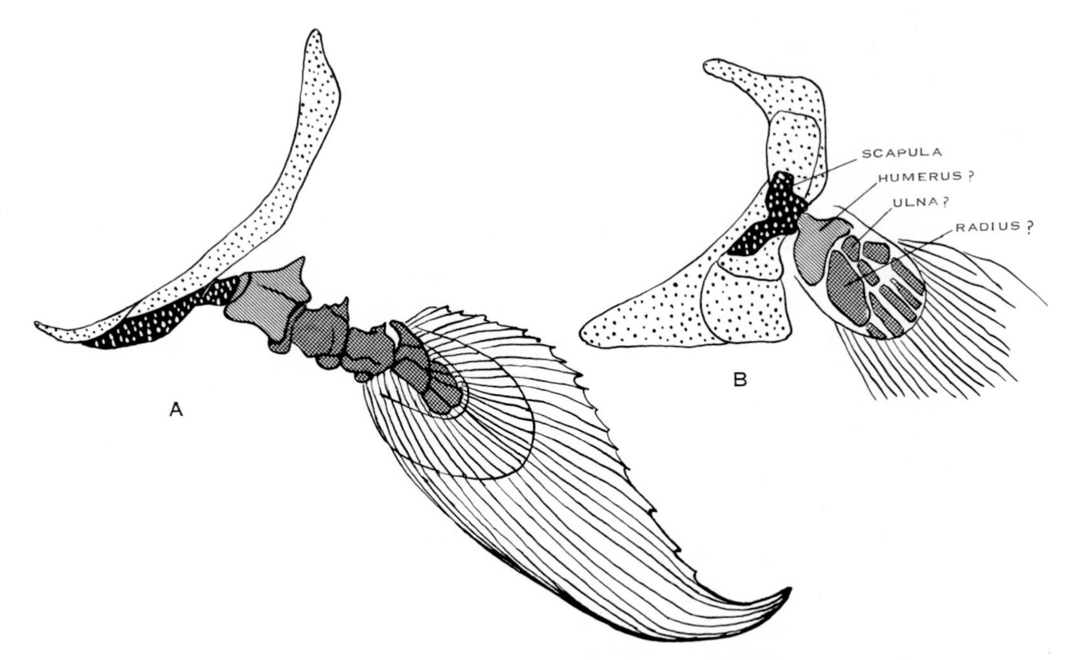

Fig. 21–8. Other pectoral fin skeleton patterns. A. *Latimeria* (recent Crossopterygian). B. *Sauripterus* (Devonian Crossopterygian).

(A after Millot and Anthony, Anatomie de Latimeria chalumnae, Tome I, 1959, by permission of Centre National de la Recherche Scientifique, Paris. B after W. K. Gregory, 1935.)

The pectoral limbs of tetrapods (Fig. 21–9) conform almost universally to the rule that there is *one* long basal element, the **humerus,** and there are *two* long radial elements in the first rank, the **radius** and **ulna,** followed by two or three ranks of short radials called **carpals,** one rank of five or fewer but somewhat longer **metacarpals,** and files of several phalanges in each of five or fewer digits. The joints at both ends of the humerus develop into diarthroses, and some of the more distal joints generally do also. No living fishes show this pattern. The tetrapod hindlimb shows a closely similar skeletal pattern distal to the hip joint. Since fossil evidence continues to be rather scanty, there are still several alternative theories as to how the tetrapod pattern arose from fish fins.

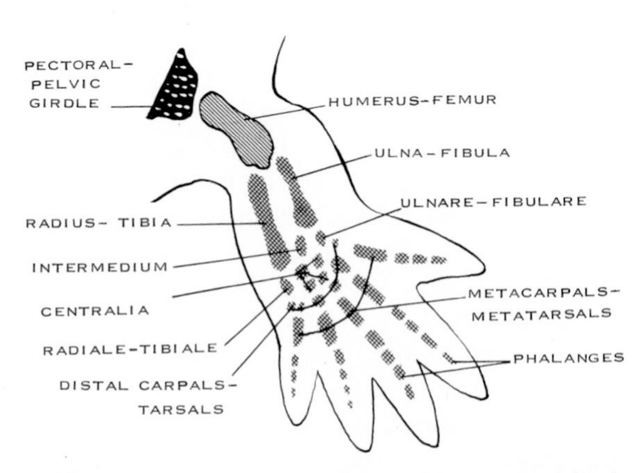

Fig. 21–9. Standard pattern of tetrapod limb skeleton.

(After A. Portmann, Einführung in die Vergleichende Morphologie der Wirbeltiere, 1948, by permission of Benno Schwabe & Co.)

2. *Muscles and Nerves.* Three categories of muscle contribute to the pectoral fin or limb, each bringing its own supply of nerves with it: (a) the appendage-bud group, (b) the myotome group, and (c) the trapezius group.

(a) The muscles which differentiate within the appendage bud arise in mesenchyme which has either sprouted into it from myotomes or wandered in from the adjacent hypomere (page 148). In either case, they are typically innervated through a **brachial plexus** made up from the ventral rami of the spinal nerves of the body segments over which the bud originally extended. This means three or four ventral rami for fins with narrow bases, or up to forty of them for the great pectoral wings of rays.

The ventral rami which join to create such a plexus are established by their pioneer fibers before the limb or fin anlage is visible. As they grow ventrolaterad, they pass out of the field in which typical flank musculature is being organized, and into a limb field in which the promuscle mesenchyme will be divided into a dorsal and a ventral mass (Fig. 21–1). As they approach the limb field, each of them divides into a dorsal and a ventral factor (Fig. 21–10), and these reach respectively into the dorsal and ventral masses of promuscle tissue.

A proponent of the theory that the nerve fiber is guided by contact with an oriented ground substance (page 59) might suggest that in the thin transition zone between the independent fields the ground substance has a somewhat jumbled structure in which the exploratory neuron tips wander, as though in confusion. At any rate, it can be observed that the bundles of fibers arriving from the nearly parallel series of neatly oriented ventral rami do divide here, meet bundles branching from their neighbors, regroup themselves, and rebranch. The normal result is the formation of a double plexus, part of dorsal factors, and part of ventral factors, distal to which the nerve fibers join up in non-segmental branches which lead to the segregated muscles of the developing fin or limb (Fig. 21–11). When one of these peripheral nerves is teased apart and its constituent neurons are followed backward from its muscle through the plexus to the spinal cord, it is usually found that the muscle has received motor fibers from the ventral rami of two or several successive spinal nerves. Any one spinal nerve supplies a number of muscles in the appendage.

The nerves which emerge from the plexus push outward in pace with the growth of the appendage bud even during its mesenchymatous stage. Thus it happens that, when procartilage condenses to form the first visible anlagen of the girdle skeleton, some of the cartilage may surround some of the nerves (Fig. 21–1). The

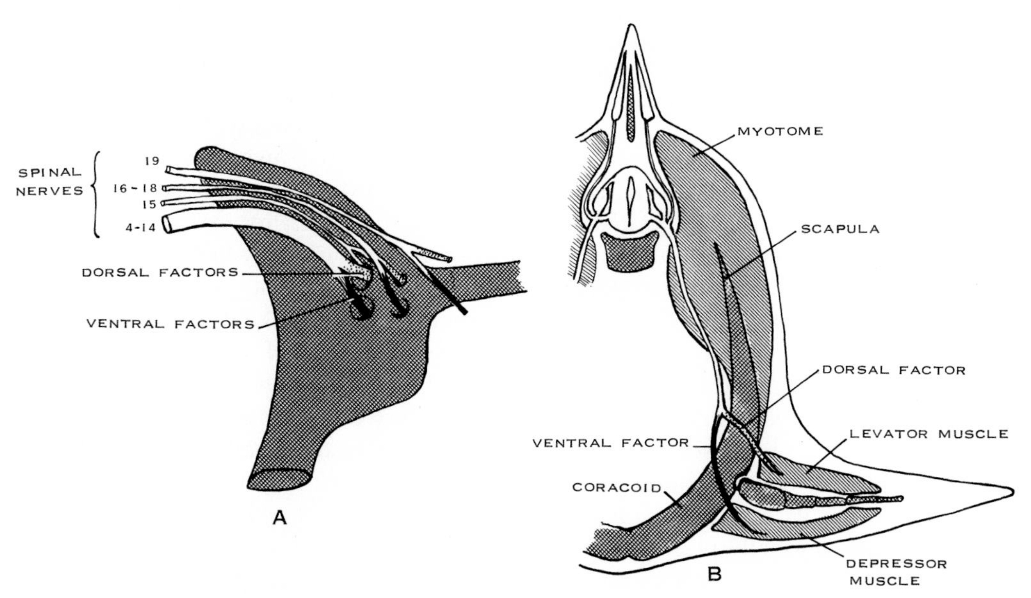

Fig. 21–10. Nerve supply to fin muscles. A. Median view of brachial plexus and pectoral girdle of the sawfish, *Pristis*. B. Cross-section of a shark at shoulder level. (After H. Braus, 1897 and 1909.)

adult pectoral girdles of the great majority of vertebrates, as a result, contain one or more foramina for nerves to peripheral muscles. In fishes, dorsal and ventral factors may pass through separate foramina (Fig. 21–10). It should not be thought however, that the nerves bored their way through established cartilage or bone to make these foramina. As with the skull and its foramina, the nerves were there first.

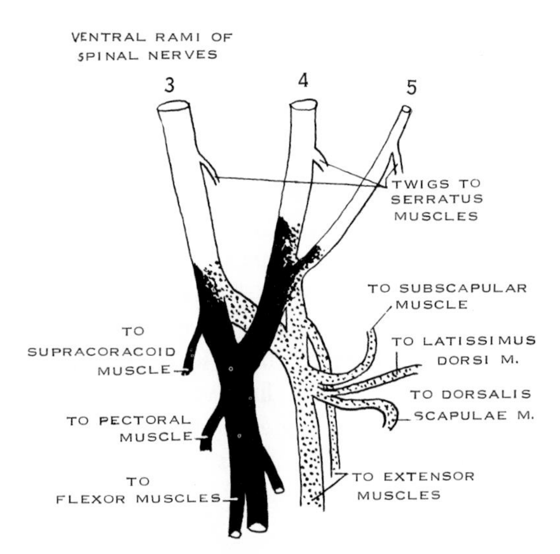

Fig. 21–11. Brachial plexus of the amblystoma, showing dorsal factors (stippled) and ventral factors (black).

The muscles derived from the fin bud, as distinct from those of the trapezius or myotome groups, form mats above and below the fin skeleton. These differentiate respectively into levators and depressors of the fin (Fig. 21–10, 21–12 A), or as in teleosts these are converted by fin bud rotation into adductor and abductor muscles. Superficial and deep parts may differentiate in each layer, and special masses are usually developed at the leading edge of the fin for protracting it or widening its membrane (Fig. 21–12 A). But simplicity is usually preserved in the muscular pattern, even in the enormous wings of rays. At the most, only six or eight functional subdivisions of these muscles can be named; all of them take origin on the rather rigidly anchored girdle, and all work over the shoulder joint.

The pattern of true limb-bud muscles in tetrapods is much more intricate. From 50 to 60 functionally individualized muscles are carved out of the mesenchyme of the bud. Some of them spread out over the trunk so that they can move the whole girdle, others work only over the shoulder joint, some only over the elbow joint, and still others only over the joints of the wrist and hand. Before all these elements are recognizable, however, one first sees the promuscle cells segregated as dorsal and ventral mats (Fig. 21–1), and the components of the brachial plexus correspondingly divided into dorsal and ventral factors to supply them (Fig. 21–11).

(b) The second category of muscles to become associated with the fin or limb arises from adjacent myotomes. In fishes, suiting the requirements for rigid anchorage, the pectoral girdle sinks into the flank, and muscle fibers of the myotomes both anterior and posterior to it insert on its cartilage or bony surfaces, just as they might to the next myoseptum (Fig. 21–12 A). These myotomic limb muscles undergo little or no specialization. They are supplied by their own segmental spinal nerves, which are not involved in the brachial plexus or if these do become superficially bound to the plexus they do not exchange fibers with the other nerves.

In tetrapods generally, the pectoral girdle does not sink into the myotome series, but lies suspended between the intercostal hypaxial muscles and the skin. Slips extend out to the scapula from the myotomes which it covers, however, and serve to move it, or to anchor it in place, keeping their origins upon the vertebrae or ribs of their segments of origin (Fig. 21–12 B). Although they become closely related to muscles of the first category in a functional sense, they retain a characteristically segmental or myotomic type of innervation, not involved in the fiber exchanges of the brachial plexus (cf. twigs to the serratus muscle, Fig. 21–11).

(c) The third category of muscles added to the pectoral complex comes from the posterodorsal limit of the pharynx-segment zone: the **trapezius** and its subdivisions. It brings the nerve supply characteristic of its origin, namely the **accessory branch of the vagus.** In sharks (Figs. 17–11, 21–12) this muscle is elongated and serves to tie the upper part of the pectoral girdle to the head, as the hypoglossal group of muscles (specialized as rectus cervicis and coracobranchiales) does ventrally. In bony fishes the trapezius musculature is reduced in size and importance because the pectoral girdle is snugged up tight against the back of the skull. But in the land animals the new freedom of the pectoral girdle and its importance in new types of locomotion open up new possibilities for use of the trapezius, and these have been exploited most notably in the mammals (compare Figs. 17–8 and 17–10). In most amniotes the nerve supply for the enlarged trapezius musculature becomes separated from the vagus during development, appearing in the adult as the **accessory nerve,** cranial nerve XI.

B. Pelvic Fins

The pelvic fins of fishes are embedded in the trunk muscles, free of any attachment by joints to the rest of the skeleton. Their location is fixed in given species, but may be anywhere along the ventral line of the belly from throat to anus, and not uncommonly they lie anterior to the pectoral fins (Fig. 21–7 B). They are relatively useless except as stabilizers. There are a number of cases of astonishingly specialized adaptations of them in isolated groups: the very different copulatory devices of elasmobranchs, holocephals, and phallostethid teleosts, the climbing organs of some sargassum fishes, the ventral suckers of gobies

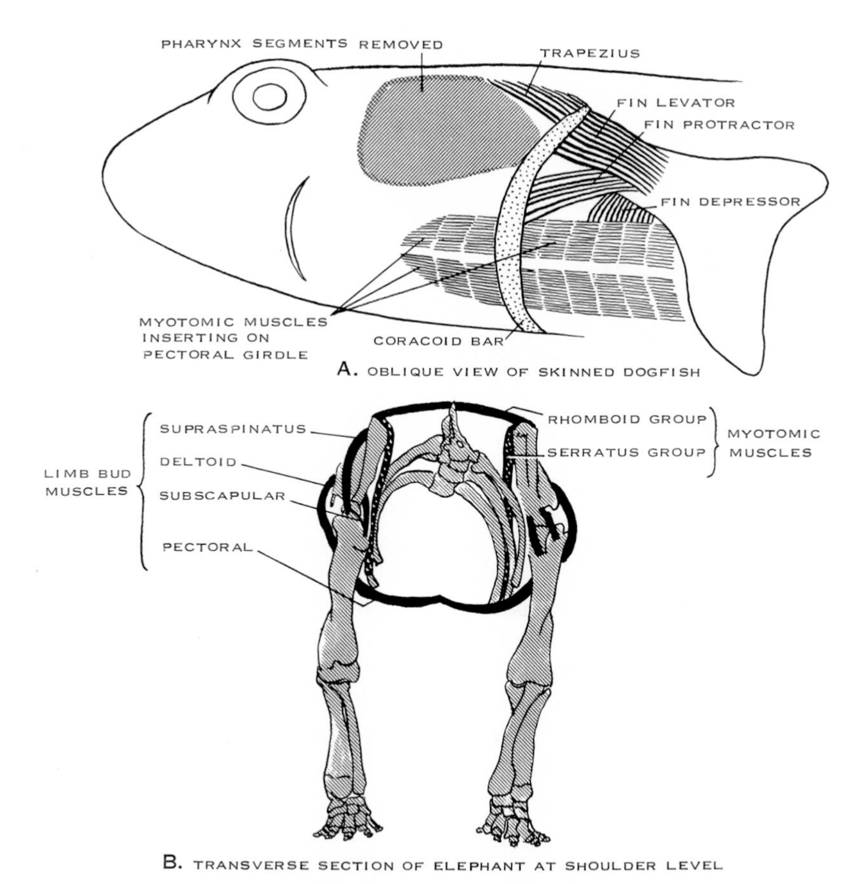

Fig. 21–12. Relations of pectoral girdles to muscles.

and clingfishes [5]. But there are many more cases of species in which pelvic fins become rudimentary or have disappeared.

Quite by contrast, pelvic appendages are heavily developed in tetrapods, and the few cases of arrested development or atrophy are limited to burrowing or aquatic forms (snakes, whales, sea cows). Their girdles are attached to the single sacral vertebra or a more stoutly built sacrum (Fig. 20–9), either directly or by way of heavy sacral ribs.

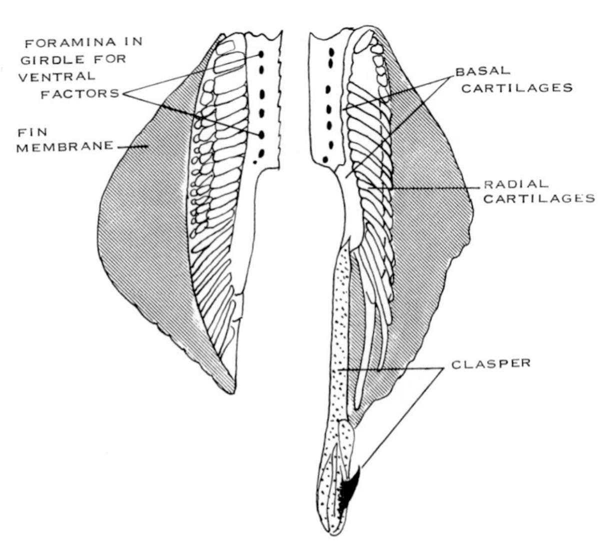

Fig. 21–13. Pelvic fins of a shark, *Chlamydoselachus*, shown on left as developed in ♀, on right as developed in ♂.
(After T. Goodey, 1910.)

The appearance and early development of the pelvic-appendage bud is like that of the pectoral one in nearly all respects. One difference is that no secondary girdle of membrane bones is ever added to the primary girdle, the whole of it being preformed in cartilage. Another follows from the physical location of the bud: nothing comparable to the trapezius musculature is added to the pelvic apparatus. The only two categories of muscle concerned with the hindlimb or pelvic fin are those developed within the bud itself, and the myotomic muscles which border the girdle. They are all supplied by ventral rami of spinal nerves, the former through a pelvic plexus, the latter not.

The supporting girdle for the pelvic fins of elasmobranchs unites from paired primordia to form a hoop of cartilage nearly encircling the body, but anchored only by being embedded in flank myotomes. The basal and radial cartilages, the fin rays, the intrinsic muscles and their nerves, are comparable to those of the pectoral fins, except for the copulatory structures or **claspers** developed by the males (Fig. 21–13). These are fashioned out of radial cartilages and intrinsic muscle slips at the posterior medial margins of the pelvic fins. Their structure varies greatly in different families and genera, but there is always a lateral groove in each one, along which semen and the secretion of a special fin gland may be guided, and always two or more distal cartilages or hooks which can be dilated with special muscles, serving as anchors when the organ is thrust into the cloaca of the female. Among other fishes only the holocephals produce structures homologous with these, though guppies and a few other families of teleosts have modified their unpaired anal fins for similar purposes.

In the general run of teleosts almost the entire pelvic fin membrane is stiffened by fin rays; basal and radial elements shrink to the vanishing point; and the girdle is usually represented by a single bony element on each side, immovably fixed in the trunk (or throat!) muscles (Fig. 21–7 B).

Quite in contrast to any known fish group, tetrapods usually develop a pelvic girdle of three parts on each side, which meet at the hip joint: **ilium** extending dorsad to make juncture with the sacrum, **ischium** extending ventrad just in front of the cloaca, and **pubis** extending ventrad anterior to the ischium. Right and left pubes generally meet in the ventral midline, and right and left ischia often do also. Fusion of elements across the midline, and on each side, and the expansion or the ankylosis of the sacroiliac joint occur in various species, and provide the strength and rigidity needed for running, jumping, climbing, digging, and other highly specialized activities.

III. TETRAPOD LIMBS

The pattern of skeletal elements and joints adopted by the tetrapods for their pectoral appendages is remarkably standardized, as mentioned above (page 434). Strong hints of a similar pattern are seen in the tetrapod pelvic appendage skeleton, and early anatomists worked hard to establish detailed serial homologies between parts of the fore- and hindlimbs. Bone homologies present little difficulty (Fig. 21–9) but the patterns of muscles and nerves are much more complex, so that the homology theories are not very helpful when it comes to understanding the whole limbs. Therefore the two pairs of appendages will be considered separately, the pectoral ones first.

The procedure in each case will be to comment on the anatomy of the amblystoma limb, and then to compare the parts of this rather simple example with those in more advanced tetrapods. It should not be assumed, because the amblystoma is the special example, that it was chosen because it is "primitive" or unusually close to the stem stock of tetrapods. On the contrary, though the antecedents of the modern urodeles are not well represented in the fossil record, many paleontologists assume that the pedagogically useful simplicity of the amblystoma is secondarily acquired through degeneration.

A. Pectoral Limb

1. Skeleton. The amblystoma pectoral girdle skeleton first appears as a single cartilage on each side, between the skin and the coelomic mesoderm. Hypaxial myotomes grow down inside this girdle between it and the parietal peritoneum, but do not lose their myotomic character in so doing. Although the girdle receives a few small slips of muscle from them, it does not become embedded in myosepta as a fish girdle does.

From the original center, cartilage spreads toward the ventral midline as a broad **coracoid** part, anteroventrad as a **procoracoid,** and dorsad as a **scapula** (Fig. 21–15 A). In most tetrapods, similar elements have origins in separate cartilage-forming centers, they are almost entirely replaced by bone, and secondary girdle elements are added to them as membrane bones. In the amblystoma, quite exceptionally, only the central part near the shoulder joint becomes replaced by bone, and no secondary-girdle elements are ever added.

The scapula is the only part of the pectoral girdle which is constant in its occurrence (except when limbs are totally absent). It is often flared dorsally, providing a broader base for muscle attachment, its triangular blade then having anterior, vertebral, and axillary borders. It may also project anterior to the shoulder joint as an **acromion process;** in mammals this is borne on the end of a strong external ridge, the **scapular spine** (Fig. 21–17 B).

Both in strength and in its manner of attachment to the rest of the body, the pectoral girdle has been many times readapted to the requirements of running, climbing, swimming, flying, digging, and other uses. The ventral part of the girdle particularly reflects this. Consideration of the homologies, hence the specific names, of the primary or secondary skeletal elements that are added to the ventral girdle, is more useful in establishing family resemblances and sorting out evolutionary lineages than it is to understanding how the limbs work. Although a triradiate pattern centered at the shoulder joint, similar to that of the amblystoma, is common, the ventral elements are not always homologous with procoracoids and coracoids. More frequently, a secondary element, a membrane bone called the **clavicle,** functionally replaces the procoracoid. Coracoids are strongly developed in most reptiles and birds but tend to disappear in mammals. Interclavicles and postclavicles and combined elements appear in some groups. In turtles, the clavicles and interclavicles apparently forsake the girdle and add themselves to the ventral shell or plastron.

Functional adaptations are richly illustrated in the skeleton of the free pectoral appendage (Fig. 21–14). Walkers or runners are divided into a primitive **plantigrade** type, in which the palms and soles are pressed to the ground; or the **digitigrade** type, such as birds and cats, which walk on their toes; or the **unguligrade**

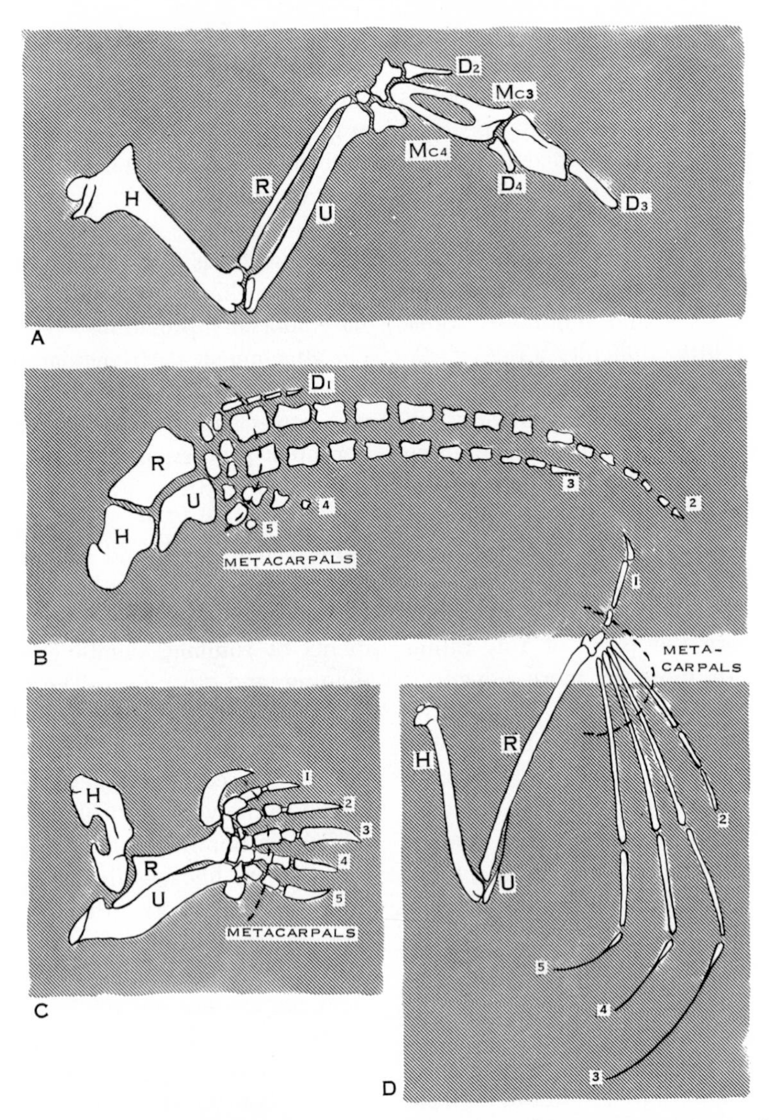

Fig. 21–14. Functional adaptations of the free pectoral appendage skeleton. A. Bird. B. Whale. C. Mole. D. Bat.

type, such as pigs and horses, which only touch their toenails or hoofs to the ground. Many species show conditions intermediate between these types of gait, and alligators are digitigrade fore and plantigrade aft. Some anteaters (Order Xenarthra) walk on the sides of their metatarsals or even on the backs of their digging hands, clanking their outsized claws as they go.

Digging and burrowing, incidentally, have been adopted as a way of life, quite independently, by certain species of marsupials and several groups of moles among the insectivores (Fig. 21–14 C) in addition to the Xenarthra. In all cases, the effect on their appendages is quite similar.

Bats support the skin webs of their wings with greatly elongated digits 2–5 of their hands, retaining the little clawed thumbs for grasping (Fig. 21–14 D). The extinct pterosaurs apparently did the same thing with just one digit on each hand, twice as long as the vertebral column (Fig. 20–10). Flying squirrels and certain marsupials and lizards have learned to glide (but not to fly) with quite generalized appendages, using a membrane of flank skin.

The wing of birds is a marvel of aerodynamics, most of the virtue of which comes from the design of the flight feathers and their exquisite control through uniquely specialized muscles [6]. The basic pattern of skeleton is recognizable beyond the shoulder joint (Fig. 21–14 A), but is both reduced and redesigned. In the chick wingbud at 6–7 days of incubation, rudiments of thirteen carpal elements and four digits are recognizable, only the thumb being missing. But during the next week the carpals fuse with each other or with the metacarpals until there are only two wrist elements left, and the more distal bones combine to produce a central rigid piece terminated by the phalanges of the middle digit, with single phalanges representing digits 2 and 4 casually attached to it [7].

Simultaneously with this reduction, the joints at elbow and wrist take on the character of hinges with strictly limited arcs of operation, all in one plane. The whole wing can be extended, locked into a straight position, or folded against the body by rather simple muscles operating through long tendons, but no energy need be wasted in resisting twist motions at elbow or wrist because the bones will not allow any. Instead, powerful muscles are designed to control the rotation of the whole wing, as well as its flapping, at the shoulder joint. The sockets which hold the great flight feathers are bound firmly but flexibly to the ulna and the middle digit by tough fascia, and special muscles and tendons are laid on to control the very slight but aerodynamically crucial adjustments of them in coordination with the movements of the whole wing in flight or soaring.

The history of reversion of tetrapod groups to an aquatic life shows a full range of adaptability in the distal limb pattern. Here is a partial list of groups which have, separately and independently, and in varying degrees, adapted themselves for swimming: ichthyosaurs, mosasaurs, mesosaurs, plesiosaurs, pythonomorphs, sea turtles, and crocodilia among the reptiles; penguins, loons, ducks, and some "toothed" birds of the Cretaceous; and among the mammals the platypus, pinniped carnivores, the beavers and muskrats, and the sirenia and cetacea (Fig. 21–14 B). Some of these water tetrapods swim by specially modified tails as though in imitation of true fishes, but most of them have transformed their limbs into paddles. The following ways to do this have been exploited in one or more of these groups, singly or in combination:

- Increase of the numbers of phalanges in each digit.
- Prolongation of a fin beyond the tips of the phalanges.
- Increase of the number of digits.
- Addition of extra wrist bones or extra bones formed in tendons.
- Elongation of metacarpals or phalanges.
- Spreading of the digits, with webbed skin between them.
- Flattening and widening of forearm or wrist bones.
- Flattening and widening of humerus.

Some species have used different sets of these devices in their two pairs of appendages. Some have reduced or lost their pelvic limbs. The effort of swimming has been reduced by other devices for stiffening the paddle, such as tightening the joints, hardening the skin or adding bony plates to it. Natural selection has apparently favored without discrimination *any* variation that improves the efficiency of swimming.

2. *Muscles.* The three categories of pectoral appendage muscles mentioned previously (page 434) occur in all tetrapods that have limbs, and with the same sorts of nerve supply. The trapezius musculature, operated chiefly if not entirely by the XI nerve or a branch of the vagus, and the myotome derivatives, innervated by spinal nerve rami which are not involved in the brachial plexus, deal almost exclusively with movements of the scapula upon the trunk. On the other hand, the muscles formed within the limb bud itself all have principal functions beyond the shoulder joint.

In the trapezius category the amblystoma (Fig.

21–15) has one muscle; in the myotome category it has two, one consisting of several segmental slips. The more complicated amniotes tend to have whole clusters and families of named muscles representing each of these groups. For instance, the trapezius anlage of man (Fig. 17–10) divides into dorsal and ventral parts, and in cats and ungulates each of these splits variously into superficial and deep layers. Hypertrophy and specialization into functionally adapted parts is the rule in the myotome-derived scapula muscles also. Adaptive effects are so widespread and pervasive that there is little profit in attending to homologies of individual muscles beyond the confines of orders or even families; nevertheless morphological patterns are easily visible in the consideration of muscle groups. Some of these will now be considered.

(a) *Trapezius Group.* The amblystoma trapezius muscle takes origin on the skull and inserts on the anterior border of the scapula (Fig. 21–15). Important parts of the trapezius group continue to do so in higher tetrapods, but other parts spread their origins down over the neural spines of neck and thorax vertebrae, forming a sheet that may completely conceal epaxial muscles in the anterior half of the trunk; and their insertions spill over onto the clavicle, the sternum, or other elements ventrally. The nerve supply of these hypertrophied trapezius groups is usually augmented posteriorly, by branches from the spinal nerves.

(b) *Myotome Group.* Two sets of muscles of this group converge on the vertebral border of the scapula for their insertion, the **rhomboid** muscles from the dorsal side, and the **serratus** muscles from the ventral side. The little weak scapula of the amblystoma has just one rhomboid muscle, usualy called a levator scapulae (Fig. 21–15 A, B) which has its origin on the skull. Lying just deep to the trapezius, it could be taken for a deep layer of that muscle except for its nerve supply. Man, cat and horse have several muscles in this rhomboid–levator set, but they are arranged differently in each species. In general their origins run far down the neural spines of the vertebrae, they insert on the vertebral border of the scapula and they serve to raise the shoulder, drag it forward, or anchor the girdle in place (Fig. 21–12 B).

The amblystoma has a serratus muscle consisting of five tiny slips which are apparently parts of the superficial external oblique muscle that move their insertions onto the scapula. In the amniotes, such slips, greatly multiplied in number and size, form overlapping and subdivided sheets whose tendons of origin arise in a long serrated curve from the ventral parts of the thoracic ribs, and from the rib-equivalents in the neck, and converge dorsad on the vertebral bor-

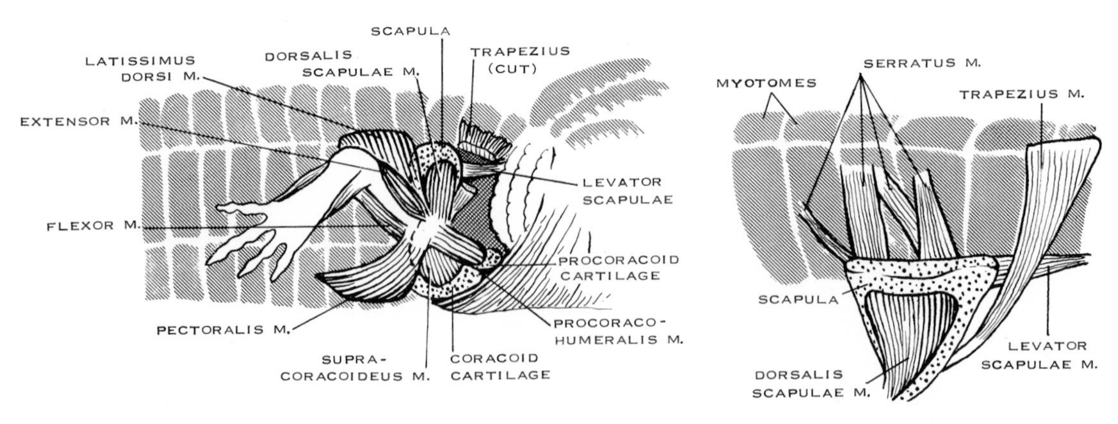

Fig. 21–15. Pectoral limb and girdle muscles of the amblystoma larva. A. Oblique lateral view of skinned specimen. B. Scapula tipped outward and viewed from above.

(B after I. H. Blount, 1935.)

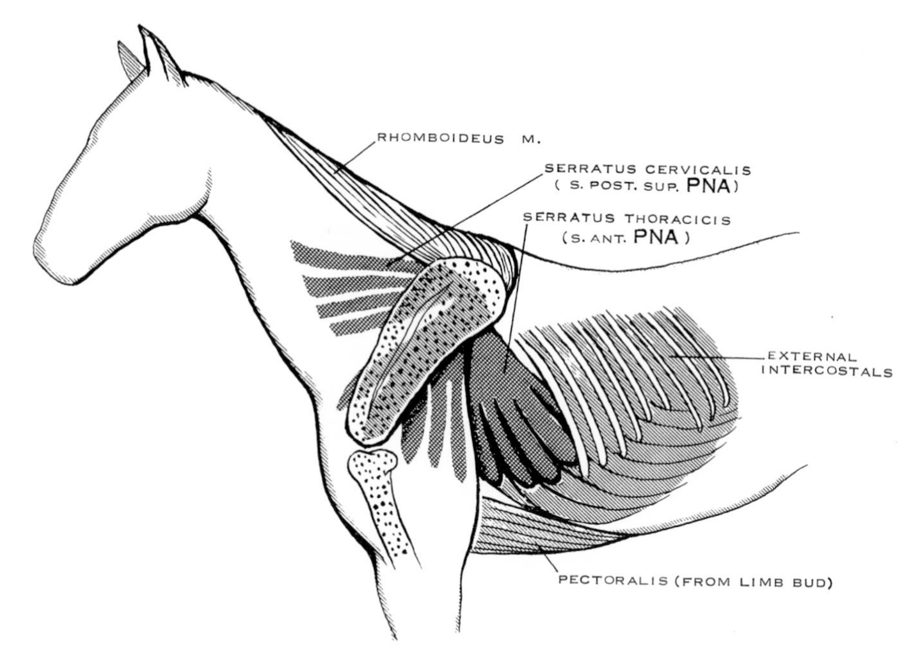

Fig. 21–16. Myotome-derived shoulder muscles of the horse.

der of the scapula. They are variously involved in girdle-anchorage, in rib-breathing, and in body support. The latter function is particularly well illustrated in elephants (Fig. 21–12 B), whose forelimbs are two columns supporting a muscular hammock in which the trunk is suspended. The pectoral skeleton is not attached by joints to any other part of the skeleton; the hammock is provided by the serratus muscles of the two sides.

(The names of the two extensive sheets of serratus muscle in man are still not corrected for the benefit of comparative anatomy. The one taking origin from rib-processes in the neck is morphologically anterior to the one taking origin from thoracic ribs (Fig. 21–16), but officially (PNA) the two are respectively called M. serratus posterior superior and M. serratus anterior, because of the erect posture.)

(*c*) *Pectoral Limb-bud Group.* The muscles that are developed directly from limb-bud mesoderm and served by nerves springing from the brachial plexus are a complex group, even in the amblystoma. In the amniotes the same generalizations as to hypertrophy, subdivision, and specialization apply. The present discussion of them will go no farther than to suggest that they are classifiable, in terms of topography, function, and nerve supply, into five groups of muscles that insert on the humerus and have their principal effect over the shoulder joint, and two other groups whose principal effect is over elbow, wrist, and digit joints. In the amblystoma, four of the five shoulder groups consist of one muscle and one nerve each. The same groups can easily be seen in mammals, though each is subdivided and specialized in a variety of ways.

The ventral rami of spinal nerves which approach the brachial plexus just inside the shoulder joint and girdle separate into dorsal and ventral factors (Figs. 21–11, 21–17), which are reminiscent of the arrangement mentioned in certain fish (Fig. 21–10). The recombination of fibers from the dorsal factors produces nerves that supply three of the five shoulder muscle groups, and one of the two groups that operate beyond. These *groups supplied by dorsal factors* are:

(1) **Latissimus dorsi** (Fig. 21–15 A), a muscle which spreads out posterodorsally over the

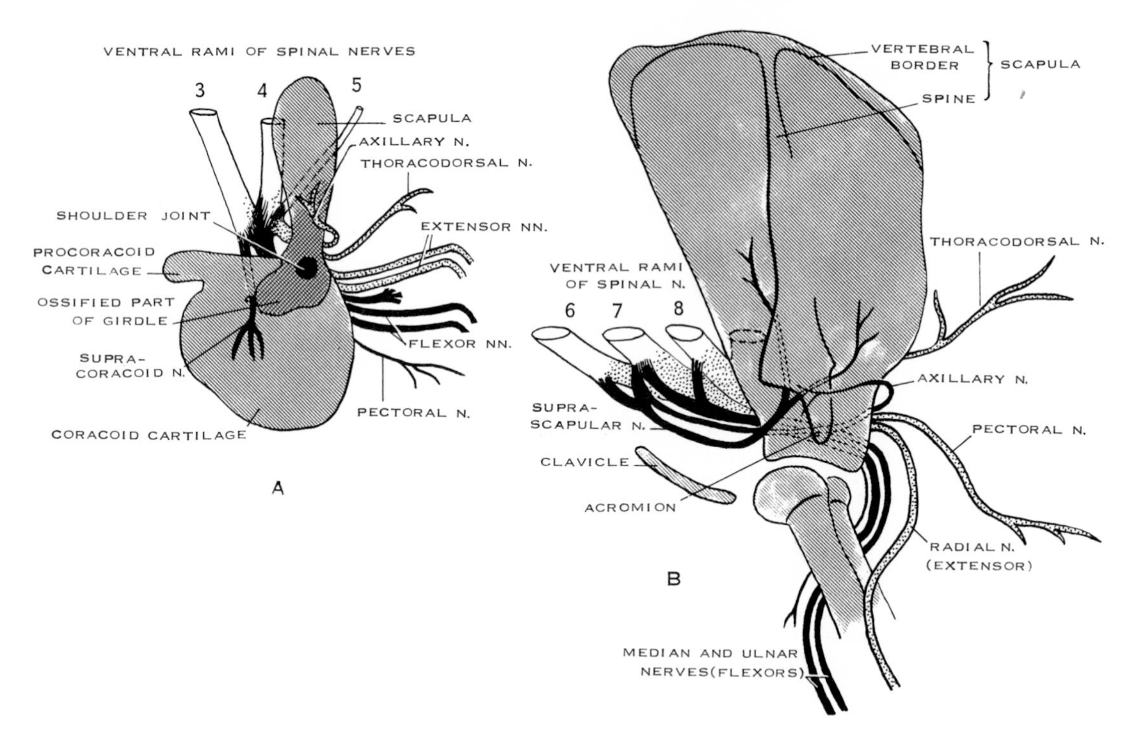

Fig. 21–17. Relations of brachial plexus and pectoral girdle. Dorsal factors stippled, ventral factors black. A. The amblystoma. B. The cat.

oblique musculature of the flank, to which it is fastened. It inserts on the posterior side of the upper end of the humerus. Tiny in the amblystoma, it becomes huge in mammals, overflowing upon the epaxial muscles of the lumbar region and producing a small subdivision called **teres major** that takes origin from the axillary border of the scapula. In quadrupeds the latissimus dorsi is an important running muscle, and in man it is used for climbing or ski-pole work. Its nerve, called the **thoracodorsal,** emerges from inside the scapula and runs along its deep surface (Fig. 21–17 A, B).

(2) **Subscapular,** a muscle whose origin occupies most of the deep surface of the scapula, and which inserts on the inside of the upper part of the humerus (Fig. 21–12 B). Its nerve supply, called **subscapular** also (Fig. 21–11), may be branched several times almost at its source.

(3) **Deltoid group:** In the amblystoma there are two muscles of this group but they share the same nerve, and both insert on the humerus. One covers the outer surface of the scapula, hence is called the dorsalis scapulae, and the other similarly covers the procoracoid cartilage as the procoraco-humeralis muscle. In higher tetrapods, and especially the mammals that climb, or slap their prey, or handle their food, deltoid muscles are much subdivided and specialized, running from the scapula, its spine and acromion, across the shoulder joint to the outside of the upper humerus. The group is called **deltoid** because of the shape of its robust principal member in man. It is supplied with an **axillary nerve,** so-called because its course from the plexus deep to the shoulder joint, around to the muscles on the outside, takes it through the axilla or armpit (Fig. 21–17). The deltoid and subscapular muscle groups produce movements of the shoulder joint which roughly oppose each other (Fig. 21–12 B).

(4) **Extensor group:** The other dorsal factors from the brachial plexus combine in one or

two trunks that pass through the axilla posterior to the shoulder joint, enter the upper arm and proceed to supply a group of muscles classed as **extensors.** The one such trunk in man or cat is called the radial nerve (Fig. 21–17 B).

The brachial plexus nerves which arise from recombination of the fibers of the ventral factors help to define the two other groups of shoulder muscles, and supply the rest of the muscles beyond the shoulder. These *groups of muscles supplied by ventral factors* are:

(1) **Anterior shoulder group:** Because of the very different forward-reaching movements in running, climbing, flying or swimming, this group has been reworked in evolution to the point that its homology can be questioned. In the amblystoma, it includes only an anteroventral muscle whose origin covers the outer surface of the coracoid cartilage (hence its name, **supracoracoid**), and whose insertion is near the proximal end of the humerus (Fig. 21–15 A). Its nerve passes to it through a foramen in the cartilage, anterior to the shoulder joint (Fig. 21–17 A). Such a nerve supply, through a coracoid foramen, is a useful marker for homology theories, but not all tetrapods have coracoids, and not all coracoids are pierced by such a foramen. When the coracoid element of the girdle is reduced, this muscle may move partly up onto the scapula for its origin. In monotremes it takes origin from both coracoid and scapula, but in placental mammals, a separate coracoid element having disappeared, it seems to have moved entirely onto the scapula, partly covered by and partly replacing the deltoid group.

Simultaneously, in man and other placentals, this anterior shoulder muscle mass has become split in two by the development of a scapular spine (Fig. 21–17 B) so that it appears as two muscles, the **supraspinatus,** and **infraspinatus,** both of which however are supplied by the same ventral-factor nerve, the suprascapular (PNA), which reaches them by winding around the anterior border of the scapula. The tendons of these two muscles are important in strengthening the vulnerable anterior surface of the shoulder joint.

(2) **Pectoral group:** In the amblystoma (Fig. 21–15 A), a single pectoral muscle spreads out from the limb bud posteroventrally, over the surface of the rudimentary sternum and the rectus muscles of the belly, to which it is tied. Its tendon of insertion fastens to the proximal part of the humerus. Its ventral-factor nerve reaches it near the shoulder joint and follows its deep surface. In both cats and pigs, pectoral musculature is very extensive and subdivided into four named parts with several nerves, but however definite the pectoral group is, the individual parts are not strictly homologous in the two species.

Pectoral muscles reach their maximum development in bats and birds, producing the driving downstroke of the wings. In birds moreover, an inner portion reaches the humerus through a sort of pulley provided by the quite rigid girdle bones above the shoulder, at such an angle that when it contracts it rotates the humerus from the downbeat position to the upbeat position, which helps the air pressures to raise the wing. In hummingbirds the alternating contractions of the inner and outer portions of the pectoral musculature follow each other at rates of sixty or more per second. The entire expanded surface of the great sternum and its keel is used by these muscles for their origin.

(3) **Flexor group:** The other ventral factors from the brachial plexus usually combine in two trunks that pass through the axilla posterior to the shoulder joint, to supply **flexor muscles** in the upper arm, forearm and hand (Fig. 21–17). In human anatomy these are the **median** and **ulnar nerves.** They and the dorsal-factor **radial nerve** are named from the positions they take up in the elbow and forearm relative to the radius and the ulna.

The primordial division of the muscle-forming mesoderm into dorsal and ventral parts, which occurs in the early pectoral limb bud, is perpetuated in a connective tissue septum that separates the extensor muscles from the flexors, all the way from the shoulder joint to the digits, with some local variations in prominence. Because the limb rotates somewhat on its long axis as it grows outward (Fig. 21–5), this septum is warped from its original plane, but the extensor and flexor nerves in general keep to their own sides of it, through most of their extent. Not always however: in many tetrapods, for obscure reasons, one of the flexor nerves regularly pierces the part of the septum which stretches as an interosseous ligament between radius and ulna in the forearm, and invades territory that might be expected to belong to the radial nerve, capturing a variable amount of the extensor muscle in the forearm and hand.

The complex pattern of forelimb flexor and extensor muscles can only be understood in complete dissection, and will not be described here. There are more than two dozen separate named muscles in the amblystoma forelimb which operate chiefly beyond the shoulder, and half of these have functional subdivisions. The specialization is far greater in the wings of birds and the running, digging, climbing, flying, or swimming forelimbs of mammals. Twenty muscles, some of them elaborately subdivided, are involved in the human wrist, and there are at least nine muscles attached to the little finger alone. Nevertheless, the most highly developed tetrapod forelimbs still retain the basic pattern which is visible in the amblystoma, if one makes allowances for subdivision, specialization, and functional adaptations of the parts.

B. Pelvic Limb

1. Skeleton. Three separate centers of cartilage formation usually appear on each side, forming a triradiate girdle of **pubis, ischium,** and **ilium** (Fig. 21–18). The two dorsal ilia make firm attachments with the sacral vertebrae, either by way of free sacral ribs or by embryonic rib-elements that fuse with the vertebrae (Fig. 20–7 C).

This basic equipment has been modified freely according to the functional requirements of various types of locomotion (digging, walking, running, jumping, climbing, etc.). Bipedal locomotion has been invented at least six times in four distinct types among tetrapods, each demanding extensive correlative adjustments of skeletal and muscular structure, and the development of appropriate special behavior mechanisms [8]. Many of the bipedal animals (some dinosaurs, birds, man) have their ilia flared dorsally, which gives more surface for the fixed ends of the muscles that maintain the upright posture. The two anteroventral pubes usually make a joint with each other across the midline, and so may the

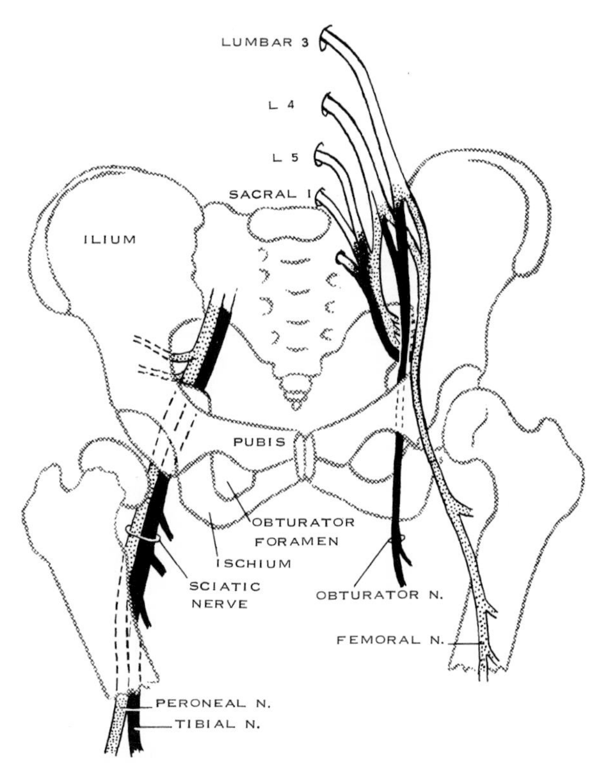

Fig. 21–18. Pelvic girdle and crural plexus of man, anterior view. Post-hip and pre-hip nerves shown on opposite sides of the drawing.

two posteroventral ischia, and the floor of the pelvis may be solidified by the joining of all four of these elements. Urodeles have a single puboischiac plate.

On the other hand, in the ornithischian dinosaurs, the pelvis was mostly soft below, the pubes and ischia being spun out into thin rods. And in flying birds, neither pubes nor ischia meet each other; the pubes have become long posteriorly directed splints while the ischia are extensively broadened and taken into the synsacrum (Fig. 20–9). The resulting wide soft floor of the bird pelvis is no doubt a convenience for the laying of eggs; but the exceptional case, in which the two pubes do unite ventrally, is the ostrich, which lays the largest eggs of all.

The resemblance between the skeletons of forelimbs and hindlimbs has been mentioned previously and shown in Fig. 21–9. The adaptation of the two pair for quite different uses, even within a single individual (man, kangaroos, moles, bats, birds, etc., etc.) disturbs this resemblance a good deal, particularly in the girdles and the digits. The effort of comparing the muscles and nerves of the forelimbs with those of the hindlimbs has in fact proved impractical.

One interesting resemblance concerns coracoid and pubis. It was mentioned (page 445) that the coracoid, if present, may be perforated by a ventral-factor brachial plexus nerve. In many of the tetrapods a similar situation exists in the pelvic girdle: the pubis may be perforated, or notched, for the passage of a ventral-factor nerve. (The nerve is called the **obturator** because, if it does not pass through a pubic foramen or notch, it goes through the gap between pubis and ischium, as in man (Fig. 21–18); this space is called the obturator foramen because it is closed or "obturated" by a tough sheet of fascia on which muscles take origin, both inside and outside of the girdle.)

The bones of the free hindlimb have undergone many functional variations. The position of the femur has been adjusted to various methods of locomotion. The crawling urodeles have quite a different stance from that of the jumping frogs. The modern lizards and crocodilians that merely run a few paces and then squat have femurs adapted to quite different engineering requirements from those of the lordly mesozoic reptiles that ran and then stood, or from those of mammals that do likewise. Birds, and the bipedal dinosaurs and other animals that have acquired the ability to walk habitually on their hind legs, have had to redesign the femur and the pelvic girdle to suit. Each of these adaptations has produced more profound changes in the muscles than in the bones: the femur, like the humerus (Fig. 21–14), remains essentially a shaft, and the effects of changing stance are seen principally in the trochanters, epicondyles, and other ridges and excrescences which grow out from it in response to the muscles that insert upon or take origin from it. But the correlated adjustments extend also into the vertebrae and the trunk muscles, not to mention the behavior mechanisms that are built into the structure of the nervous system [8].

In many mammals and most birds, the fibula may be considerably reduced, and fused to the tibia either at its distal end or throughout. The number of toes is reduced in various tetrapod orders, from five to four, three, two, or one. The hinge joint at the ankle occurs between the tibia–fibula and the tarsal bones in mammals, but in birds and many reptiles it is between the proximal and the distal rows of tarsal elements. In birds, the ankle bones have fused with their neighbors, so that *three* long bones are found in succession from hip to foot: femur, **tibiotarsus** (there is no free fibula), and **tarsometatarsus.** All the metatarsals are fused with the distal tarsals in one piece. Wading herons and flamingos get extra height through the elongation of the tarsometatarsus, which may become twice as long as the femur.

2. *Muscles.* The muscles of the hindlimb apparatus may be divided into (a) those derived from myotomes, and not innervated through a plexus, and (b) those derived from the limb-bud mesenchyme itself.

Whereas there is a strong development of myotome-derived muscles in the thorax for restraining and supporting the freely movable scapula, such muscles play a quite minor role in relation to the firmly attached hindlimb. The pelvic girdle is generally held quite tight by the sacral joints, and the epaxial (iliocostal, etc.) and hypaxial (rectus abdominis, the oblique layers) attachments to the pelvic girdle are for the convenience of other functions of trunk and ribs, not as direct contributions to locomotion.

All the largest muscles of the thigh take origin mostly from the pelvic girdle and insert beyond the knee, operating over both the hip and knee joints. A number of shorter muscles operate only over the hip joint. Of these, one set anterior to the hip tend to spread up along the centra and transverse processes of the lumbar vertebrae in mammals (the "tenderloin" muscles), and another set posterior to the hip spread similarly along the sacrum and base of the tail. They are powerfully developed in running mammals. Other sets tend to be concealed inside the origins of the long thigh muscles. Earnest efforts have been made to develop a comparative classification of these muscles, but they intergrade confusingly and they have been freely remodeled in the many adaptations to types of stance and locomotion. As a result, their homologies are often in doubt beyond the limits of families and orders.

3. *Hindlimb nerves.* All muscles formed in the hindlimb buds get their innervation from branches of a plexus produced by the ventral rami of several spinal nerves. This is the **lumbosacral plexus** of human anatomy, but since there are many tetrapods in which caudal nerves, and even posterior thoracics, are added to those of the lumbar or sacral regions, the more general name **crural plexus** can be defended.

Like the brachial plexus, the crural plexus lies inside the joint between girdle and free appendage (Fig. 21–18), and sends branches to the limb muscles both anterior and posterior to the joint. In the majority of amniotes also, the ventral rami of the spinal nerves divide into dorsal and ventral factors as they approach the crural plexus, the more distal nerves arising from one or the other set of factors. Usually only one ventral ramus forks and sends fibers both sides of the hip joint; in the few species or exceptional individuals which do not have such a "furcal nerve," there is a pre-hip plexus, separate from a post-hip one.

In addition to various sensory nerves that scatter to the hindlimb skin from the crural plexus, it is usual to find two important motor nerves given off into the thigh anterior to the hip joint, and two posterior to it (Fig. 21–18). In each pair, one of the nerves is made up of ventral factors, and the other of dorsal factors. The pre-hip ventral-factor branch is the **obturator nerve,** previously mentioned as running through a pubic foramen or notch, if not through the obturator foramen. The pre-hip dorsal-factor branch, called the **femoral nerve,** enters the thigh anterior to the pubis. The post-hip nerves, in a common but by no means standardized arrangement, consist of the **tibial** (ventral factors) and the **peroneal** (dorsal factors). Or (as in man) there may be a huge common trunk, the **sciatic nerve,** passing into the thigh behind the hip joint and ischium, there to divide into tibial and peroneal nerves; and some of the short muscles that operate only over the hip joint may get their own nerves direct from the plexus.

The simplicity of this generalized arrangement of thigh nerves is matched in many tetrapods by thigh muscles developed in four quadrant masses, displaced by the rotation of the limb-bud tissues into dorsal (knee extensor), ventral (knee flexor), anterior (adductor), and posterior (abductor) groups. The tetrapod hindlimb, however, has not evolved by simple transformations of a set of geometric relationships. Comparative dissections within orders and classes show that these muscle groups are freely intergrading and not at all committed to stereotyped innervations. Knee extensor muscles are usually supplied by the femoral nerve, but in some species they are partly or wholly supplied by the sciatic. The easily recognized knee-flexor group, called the hamstring muscles, are usually served by the ventral division of the sciatic nerve, i.e. the tibial, but there are many tetrapods in which they are served by the obturator. One of the four main motor nerves may occasionally be completely replaced by others, and what might be expected to be minor branches of one of them may arise independently from the plexus. Even within a species, the distribution of motor fibers from particular spinal nerves through and beyond the plexus is subject to many individual variations. Minor differences commonly occur on the two sides of a single animal.

In short, while there is a normal hindlimb anatomy for a species, and the range of variation is narrower in genera than in families, etc., the homologies established for hindlimb muscles and nerves become rapidly less useful as the attempt is made to broaden their application.

C. Correlative Developments of Spinal Cord and Limbs

During the time that the limb bud is differentiating and its muscles are being supplied with nerves from the spinal cord, interactions go on between these parts, that have both anatomical and behavioral results. The anatomical results include (a) the complicated but species-specific patterns of the nerves as they extend through the plexus to the individual muscles, and also (b) certain effects of size and proportion within the spinal cord itself. The obvious behavioral result is (c) the coordination of muscles in effective and meaningful acts. Both groups of interactions are in process of analysis by new types of experimentation, samples of which will now be considered.

1. Factors Controlling Nerve Paths. The limb bud will differentiate its skeleton, muscles and blood vessels with fair success whether transplanted to the tail, the head, the mid-flank or the midventral line. Whatever nerves are present in one of these transplantation sites can be induced to grow into it. If it is grown on a site where no nerves can reach it, differentiation of its other tissues nevertheless takes place. If such a limb remains nerveless it eventually regresses and disappears, but if it is soon enough transplanted into the brachial plexus region it can acquire nerves and function normally thereafter [9].

The pattern of nerves produced within the transplanted limb is usually quite close to the normal one for the species, irrespective of whether its nerve fibers are from the whole normal brachial plexus or from only one of the ventral roots usually belonging to the plexus.

Why do they weave this standard pattern rather than random unpredictable ones? It has been suggested that the early limb bud prepares a pattern of suitable pathways for the nerve fibers before they enter it, and then the nerves simply fill all the pathways. But there are really two nerve patterns which do not wholly overlap in the limb, one consisting of long, primarily motor nerves ending in muscles, and the other of long superficially located sensory nerves ending in the skin. So it was later suggested that not all the paths are prepared at the same time; the motor nerves, which enter the limb first, fill the early paths, and sensory nerves, arriving later, find some paths which were not available for the motor nerves.

However, if the salamander limb is cut off at the shoulder and allowed to regenerate, the sprouting fibers from the brachial plexus all swarm into the blastema before any signs of differentiation have shown in it, establishing their normal patterns of sensory and motor branches simultaneously. Also, in frogs, the hindlimb bud is normally formed very late and gets its sensory and motor fibers at the same time; if its sensory ganglia have been removed, the motor fibers will form their own part of the nerve pattern and no more, and if the ventral half of the spinal cord has been removed the sensory fibers will fill only *their* portion of the normal nerve pattern.

Further evidence that timing is not a normal factor is seen when a differentiated forelimb, raised in the absence of nerves, is transplanted to a brachial plexus region from which the normal limb has been cut away. The regenerating neurons that enter it must traverse relatively long distances through well established tissues to reach their proper end organs and skin areas, but they do this, establishing the *normal* nerve pattern. Are they merely filling all the possible pathways? If such a differentiated but nerveless forelimb is transplanted to the hindlimb site, or if other sections of the neural tube are substituted for the brachial section in a young embryo, the nerves that grow into the forelimb form a *chaotic* pattern [10]. The question whether the nerves decide their paths for themselves or whether they are the creatures of their environment seems to be still open [11].

2. Repercussions in the Spinal Cord. The spinal cords of tetrapods show swellings (**intumescences,** PNA) at the levels which supply the limbs. The size of these swellings has a functional correlate. For instance, frogs (Fig. 20–20) show bigger ones than salamanders; there are larger pectoral-level swellings than pelvic ones in bats, and it is the other way around in kangaroos. Spinal cords of snakes and limbless lizards show no such swellings; nor do those of fishes, in correlation with their weakly developed paired-fin musculature.

These swellings are always found in much reduced form in experimental animals which have been deprived of their limb buds at early stages, or in the anomalous individuals of whatever species, which spontaneously fail to develop limbs.

Increasing the "peripheral load" of a few segments of the spinal cord by grafting limbs onto a normally limbless section of the trunk, or by crowding one or two extra limbs into the normal limb area, regularly produces a local increase in the size of both the dorsal root ganglia and the sensory and motor areas of that part of the cord. Under these circumstances, certain cells which would normally have remained small and unspecialized become large sensory or motor neurons with extensive processes; this accounts for most of the size increase. But it is also certain that the spinal ganglia also acquire more cells in these segments, either by migration or by local increase of cell division. Another factor is noted in chick embryos: epidemics of cell death normally occur in most levels of the spinal cord, but are forestalled in the areas influenced by the limb buds [12].

The mechanism by which the peripheral connections bring about these anatomical effects in the spinal cord is quite unknown. Calling it "assimilative induction" suggests that a nutritive factor may be transmitted. The influence operates not only in parallel, as when pioneer motor fibers influence other potential motor fibers to follow them out to the expanding frontier, but also in series: for when a peripheral overload stimulates the hypertrophy of primary sensory fibers whose somata lie in the dorsal-root ganglia, this is followed by a spurt of growth and differentiation in the secondary sensory neurons with which they are associated.

3. Development of Limb Muscle Coordination. Leaving these unsolved questions of how one cell affects another in development, we may turn to the behavioral aspect of the interaction of spinal cord and limb buds, and ask how a whole host of neurons and muscle cells can coordinate their activities to produce a meaningful act. It looks simple when a man reaches to pick up a drink or a hawk beats its wings in a power dive. The quite stupid trance-like walking of an amblystoma seems even simpler, but this is before one considers the neural and muscular anatomy that is involved. When the individual contractions and relaxations of even a few of the muscles are timed and recorded in parallel lines like the score of a symphony [13], any illusion of simplicity vanishes. Some servomechanism of unknown structure in the spinal cord delivers volleys of signals to each muscle over its own specific nerve at the precisely required times and intensities so as to produce a coordinated and meaningful combination of movements, not spasms or chaotic twitches. How is this marvelous trick brought off?

It is no longer possible to believe that each animal acquires the basic elements of its behavior in trial and error, by a learning process, any more than that it learns to see by experimenting with epithelia arranged in possibly meaningful optical designs. Instead, a behavior pattern has been evolved by its ancestors through a long history of evolution, by random variation culled by forces of natural selection; and the individual inherits the coded instructions for developing the apparatus which will continue this behavior pattern. The behavior is developed in its perfected state like a house from its blueprints, without the intervention of architect or owner. An amblystoma embryo can be raised from a non-motile stage to hatching under complete anesthesia, and then can wake up and perform complicated acts of swimming and feeding that it has never even practised, much less learned by random trial and error.

Setting aside for the moment the question how the spinal-cord command center chooses its strategy and sets up its tactical communications, let us ask how the commands get to the right muscles? The spinal cord and the limb muscles develop quite separate from each other. The nervous connections that are eventually established between them are more complex than the wiring of a TV set. How do the wires get soldered to the right terminals?

Experiments with amphibian embryos reveal new complications rather than simple explanations, but the development of a theory on this question must be limited and guided by such findings as these:

(a) The normal nerve paths to and beyond the brachial plexus are not essential; the brachial section of the amblystoma spinal cord can regulate coordinated behavior of a limb even if any one or any two of the three spinal nerves that normally enter the plexus are eliminated during early development or regeneration.

(b) The cord gives its precise instructions to the individual muscles of the limb with complete unconcern as to whether the limb has been experimentally installed upside down or in some mirror-image relation to the normal. Thus, if right and left forelimbs are exchanged as in Figure 21–4 C, each of their muscles continues to get instructions which would be meaningful in the normal position, but which under the circumstances contribute to a total action which is the exact opposite of what the spinal cord "has in mind." Such an animal cannot walk successfully. Its forelimbs and hindlimbs cancel out each other's efforts. All its life it continues to behave like a racing shell with two pairs of oarsmen back to back, rowing in opposite directions [14].

(c) Experimentally it is easy to produce two forelimbs side by side where one should be, but mirror images of each other. In such a situation, whatever is done by one of the two is done simultaneously but in mirror image by the other. Their homologous muscles contract exactly together in the same sequences, but the total effect is that the two limbs work against each other, pushing in opposite directions or locking elbows in frustration.

Coming back now to the nature of the command center itself, next to nothing is known of its design, though theories are being advanced from the experience of engineers who build servomechanisms for similar jobs in commerce, industry and war. Experiments with amblystoma embryos have shown that the brachial section of the spinal cord can mediate coordinated and meaningful activities in its limbs even if, at early embryonic stages, it has been reduced to half or a third of its normal volume, or turned upside down, or deprived of normal connections with the rest of the central nervous system (or given quite abnormal ones). In other words, its development is a field phenomenon.

Also, only the brachial part of the spinal cord normally develops this capacity. Though transplanted amblystoma forelimbs can be innervated from cranial or mid-flank parts of the neural tube, they never get coordinated commands from these sources, they merely show spasms or chaotic twitches, not meaningful actions. However there are some experimental indications that other parts of the embryonic neural plate can be organized in this way if they are transplanted into the future brachial region at an early enough date. That is, a limb command field can be set up in them by inductive influences that operate only at this level of the trunk.

Nevertheless, the structure and the mode of development of the limb-command center is almost a complete mystery. As to the problem of getting its distributor terminals linked up with the right muscles, there is the following theory: (1) Each muscle in the limb differentiates from the others not only in an anatomical sense but also in some more subtle, perhaps biochemical, sense. The nature of these specificities (x, y, z...) is not revealed by any procedures yet known; in fact the existence of them is an assumption suggested by phenomena like those described for the skin on page 381. (2) Matching specificities (x′, y′, z′) are induced in groups of neurons or perhaps individual neurons in the presumptive limb-command center in the spinal cord at brachial levels, but as an independent development. By some completely unknown process of differentiation these specified neurons develop into the distributor channels of the command center. (3) Motor neurons, which grow out in rather random fashion from the brachial spinal cord and reach and form functional contacts with the anlagen of muscles, acquire specificities like those of the particular muscles with which they form motor end plates, as though by infection. Once such a neuron has made contact with the muscle carrying specificity x, it loses the capacity to make functional synapse with any neurons in the central nervous system except the ones which have the matching specificity x'. (Nerve specifications of this sort have been discussed previously, pages 352–354). The dendrites of this neuron then explore the spinal cord refusing all synaptic contacts until they find neurons with specificities that match the one each got from its own muscle. Thus the wires get soldered to the right terminals [15].

It would be surprising indeed if this theory is not transformed out of recognition as new analytical experiments bring in new facts and new clues. The purpose of outlining it is to call attention to an unsolved problem which is basic alike to neuroanatomy, neurophysiology, and behavioral science.

REFERENCES

1. Bertin, L., 1958. *In* P. P. Grassé (ed.), *Traité de zoologie,* Tome XIII (1). Masson, Paris. Also Nursall, J. R., 1962, *Am. Zoologist* 2: 127. Origin of paired appendages in evolution.
2. Saunders, J., 1948. *J. Exptl. Zool.* 108: 363. Also Zwilling, E., 1956. *J. Exptl. Zool.* 132: 241. Also Zwilling, E., 1961. *Advances in Morphogenesis* 1: 301. Interaction of factors in limb development.
3. Balinsky, B. I., 1956. *Proc. Nat. Acad. Sci.* 42: 781.
4. Goodrich, E. S., 1930. *Studies on the structure and development of vertebrates.* Macmillan & Co., Ltd., London.
5. Gregory, W. K., 1951. *Evolution emerging.* Macmillan Co., New York.
6. Saville, D. B. O., 1962. *Am. Zoologist* 2: 161.
7. Montagna, W., 1945. *J. Morphol.* 76: 87.
8. Snyder, R. C., 1962. *Am. Zoologist,* 2: 191. Also Du Brul, E. L., 1962. *Am. Zoologist* 2: 205. Bipedal adaptations.
9. Piatt, J., 1951. *In* P. A. Weiss (ed.), *Genetic neurology.* University of Chicago Press, Chicago.
10. Piatt, J., 1952. *J. Exptl. Zool.* 120: 247. Also, 1957, *J. Exptl. Zool.* 134: 103.
11. Weiss, P. A., 1955. Neurogenesis. *In* B. H. Willier, P. A. Weiss, and V. Hamburger (eds.), *Analysis of development.* W. B. Saunders Co., Philadelphia.
12. Hamburger, V., 1952. Development of the nervous system. *Ann. N. Y. Acad. Sci.* 55: 117.
13. Weiss, P. A., 1941. *Comp. Psychol. Monographs* 17, No. 4.
14. Weiss, P. A., 1937. *J. Comp. Neurol.* 67: 269.
15. Sperry, R. W., 1951. *In* S. S. Stevens (ed.), *Handbook of experimental psychology.* John Wiley & Sons, New York.

Part VI

VISCERAL, REPRODUCTIVE, AND REGULATIVE APPARATUS

Some of the lower chordates are little worm-like or bag-shaped creatures that burrow in marine muck. They draw water into their slit pharynx cavities and feed by straining out microorganisms. It is an entertaining hypothesis, for which direct evidence is not likely to become available, that the vertebrates came from ancestors like these, their greatest evolutionary progress having been the addition of a head (described in Part IV) and a rugged locomotor body (described in Part V) to the original thin bag of digestive and reproductive viscera. In Part VI we turn at last to that inner and more ancient apparatus.

The unpaired food-processing viscera will first be described. Later come the paired viscera, those concerned with excretion and reproduction. Interspersed with these are other chapters which deal with the circulatory and regulatory apparatus of the trunk. As usual one finds that the anatomy of the adult is best understood as the product of developmental processes, and that the differences between the classes and orders of vertebrates can be interpreted as the realization of different potentialities that lie unseen in the relatively standardized structure of the pharyngula stage.

22

The Digestive Apparatus

I. EARLY ENDODERMAL DEVELOPMENTS

The endoderm, which is the rallying ground for all the tissues used in constructing the digestive apparatus, varies more in its early appearance and behavior than the other germ layers. It has already been described (page 135) how the yolk-rich endoderm cells of the amphibia, and the yolk-excluding endoderm sheets of teleosts maneuver themselves into the form of primitive gut tubes (Figs. 7–10, 8–7). In the meroblastic elasmobranchs and amniotes (Fig. 11–1), the yolk-encompassing endoderm sheets accomplish this task with much more difficulty (Fig. 22–1). As the axis of these embryos begins to lengthen and lift itself up off the yolk mass, first the anterior end and then the posterior end of the definitive gut tube are formed, and these grow toward each other, the middle of the tube being formed last.

At its anterior end, the sheet of endoderm stretches along the midline while at the same time its more lateral parts are wheeling posteromedially[1]. This changes it into a tube of tissue which has a blind end anteriorly, where the mouth opening is destined to be, and an opening posteriorly into the yolk sac (Fig. 22–1). This tubular cave is called the **foregut** and its opening into the yolk sac is called the **anterior intestinal portal.** A **hindgut** forms later by similar modelling of the endoderm sheet. It can be entered from the yolk sac through a **posterior intestinal portal,** and the cloaca will eventually form at its blind end.

The anterior and posterior intestinal portals face each other, and are brought closer and closer together as the foregut and hindgut lengthen. This completes the middle part of the gut tube, the last step being the closure of the umbilical opening to the yolk sac. By this time, the entrance to the yolk sac has been narrowed to a vitelline duct (Fig. 11–1). In these gut-forming maneuvers of the meroblastic embryos, the endoderm sheet is already closely associated with hypomeric mesoderm; the relative roles of the two components in the tissue-modelling movements have not been fully analyzed.

Experiments with the explantation of cell clumps from embryos of both amphibian and bird embryos suggest that the capacity for self-differentiation of tissues like those of the normal gut tube arise very early. These potentialities reside chiefly in the prospective endoderm areas of amphibia, but are also represented in the very wide range of capacities possessed by the prospective chorda-mesoderm cells. In the chick, they appear first in the epiblast, then in epiblast, hypoblast, and intervening primitive streak areas,

gathered through the hepatic duct system. It may be emptied into the intestine, or it may be backed up into the gallbladder and stored there until digestive reflexes call for it. The species which lack gallbladders use the duct system itself for storage of bile.

This complex fluid contains bile pigments, which are a waste substance, and bile acids which will be needed in the intestine for the emulsification of fats in preparation for their digestion.

The big polyhedral cells, besides carrying on this function with those of their surfaces that are brought together around the bile canaliculi, are engaged in many other and different activities on the rest of their surfaces which come into intimate relation with blood. The early development and the anatomy of liver veins will be considered later (page 468) in functional relationship with the digestive tract, and it is necessary here merely to mention the behavior of the capillaries which penetrate the proliferating liver mass at very early stages.

At first these venous capillaries form a rather regular three-dimensional network braiding through and among the liver plates, but then they transform into **sinusoids.** That is, they give up their tubular form and enlarge into irregular spaces that wrap over the free surfaces of the epithelial plates, molding their form to the bulging facets of the big cells. Across these blood-lined cell walls, the polyhedral cells can now receive digested food and other chemicals from the blood, and they can discharge in the opposite direction a most remarkable miscellany of their own products. They have submicroscopic enzyme-and-template factories for degrading and rebuilding the food materials brought in, and either store them in the form of glycogen (a ready source of energy) or discharge similar fuels into the blood.

Among the other substances secreted back into the blood sinusoids through the outer surfaces of the polyhedral cells, some are wastes (urea, etc.), some are hormones (heparin, etc.) and some are fuels for the rest of the body (glucose, from the splitting of the stored glycogen molecules). Research is still adding to the list of the synthetic and regulatory processes carried on by these simple-appearing but extraordinarily specialized two-faced cells.

Besides the fact that the liver in an adult vertebrate always lies just back of the heart in the body cavity, and that venous blood trickles through its sinusoids on the way from the digestive tract to the heart, there is nothing constant about the gross anatomy of the liver. The whole organ may be elongate or compact, and may be deeply cut into lobes, or hardly grooved at all. It is bound up in a peritoneal capsule, just inside which the fetus produces a certain amount of blood-corpuscle-forming tissue; this persists in adults of many anamniotes, but not in others. All the bile channels may join into a single **common bile duct** (Fig. 22–5) in some species, and the duct of the ventral pancreas may join it; or there may be separate ducts draining the right and left halves of the liver, the gallbladder usually being connected only with the right one.

2. *Pancreas.* Although recognizable pancreatic tissue can be found in all the vertebrates, formed in association with the duodenum, it does not evaginate far enough in cyclostomes and the dipnoi to free itself from the gut wall. In other groups, it buds out into the mesentery from its customary dorsal and paired ventral points of origin and spreads there in a variety of ways. Usually the dorsal and ventral pancreates join to form a single compact gland lying against the duodenum, but there are also many species in which it spreads diffusely along intestinal veins. Not uncommonly, in teleosts and some others it grows into the substance of the liver along the main branches of the hepatic portal vein, where in fact it may lie entirely concealed in gross dissection. Similarly there are species in which it invades the spleen.

As soon as a pancreatic anlage is visibly established, it begins to take shape as a branching tree of hollow tubules, the tips of whose twigs later form glandular **acini** of large clear cells, the stems forming ducts lined by pavement epithelium. The acini eventually secrete a fluid containing powerful digestive enzymes which become activated when they flow into the intestine from the ducts.

The characteristic endocrine tissue that is scattered as **pancreatic islands** through this exocrine tissue is apparently produced by groups of cells that simply withdraw from the duct system. Each island attracts to itself a slight capsule of connective tissue and a rich blood supply.

Evidence from certain favorable species suggests that the island tissue may be produced only in the dorsal rudiment of the pancreas and becomes secondarily scattered through the fused gland mass. In a few teleosts, sizeable nodules of the island tissue come to rest in nearby mesentery, separate from the rest of the pancreas. Similar "giant islands" occur at the anterior pole of the pancreas in some snakes, in contact with the spherical spleen.

Two main kinds of cells can be distinguished in the pancreatic islands, each with its quite distinct secretion. The so-called B-cells are by far the most numerous in mammals. They secrete a protein hormone called **insulin,** which regulates the uptake of glucose elsewhere in the body, and its conversion to storage or building materials. Insulin is thus vital for growth, and for making sources of energy available to muscles and other tissues. Deprivation of insulin in a disease called diabetes, or after surgical removal of the pancreas, or by specific poisoning of its B-cells with alloxan, leads to wastage of carbohydrate reserves through the urine, bringing on shock and death.

A-cells, which are not very numerous in mammals but are the principal element in many of the pancreatic islands of birds and reptiles, are apparently the source of another substance called **glucagon.** Though quite different from insulin chemically, glucagon is associated with insulin in a variety of metabolic disorders, and is potent in causing the liver to reduce glycogen to glucose. Its normal general role is not yet clear [5].

Much of the variation in pancreatic ducts which is found among the vertebrates is explained by developmental studies. Three ducts may be present in one pancreas, representing the three primary anlagen; or variable combinations and reductions may be found. Where only one duct persists, it may be either the dorsal or a ventral one, according to the species. Usually two of them persist, one entering the duodenum on its ventral side in association with the common bile duct or actually sharing an opening with it, and the other entering dorsally at a little distance. In a species showing this condition (man for instance, Fig. 22–9), individual variations exist in the proportions of the whole gland drained by the two ducts. One might guess that each anlage competes with the others to produce the most pancreatic tissue until the body

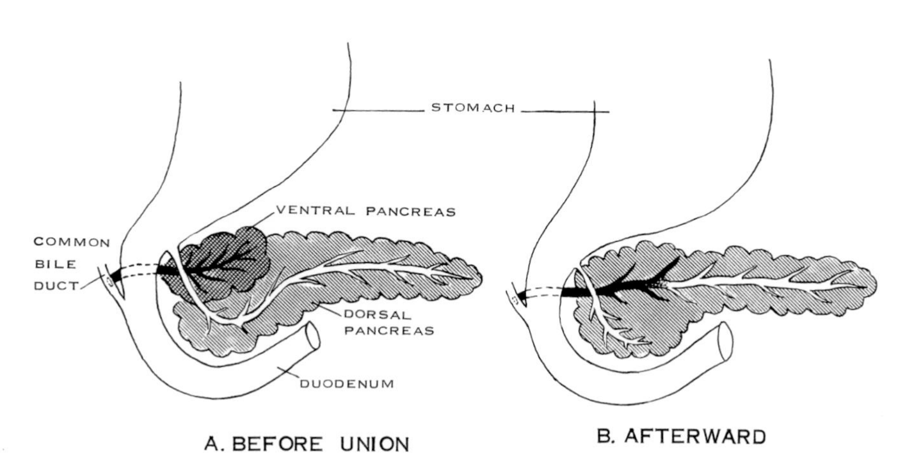

Fig. 22–9. Union of two pancreates, and transformation of their ducts, in man.
(After I. Broman, 1937, in Handbuch der Vergleichenden Anatomie der Wirbeltiere, by permission of Urban u. Schwarzenberg.)

has enough of it and the race is called off. But the control mechanisms are completely unknown (pages 184–187).

In rare species more than three ducts are found entering the duodenum from the pancreas. This may happen because the base of a branching duct system has been absorbed into the wall of the gut, up to or beyond the first branchings. Or it may be due to the formation of accessory pancreas anlagen. Small nodules of pancreatic tissue are occasionally found scattered along the intestine.

E. Post-Hepatic Parts

By the time food has been moved as far down the gut as the entrances of the liver and pancreas ducts, it may be assumed that it has been reduced to very tiny particles and a soupy condition, either by mechanical devices (teeth, pharyngeal mills, gizzards, etc.) or by chemical action (HCl secreted by stomach glands, and enzymes carried in the juices from salivary, esophageal, and stomach glands). The smaller the particle size, the greater its surface/volume ratio, and the faster the enzymes can work upon it.

Beyond the liver, the food is further macerated by enzymatic destruction of its binding tissues, and the emulsification of its fats by bile. Three important tasks remain to be carried out on it: (a) enzymatic splitting into molecules that can be later taken across living cells and put into the circulatory system; (b) the transfer process itself, which might be called absorption; and (c) the dehydration, storage, and elimination of the unused material, as feces. Each of these tasks is in charge of its own specialized cells, which are chiefly epithelial, so that a comparative survey of the post-hepatic digestive tract becomes principally a study in the arrangement of epithelia. The submucous, muscular and serosal layers of the standard gut transverse section (Fig. 4–17) are modified in these parts of the body to suit the local adaptations of the epithelia. The sizes, coilings, and corrugations of the parts are also in the service of the digestive, absorptive, and storage functions.

Three ways are available for increasing the epithelial surfaces of the post-hepatic gut so that they can keep pace with the requirements of the whole animal: lengthening the tube itself, sending invaginations into the submucosa from its endodermal lining, or folding the mucosa the other way, out into the gut cavity.

The whole alimentary canal is short and straight at the pharyngula stage. While there are some vertebrates which have uncomplicated straight guts as adults (cyclostomes, holocephals, dipnoi, a few teleosts, a few eel-like amphibia, snakes), the vast majority of species grow intestines from two to thirty times as long as the body. Most of this is accomplished during the fetal stages, but in some amphibia and teleosts the character of the diet has some effect on the degree of lengthening in later life.

If the intestine is to be contained within the body cavity, it must coil as it lengthens. At early stages the pattern of coiling is not random but predictable according to the species. In the amblystoma and many others, the first bend, a prehepatic one, clockwise in ventral view, swings from the stomach to the left. It is the duodenal section of the intestine which crosses the midline. Beyond the entrance of the ducts of the great glands the intestine makes the second bend, counter-clockwise. A third bend, this time clockwise, returns it to the midline near the cloaca. To the second and third of these primary coils there are freely added a number of secondary coils so that a great deal of variety is produced in later development.

The lengthening and bending of the gut takes place in amniotes while the umbilical passage to the yolk sac is still wide open. This provides a temporary escape for the skein of intestine from the confines of the coelom, and incidentally demonstrates that its contortion is not caused by the lack of stretching-room. The extruded coil of intestine, with its dwindling connection to the yolk sac, is gradually pulled back into the abdominal cavity as belly proportions change, and this normal **umbilical hernia** is normally closed and healed before birth or hatching. Delay of the process, however, produces a quite common birth defect.

While all this lengthening of the gut automatically increases the amount of epithelial surface for enzyme secretion, absorption and storage, it is greatly augmented in birds, mammals, and some reptiles and teleosts, by sharply localized invaginations and evaginations of the surface, particularly at duodenal levels. Crypts and tubular glands sprout away from the lining of the central cavity in huge numbers. They fail to continue growth to the point of forming bulky glandular masses like the pancreas, yet in the aggregate they secrete an even greater volume of digestive juice than it does. This is strongly alkaline and contains enzymes which, like those of the pancreatic juice, act specifically on proteins, carbohydrates, or fats, breaking them into their basic constituents, the smaller sugar, amino-acid, or fatty-acid molecules. The corrosive intestinal fluid is called forth by nervous reflexes in the course of digestion. A still inadequately answered question is how the mucous membrane which lines the living gut resists the potent digestive action of the fluid with which it is periodically flooded.

Another very common device for increasing the secretory, or particularly the absorptive, surface of the gut cavity is the formation of minute finger-like or leaflike projections from the mucous membrane into the central gut tube. Such **villi** are produced by all vertebrates, whether their intestines are straight and short or long and coiled. The villi are not stretched out of existence when the tube is bulged with food, which distinguishes them from the temporary ridges found in the esophagus, the stomach and other parts of the intestine in various species, and which are themselves covered by multitudes of villi.

There is still another device for increasing internal surface which is less common but sometimes spectacular. In the posterior part of the intestine of mammals and some large lizards, permanent folds of the mucous membrane, called **plicae**, project into the food canal. They are covered with villi and are commonly arranged in semicircular fashion, but they may link up in long spirally arranged folds. Thus, the greatly elongated cecum of many rodents contains a spiral fold which may take a number of turns around its length (23–25 in some rabbits). The ostrich has two ceca of unusual length, each containing spiral folds that take up to 30 turns.

It is in the intestines of fishes that the device of spiral folds reaches its greatest development. A fold of mucous membrane projects into the cavity of the straight intestine of an adult lamprey, its line of attachment marking a spiral of

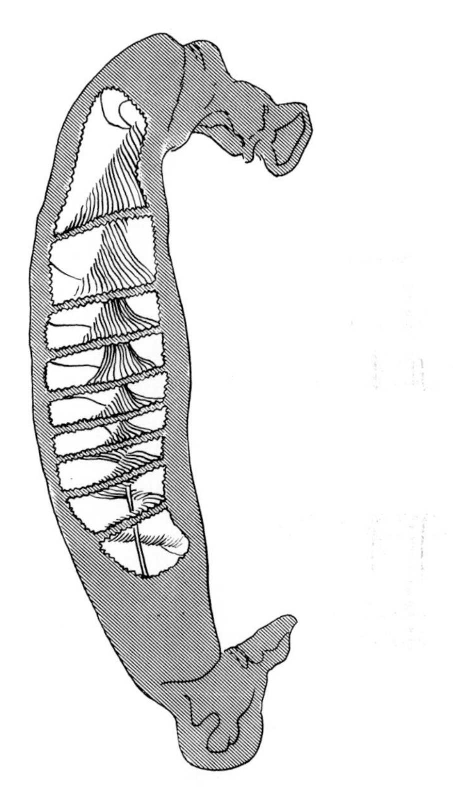

Fig. 22–10. Spiral valve in a skate intestine. (After P. Mayer, 1897.)

several complete turns. In holocephals, elasmobranchs, dipnoi, *Polypterus, Latimeria,* chondrostei, and holostei, part of the intestine is given over to a similar but usually more elaborate **spiral valve.** In the elasmobranchs (Fig. 22–10) the number of turns taken by the spiral is usually 10 or more and in certain species may be as high as 50; in other fish groups it ranges from 2 to 8.

The spiraled line of attachment of the mucous membrane fold is not achieved, as some have thought, by a twisting of the inner lining of the gut during development. It remains attached at both ends at all times, and there is no counter-coiling. The distribution of arteries and nerves within the intestine leaves no record of any such twisting; instead, these vessels wrap symmetrically around the right and left sides of the intestine from the dorsal mesentery. Models of stages in the development of the intestine show a growth zone in the form of a spiral line appearing first as a flange at the posterior end for a time not reaching beyond the middle. It pushes farther and farther forward through the prospective valvular intestine, adding more coils to the fold, but coincidentally the earlier coils are being packed down closer to each other in the posterior part. In other words, there is a spirally spreading zone of growth, but no significant spiralling movement of the established mucous membrane.

In one family of sharks there is a departure from this pattern to the extent that the line of attachment of the epithelial flange does not describe a spiral inside the intestine but zigzags back and forth, never making more than three-fourths of a turn before reversing itself. When the flange is fully grown it is narrow at both ends but in the middle it may be half as wide, or fully as wide as it is long. In the circumscribed intestinal cavity it must therefore wrap itself into a scroll. Both the scroll fold and the much more common spiral fold of mucous membrane are spoken of as **valves.** They greatly increase the surface with which the food is brought into contact and through which it is absorbed. The **valvular intestine** is usually preceded by a duodenal section for rapid digestion, and succeeded by a short and uncomplicated rectum for storage of feces.

In the tetrapods, a more or less distinct transition takes place between an intestinal section showing the secretory epithelium of a digestive organ, and a more posterior section which acts as a temporary storage space for feces and carries on further absorptive activity, but has a less glandular mucous membrane. In mammals the two sections are properly named the small intestine and the large intestine. Any butcher would notice the transition between them, which is very sudden (Fig. 22–5). The place where the small intestine empties into the large is almost always marked by a constricted valve and the development of a blind pouch or **cecum.** The latter may be rudimentary (cats, Fig. 22–5) or enormous (rabbits); and in man and a scattering few other mammals it terminates in an **appendix** (Fig. 22–7), normally on the right side.

In mammals, the whole large intestine is used for the consolidation of feces, and a terminal section, usually with undefined anterior limit, is called the **rectum.** In amphibia there is also a special terminal section of the general intestine, clearly set off for this function. It is not possible to make specific homologies of the various sections of the intestine, for instance between the elasmobranch valvular intestine and either the small or the large intestine of mammals, or between the amphibian rectum and either the whole mammalian large intestine or the rectal part of it. Storage of feces is a function which is commonly restricted to the cloaca in reptiles and birds.

In birds and some lizards and turtles, one or two ceca may be formed near the posterior end of the intestine. The avian **cloacal bursa** is known as a site of origin, in common with the thymus (page 327) of the cells which produce antibodies in immunity reactions (cf. page 529). A **digital gland** always projects upward into the dorsal mesentery above the rectum of elasmobranchs, and is reported to be a device for excreting excess salt [6]. Rodents have a huge **cecum** growing out from their large intestine, which is known to be used as a site for prolonged bacterial digestion of plant food.

F. Veins of the Intestine and Liver

The blood that has been through capillaries in most organs is taken by veins directly to the heart. Not so the blood from the digestive organs. In all adult vertebrates without significant exception, veins first take it to the liver, where it is trickled through the sinusoid network in close contact with the big polyhedral cells before being delivered to the heart. The veins that collect from the gut capillaries and deliver it to the sinusoids constitute the **hepatic portal vein system; hepatic veins** in turn drain the sinusoids and deliver their blood to the heart.

This almost invariable arrangement, curiously enough, arises in quite different ways in the different classes of vertebrates. To understand why this must be so, one must remember the following contrasts: (a) the tailbud has an early and massive development with a strong blood supply in anamniotes, but remains relatively insignificant in amniotes; (b) the amniotes have fetal membranes which acquire a vigorous blood flow at an extremely early stage, and these are totally unrepresented in anamniotes; (c) blood flow is from yolk to liver to heart in most vertebrates, but from liver to yolk to heart in most teleosts. The result of these contrasts is that quite different veins come into functional relationships with the embryonic liver in the different classes. Nevertheless, these relationships (and other experimentally produced ones) always have equivalent results: any vein that touches the early liver anlage grows in amongst the liver plates and ravels into a network of sinusoids. Arteries are not affected this way, nor is the postcaval vein at a much later stage.

Vitelline veins are present in all vertebrate embryos, and are prominent in all except the practically yolkless mammals. They are the first veins to form, and they usually carry the first blood corpuscles toward the heart. Later, they deliver the yolk-derived food into the rest of the circulation. In all but the teleosts, it is their path which is first encroached upon by the bulging early liver anlage, and it is they which are first induced to send a mesh of capillaries (later sinusoids) through its mesenchymal matrix. In fact, each

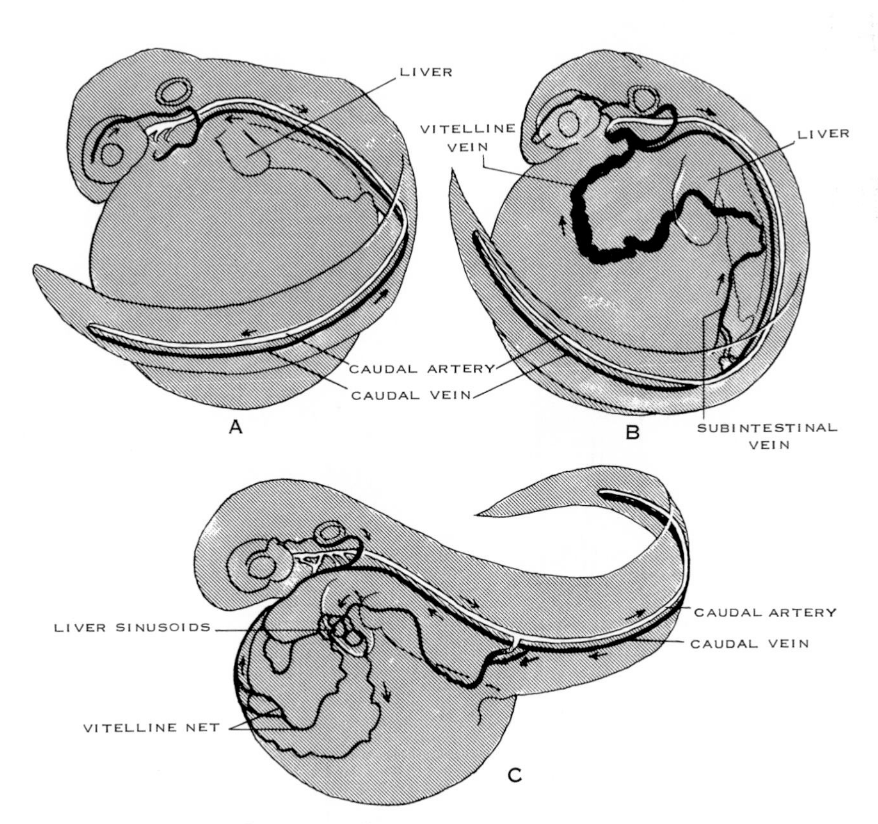

Fig. 22–11. Development of veins in young teleost embryos (*Cottus*).
(After G. Portmann, 1927.)

vitelline vein (except in the teleosts) is thereby separated into a posterior part that ends in the liver, and an anterior part leading from the liver to the heart.

In anamniote embryos with their relatively massive tails, the dorsal aorta continues with only gradual diminution to the very end of the body. Its posterior section is renamed the caudal artery, and it delivers a substantial volume of blood through segmental branches to the caudal myotomes. This blood is brought back by a **caudal vein** through the hemal canals of the caudal vertebrae, and continues by way of a **subintestinal vein,** or a pair of them, through the body cavity anterior to the cloaca (Fig. 22–11).

In many teleost fishes, the liver anlage grows down from the little tubular intestine directly into the path of this subintestinal flow, with the prompt result that the latter is forced to detour into the liver and through a sinusoidal network. Collected again beyond the liver, the blood is separated from the heart by the bulging yolk sac, over which it then travels in an expanding braided system of vitelline veins, which eventually recombine and flow into the heart.

In the rest of the anamniotes the subintestinal veins, continuing forward from the cloaca level toward the heart, make themselves tributaries of the vitelline veins (Fig. 22–12 B), which then empty into the liver sinusoids. Later the subintestinals are more or less cut off from the caudal veins (Fig. 22–12 C), which find more direct paths to the heart through posterior cardinal veins. After this, the subintestinal veins persist as tributaries of the vitelline veins, which drain away the blood that the intestine has received from the dorsal aorta, carrying it to the liver.

In the amniotes, the intestine is for a long time wide open to the yolk sac, and the tail is a relatively late and feeble development (Fig. 11–3). A subintestinal vein is never a significant factor, and may not form at all. The vitelline veins, which find their direct path to the heart around the sides of the anterior intestinal portal, are soon interrupted by the liver, and their post-hepatic parts send their own tributaries back into the intestinal walls as these are gathered together from the endoderm sheet.

At this stage in the formation of the hepatic portal system the sequence of blood flow in the

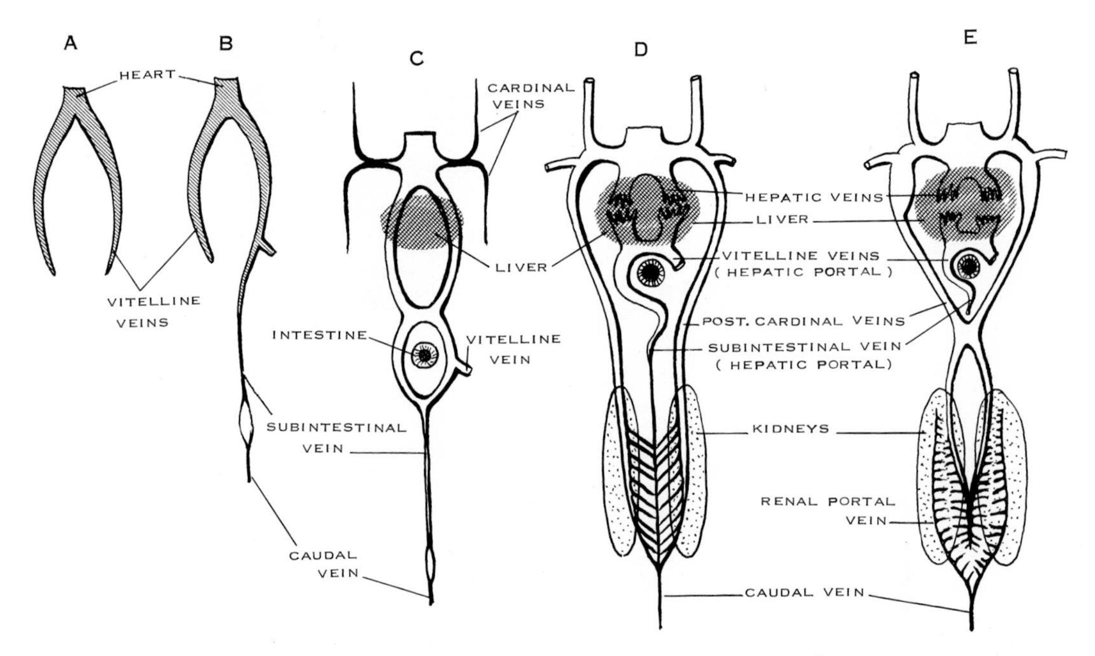

Fig. 22–12. Development of trunk veins in sharks.
(After F. Hochstetter, 1906.)

embryos of a shark, an amniote, and a teleost would be approximately as follows:

Shark (Fig. 22–12 D)	*Amniote*	*Teleost* (Fig. 22–11 C)
Gut capillaries	Gut capillaries	Gut capillaries
Subintestinal vein		Subintestinal vein
Vitelline vein (toward liver)	Vitelline vein (toward liver)	Liver sinusoids
Liver sinusoids	Liver sinusoids	Vitelline network (toward yolk)
Vitelline (hepatic) veins (away from liver)	Vitelline (hepatic) veins (away from liver)	Vitelline veins (away from yolk)
Heart	Heart	Heart

These differences are striking in the embryo but they are temporary. With the disappearance of the yolk, the sequence in all vertebrates becomes:

Gut capillaries
Hepatic portal vein system
Liver sinusoids
Hepatic veins
Heart

Other temporary complications are added in the amniotes, for in them a relatively huge amount of blood is circulated through the allantois and/or the placenta during late embryonic

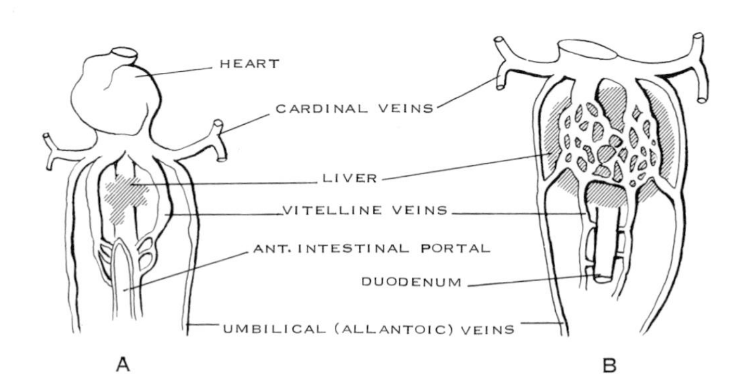

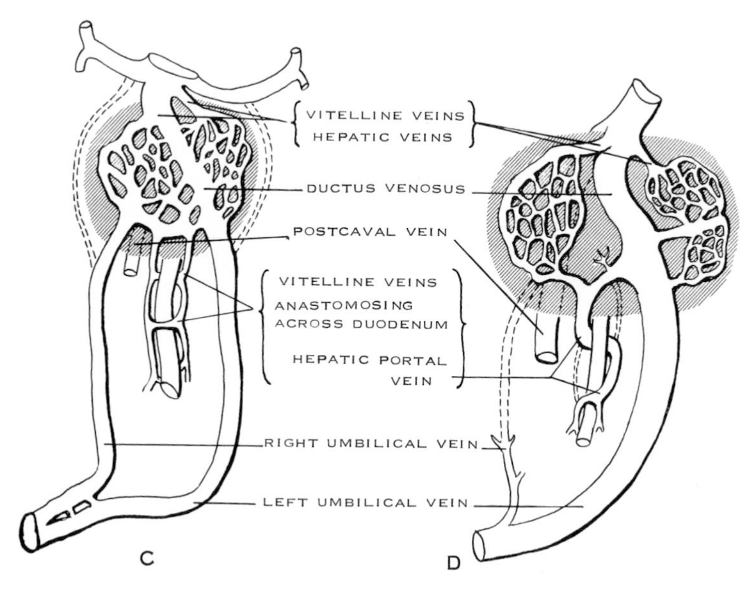

Fig. 22–13. Development of mammalian veins related to the liver.
(Redrawn from B. M. Patten, Human Embryology, 1946, by permission of McGraw-Hill Book Co., Inc.)

and fetal stages, to be returned through the umbilicus and the somatopleure to the heart (Figs. 11–3, 22–13). When the liver has grown to the size that crowds it against these more laterally placed veins, they yield to its influence as the vitellines did before them, and lose much or all of their blood into the sinusoids. But when the current of blood running through the liver becomes too strong, a sizeable direct path called the **ductus venosus** is opened through it to the hepatic vein. When the allantoic or umbilical veins finally dry up at birth or hatching, the ductus venosus collapses and is converted into a strand of connective tissue that may remain in the adult liver throughout life.

From the foregoing account, it may be seen that most of the teleostean hepatic portal vein system is derived from the subintestinal veins; in other anamniotes the parts near the liver are derived from the vitelline veins and the more posterior branches from the subintestinals; and in amniotes nearly the whole is derived from the vitelline veins.

Usually in adult vertebrates the blood of the hepatic portal vein system enters the liver through a single trunk, though branches may be given off into the liver substance almost immediately after the last tributary has been received, or even before. In a good many teleosts and birds there are two hepatic portal veins, since the part of the system draining the stomach fails to meet the part draining the main intestine. In a few teleosts there may be several veins entering separately.

The hepatic portal vein system primarily drains the digestive tract, but as a matter of convenience it also drains the spleen which has nothing to do with digestion (cf. Chapter 26). In the tetrapods, venous anastomoses commonly occur in the pelvic region between the somatic and visceral systems, so that some blood may be drawn into the hepatic portal drainage from the hindlimbs and tail. Much of the blood from the hindlegs in amphibia and reptiles finds its way direct to the liver through **abdominal veins.** In equally illogical fashion, blood from the heart muscle flows into the hepatic portal system in frogs and crocodiles, and blood from intercostal veins in lizards. The most aberrant hepatic portal system is found in hagfishes, where the persistent subintestinal vein bypasses the liver and empties into the heart, while the principal head vein of the right side develops a pulsating heartlike structure and empties into the hepatic portal vein along with a supraintestinal vein. The embryonic development of this radical arrangement is unknown.

The liver of the amniotes seems to lose its curious effect on nearby veins after it has had its way with the allantoic or umbilical veins. In mid-fetal stages (Fig. 22–13 C, D) a new centralized somatic vein is assembled alongside the dorsal aorta in the abdominal cavity, to take over the drainage of substantial portions of the flanks, paired viscera, hindlimbs, etc. It is called the **postcaval vein** (cf. page 552). It empties into the hepatic vein at the anterior end of the peritoneal cavity, and becomes gradually enveloped by the spreading mass of the liver; yet it never forms sinusoids and it remains quite independent of the hepatic portal vein. This also occurs in dipnoi, *Latimeria*, and amphibia.

REFERENCES

1. Bellairs, R., 1953. *J. Embryol. Exptl. Morphol.* 1: 369.
2. Kemp, N. E., 1951. *J. Exptl. Zool.* 116: 259.
3. Copenhaver, W. M., 1955. *In* B. H. Willier, P. A. Weiss, and V. Hamburger (eds.), *Analysis of development.* W. B. Saunders Co., Philadelphia.
4. Elias, H., 1955. *Anat. Anz.* 101: 153.
5. Turner, C. D., 1960. *General endocrinology.* 3d ed. W. B. Saunders Co., Philadelphia.
6. Burger, J. W., and W. M. Hess, 1959. *Science* 131: 670.

23

Gas Bladders and Lungs

I. GENERAL CONSIDERATIONS

Practically all the living vertebrates have gas-filled organs lying among their trunk viscera. A scattering of teleosts and one family of urodele amphibians do not, but they presumably came from ancestors that did. The modern cyclostomes, and elasmobranchs and holocephals, also lack gas chambers, and the fossil record is not adequate to decide whether these are also cases of evolutionary simplification, or whether they came from lines that never had any.

There are two main types of gas organs: the lungs of tetrapods and the gas bladders of bony fishes. These both arise as outpouchings of the embryonic foregut and receive branches from the vagus nerves, but beyond that they are so strongly contrasted in most anatomical details that they must be described separately. The few surviving fishes that have genuine functional lungs (the dipnoi and polypterini) are probably not closely related to the first tetrapods but they come from extremely ancient stocks. For this reason, and also because certain aspects of the anatomy of gas bladders of those other "living fossil" fishes, the chondrostei and the holostei, are uncommonly reminiscent of lungs, the guess is hazarded by some paleontologists that lungs evolved earlier than gas bladders. Some antiarchs of the Devonian era, which were placoderm fishes more primitive than any surviving gnathostomes, had paired sacs like lungs, opening into the pharynx [1]. Though fossil evidence is lacking, there is little reason to doubt that, whichever flowered first, lungs and gas bladders had a common origin.

The following table summarizes the distinctions between representative lungs and representative gas bladders:

	Lungs	*Gas Bladders*
Chief function	Respiratory	Hydrostatic
Time of origin	Early pharyngula	Late pharyngula
Manner of origin	Paired ventral out-pouchings	Unpaired dorsal out-pouchings
Level of origin	Posterior pharynx	Esophagus or stomach
Arteries	From VI aortic arch	From dorsal aorta and coeliac artery
Veins	To right atrium (pulmonary veins)	To hepatic portal or postcardinal veins
Air duct	Persistent, with special laryngeal structures	Usually obliterated; if present, unadorned
Present in	Polypterini, dipnoi, tetrapods	Chondrostei, holostei, teleostei

Exceptional *intergrading structures* are found in a few species, softening most of the distinctions that are shown in the above table. (a) Functionally, for instance, the lungs of urodeles are hydrostatic like gas bladders, and of little respiratory use. The gas bladders of holostei and a very few teleosts are respiratory, like lungs. The air cell structure on the inside of the true lung of the dipnoan *Lepidosiren* is precisely like that of the gas bladders of living holostei, or of the archaic teleost *Gymnarchus*.

(b) Lungs are not always clearly paired in origin, while the gas bladder of the sturgeon (chondrostei) is described as arising from the coalescence of paired rudiments. The distinction between dorsal and ventral origins generally applies, but some lungs arise off center, and so do some gas bladders. The morphologic importance of these points may be challenged anyhow, since the liver may arise as a paired organ in some forms, apparently unpaired in others, and the pancreas is a pancreas in spite of the fact that it usually arises from separate dorsal and ventral rudiments. The gas bladder's level of origin is subject to variation and sometimes it comes from the pharynx, or very close to it.

(c) Two fishes are known, the holostean *Amia* and the teleost *Gymnarchus*, whose gas bladders get blood from gill arches, i.e., by pulmonary arteries.

(d) The air ducts of the *Polypterus* lungs are not provided with special glottis structures, and on the other hand the gas bladder of the holostean *Lepidosteus* has a primitive "dorsal larynx" developed in relation to its "glottis."

(e) *Latimeria*, the newly discovered coelacanth fish, has a large abdominal structure which is single like a gas bladder but arises ventrally from the alimentary canal like a lung; it has degenerated to a thick sac of fat.

II. GAS BLADDERS

A. Development

The first indication of the embryonic gas bladder in the holosts and chondrosts is an elongated ridge, which pinches off from the dorsal side of the esophagus, leaving a duct opening close to the pharynx. In the other bony fishes, the more usual opening is to the esophagus or the stomach (Fig. 22–3 C). The bladder itself lies at first in the dorsal mesentery, but as it gets larger it is incorporated into the body wall, the entire coelom and gut lying ventral to it. The dorsal aorta, the kidneys, and the vertebral column lie just above it.

Practically all the teleosts which have been studied as embryos develop a rudiment of a gas bladder, but a good many bottom-living species have lost all trace of it in the adult condition. Their way of life does not require a hydrostatic organ. This ecological correlation is not a strict one: some bottom fishes have elaborate gas bladders used for non-hydrostatic purposes; many groups of deep-sea fish lack the bladder, but not all; and there are a few cases of surface-roving teleosts that get along without one.

The gas bladder duct remains primitively short and wide in holosts and chondrosts, but in teleosts it generally becomes long and narrow, dwindles to a thread, and may disappear altogether. Loss of the duct is very common in the groups of advanced spiny-rayed teleosts. Retention or loss of the duct of the gas bladder was once thought to be a useful criterion for separating two great groups of teleosts, called respectively the Physostomi and Physoclisti. However, there are too many exceptional cases: many physoclist species turn up in what would otherwise be clear-cut families and even genera of physostome fishes. No doubt, loss of the duct has occurred independently in a number of evolutionary lines.

There are small simple gas bladders and large complex ones, in great variety. As the pouch-like anlage expands from the esophagus it may form a straight sac (Fig. 23–1 A) or branch T-wise into anterior and posterior lobes (Fig. 22–3 C) or bend sharply forward. The duct may open into it in these various cases at its anterior or posterior end, or in the middle. Continued expansion may carry the sac beyond the limits of the coelom. The gas bladder of the Atlantic herring extends into the skull and comes into intimate contact with the ears, and at a late post-larval stage it

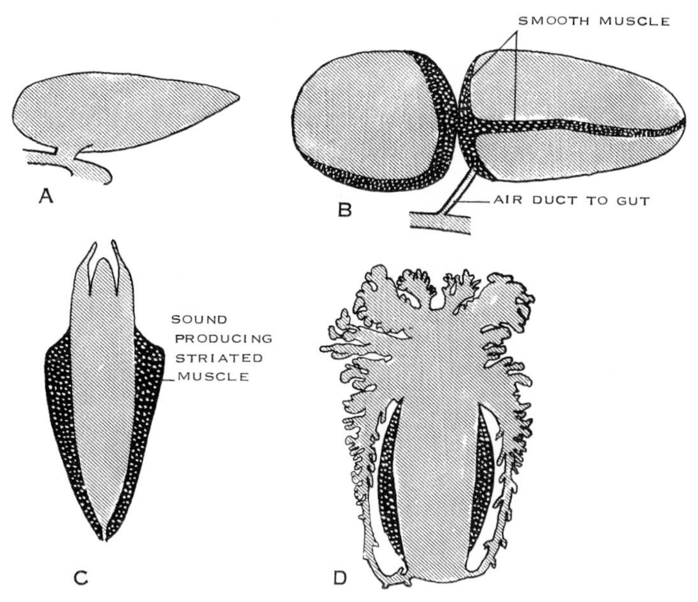

Fig. 23–1. Gas bladders of some bony fishes. A. Sturgeon (*Acipenser*). B. Carp (*Cyprinus*). C. Squeteague (*Cynoscion*). D. Sea drum (*Pogonias*).
(After L. Bertin, 1958, in Traité de Zoologie, by permission of Masson et Cie.)

also develops an opening to the outside behind the anus. In many species the bladder becomes constricted by a waist into anterior and posterior chambers which serve different functions. Arms, bizzarre lobes, and frills may grow out from it (Fig. 23–1 C, D). The coelomic lining may contribute a coating of smooth muscle to the gas bladder, but striated muscles from the trunk may also insert upon it, or bands or caps of muscle be superimposed.

B. Functional Specializations

1. Hydrostatic Gas Bladders. If a fish has the ability to adjust its specific gravity to equal that of the surrounding water it can float with minimum effort at a desired depth. The gas bladder commonly serves this hydrostatic function, like the float of a bathyscaph. In the simplest cases, air is gulped in at the surface and swallowed into the bladder. Newly hatched fish larvae, even of species which eventually lose the duct, do this. The practice continues in the adults of some groups, such as cyprinids and salmonids. Usually, however, the duct only functions as a safety valve for gas escape, and the gas is secreted into the bladder by a special gland, which takes it from the blood.

In the predominantly hydrostatic gas bladders of the spiny-rayed teleosts and others, structure is relatively uniform. There are anterior and posterior chambers or areas, the former gas-producing and the latter gas-absorbing. The posterior one may be either large and set apart by a constricted waist, or a small flattened "oval" which can be closed off by means of a diaphragm containing radial and circular smooth muscle (Fig. 23–2). In other cases, no waist or diaphragm is present but the gas-absorbing chamber is distinguishable by its thin wall and simple epithelium. It is richly supplied with capillaries.

The gas-secreting organ usually consists of a glandular epithelium which has one face toward the cavity of the bladder and the other in contact with a remarkably organized double **rete mirabile** (cf. page 532) of alternately spaced arteries and veins. In the common eel (Fig. 23–3), a branch of the coeliac artery which approaches this tissue breaks up into many thousands of parallel branches which assemble again

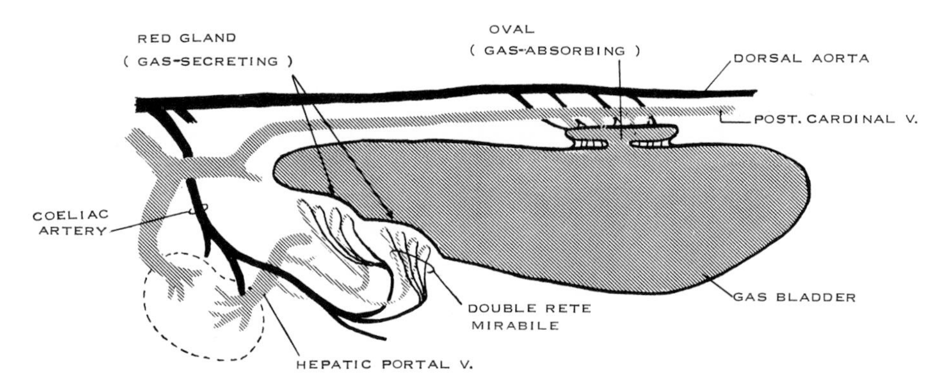

Fig. 23–2. Diagram of a hydrostatic gas bladder.
(After E. S. Goodrich, Studies on the Structure and Development of the Vertebrates, 1930, by permission of Macmillan & Co., Ltd., London.)

into one artery before distributing to the capillaries of the glandular epithelium. The veins draining the epithelium likewise break up into thousands of parallel branches which alternate geometrically in ranks and files with those of the arteries, before assembling again into veins that enter the hepatic portal system. The combination of the double rete mirabile and the glandular epithelium is called the red body or the **red gland.**

Many variations of this red-gland structure are found. It may be scattered or condensed. It usually has an anterior and ventral location (Fig. 23–2). The epithelium may be smooth, or thickened and fissured, or penetrated by crypts. There is no red gland at all in salmonids, many clupeiformes etc.; in other fishes (*Fundulus, Hippocampus*) it may cover the whole anterior surface of the bladder.

There is no doubt that these organs can secrete and absorb gases, for when the gas bladders are emptied they fill up again quickly, even in the absence of a duct. Shortly after experimental emptying, the refilled gas bladders of some fishes have been found to contain mostly carbon dioxide, but somewhat later they have a preponderance of oxygen. The closed bladders of deep-water fish commonly contain partial pressures of these gases and nitrogen which are many times greater than what is found either in their blood or in the surrounding water, which clearly shows that they must have been actively secreted against strong diffusion gradients [2].

The formation of new gas in the bladder is the function of the red gland, as indicated by excision experiments. How it happens is another question. Gas bubbles are not formed in the cells of the glandular epithelium. The mechanisms are probably different for each kind of gas.

Where the two ends of the gas bladder serve their separate functions of gas secreting and gas absorbing, they have different relations to the circulatory and nervous systems. The anterior gas-secreting part is supplied from the coeliac artery and drained to the hepatic portal vein. The posterior gas-absorbing part is supplied by local branches of the dorsal aorta and is drained by tributaries of the posterior cardinal veins (Fig. 23–2). Branches of the vagus nerve are traceable to the red gland, and nerve fibers from local motor ganglia of the sympathetic system reach the bladder from dorsally and posteriorly.

The gas volume in the bladder, and hence the specific gravity of the fish, is under nervous control through the vagus. Secretion of gas into the bladder may be induced by withdrawing some of it by hypodermic syringe, or by hanging weights on the free-swimming fish. When the gas bladder is emptied and the fish is supported at the surface of the water or forced to swim downward, the gas is restored more slowly, and if the fish has to swim upward the gas is restored faster than in free-swimming controls, with the outside pressure constant [3].

2. *Noise-Producing Gas Bladders.* The vocal aspects of fish life are only beginning to be studied, but it is known that many teleosts make purring, grunting, bumping, or rattling noises. Certain species are known to call and answer each other [4]. The "voice" may be produced by a

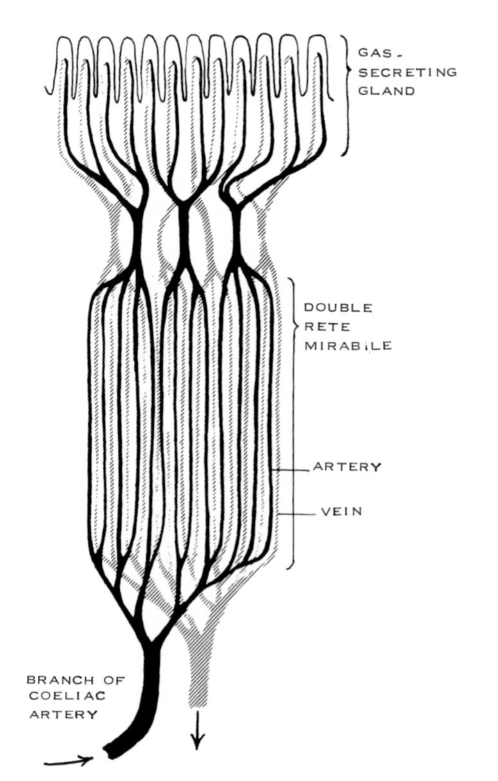

Fig. 23–3. Components of the red body in the gas bladder of an eel.
(After W. N. F. Woodland, 1911.)

stridulating of one shoulder girdle bone on another, resonated by the gas bladder, as in the triggerfish *Balistes,* but usually the noise originates in the gas bladder itself. Many catfishes can make sounds by vibrating certain strong striated muscles which take origin from the skull and insert on the anterior end of the bladder.

In a more complex version of this arrangement, the transverse processes of the 4th vertebrae are flared out into elastic springs which rest on the anterior pole of the bladder. The skull muscles insert on the bony springs, and can set up vibrations in them which are transmitted directly to the contained gas.

The sciaenid fishes, which are locally called "drums," "croakers," etc., get their names from the sound produced by heavy bands of striated muscle laid lengthwise on the gas bladder (Fig. 23–1 C). Some of these noise-making bladders are fitted with perforated internal diaphragms which can be set in motion like vocal cords, by the forcing of air from one chamber to another.

3. *Associations Between Gas Bladders and Ears.* In two very different ways, separate groups of teleosts have achieved connections which probably allow the ears to register pressures and audible vibrations from the outside through the gas bladder.

One pattern has the gas bladder sending out long anterior diverticula, which penetrate the skull and lie close to or actually in contact with the membranous parts of the ear. Variations on this pattern are found in many, but by no means all members of the most primitive group of teleosts, the Malacopterygii or Clupeiformes. Other variations are found in at least three isolated groups of physoclists: the Berycidae, the Sparidae (scup), and Gadidae (cod). Closely related genera of these groups may show varied stages of forward growth, skull penetration and contact with the ears and it is hard to believe that any but the completed-contact stages actually acquire the special functions under discussion.

In clupeids (herring, shad, sardine, menhaden) the apparatus is perfected; the cranial extensions of the bladder end in little ampullae that grasp both the sacculus and the utriculus of each ear (Fig. 23–4).

In the other pattern, a chain of specially contrived bones ("Weberian ossicles") on each side bridges the long gap between the gas bladder and the ear. It is developed rather uniformly in the four great orders of Ostariophysi: the Eventognathi (the cyprinoids: carp, suckers and dace), the Heterognathi (characins), the Nematognathi (the siluroids: catfishes), and the gymnotids (electric eel) (Fig. 23–5).

The apparatus involves four elements: the gas

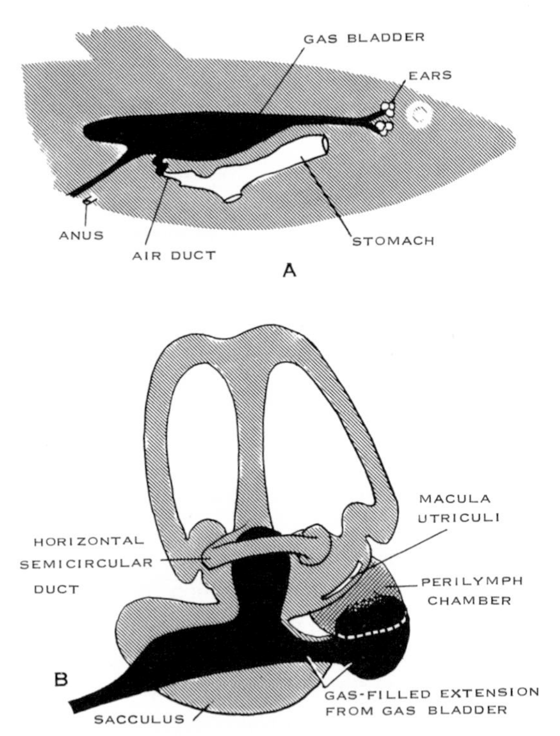

Fig. 23–4. Relations of the gas bladder to the ears in a herring (*Clupea*). A. Full extent of gas bladder. B. Detail of relationship to right ear.

(After H. M. de Burlet, 1934, in Handbuch de Vergleichenden Anatomie der Wirbeltiere, by permission of Urban u. Schwarzenberg.)

bladder itself, a group of anterior vertebrae, a single forked perilymph chamber that communicates with both ears, and a chain of three or four ossicles on each side connecting the forks of this chamber with the bladder. The relations with the ear were mentioned earlier (page 268).

The gas bladder itself is usually divided into an anterior and a posterior chamber by a waist or by an internal diaphragm, but these do not correspond to those of the primarily hydrostatic physoclist bladder, since the red gland, when present, is confined to the posterior chamber. The connective tissue wall of the anterior chamber either remains a tough membrane or becomes bony by the spread of ossification from the transverse processes of the vertebrae that grasp it from above. In catfishes, the posterior chamber is suppressed, and the anterior chamber pinches partly or quite into two lateral lobes which may come into close contact with the skin back of the shoulder on the right and left sides, forming what are known as "tympani" from their resemblance to eardrums. A similar contact is made in a few bottom-dwelling cyprinids through the in-pouching of lateral skin sacs.

The front part of the vertebral column is stiffened by the fusion of several vertebrae, which send rib processes out to grasp the dorsal surface

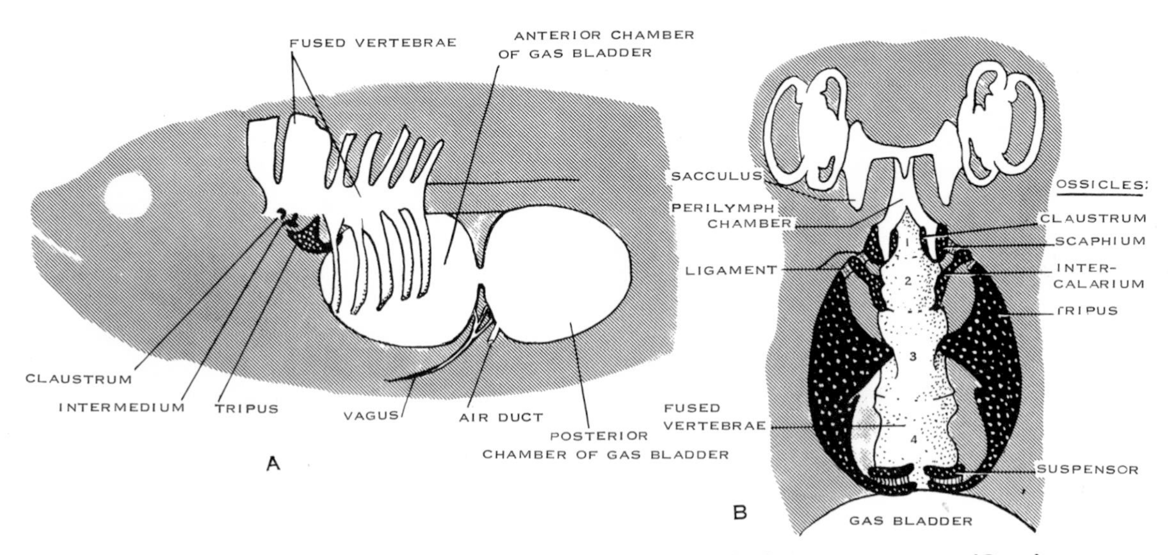

Fig. 23–5. Ossicles connecting the gas bladder with the ears in a carp (*Cyprinus*). A. Dissection from left side. B. Diagram, dorsal view.

(A after Evans, 1925. B after N. S. Chranilov, 1927.)

of the gas bladder. The considerable gap between the gas bladder and the ear on each side is bridged by a chain of "Weberian ossicles," mostly formed from parts of the first several embryonic vertebra rudiments. The little **claustrum** (when present) forms a medial wall for the backward-projecting fork of the membranous perilymph chamber. The lateral wall of the membranous fork is in contact with a little cap of bone called the **scaphium,** alongside the remains of the first vertebra. Much the largest of the ossicles is a crescentic piece called the **tripus** because of its three prongs. The anterior prong is attached by a ligament to the scaphium, and a tiny ossicle, the **intercalarium,** may lie in this ligament. The medial prong of the tripus is attached to the remains of the third vertebra (from which it was chiefly derived), and its posterior prong is bound to the gas bladder. If the bladder has a bony capsule, a foramen is left in it for this latter attachment.

The mode of action of the tripus–intercalarium–scaphium chain is slightly different in the fishes with an ossified gas bladder from what it is in the fishes with a soft one, but the result is the same. Volume changes or coarse vibrations of air in the bladder will be recorded in movements against the fluid-filled ear-bulbs and so transmitted to the sensory patches of the inner ear [5].

The function of this extraordinary apparatus has not yet been fully explored. One would expect the sound waves to travel quite as well through the exposed skull bones to the ear as through the bladder and the wall-embedded ossicles. Nevertheless, conditioned-reflex experiments with various common European freshwater species indicate that those which normally lack an ossicle chain (*Salmo, Umbra, Perca, Cottus*) have a very limited sense of hearing. In the European minnow, *Phoxinus,* which has such apparatus, there is a considerable range of normal sensitivity to sound and remarkable ability for pitch discrimination, which is much disturbed by removal of the gas bladder [6].

Other possible functions of this apparatus have been suggested, and also deserve wider investigation. For instance they might serve as a sort of barometer for measuring water pressure, or as a means of calling forth reflexes to produce hydrostatic adjustments in the bladder [2].

4. Respiratory Gas Bladders. Some of these bladders are called pulmonoid, since they have their internal surface broken up into chambers and air cells that greatly increase the exposed area. They occur in the holostei, and in isolated cases among teleosts. The adaptation is notable for its rarity.

The division of the inner surface of the bladder into lunglike air cells takes place in some of the teleosts that gulp air, but not in all. Also it takes place in a considerable number of species which do not breathe air. Teleosts that are able to travel across wet meadows, or to climb trees, breathe air with specialized gills or the skin, and not with their gas bladders.

In tropical lands, the dissolved oxygen of standing waters is often completely taken up by suspended organic material that is washed in by torrential rains. Fish can live in such brown or black waters only by gulping air at the surface, and swallowing it into regions specially adapted for uptake of oxygen through suitably rich capillary beds. These may lie in the pharynx itself, or in pharyngeal diverticula that invade other head or shoulder regions, or in the gut [2].

III. LUNGS

A. Development

In amphibia, the lung rudiments are first seen as a pair of outgrowths from the endoderm lining of the narrowing pharynx cavity. They look convincingly like final members of the series of pharyngeal pouches, sprouting posteroventrally towrd the coelom rather than laterally toward the skin (Fig. 23–6). In the adult condition the two lungs share a single slitlike opening into the pharynx, called the **glottis,** and a small central space just underneath it, called the **laryngotracheal chamber.** The actual formation of a tracheal tube is found among amphibia only in the wormlike gymnophiona.

In the amniotes, as part of the general activity that forms the neck, the glottis remains in the

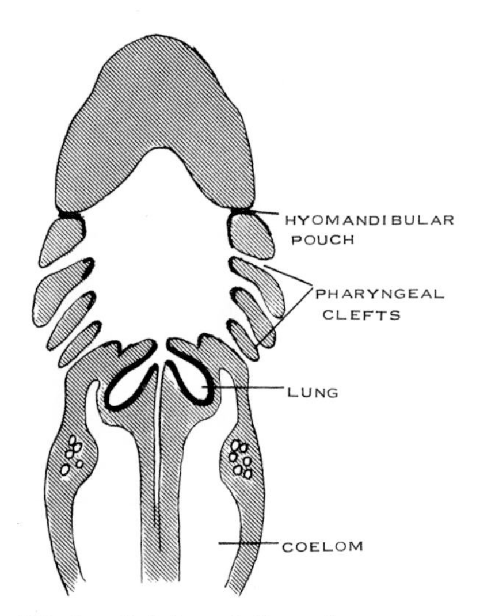

Fig. 23–6. Origin of frog lungs as seen in frontal section of a very young tadpole.
(After Goette, 1905, and Makuschok, 1911.)

floor of the pharynx, and the lungs are carried posteriorly from it into the thorax at the end of a long **tracheal tube.** The upper part of the trachea regularly specializes as a **larynx.** The lower end of it forks into the right and left **bronchi,** each bronchus entering its own lung.

In some cases the lungs arise as a pair of buds directly on the floor of the pharynx just as described for the amphibia. In other cases (man for instance) an unpaired groove (Fig. 23–7 A) is pinched off the floor of the pharynx to form a tracheal tube (Fig. 23–7 B) and the lungs are first seen as a pair of buds at the end of the trachea.

B. Asymmetries

A great many tetrapods show characteristic differences between the right and left lung buds. As will be seen in the next chapter, this leads to rather complex asymmetries in the coelom and mesenteries of many of them, but the marks may be left on the adult lungs also. Usually the left primary lung bud is small and at right angles to the right one (Fig. 23–7 C, D). In adult gymnophiona, the left lung remains smaller than the right. In a few snakes it persists in rudimentary form, but in many more of them it is absent altogether and all breathing centers in the right lung.

There are asymmetries in the pulmonary apparatus of all the surviving fishes that have true lungs. The Australian lungfish, *Neoceratodus,* has only one lung, and in other genera the left lung is said to lag in development. Asymmetries also occur in the arterial and nervous supply, and in the position of the glottis in these lungs. *Latimeria* has a single degenerate lunglike structure dorsal to the stomach, connecting to the ventral side of the esophagus on the right side.

C. Glottis

In all tetrapods, the glottis arises as a midline slit in the posterior floor of the embryonic pharynx. Variations in growth rates of associated structures give it a remarkable range of positions in the adults. It always lies posterior to the tongue. In species which have evolved a bulky muscular tongue (page 330) the glottis is crowded down into the neck.

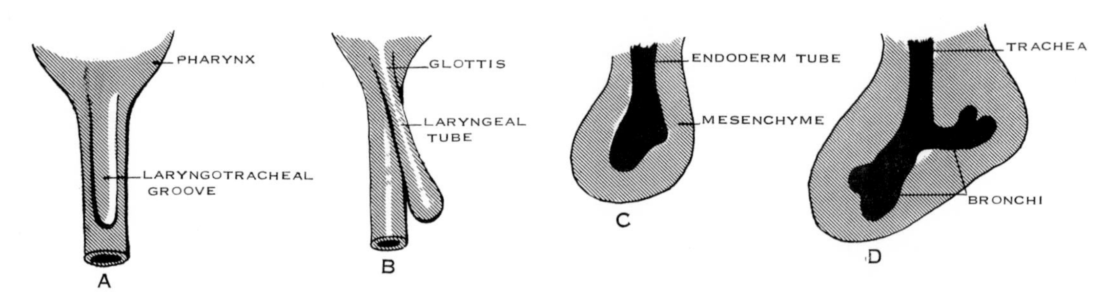

Fig. 23–7. Origin of mammalian lungs. A. Ventral view, 2.5-millimeter pig embryo. B. Oblique ventral view, 3 millimeters. C. 4-millimeter embryo. D. 6-millimeter embryo.
(After J. M. Flint, 1906.)

In the amphibia there is no functional or anatomical relation between the location of the choanae and the glottis, but in the amniotes the glottis invariably lies close under the choanae wherever they may be (Fig. 23–8). In animals with a short hard palate (snakes, turtles, lizards) the glottis lies near the front of the mouth, and in those with a long one (birds, crocodilia, mammals) it lies far back. This spatial relationship is a useful one, and is doubly remarkable, since lung buds and the hard palate must have had independent evolutionary origins and certainly arise at quite different times and places in the amniote embryo. It is an interesting question what brought them into such a close and functionally appropriate correlation.

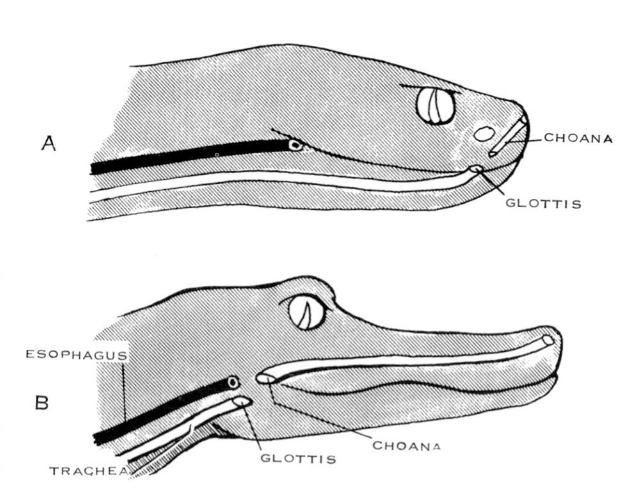

Fig. 23–8. Position of choanae and glottis in reptiles. A. Rattlesnake. B. Alligator.

The accomplishment of this correlation gives the animal the ability to close off the breathing track from the feeding track. Amphibia cannot breathe while they are taking in food, but mammals can chew and salivate their food for long intervals without interrupting their breathing. Choanae and glottis are placed far back, actually in the throat, and a combination of the fleshy base of tongue, the soft muscular sidewalls of the back of the mouth, a movable soft palate, and the epiglottis (see below) can wall off the mouth cavity during the chewing period, and also clap shut both the nasopharyngeal and the laryngeal parts of the breathing track during the instant of swallowing.

The choanae and glottis are placed far back in the crocodilia also (Fig. 23–8 B). In this case, the mouth cavity can be blocked off by means of a strong special fold that descends from the back of the hard palate and meets a fold that can be lifted from below on the back of the tongue. This enables an alligator to breathe comfortably with only the tip of its snout out of water, all the while it is drowning the prey which is grasped in its open jaws.

Snakes (Fig. 23–8 A) have a uniquely mobile glottis, which lies near the front of the mouth cavity but can be either retracted or moved still farther forward by the action of special derivatives of the hypoglossal musculature. A snake can swallow a frog that is larger than its own head, and needless to say its whole mouth is fully occupied during the half hour that the process takes. Nevertheless, it does not have to stop breathing all that time, for it can protrude its glottis outside the mouth, between the separated halves of the lower jaw.

D. Larynx and Trachea

Placement of the lungs at the end of a long neck in the amniotes introduces the functional requirement that the tracheal and bronchial air passages be provided with stiff walls so that they remain open for the free passage of the breath at all times. Also, since the air passage from nasal chambers and choanae to glottis and trachea must cross the food passage from mouth to esophagus (Fig. 23–9) some provision has to be made for closing the glottis during the act of swallowing. Both these needs have been met in evolutionary selection, and the devices that have been produced are foreshadowed in the amphibia.

All the amniotes have an enlarged laryngeal chamber just below or behind the glottis. The lateral walls of the glottis are stiffened by a pair of **arytenoid cartilages,** and the larynx has a separate **cricoid cartilage** wrapped around it. This pattern is subject to many variations, including augmentation. Mammals for instance (Fig. 23–9) turn the cricoid into the shape of a

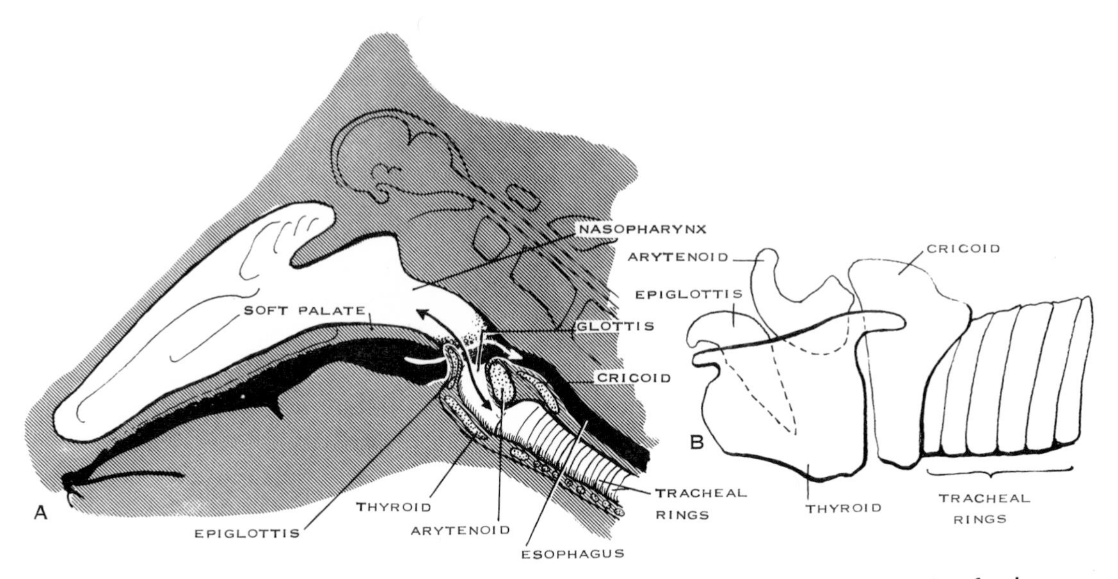

Fig. 23–9. Larynx of a cow. A. Sagittal section, showing air passage crossing food passage at glottis. B. Laryngeal cartilages, from left side.

(After Sisson-Grossman, Anatomy of the Domestic Animals, 3d edition, 1938, by permission of W. B. Saunders Co.)

signet ring by a dorsal enlargement, the two arytenoids resting on the anterior surface of the signet part; and they also add two uniquely mammalian cartilages to the anatomy of the larynx, both straddling the ventral midline. The larger of the two is a shield-shaped **thyroid cartilage,** whose side wings wrap around the arytenoids. Anterior to this, an **epiglottis** is formed, which lies between the glottis and the base of the tongue and acts as a cover for the glottis during the act of swallowing.

Beyond these laryngeal cartilages, the trachea and bronchi are propped open by a succession of hoops of cartilage. These may be either complete rings, or they may be open dorsally, like tipped C's. In birds they become ossified, and at the place where the bronchi fork from the trachea several of them, together with the membrane that lines them internally, are exquisitely specialized as the **syrinx,** the organ that produces bird song.

The tracheal rings are unrepresented in neckless amphibia, except in one family of toads. Laryngeal cartilages occur, but in many cases they consist merely of slivers which stiffen the walls of the glottis (Fig. 23–10). Even these, however, serve the requirement of opening the air passage for breathing and closing it for swallowing. It is as though the laryngeal cartilages were the skeletal bars of a rudimentary VII pharynx segment. Tiny strips of dilatator muscle come down to insert upon them from the dorsal pharynx wall, like C_7d levators, appropriately supplied by twigs from the vagus nerves. In action they pull the cartilages apart and open the glottis. Where the air passage perforates the transversus ventralis sheet of pharynx-segment muscle ($C_{3\text{-}6}$v, in Fig. 17–9), little sheets of this muscle surround the glottis, commonly joining to enclose it in a sphincter. This, in contraction, closes the glottis. Larval urodeles show these arrangements in their simplest form: both the cartilages and their muscles achieve more elaborate and variable arrangements during metamorphosis.

The origins and nerve supply of the muscles that open and close the amniote glottis are reminiscent of these in amphibia, but both the muscles and the cartilages on which they work are greatly increased in size and complexity, and along different lines in different classes and orders. The dilatator muscles insert on the aryte-

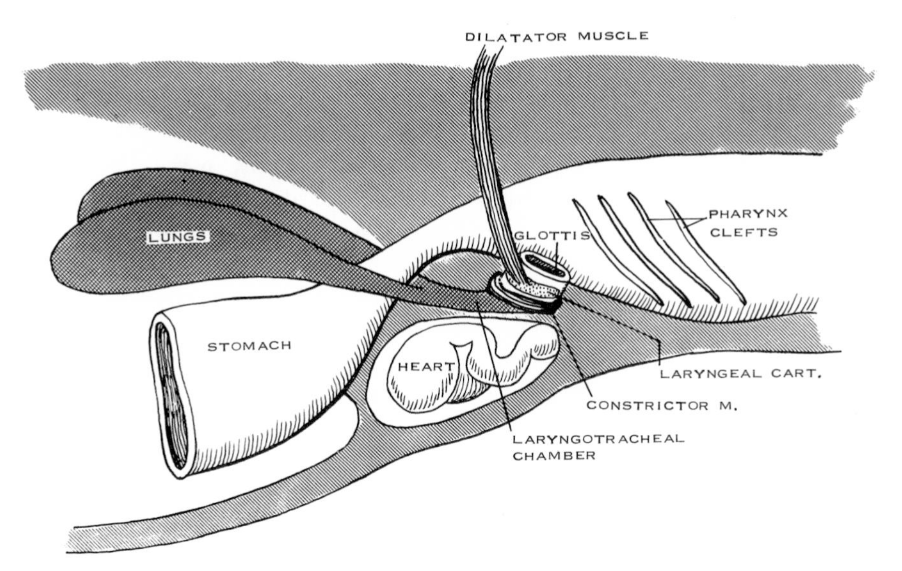

Fig. 23–10. Respiratory tract of a larval amblystoma. Sagittal dissection from the right side, liver and mesenteries removed.

noid cartilages and usually take origin from the cricoid, but may extend farther out to origins on the hyobranchial skeleton. The sphincters also become subdivided and specialized. In mammals, a climax condition is reached, in which a dozen or more separate laryngeal muscles provide various combinations of movement of the cricoid, thyroid, and arytenoid cartilages upon one another. They are all supplied by the vagus nerve. Obviously this is a far more complex apparatus than is needed for merely opening and closing the glottis. The explanation is that the larynx has here developed a new function. It is a voice box.

Nothing has yet been said about the vocal cords. This is because most tetrapods do not develop any. The whole tract from glottis to lung is lined with endodermal mucous membrane. All that is needed for a voice is to stretch strands of this membrane from one cartilage to another where they can be set vibrating by the respiratory air currents.

There are no such vocal cords in the silent urodeles. Anura produce them in the laryngotracheal chamber, with sexual differences, and their species-specific grunting, whistling, and trilling calls are well known. The vocal ability of most reptiles begins and ends with hissing, though the African chameleon, lizards, and crocodilians have a true voice. The larynx of birds is quite devoid of vocal cords, but the syrinx does the job better, being composed of essentially similar but highly specialized components.

Monotremes and cetacea lack vocal cords, and the marsupials have quite rudimentary ones. In most other mammals the larynx is notably enlarged, with right and left recesses in its walls, at the openings of which vibratile membranous cords are stretched. Particular movements of muscles that run from one laryngeal cartilage to another can alter the position of these cords and expose them to, or move them out of, the exhaled air stream. It is these movements that determine whether or not the cords are set in vibration, and control their pitch.

E. The Lung Itself

All three principal germ layers are represented in the anatomy of the lung. The endoderm produces the inner epithelial lining, the mesoderm contributes connective tissue, smooth muscle, and blood and lymph vessels, and the ectoderm sends in a nerve supply.

The form taken by the lung is extremely variable in the different classes and orders of tetrapods, perhaps as a resultant of the opposed tendencies of the endodermal epithelium to expand and of the mesoderm to restrain it from doing so.

In amphibia, each endodermal lung bud is covered only by a sparse layer of delicate connective tissue, and it expands rapidly within the coelom, forming a large simple bag which may reach the cloaca. The inner respiratory surface is increased only by a network of minor in-foldings (Fig. 23–11 A). These animals do not rely exclusively on their lungs for breathing, but use gills or their skin in addition, or instead. There is even a large and successful family of air-breathing urodeles (Plethodontidae) which lack lungs and glottis altogether. Nevertheless, equally simple baglike lungs serve adequately as the only breathing organs in the sphenodon and a number of lizards.

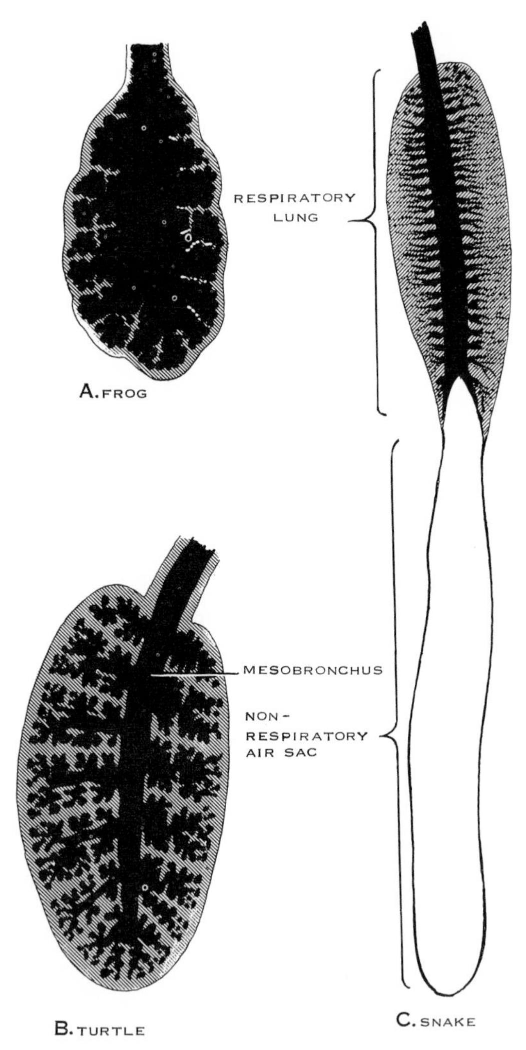

Fig. 23–11. Diagrams of lung types.

In most reptiles the mesodermal partitions become far more prominent (Fig. 23–11 B). The endodermal lung bud seems at first to be relatively uninhibited in its expansion, but then it is restrained by the surrounding connective tissue so that its surface is honeycombed with intersecting partitions. In dissection of relatively simple lungs of adult turtles, one can discern primary partitions bearing secondary partitions, which bear tertiary ones, etc. But it must not be thought that this tripelike architecture develops by growth of the partitions inward. The whole lung is growing continuously outward from the center, and the connective tissue lays down a finer and finer restraining net, through the interstices of which the endodermal epithelium must expand. Pulmonary blood vessels, branching through the connective tissue, lay down a rich bed of capillaries against the epithelium.

Lungs show exceedingly variable internal structure within the class of reptiles. They may be simple bags like those of frogs, or they may be uniformly spongy like those of mammals. Usually however, there is a roomy central chamber called the **mesobronchus,** directly continued from the bronchus (Fig. 23–11 B, C). Like the latter it is non-respiratory, with a lining of mucous membrane stiffened by connective tissue, or muscle, or even by cartilage rings. A number of prominent and radially arranged **parabronchial air tubes** may lead out from the mesobronchus toward the finer passages and the chambers where the respiratory exchanges of gases actually take place.

In most snakes and many lizards, the mesobronchus may open out posteriorly into a thin-walled, uncomplicated, almost bloodless **air sac** (Fig. 23–11 C). One may suspect that in these species the potency to restrict and partition the wall of the endodermal lung bag resides only in the mesoderm that coats the anterior part of the anlage, leaving the posterior part to expand without restraint. In a few species, the parabronchi may expand at their tips in this way also. The African chameleons have a number of such non-respiratory air sacs, which are prolonged among the viscera as far as the pelvis. These animals, like certain snakes, have the habit of suddenly inflating themselves when molested, by filling the air sacs, as though to frighten off aggressors.

IV. SPECIAL TYPES OF LUNGS

A. Mammalian Lungs

Embryonic lungs of mammals are embedded from the beginning in thick strong mesenchyme (Fig. 23–7 C, D). Their endodermal components form into tubules which branch repeatedly in it, each bronchus giving rise to a tree of bronchioles (Fig. 23–12 A). The pattern is remarkably like that of a compound tubular gland. No other vertebrates build their lungs in quite this way. The ciliated columnar epithelium of the proximal bronchioles gives over to thin cuboidal epithelium distally, and eventually at the outermost twigs of the tree some areas expand, forming tiny air cells or **alveoli** (Fig. 23–12 B). These are richly encased in a capillary bed, and the endodermal lining in them thins out so much that even though it completely lines the capillaries this can only be conclusively demonstrated with the electron microscope. In a mature mammalian lung, the tissue that separates the blood from the air in an alveolus, i.e., the capillary wall and its endodermal covering, may be less than half a micron in thickness.

Alveoli are not produced from the terminal bronchioles of the human lung until the sixth month of pregnancy, by which time as many as 17 successive branchings have occurred in the bronchial tree. Premature infants born before this cannot survive, partly because they do not have enough alveolar surface to carry on the necessary gaseous exchanges. After birth, the bronchioles resume their growth and by mid-childhood have carried their branchings out to the twenty-fourth series. The proportion of tissue expanded into alveoli, alveolar ducts, and other areas capable of supporting respiration continues to increase.

The pouch young of marsupials, which are born so young that toe buds are scarcely formed on their hindlimbs, must develop respiratory

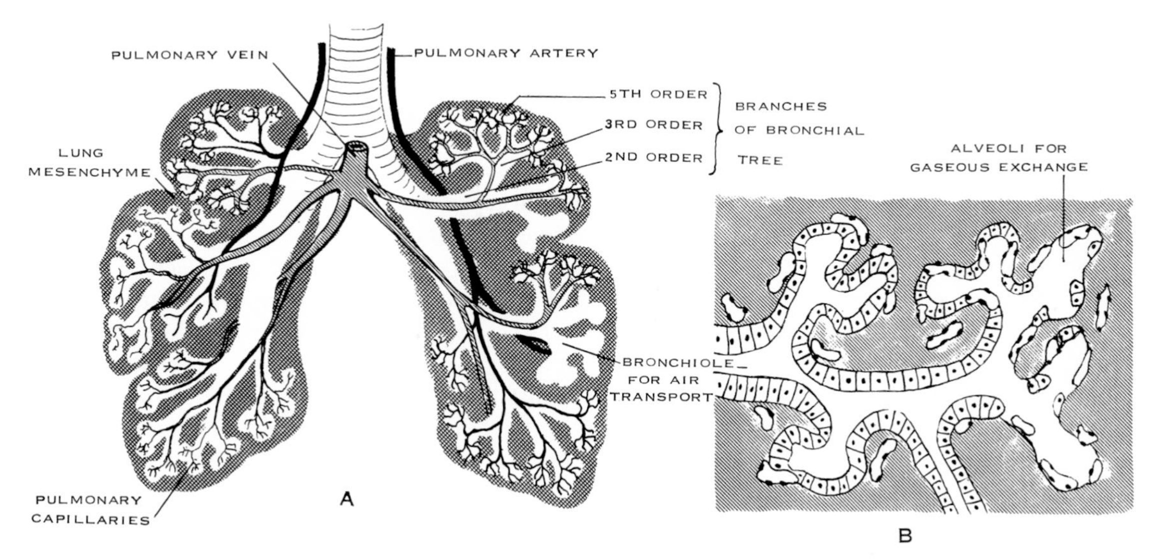

Fig. 23–12. Further development of the lung in man. A. Bronchial trees at 8 weeks. B. Lung tissue section at 8 months.

(A after His, 1887. B after L. B. Arey, Developmental Anatomy, 6th edition, 1954, by permission of W. B. Saunders Co.)

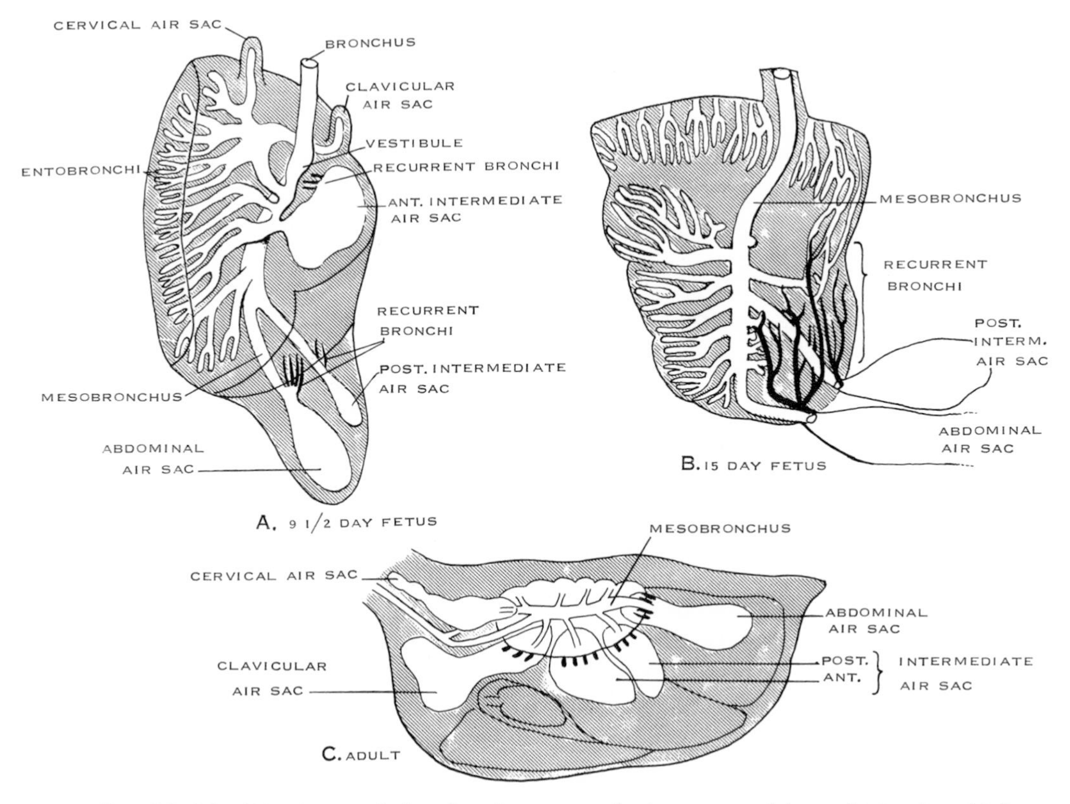

Fig. 23–13. Diagrams of the development of air sacs and bronchi in the chick.
(A and B after Locy and Larsell, 1916. C after E. S. Goodrich, Studies on the Structure and Development of Vertebrates, 1930, by permission of Macmillan & Co., Ltd., London.)

surfaces at a far earlier stage. Alveoli are reported forming when the bronchi have branched only twice or three times in the lung mesenchyme.

The oxygen requirements of mammals are markedly increased by their high body temperature and generally active metabolism. This is reflected in a great increase in the area of respiratory epithelium in the lungs per body weight, which does not exceed 5 cm^2 per gram in pythons and alligators, but is estimated to reach 7 for man, 11 for horses, 28 for cats, 54 for mice, and 100 for bats. An individual's alveolar area is vastly larger than the area of his skin.

Respiratory interchange between the air and the blood takes place only at the blind alveoli of mammal lungs, not in the thick-walled bronchioles. The diameter of these alveoli varies from 400 microns in sloths, to 150 microns in man and 25 in bats. To have the gas exchange between blood and air located in these tiny spaces at the far ends of blind passages introduces a large factor of inefficiency into the respiratory process. Since only a small fraction of the air contained within the chest can be exhaled at each normal breath, the incoming air must be mixed with several times its volume of stale residual air. The highest concentration of oxygen remains in the air of the trachea and bronchi, where it is physiologically unavailable. Removal of this handicap could only be accomplished by a fundamental redesigning of the lung architecture, along lines wihch only birds have discovered.

B. Bird Lungs

1. Development. The respiratory system unquestionably finds its highest development in birds. Several radical new lines of specialization appear quite late in the fetal period, producing structures not foreshadowed in any other living vertebrates. The lung buds start off their development in a quite reptilian fashion, except that the mesenchyme which coats their early branchings is notably thicker. Each bronchus is continued internally by a **mesobronchus** which runs the full length of the lung and gives off a small series of branches of the second order, which are named from their position (Fig. 23–13). The 9½ day chick shows 4 ventral **entobronchi,** 8 dorsal **ectobronchi** and 6 **laterobronchi.** These have in their turn given off numerous tertiary air passages called **parabronchi,** which reach into all parts of the lung without substantial diminution in their diameter.

Up to this point the bird lung has followed a crocodilian pattern, with its clearly defined mesobronchus, rather than the bronchial tree pattern of the mammal. If the parabronchi were now to give off several more generations of air-passages ending in blind air cells, the crocodilian pattern would be complete. However, the distal ends of the mesobronchus and several of the secondary branches have already, one may suppose, escaped from the control of the pulmonary mesenchyme and are expanding in various directions as **air sacs** (Fig. 23–13), and the parabronchi that are embedded in the thick mesenchyme also begin to behave in a radically new way at this time.

Each parabronchus proceeds to make multiple end-to-end or lateral anastomoses with its neighbors (Fig. 23–14 A), and gives off multitudes of little branching air capillaries on all its sides (Fig. 23–14 B). These tiny air capillaries also anastomose with each other and with those of neighboring parabronchi to make a three-dimensional lattice-work of passageways, comparable to an old-fashioned steam radiator infinitely complicated and reduced in size. The smallest of these air tubes are from a half to an eighth the diameter of the smallest known mammalian lung alveoli and their epithelial lining is too thin to be visible with the light microscope. Meanwhile the mesenchyme in which they are proliferating is producing an equally rich pulmonary capillary bed, and the capillaries that are to carry air are completely interwoven with those that carry blood.

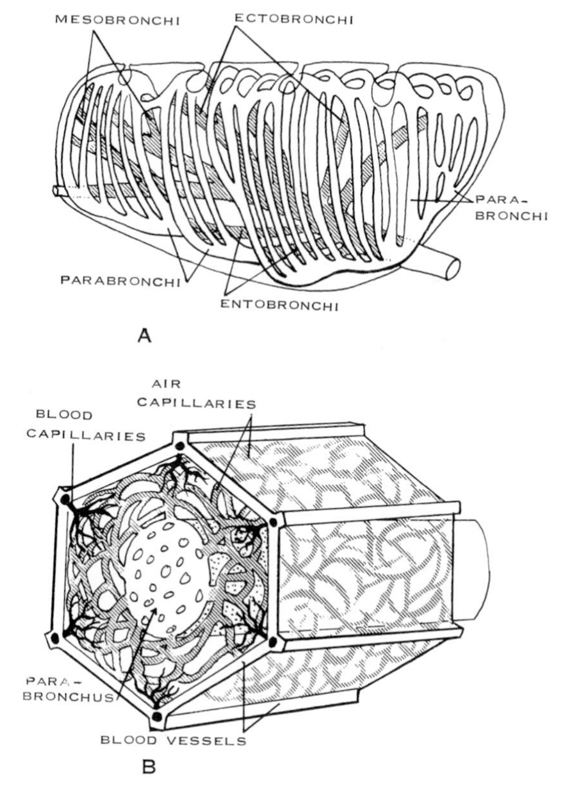

Fig. 23–14. Diagrams of lung architecture in a bird. A. Anastomosis of secondary bronchi and parabronchi. B. Relation of parabronchus to blood and air capillaries.

(After Locy and Larsell, 1916.)

Thus, the branching of blind sprouts, which produces the mammalian bronchial tree, stops in the bird after the third generation and is replaced by the development of finer and finer sets of anastomoses. There are no blind air cells in the bird lung. Instead there is an almost inconceivable richness of air capillaries through which the air can pass from any part of the lung to any other if not temporarily obstructed by the action of smooth muscle sphincters in the parabronchial walls. It is estimated that a pigeon has about 8 billion (8×10^9) air capillaries, with a respiratory surface twenty-five times greater than that of man per unit of body weight. It is nearly a hundred times greater in a hummingbird than in man, per weight.

2. *Air Sacs and Recurrent Bronchi.* Certain peripheral spots on some of the secondary bronchi, as well as the far end of the mesobronchus itself, expand beyond the respiratory area to form extrapulmonary non-respiratory air sacs (Fig. 23–13). There are characteristically five pairs of these, namely **cervical, interclavicular, anterior intermediate, posterior intermediate,** and **abdominal.** The two interclavicular sacs usually join to form a single one. The intermediates lie inside the ribs in mid-trunk and the abdominals lie sometimes dorsal and sometimes ventral to the viscera. Their pattern and extent is subject to some variation in the different orders and families of birds, but they are present in all birds and nothing quite like them is found in any other vertebrates.

The non-respiratory expansions of snake and lizard lungs are wide open to large central lung cavities. In sharp contrast, the avian air sacs are connected with secondary bronchi by quite restricted openings. Near these openings the air sacs proceed to develop clusters of small **recurrent bronchi** (Fig. 23–13 A) which secondarily invade the respiratory part of the lung and, after growing and branching for some distance, anastomose with the parabronchi (Fig. 23–13 B).

This creates the anatomical possibility of a circulation of air from the mesobronchus or a secondary bronchus through an air sac to recurrent bronchi and back to the mesobronchus through other parabronchi. What actually happens is a difficult question to study, and events may be quite different in a bird when it is standing from what they are during flight. A good guess is that much of the air which the bird inhales goes directly to the intermediate and abdominal air sacs. These then act not only as reservoirs of fairly fresh air but as bellows chambers from which, by the action of body and wing muscles, streams of air are injected back into the pervasive gridwork of parabronchi. It has not been possible to demonstrate that moving valves control the circulation of air in the bird lung, but there is an aerodynamic possibility that the exits from the posterior intermediate and perhaps other air sacs create eddies that prevent much of the air that reached the abdominal sacs by way of the mesobronchus from being exhaled by the same path, and encourage it to detour through parabronchi. There is a continuing dispute as to whether air circulates in one direction, or in both, through the parabronchi during inspiration and expiration, but there is general agreement that the large air tubes which permeate the bird lung are swiftly washed by fresh air, and that there are no blind pockets in the respiratory parts of the lung, in contrast to mammals and reptiles. Though the air in the air capillaries must presumably be replaced by diffusion, the distances are extremely short and the gaseous exchange is very efficient indeed[6].

3. *Pneumatization.* The avian air sacs make extensive invasions into all parts of the body, though with much variation in the different orders and families. The cervical sacs usually extend far up the neck, and pass into the interior of certain bones, such as the upper ribs, the vertebrae, and parts of the skull. The interclavicular sac usually forms axillary sacs, pushes between the outer and inner pectoral muscles of flight (thus being massaged at each wingbeat), and invades humerus, scapula, wishbone, sternum, and lower ribs. The abdominal air sacs may not only form extensive spaces outside the flight muscles beneath the skin, but also commonly invade the trunk vertebrae and the bones of the synsacrum and proximal hindlimb. This **pneumatization** of the bones is not found in the earliest fossil birds, and is lacking or very slightly developed in a number of groups to whom it would be of real disadvantage: the diving penguins, loons, grebes, and sea ducks. Some

virtuoso fliers like the frigate-birds have their bones pneumatized clear out to the metatarsals. In general however the greatly variable degree of pneumatization is not correlated with the way of life. Invasion of bones by air spaces is known in a few other vertebrates (page 238), but only birds accomplish it with extensions from the lungs.

4. Function of Bird Air Sacs. Besides their undoubted but still poorly understood involvement in the breathing process, the air sacs of birds may aid in heat regulation by furnishing a large internal surface for evaporation. Panting is the standard reaction of birds to overheating. An individual on a long migration flight may lose up to 50 per cent of its weight while in the air, and a good deal of this is by evaporation of water produced in metabolism [6].

Air sacs also serve to distribute the weight by confining the viscera to particular parts of the body, which is important in adjusting balance to make flight possible. They facilitate the development of a streamlined body, which is needed both in the water and in the air. They lower the specific gravity of the whole animal somewhat, to the advantage of swimming birds, but to the disadvantage of divers, some of which have been observed to exhale just before going under. The subcutaneous expansions of the air sacs serve as insulation against cold, just as the trapped air in the feather coat does.

It has often been suggested that the oxygen required by loons and other birds in their long dives (up to 15 minutes) is supplied by stored air which is pumped back and forth through the lungs between anterior and posterior air sacs. There seems to be no evidence for this idea. Large reserves of oxygen can be stored before diving, in the rich supply of hemoglobin in the remarkably high volume of blood, and also in myoglobin throughout the dark red musculature. Diving birds can also tolerate unusually high concentrations of carbon dioxide in their blood [7].

5. The Syrinx. No birds have laryngeal vocal cords. They make their songs or calls with a special organ, the **syrinx,** located at the cleft of the trachea and surrounded by the interclavicular air sac. It may be exclusively bronchial, or tracheal, but is usually both. All birds, and only birds, have a syrinx.

In its usual forms (Fig. 23–15), this organ is double, involving both bronchi. The cartilage hoops, uncompleted medially, are passive, but the membranes between them are thinned out at special points and so disposed that they can be set in vibration by a passing current of air. Other internal ridges are so disposed as to direct the air against these vibratile membranes, or not, according to the action of special syrinx mus-

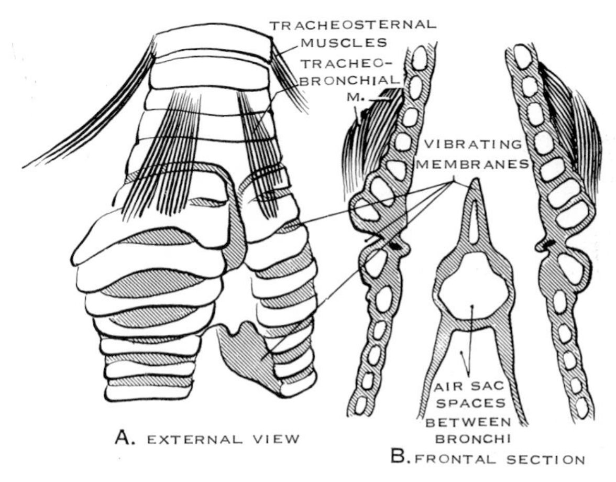

Fig. 23–15. Syrinx of a magpie.
(After Haecker, 1900.)

cles. The partition between the two bronchi at their fork is variously projected upward into the trachea in the midline, with another membrane at its tip.

The whole syrinx can be carried backward toward the sternum, or forward, by special muscles of the rectus group. Both these and some small vagus-innervated intrinsic syrinx muscles (tracheobronchials, Fig. 23–15 B) can also buckle the cartilages and control the disposition of the air passages. Since the bird becomes mute if its interclavicular air sac is opened, and recovers its voice after closure of the wound, it is supposed that pressure of air within the sac may help force the vibratile membranes inward across the bronchial air currents. Some species show enlargement of the tracheal rings nearest the syrinx, to form a resonating chamber, particularly prominent in males. The detailed structure of the syrinx is as variable from species to species as bird song itself is.

V. BREATHING MECHANISMS

A. Amphibia

When terrestrial amphibia breathe, they take only an occasional gulp of fresh air, and pump it back and forth between the lungs and the mouth cavity, by alternating actions of two force-pumps. One of these, contrived out of the hyobranchial skeleton and muscles, may be observed rhythmically raising the floor of the mouth, driving air down into the lungs. The other, operated by the belly muscles, presses air back into the mouth, lowering its floor. During this pumping process, the glottis is held open and the mouth and nostrils closed. After a while the glottis is closed, the nostrils are opened, and a fresh mouthful of air is taken in. This mechanism is used even by the lungless plethodontid salamanders, which substitute a highly vascularized pharynx lining for the lungs.

Anura have a variety of cheek- or throat-pouches which can be inflated from the lungs when the mouth and nostrils are closed. Vocal cords that are placed in the walls of the laryngotracheal chamber can be set in vibration by these currents of air, which produces the peeping, whistling, trilling, snoring, bleating, or booming calls characteristic of the species. Since the circulation of air back and forth between lungs and throat pouches can go on with the mouth closed and much of the gas exchange takes place through the skin, frogs and toads can sing under water, and some of them regularly do. Both the vocalization and the force-pump mechanism for inspiration of air are rendered useless if the mouth is propped open.

B. Reptiles

This hyoid-arch *force-pump* mechanism of breathing with nostrils and mouth closed except for occasional gulps of air does occur in some reptiles. Two new methods of *suction-pump* breathing have been developed, however, one characteristic of most of the reptiles and the other found only in turtles. In the larger group, there are always freely movable ribs, and these are attached to the vertebrae in such a way that when the trunk muscles drag them forward they swing outward, expanding the volume of the chest. The partial vacuum thus created in the thorax sucks in air if the glottis is held open. An alarmed puff-adder can double his size in this way, filling the air sac of his lung all the way to the cloaca with one inspiration, and then, though lacking vocal cords, forcing his wind out with a long loud hiss, wonderfully frightening for such a harmless creature. Birds and mammals have their own modified versions of this suction-pump rib breathing mechanism.

But in the turtles the developing ribs become embedded in the carapace, and the flank musculature is mostly obliterated. It was once thought that turtles set up a force-pump mechanism for breathing by means of the hyoid arch, or a suction-pump mechanism by means of limb movements. Experiments show, however, that if such devices exist they are unnecessary and unusual. Instead, some surviving elements of the abdominal musculature, lying inside the shell, provide anterolateral and posterolateral pairs of breathing muscles which either directly pull on the lungs themselves, or enlarge the body cavity, which has the same effect. These muscles, though they perform a function quite analogous to that of the mammalian diaphragm, are not homologous with it.

C. Mammals

An improved arrangement of the rib joints and specially modified scalene muscles on the anterior thorax (Fig. 20–17) enable the mammals to increase the volume of the chest cavity considerably by rocking the ribs ventrad and forward. This means of creating a partial vacuum in the pleura cavities is entirely adequate to support life, but normally the same effect is produced rhythmically by the contraction of the uniquely mammalian **diaphragm.** This is a dome-shaped muscle which flattens when it contracts, thus increasing the chest volume at the expense of the abdomen, and sucking in air. When it relaxes, the diaphragm is pushed upward again by the contraction of the belly muscles. Thus the mammal can continue to breathe even with the entire thorax immobilized in a plaster cast, if its belly is free.

D. Birds

Avian lungs are extremely small in comparison with those of mammals of equivalent weight. They do not change much in volume during normal breathing, nor do they slide freely in a pleural or peritoneal cavity. Normally, tides of air are maintained inward and outward through the lung by the effect of body movements on the air sacs. These tides can be maintained in abnormal directions. For instance, a pigeon with a stoppered trachea and a broken wing can breathe successfully through the hole in its pneumatized humerus. On the other hand it has been shown experimentally that small birds can survive also if the air sacs are opened or tied off. This suggests that air can be kept circulating through the lungs by exaggerated movements of the ribs, which normally lie partly embedded in the lung tissue. The role of muscle tissue within the lung, and in the membrane which supports its ventral surface, is not known.

REFERENCES

1. Denison, R. H., 1941. *J. Paleontol.* 15: 553.
2. Jones, F. R. H., 1957. *In* M. E. Brown (ed.), *The physiology of fishes,* Vol. 2. Academic Press, Inc., New York.
3. Copeland, D. E., 1952. *J. Exptl. Zool.* 120: 203.
4. Fish, M. P., 1954. *Bingham Oceanog. Coll.* 14: 1.
5. Grassé, P.-P., 1958. *In* P.-P. Grassé (ed.), *Traité de zoologie,* Tome XIII (2). Masson, Paris.
6. Lowenstein, O., 1957. *In* Brown (ed.); see Ref. 2.
7. Salt, G. W., and E. Zeuthen, 1960. *In* A. J. Marshall (ed.), *Biology and comparative physiology of birds,* Vol. 1. Academic Press, Inc., New York.

24

Coelom and Mesenteries

I. INTRODUCTION

In all vertebrates, the hypomeric mesoderm sheet of the early embryo splits into inner and outer layers, enclosing a **coelomic cavity** (Figs. 7–12, 7–20, 8–14, 8–15). In animals without an umbilical connection to a yolk sac (amphibia, teleosts, etc.), the coelom is one continuous head-and-trunk cavity; the heart and gut rudiments are suspended in this by a continuous **dorsal mesentery** system, and there is no primary ventral mesentery. In elasmobranchs and amniotes, however, the hypomere cavities are formed in mesoderm sheets that extend far outward over a huge yolk mass (or empty yolk sac, mammals). As these split to form coelomic cavities, one first distinguishes a U-shaped space in the head. Its arms point caudad and become confluent, as do the coelomic spaces of the trunk, with vast extraembryonic cavities between the amnion and the yolk sac (Figs. 24–1, 24–2 A).

Furthermore, as the embryonic head is lifted off the flat sheet of the area pellucida, the two arms of the U-shaped anterior coelom are swung together ventrally, the space between them constituting a primary **ventral mesentery,** which contains the rudiments of the heart and liver. This ventral mesentery (Fig. 24–2 B) is soon reduced to scraps or disappears altogether at the pericardial level, mostly absorbed into the septum transversum at the anterior border of the liver.

The roles of the common cardinal veins and the liver in constricting the coelom into an anterior **pericardial cavity** and a posterior **peritoneal cavity** have already been considered (pages 146–147). Disregarding the exceptional case of the teleosts (page 140), it is usual to find the common cardinals taking the first steps in establishing the septum transversum that intrudes between these two cavities. Each vein makes a broad bridge from the somatopleure to the splanchnopleure on its way to the heart (Figs. 5–16, 8–19). The liver quickly occludes the passageways that might have remained ventral to these bridges, leaving the pericardial and peritoneal cavities in communication only dorsally, through pericardioperitoneal tunnels, which will be referred to hereafter simply as **pleural canals** (Fig. 8–19). These lie on the right and left sides of the esophagus and its mesentery, where lung buds (if there are any) may bulge into them.

Since the lateral walls of these tiny pleural canals are being crowded by the common cardinal veins, it would take very little spreading of the mesoderm tissues around the esophagus to choke the canals off completely. In fact this regularly happens during or soon after the pharyngula stage, completing the separation of the pericardial cavity from the rest of the coelom. Only in larval lampreys and in adult hagfishes

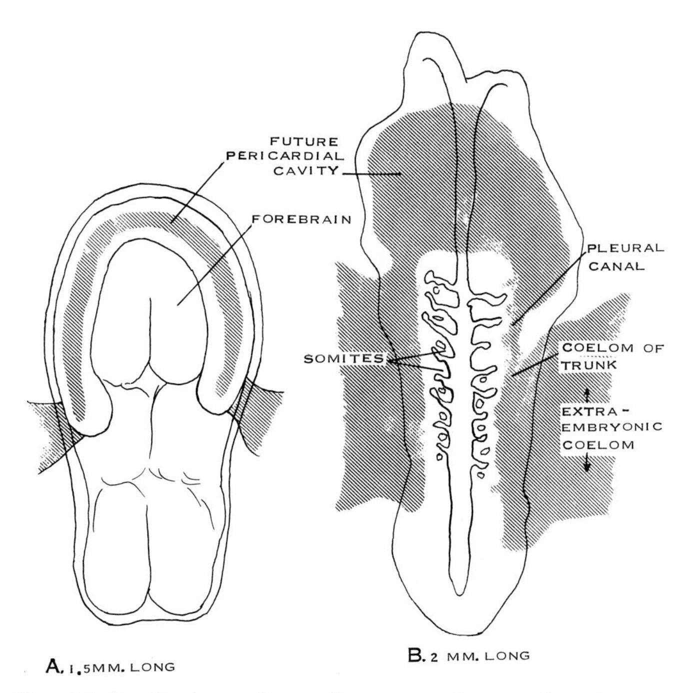

Fig. 24–1. Coelom of two human embryos, dorsal view.

and elasmobranchs do the dorsal tunnels still remain open to the pericardial chamber.

Except in teleosts, the liver spreads out over, and adheres to, the entire posterior surface of the septum transversum (Figs. 5–16, 8–19, 24–3 A). In later development this attachment expands less rapidly than the adjacent cavities, so that the adult liver is found attached at its anterior surface by a relatively restricted mesenteric bridge, the **coronary ligament** (Fig. 24–3 B) across which hepatic veins (of fishes) or a postcaval vein (of tetrapods) find the way to the heart. In many, but not all, mammals, a mesenteric attachment is produced between the liver and the midventral line of the body wall, called the **falciform ligament** Figs. 24–3 B, 24–4, 24–14); it is a secondary development, not a surviver of the original ventral mesentery, which was lost sight of when the liver began its precocious expansion.

The parts of the dorsal mesentery system that support different levels of the intestine of the adult are given appropriate names to distinguish them: **mesoesophagus, mesogastrium, mesoduodenum, mesorectum,** etc. The part that supports the general intestine is sometimes distinguished from these by such names as mesentery proper, mesentery sensu strictu, etc.; in the anatomy of adult man it is simply called *the* **mesentery.**

Fetal developments produce some remarkable differences in the adult anatomy of the coelom and mesenteries, characteristic of separate classes of the tetrapods. Mesenteric variations occur so freely that they often cannot be predicted in detail, even within a given family, but must be determined for each genus by dissection. Only generalizations as to the types of such variations are pertinent here. There has been no experimental analysis of the factors governing the establishment of mesenteries.

This chapter will focus on developmental explanations for the following major types of contrast:

1. Relations of the lungs to the coelom. In anuran amphibians, the posterior section of the coelom must be called a **pleuroperitoneal cavity,** since the baglike lungs lie completely within it.

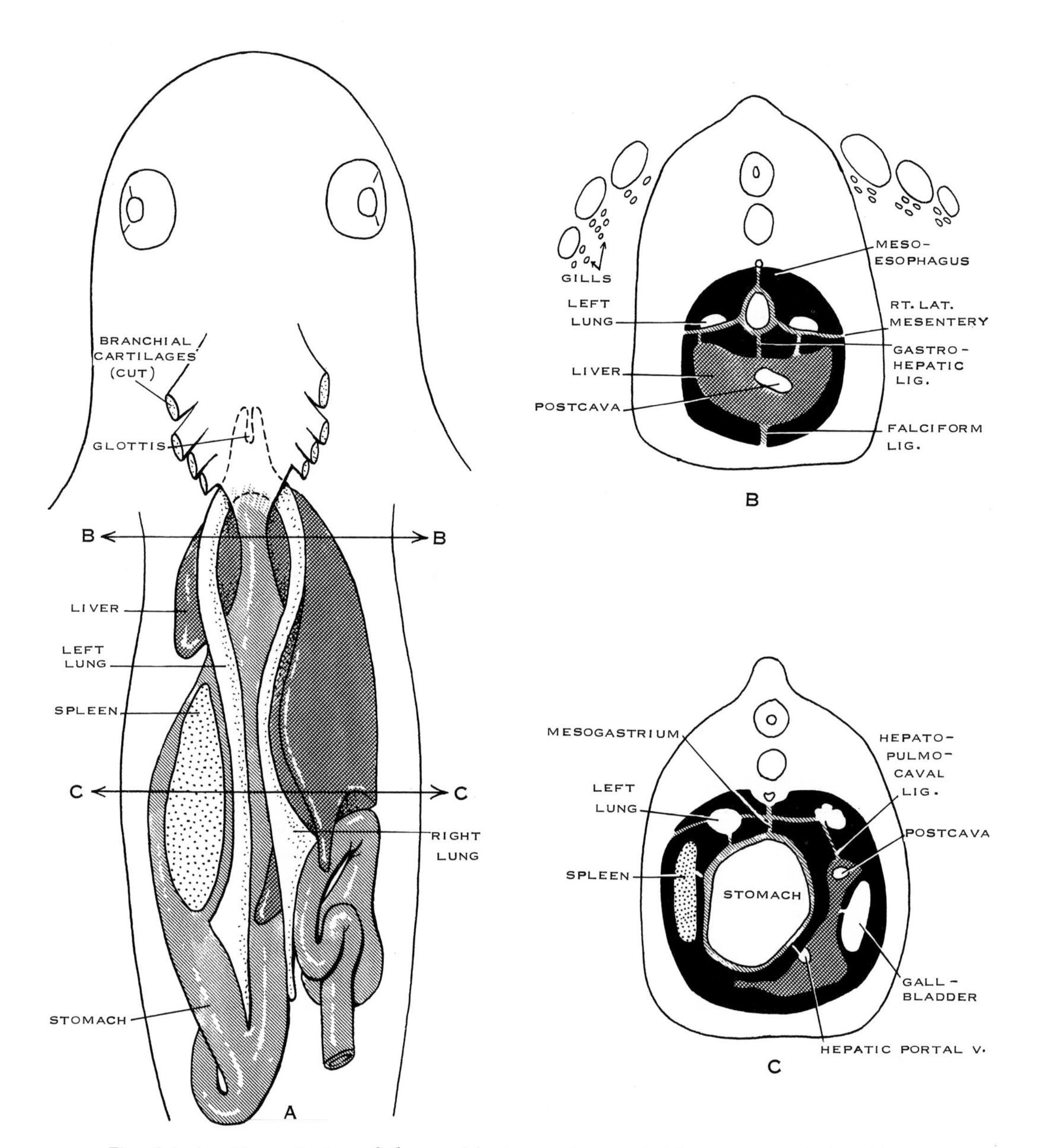

Fig. 24–4. Mesenteries of the amblystoma larva. A. Viscera, dorsal view. B. Section through esophagus (B—B). C. Section through mid-stomach (C—C).

lungs on both sides (Fig. 24–6). Usually in other groups the left recess stops spreading and the left lateral mesentery becomes defective; in some mammals the recess and the lateral mesentery that bounds it are never even formed on the left side (Fig. 24–15 A). On the right side, however, the recess and lateral mesentery are always developed with more vigor, and the ventral part of the mesentery, meeting the anteriorly spreading liver, transfers to its upper surface, becoming a **hepatopulmocaval ligament** (Fig. 24–4 C).

As the lungs stretch beyond the pleural canals and into the pleuroperitoneal cavity, these lateral mesenteries may become extensive, delimiting a pair of **pulmo-enteric recesses** medially, and a pair of **pleural recesses** laterally (Fig. 24–7). The pulmo-enteric recesses are separated from each other by the midline mesenteries (**mesogastrium** above the stomach, **gastrohepatic ligament** below it), and have the liver for their floor. Both they and the pleural recesses are open to the general peritoneal cavity posteriorly. The pleural recesses, which are bounded laterally by the somatopleure, are also open to the general cavity ventrally, around the sides of the liver, unless the lateral ligament makes a line of fusion with the somatopleure (compare Fig. 24–7 with Fig. 24–4 B).

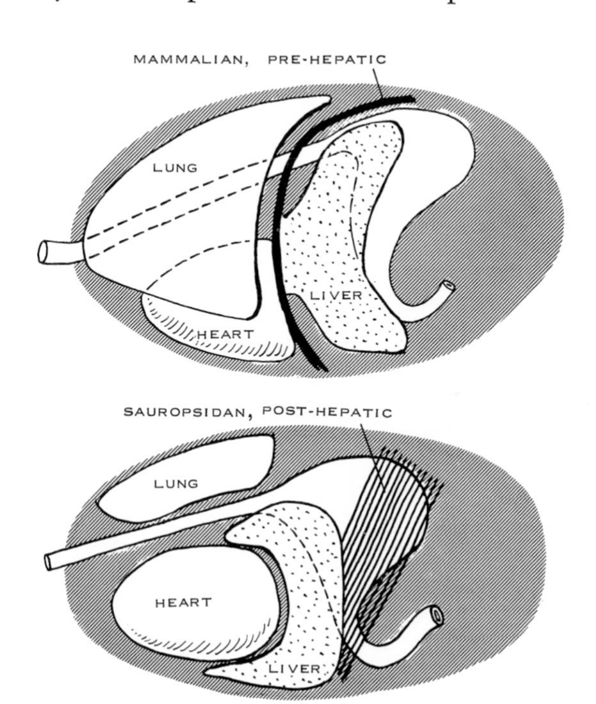

Fig. 24–5. Types of diaphragms.

Although such recesses are recognizable in some adult urodeles and lizards, they regularly become transformed in other amniotes during post-pharyngular development. In turtles, alligators, and birds, the pleural recesses are provided with a mesenteric floor by the formation and spread of an attachment of the lateral mesenteries to the somatopleure, which walls off their contained lungs in **pleural cavities** (Fig. 24–8). Primitively, these pleural cavities are open to the peritoneal cavity posteriorly, as they still are found to be in many adult turtles. But in other species they are progressively walled off, almost, or quite, to the point of closure.

Since this closure of pleural cavities is accomplished by the part of each lateral mesentery that lies between its lung and the liver, another result is achieved at the same time, namely that the liver becomes tied to the lateral body wall on each side also. Now if the mesogastrium remains complete in the dorsal mesentery, and if the gastrohepatic and falciform ligaments are

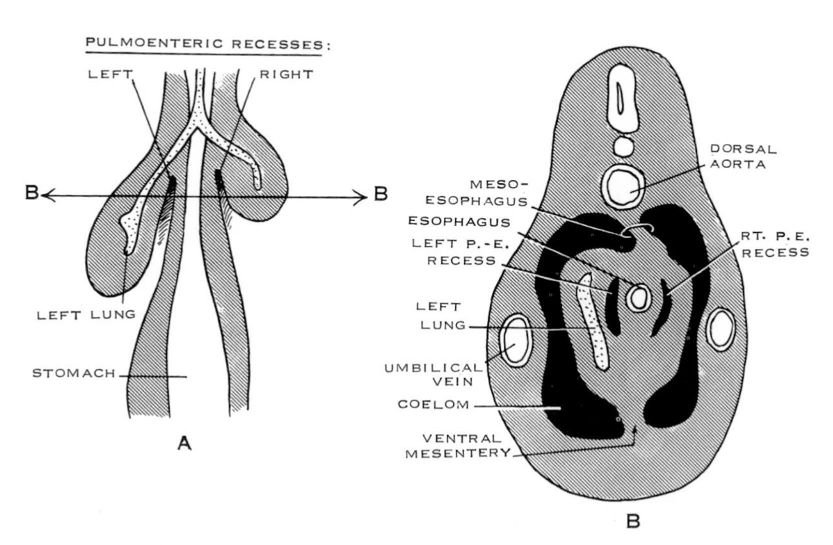

Fig. 24–6. Coelom relations of the lung buds in a chick pharyngula. A. Diagram, ventral view. B. Section of whole embryo through plane of arrow in A.

present to support the liver below it, *six* pockets may be present in the anterior part of the coelom, all of them open posteriorly to the general peritoneum at least in their early stages of

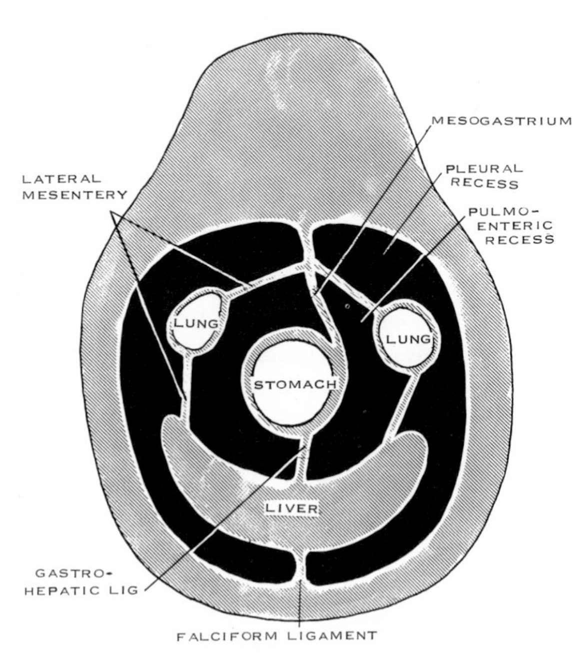

Fig. 24–7. Diagram of anterior peritoneal recesses.

development: the two **pleural cavities** (isolated from the rest by the dorsal parts of the lateral mesenteries), and the two **pulmo-enteric recesses** (below the pleural cavities and separated from each other by the gastrohepatic ligament), and two **liver sacs** (separated from each other by the falciform ligament, and from the pulmonary recesses by the fusion of lateral mesenteries to the somatopleure) (right side of Fig. 24–8).

In crocodilia and birds, not only may the pleural cavities be isolated from the rest of the peritoneal cavity, but also the liver sacs and pulmo-enteric spaces are walled off by the formation of a post-hepatic diaphragm. Various pairs or combinations of these spaces may break through to each other in particular species, by secondary loss of their mesenteric walls. Or some or all of them may be obliterated by secondary adhesions in later development. In snakes, for instance, all traces of pleural cavities or pulmo-enteric recesses disappear during fetal growth, and nothing remains of the peritoneal cavity anterior to the free hind end of the liver except vestiges of the liver sacs.

Conditions in birds are further complicated by the air sacs, which push into the floors of the pleural cavities, and into the abdomen (see page 487).

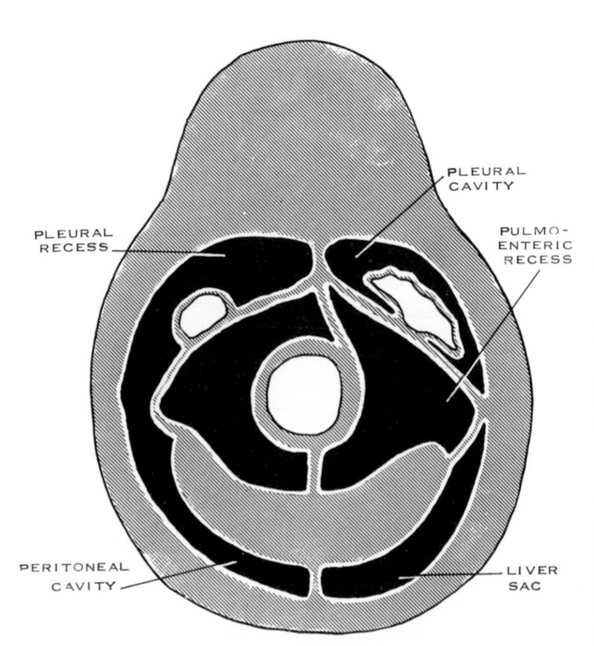

Fig. 24–8. Fixation of the lateral mesenteries in sauropsida. Early stage shown left, later at right.

III. THE PLEURAL CAVITIES AND DIAPHRAGMS OF MAMMALS

A. Development

The lung buds of mammals project posteroventrally into the pleural canals from the mesoesophagus. The right one develops a lateral mesentery, complete with an attachment to the liver, but the left one does not. Anteriorly the pleural canals are promptly closed off from the pericardial cavity, but posteriorly they remain open to the general peritoneal cavity for some time, dorsal to the liver. When they do close posteriorly—and this does not happen in man until the body is about 20 millimeters long—this traps the lungs in pleural cavities, and forces them to expand ventrally rather than posteriorly. Furthermore, the active agent in closing the pleural cavities off in this case is not the lateral mesenteries but the dorsal part of the diaphragm. The resulting anatomical situation is uniquely mammalian.

This diaphragm is formed from three principal components, and in several stages. The first or *ventral component* is the septum transversum, whose establishment has already been described (page 146). The two pleural canals and their contained lung buds lie dorsal to this, closed off early from the pericardial cavity, but still open for a time posteriorly. The second or *dorsal component* is what isolates these canals from the peritoneal cavity. There is a third, or *muscular component:* a migrating cluster of promuscle cells grows in from the somatopleure on each side, towing behind it a **phrenic nerve** made up of branches from several cervical spinal nerves. It is natural that these muscles and nerves should be from cervical segments because the diaphragm is being assembled at just that trunk level. The elongation of the neck and relocation of the thoracic viscera caudad has only just started at that stage.

The dorsal part of the diaphragm is assembled on each side in twin operations, each one involving two factors which meet like the pinch of a pair of scissors to close off the pleural canal of that side. The lateral blade of each scissor is a **nephric fold** (also called a pleuroperitoneal membrane)—a flange of mesoderm jutting medially from the kidney ridge. The medial blade is a bulge of mesenchymatous tissue from the splanchnopleure, called the **posterior closing fold** (Fig. 24–9). Both the disposition and the relative importance of the two pairs of components of the dorsal diaphragm vary with the species, but it is no great problem for the medial and lateral folds to meet on each side, each scissor closing off the posterior end of its own canal: the openings are in any case only a small fraction of a millimeter across. Nevertheless a failure of closure does rarely occur, usually on the left side, and this leaves the stomach of the adult individual free to bulge into the thorax. The anomaly is called a **diaphragmatic hernia.**

The muscles spread into both ventral and dorsal parts of the diaphragm, disposing themselves radially about a central tendon. The junctions of the two phrenic nerves with the adult

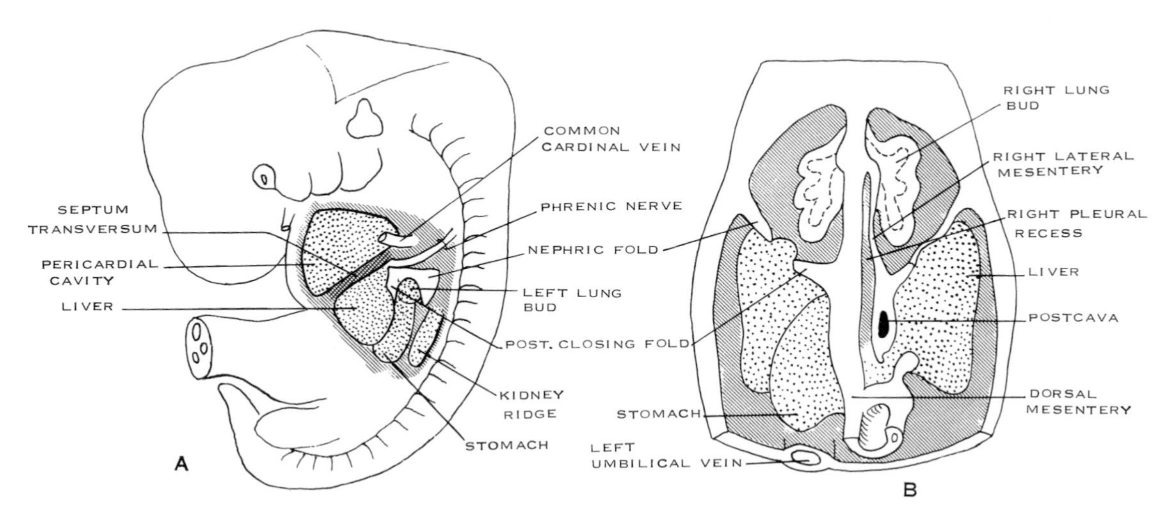

Fig. 24–9. Establishment of the mammalian diaphragm. A. 9-millimeter human embryo. Viscera exposed through window cut in left body wall. B. Diagram of same stage, body cavity dissected open from dorsal side.

(B after E. S. Goodrich, 1930, Studies on Structure and Development of Vertebrates, by permission of Macmillan & Co., Ltd., London.)

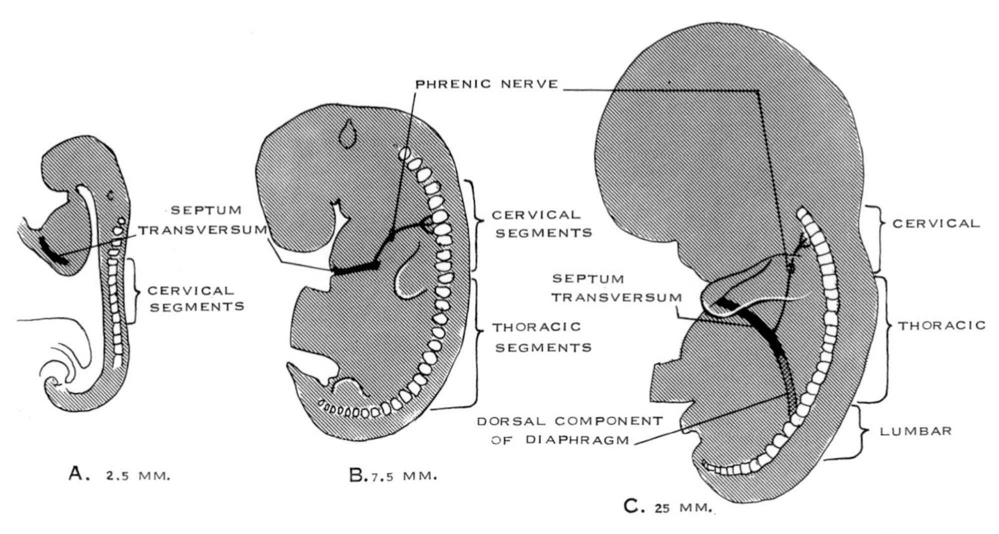

Fig. 24–10. Posterior drift of diaphragm components in the growing human embryo.

diaphragm remain as convenient markers of the effaced boundary between dorsal and ventral components of the pre-muscular diaphragm.

Two other remarkable growth phenomena are already in operation by the time the diaphragm has been assembled and the posterior ends of the pleural canals finally stoppered. One is the general shift of the ventral viscera caudad into the thorax and out of the neck. Since the diaphragm is planted between the liver and the heart, both of which are moving backward, it also must shift in the same direction, while its phrenic nerves correspondingly spin out their length from the cervical spinal cord (Fig. 24–10). In adult mammals, a record of this shift of the diaphragm remains in the long posterior course of the two phrenic nerves, through the posterior half of the neck and the whole length of the thorax—a distance of as much as 5 feet in a large giraffe.

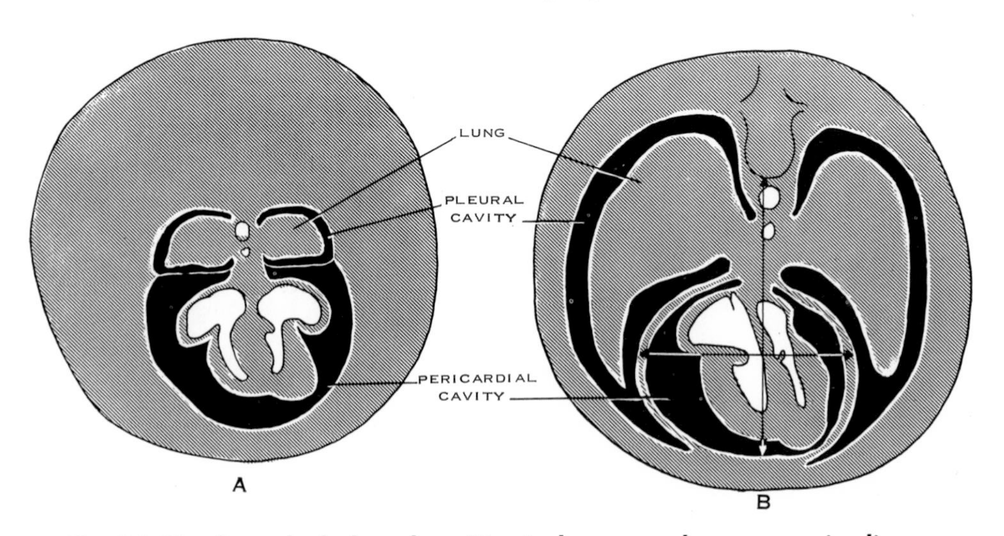

Fig. 24–11. Spread of pleural cavities in human embryos, seen in diagrammatic transverse sections of the thorax. A. At 7 weeks. B. At 9 weeks. Arrows indicate extent of mediastinum.

The other growth phenomenon is the expansion of the pleural cavities themselves (Fig. 24–11). However fast the lungs expand, the pleural cavities keep well in advance of them, pushing caudad and ventrad, forcing the established tissues that lie outside to give way and remodel themselves constantly. The phenomenon recalls the expansion of the semicircular canals through a rearrangement of the rigid skull tissues, to make way for the enlarging semicircular ducts of the inner ear. The mechanics of the process are completely unexplored.

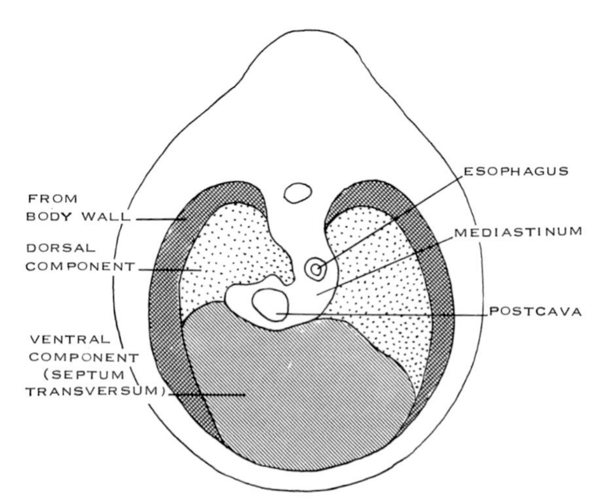

Fig. 24–12. Components of the adult human diaphragm, viewed from above.
(After I. Broman, 1904.)

The result of these growth processes is that the lungs of mammals, instead of remaining in a high dorsal position as they would in birds and turtles, or passing caudad among the abdominal viscera as they would in amphibia and most lizards and snakes, proceed to spread ventrad around the sides of the pericardial cavity. They also encroach somewhat upon the edges of the diaphragm, so that its boundaries are extended posteriorly upon all sides of the flanks. Not only does the diaphragm acquire its dome in this way, but as its line of attachment to the body wall recedes posteriorly it acquires more surface area. Thus the definitive diaphragm contains not only a ventral component from the septum transversum and dorsal components from the scissors-folds of the pleuroperitoneal membranes, but also an outer rim carved from the previously established body wall (Fig. 24–12).

B. The Mediastinum

When the lungs in their pleural cavities have finished wrapping themselves around the pericardial cavity and the heart, and when they have expanded farther to fill all the rest of the available space in the thoracic cavity, a body area called the **mediastinum** is established. It is defined as the space between the two pleural cavities. Nothing like this compartment exists in other tetrapods. Some of the non-mammals never form pleural cavities at all, and some obliterate them during fetal development. Those that do retain closed pleural cavities in the adult condition carry them high dorsally (Fig. 24–5 B), where nothing is included between them except the bodies of thoracic vertebrae and the dorsal aorta.

The entire mammalian pericardial cavity, together with the heart and the great veins and arteries that enter and leave it, are all contained in the mammalian mediastinum. So are the esophagus and its mesentery, the lower end of the trachea and its bronchial fork, the thoracic parts of the vagus nerves, and the attenuated phrenic nerves, not to mention vestiges of the thymus glands and parts of the lymphatic system and autonomic nerves. In fact, everything inside the ribs has been enveloped by the spread of the pleural cavities, and herded into the mediastinum.

Of passing interest is a usually well-defined but empty space within the posterior part of the mediastinum. Called the **infracardiac bursa,** it is the remnant of the embryonic right pulmo-enteric recess of the coelom (Fig. 24–6), which had been formed by projection of the lateral mesentery onto the liver, as in other tetrapods. It was completely isolated from the peritoneal cavity in early fetal development by the completion of the diaphragm. Normally obliterated in man, it is usually found in other adult mammals and is sometimes large enough to be referred to as an empty third pleural cavity (Fig. 24–15 B).

IV. POST-HEPATIC DIAPHRAGMS

The pre-hepatic muscular diaphragm is not achieved in any lizards, though all the constituents, including the septum transversum, nephric folds, midline mesentery (bulging with liver), and a ready source of myotomic striated muscle, are all present. In one family (Agamidae) it is reported that a pleural cavity is actually completed on one side by the joining of all these elements except the muscles.

On the other hand a few lizards of another family (Tejidae) develop a fairly complete *post-hepatic* partition, which walls off the pleural cavities, completely on the right side and incompletely on the left. It is produced by a spreading growth from the gastrohepatic ligament, and acquires smooth muscle fibers.

In crocodilians this **post-hepatic diaphragm** becomes complete and prominent. The falciform and gastrohepatoduodenal ligaments of the ventral mesentery system spread out ventrally and laterally and form adhesions to the body wall, in which the stomach and liver also join. Striated muscle fibers from the posterior body wall spread out over this connective tissue wall, and it thus resembles the mammalian diaphragm in all but the crucial morphologic details: it is on the wrong side of the liver and formed from entirely different elements. Its muscles are supplied by lumbar spinal nerves, not by phrenics. Closed liver sacs lie anterior to it (Fig. 24–5 B; right side of Fig. 24–8).

Birds have a post-hepatic diaphragm which is directly comparable both in origin and in structure with that of crocodilia. It divides a posterior peritoneal space containing the abdominal air sac, intestines and urogenital organs from anterior peritoneal spaces containing the liver.

Since the liver itself is anchored by four mesenteries (the gastrohepatic and falciform ligaments which lie respectively above and below it in the midline, plus the two lateral mesenteries) it occupies four more or less isolated coelomic spaces: two **pulmo-enteric recesses** dorsally and two **liver sacs** ventrally. Since the post-hepatic diaphragm is constructed partly out of both the dorsal and the ventral mesenteries of the stomach, the gizzard is embedded in it.

V. AVIAN PRE-HEPATIC SEPTA

The lungs, heart, liver and intestines of birds are anchored in place and propped apart from

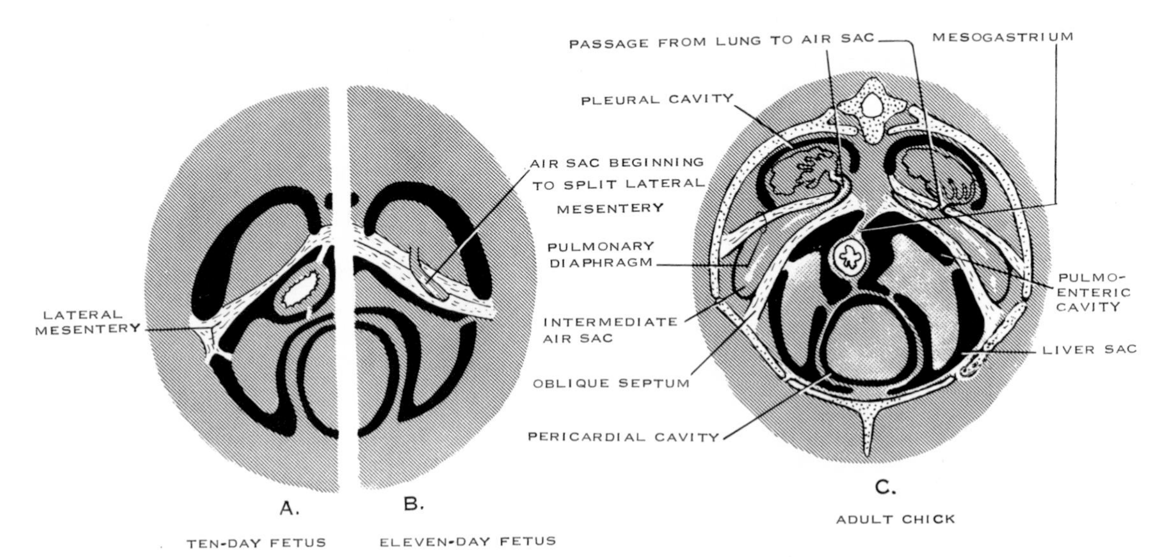

Fig. 24–13. History of the lateral mesenteries in the chick, seen in diagrammatic transverse sections of the thorax.

(C after E. S. Goodrich, Studies on the Structure and Development of Vertebrates, 1930, by permission of Macmillan & Co., Ltd., London.)

one another by a formidable array of partitions, whose relations with those of other animals could not have been understood until their development had been studied. Up to the fifth day of incubation the chick embryo shows quite the usual array of midline mesenteries, septum transversum, lateral mesenteries for the lungs, pleural and pulmo-enteric recesses, and nephric folds. Later, however, one finds not only the post-hepatic diaphragm and the four liver-containing coelomic divisions as described above, but also two paired sets of pre-hepatic septa.

One pair of these occupies a high dorsal and almost horizontal position in the thorax, each member forming the floor of its own pleural cavity and supporting the lung of its own side (Fig. 24–13 C). These two together may be called the **pulmonary diaphragm;** they are separated from each other by the dorsal mesentery and the dorsal aorta. The other pair are properly described from their adult position as oblique septa, and they are widely separated from each other both by the heart in its pericardial cavity, and by the liver in its coelomic chambers. As may be seen from Figure 24–13 A and B, these four partitions are all produced from the lateral mesenteries, each of which is split into upper and lower layers by the invasion of intermediate air sacs from the lungs. All four of them extend toward the body wall from the midline mesentery, and all are cut off posteriorly by the late formation of the post-hepatic diaphragm (Fig. 24–14). Each of them is originally in contact with coelom-derived space on one surface, but the space between the two right ones, or the two left ones, is not coelomic, it is air-filled, at least after hatching.

With further growth of the lungs, the pleural cavities of most birds are obliterated. The pulmonary diaphragm, which acquires muscles from the hypaxial (intercostal) myotomes of the thoracic segments, holds the lungs tightly against the ribs. Since birds can breathe enough to stay alive when all their air sacs are opened to the outside, it is thought that the musculature of the pulmonary diaphragm, in conjunction with rib-moving muscles and the elasticity of the lung tissues, can keep air moving through the parabronchial tubes.

The oblique septa sometimes acquire smooth muscles. It has been suggested that these might have to do with manipulation of tides of air from the intermediate air sacs back into the lung.

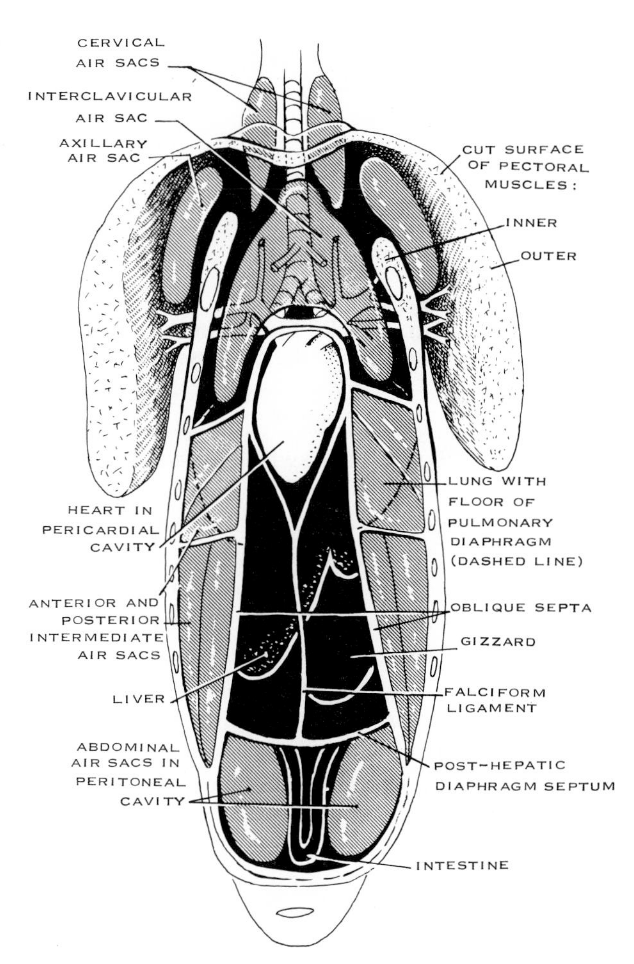

Fig. 24–14. Body cavities and partitions in a duck.
(After H. Strasser, 1877.)

VI. THE OMENTAL BURSA

When the stomach is first beginning to enlarge and to bend to the left, the thick mesenchyme of its mesogastrium develops a pocket or cavitation on its right side. This not only happens in all tetrapod embryos, it has been reported in some fish also. In the tetrapods, with rare exceptions, this pocket, called the **omental bursa,** becomes confluent with the pulmo-enteric

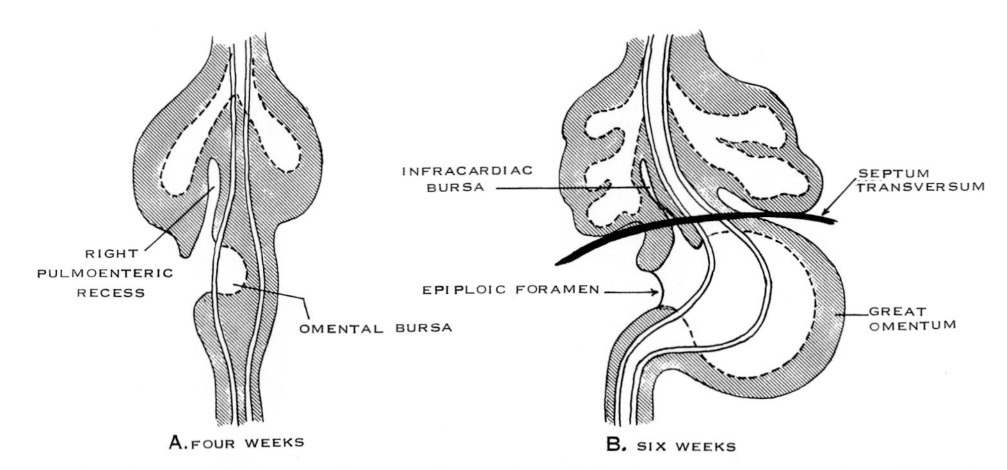

Fig. 24–15. Stages in the transformation of the human mesogastrium. Ventral view diagrams, the gut dissected to the frontal plane.

(After L. B. Arey, Developmental Anatomy, 6th edition, 1954, by permission of W. B. Saunders Co.)

recess of the right side, which is extending posteriorly along the dorsal surface of the liver through the agency of the right lateral mesentery (Fig. 24–15 A). The opening into the bursa, which is called the **epiploic foramen,** is bounded anteriorly and posteriorly by the liver and the duodenum; and dorsally and ventrally by the postcava and the hepatic portal vein.

Both the omental bursa and the epiploic foramen have many fates among the tetrapods, leading to curious differences in the disposition of the coelom and mesenteries.

The epiploic foramen may get bigger as development proceeds, until the whole bursa is secondarily opened into the general coelom and disappears, as in many adult lizards. Contrariwise, it may become narrowed (most mammals), or closed up tight (most urodeles, some turtles, the crocodilia and birds, etc.). When it becomes closed, the omental bursa may rarely remain as a completely closed chamber, but it generally either disappears by obliteration (crocodilia), or by the breaking through of the mesogastrium, which opens it up to the *left* side of the body cavity (urodeles, birds).

In mammal embryos, the dorsal mesogastrium is especially thick and soft, and the omental bursa excavates it to an exceptional depth (Fig. 24–15 B). At the same time, the mesogastrium proliferates actively from the greater curvature (original dorsal but now left side) of the stomach, forming a loose sheet of mesentery, the **great omentum,** which extends to the left and posteriorly. The excavation of the omental bursa spreads to this, so that the original chamber between duodenum and liver is much augmented by the cavity of the great omentum. In some mammals this omental outgrowth from the mesogastrium spreads down over the entire ventral part of the abdominal cavity to the pelvis. The cavity may reach to the farthest extent of the omentum, or only part-way, depending on the species. As previously mentioned, the right pulmo-enteric recess or infracardiac bursa (page 501) becomes cut off from the omental bursa and the rest of the coelom by the development of the dorsal diaphragm (Fig. 24–15 B).

VII. ADHESIONS AND OBLITERATIONS OF MESENTERIES

In the primitive embryonic condition, the large viscera are loosely tied in place by a complete simple dorsal mesentery and fragments of ventral mesentery. Subject to these restrictions they may slither comfortably about in a lubricated or serous cavity, the coelom. The walling off of the pericardial and then the paired pleural cavities, and the formation of further diaphragmatic partitions, increases the restrictions on their move-

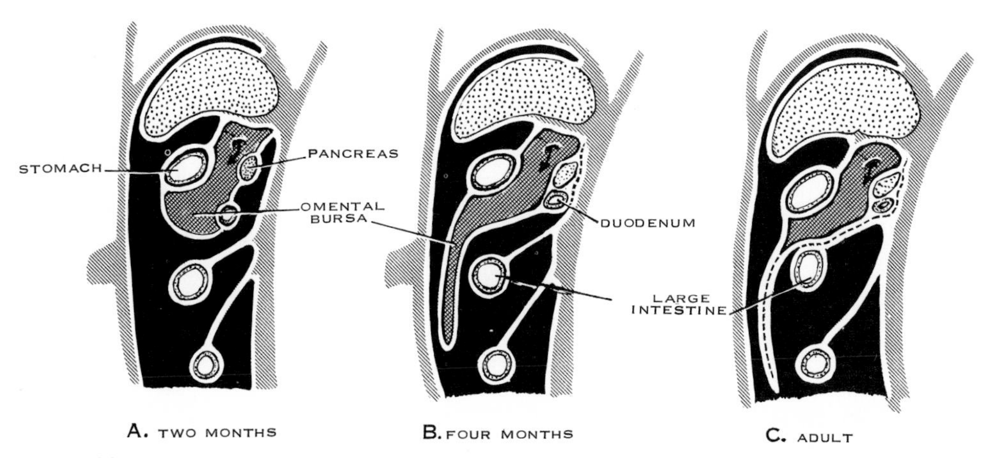

Fig. 24–16. Adhesions of mesenteries during human development.
(After L. B. Arey, Developmental Anatomy, 6th edition, 1954, by permission of W. B. Saunders Co.)

ment. The process is carried still further in many vertebrate species by the adhesion of one mesentery to another, or the adhesion of mesenteries or viscera to the body wall.

This is seen even in fishes. The peritoneal cavity of adult members of some carp species for instance, is bound up in large numbers of connective tissue threads that almost hide the simple arrangement of mesenteries formed in their embryos. One of the dipnoan fishes, *Lepidosiren,* has lost the anterior third of its peritoneal cavity by complete adhesion of stomach and liver with each other and with the body wall. Similar adhesions fix the viscera anterior to the duodenum in snakes and lizards. Lungs develop adhesions to the body wall in turtles, birds, elephants, etc.

Secondary fusions of overlapping mesenteries are common. In many mammals the coiling of the gut brings the mesentery of the large intestine (mesocolon) up against the mesogastrium and mesoduodenum or the mesentery proper, and at the areas of contact these mesenteries may variously fuse together.

In anthropoids including man (but not monkeys), great areas of the mesentery of the large intestine fuse with the dorsal body wall, "fixing" the ascending and descending limbs of the large intestine. The name of the duodenum, or 12-finger gut, comes from the fact that in man a post-pyloric section of gut about 12 fingers wide becomes fixed to the body wall in this way (Fig. 24–16 B). Thus the mesoduodenum which exists normally in the human embryo is obliterated in the adult. It is an exceptional thing, occurring in few other species, even of mammals. Unfortunately the definition of the duodenum, which rests on this peculiarity, is inapplicable to other animals.

Mesenterial adhesions of endless variety are found among vertebrates, spectacular cases being found in many teleosts, the vegetarian turtles, and birds. Investigations of embryos of such animals always show that the coelom and mesenteries are simple when first formed, and the puzzling adult arrangements are late secondary developments.

REFERENCE

1. Goodrich, E. S., 1930. *Studies on the structure and development of vertebrates.* Macmillan & Co., Ltd., London. Also Broman, I., 1937. *In* L. Bolk, E. Göppert, E. Kallius, and W. Lubosch (eds.), *Handbuch der vergleichenden Anatomie der Wirbeltiere.* Urban u. Schwarzenberg, Berlin.

25

The Heart

I. FORMATION OF TUBE AND CHAMBERS

The early embryology of the heart has already been described in general terms (pages 144–146). Conspicuous variations occur in the different classes, depending on the amount and distribution of yolk and the patterns of morphogenetic movements, but there is also uniformity. Two heart fields always form (page 185) on the future ventral borders of the right and left lateral plates of mesoderm, and are gradually swung together and merged into one. The cells which produce the first visible heart anlage (endocardial cells, Fig. 8–16 A) first aggregate in a loose string, then proliferate into a loose mesenchyme, and finally organize into a tube which starts to twist almost at once (Fig. 25–1). Merging of the two heart anlagen takes place in fishes at the cell-strand stage and in sauropsida (Fig. 8–17) commonly at the mesenchymal stage, but in mammals not until after the precocious formation of right and left tubes and the onset of blood flow. Whatever the timing, the end result in all cases is the appearance of a single heart tube in the midventral line, even though potentiality exists for forming two (Fig. 10–10).

First the tube differentiates a thin endocardial lining, around which accumulates the **epimyocardium** (Fig. 25–2 B). Most of the cells of the latter gradually convert into syncytial nets of branching striated muscle fibers joined end to end, and laid on in a complex continuum of layered helices. Outside these, a thin layer differentiates as the **epicardium,** the visceral lining of the pericardial cavity. The thickening layer of muscle between epi- and endocardium is distinguished as the **myocardium.**

As the tube bends into its first S-form (Fig. 25–1), it bulges at intervals so as to form the four chambers characteristic of the pharyngula stage (pages 77, 144). The myocardium thickens regionally at different rates, remaining quite thin in the sinus venosus, less so in the atrium, and developing into a rugged wall in the ventricle (Fig. 25–2 D). Indeed, the interior of the ventricle soon becomes a spongy, pitted surface of whorled fibers, collected—clearly in some species, in more disordered fashion in others—into ridges arranged across the direction of blood flow (Fig. 25–4).

The earliest vessels to bring blood to the sinus venosus are the vitelline and common cardinal veins (Fig. 5–15, 26–2). Their relationships to the viscera and the septum transversum have been described earlier (pages 77, 146, 492). Even before valves have been formed in the twisted tube,

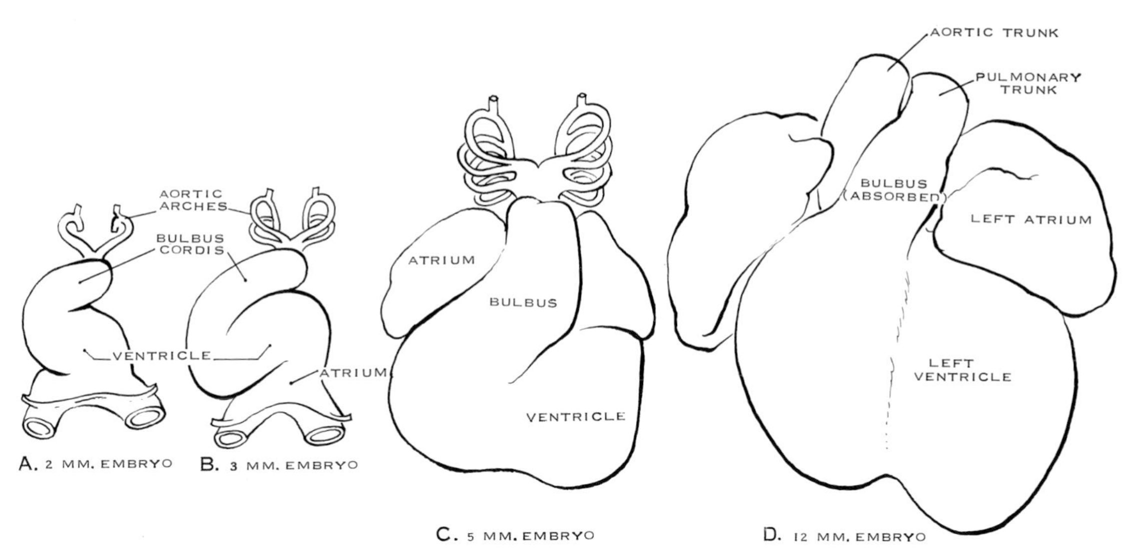

Fig. 25–1. Changing form of the developing human heart (ventral views).
(A, B, and C after T. C. Kramer, 1942.)

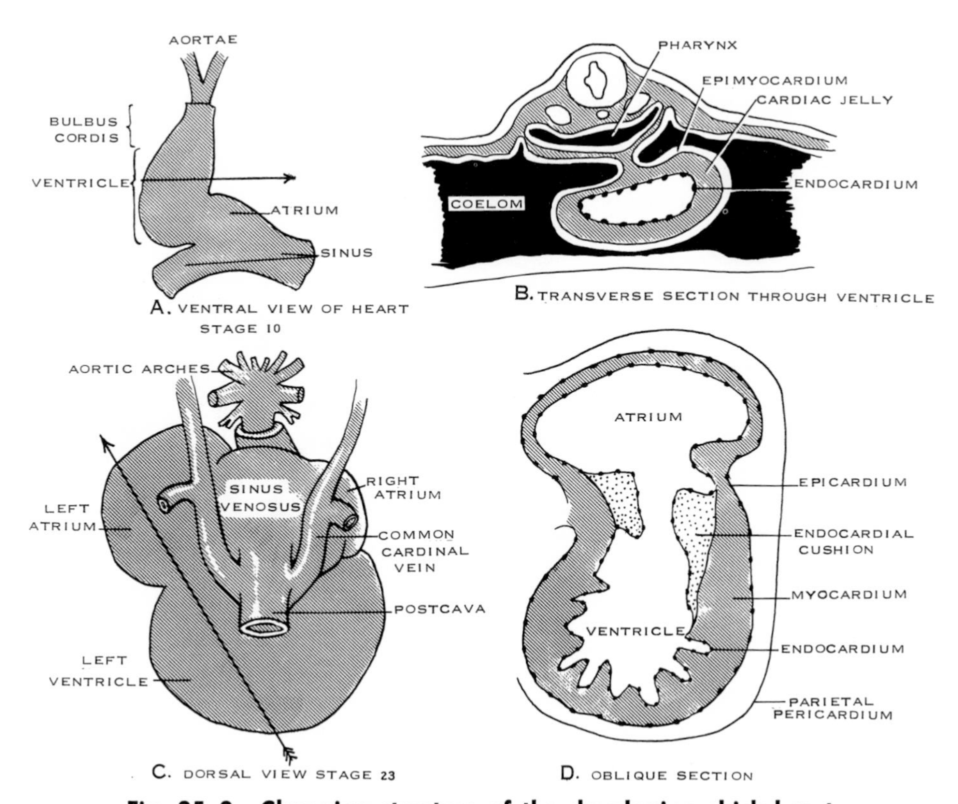

Fig. 25–2. Changing structure of the developing chick heart.

blood swirls smoothly through it because the beating of the chambers is coordinated. This is the result of three facts: (a) Since the fibers of cardiac muscle are all interconnected in a syncytium, a beat starting anywhere in the heart will spread to all the other parts. (b) Although each part has its own intrinsic rate of pulsation, which can be demonstrated by cutting it out and watching it continue to beat in isotonic salt solution, a pulse reaching it from another part can induce it to beat sooner. (c) The intrinsic rate for the atrium is faster than that for the ventricle, and the rate for the sinus venosus is still faster.

So, as soon as the atrium acquires the ability to pulsate, it imposes its quicker rhythm on the previously beating ventricle; i.e., it becomes the **pacemaker.** When the sinus venosus starts up, this in turn becomes the pacemaker for the whole heart. Since the beat starts at the sinus and sweeps progressively through atrium, ventricle, and bulbus cordis, blood is grasped as it enters from the great veins and propelled in an orderly way to the aortic arches, with no appreciable backflow.

Already at the pharyngula stage, however, the three relatively constricted rings that appear between the four bulging chambers of the heart tube acquire thickened linings, the **endocardial cushions** (Fig. 25–2 D). These quickly become excavated and transformed into pocket valves (sinoatrial, atrioventricular, etc.), which prevent the backflow that would otherwise occur in the larger, more powerfully contracting heart. In amniotes, the rapid temporary appearance of a transparent stiff **cardiac jelly** between the endocardium and the myocardium of the ventricle-bulbus section of the heart tube (Fig. 25–2 B) precedes the definition of these valves and increases the efficiency of the pump. Lastly, in the bulbus cordis section of the tube, two or more (usually four) longitudinal endocardial ridges appear, whose derivatives figure importantly in the comparative anatomy of the adult hearts, taking the form of valves or spiral partitions.

The ability of most parts of the embryonic heart to contract automatically in a definite rhythm seems to become restricted during later development in many vertebrates, persisting only in certain localized bundles of cardiac tissue, which can be recognized physiologically and cytologically as the **stimulation fibers.** Most of the heart musculature, composed of **contraction fibers,** loses this autonomy, and contracts only when triggered off by the spreading impulses from the stimulator fibers. There is much variation in the degree of this specialization, even among members of the same class of vertebrates. The sinus venosus and/or the constricted sino-

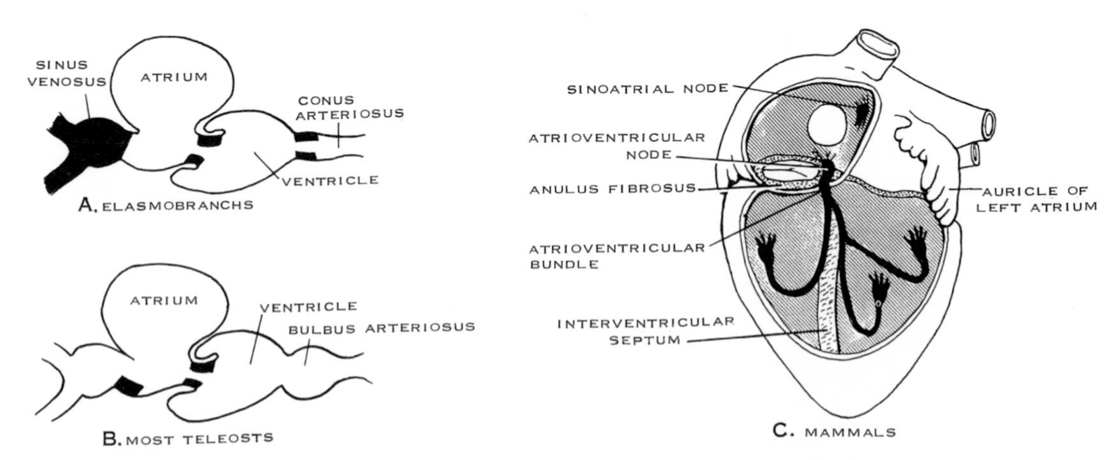

Fig. 25–3. Sites of pacemaker tissues in various adult hearts.

(A and B after von Skramlik, 1955, in Ergebnisse der Biologie, 11, by permission of Springer Verlag. C after A. Benninghoff, 1933, in Handbuch der Vergleichenden Anatomie der Wirbeltiere, by permission of Urban u. Schwarzenberg.)

atrial and atrioventricular rings are the common sites for the stimulation tissues or pacemakers (Fig. 25–3).

II. BASIC DIFFERENCES IN VERTEBRATE HEARTS

The main subject of this chapter is the ways in which the relatively standardized pattern of the heart at the pharyngula stage becomes adapted to serve different respiratory devices in the adults of aquatic, amphibious, and terrestrial vertebrates. Most of these specializations and differences arise in development after the pharyngula stage.

No false biological statement has had a longer or more popular life than the one about the ontogeny of the four-chambered mammalian heart recapitulating its phylogeny from the two-chambered fish heart and the three-chambered amphibian or reptilian heart. Often repeated in the days when Haeckel's so-called biogenetic law was widely and uncritically accepted, it can still be found in some elementary texts, side-by-side with correctly labelled diagrams of the four-chambered fish heart and the five-chambered frog heart.

In real life, all vertebrate hearts are composed of the same four chambers at the pharyngula stage (Fig. 5–12). A **truncus arteriosus** leads from the bulbus cordis to the aortic arches. Not strictly a part of the heart, the truncus lies at first outside the pericardial cavity and develops smooth rather than striated muscle. It becomes variously involved with the growing heart and aortic arches (Fig. 25–4).

In post-pharyngular development the four chambers of the heart and the truncus arteriosus may be reduced, or augmented, or specialized in different ways, in combinations specially suited to aquatic, or amphibious, or terrestrial life. These adaptations are directly concerned with different kinds of respiratory organs, and the hearts will therefore be contrasted as **gill-hearts, intermediate hearts,** and **lung-hearts.** Each one of these has evolved its own peculiar features, and it is easy to demonstrate that no one of them "recapitulates" or shows traces of the specializations of the others in its later development. Their ways part at or even before the pharyngula stage.

III. GILL-HEARTS

Except for the complexity of histological detail that comes with larger size, the gill-hearts of fishes are readily comparable with those of the pharyngula, except at their anterior ends. Just one current of blood passes through, from sinus to atrium, to ventricle; and the backflow is prevented by flap-valves, usually two at the sinoatrial and two (occasionally more) at the atrioventricular constrictions (Fig. 25–4). The heart remains a relatively simple S-tube in the sagittal plane, the arterial exit well removed from the venous intake. Its location is close behind the gill structures that develop from the pharyngeal pouches, and the truncus arteriosus delivers all of its blood to these gills by symmetrical aortic arches (Fig. 5–13).

The flabby atrium lies dorsal to the stout ventricle and there is always a bold contrast in the muscle walls of the two chambers. The lacework of muscle fibers in the atrial wall creases the endocardium only slightly, whereas the thick ventricular muscle is apt to be deeply cut by endocardium-lined crypts and pockets. In adult elasmobranchs and lampreys these pockets lie between radial septa arranged at right angles to the blood current, and this arrangement appears in embryonic hearts of some teleosts, but becomes obscured in adults.

The bulbus cordis and truncus arteriosus of adult gill-hearts are much transformed from their simple condition in the pharyngula, not always in the same way, but in response to the same mechanical necessity, of equalizing blood pressure. This problem exists in all vertebrates, but is accentuated in fishes because the blood, as soon as it leaves the heart, must pass through a first set of capillaries in the gills; and then, after it has been distributed by the dorsal aorta, it must pass through a second set of somatic or visceral capillaries. The blood pressure must be raised high enough in the heart to drive it through both sets of capillaries (not to mention a third set in

an artery enters and a vein leaves. They also have several, or numerous, lymph capillaries entering at various points around the capsule, and the pulp of lymphoid tissue is embedded in a swamp of lymph channels, along which phagocytic cells lie in wait. The lymph is drained out at the hilus, and both the incoming and outgoing lymph channels have valves that permit flow in one direction only.

The lymph nodes of mammals have several functions in common with the spleen. They are an important source of new leucocytes, they destroy old erythrocytes, and they are involved in the production of antibodies and the maintenance of immunities. They also have important additional functions in relation to the lymph stream, for their phagocytes arrest or devour particles being carried past them. In this way they filter out and even destroy invading bacteria, impede the migration of metastatic cancer cells, and remove cellular debris. Some of the heavy dust that settles in the lungs is drawn into the tissues and accumulates in lymph nodes along the bronchial passageways by way of the lymph stream.

In some mammals (but not in man) encapsulated patches of lymphoid tissue occur near the kidneys and spleen and along large blood vessels. They are called **hemal nodes** since they are penetrated by blood vessels but not by lymphatics. In this and other respects they *are* little spleens. Intergradations between these and the more common lymph nodes are also known.

Still more lymphoid tissue is present throughout the digestive tract of mammals, in the form of tiny solitary patches of lymphocytes scattered among the tissue layers, or in aggregations large enough to be visible to the naked eye, such as the tonsillar patches which surround the posterior part of the pharynx. The lower vertebrates do not generally show this histological arrangement, though "tonsils," i.e., lymphocyte aggregations lying in deep crypts of the mucous membrane, occur sporadically among the amphibia. But all vertebrates have an abundance of lymphoid tissue tucked away in various organs, particularly in the liver, kidneys, and intestine, and along the great blood vessels.

III. HISTOGENESIS OF BLOOD VESSELS

A. Sources

Blood vessels come from local mesenchyme, but there is no information as to whether all mesenchyme cells can act this way, or what determines that certain ones shall do so. The first steps in the formation of endothelium-lined blood spaces occur in the blood islands, but similar rearrangements of cells soon take place all over the embryo, and the agents are local cells, reacting to local conditions. The principal arteries will form in the complete absence of blood, or of the heart.

The very earliest vessels, such as the first of the aortic arches, the anterior part of the dorsal aorta and the vitelline veins, are normally established as major tubes before blood begins to flow. In other parts of the embryo, a diffuse network of extremely fine channels is established, from which certain pathways are then selected for more substantial differentiation. Most of the alternative pathways are then discarded. This emergence of enduring and individualized arteries and veins takes place gradually. In the chick embryo, for instance, the posterior parts of the future dorsal aorta are diffuse networks long after the anterior part is a busy thoroughfare of circulating blood (Fig. 26–2). And some time after the dorsal aorta has reached an advanced state of differentiation all the way to the tail, the new limb buds are permeated with nothing but a capillary network from which the definitive arteries and veins are gradually selected.

The development of these provisional capillary networks is probably favored by metabolic conditions in the tissues, such as the accumulation of carbon dioxide and nitrogenous wastes, conditions which can be corrected by the circulating blood. Even in adult life, wherever more capillaries are needed, as in wound repair, growth, regeneration, temporary adaptations to pregnancy, etc., more capillaries are quickly produced.

Substitution of better pathways for earlier ones is repeatedly observed in the development of the circulatory system. Selection from the

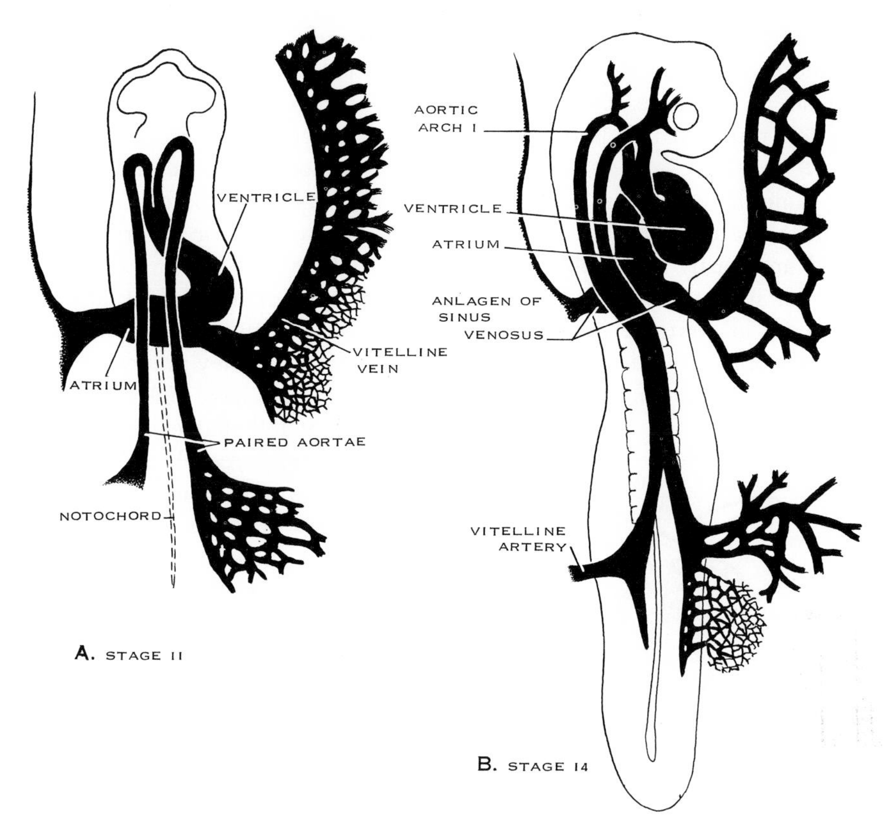

Fig. 26–2. Early blood vessels in the chick embryo.

multitudes of alternative pathways is probably decided by differential pressures within the blood stream, each vessel developing the size and strength demanded of it. The vessels are extraordinarily sensitive to the use that is made of them. If a young chick embryo is cultured without blood, its dorsal aorta survives no more than four or five hours.

B. Structure of Blood Vessels

Arteries have a smaller bore in relation to their diameter than veins do, because they develop tough walls reinforced by muscle and connective tissue. This makes them resistant to the higher blood pressure within them, and they are not so easily collapsed by outside pressure as capillaries and veins. Three layers can be distinguished in an artery wall. The cellular and fibrous elements of the inner and outer layers tend to dispose themselves lengthwise, the intermediate one circularly. The inner layer, called **tunica intima,** is a sleeve composed of flattened endothelial cells strengthened by an inner elastic membrane of longitudinal fibers. The middle layer or **tunica media** is usually the thickest of all, and is composed chiefly of smooth muscle cells wrapped around the tube at right angles to its length, interwoven with reticular or elastic fibers of connective tissue. The outermost layer, called **tunica externa,** is looser elastic and fibrous connective tissue laid on longitudinally, and intergrading with similar tissue in its neighborhood (Fig. 26–3).

The proportions of these three layers, and the types of tissues in them, vary according to circumstances and adapt to the needs of the animal. In the large amniotes there is no shock-absorbing device developed in the heart or ventral aorta comparable to the bulbus arteriosus of the teleost or the conus arteriosus of the shark (page

510), so that this function has to be served by the dorsal aorta and the stems of the large arteries that spring from it. In these, the muscular tissue is more or less replaced by elastic fibrous tissue [2].

Veins have the same three layers in their walls as the arteries, but they are comparatively large-bored, thin-walled and easily collapsible. Folds of the tunica intima may produce valves projecting into the cavity at strategic points to insure that blood flows only toward the heart. No such device is needed in the arteries because their blood is propelled at high pressure. The connective tissue of the tunica media is more prominent than the muscle, and the whole layer may be indistinct and poorly set apart from the others.

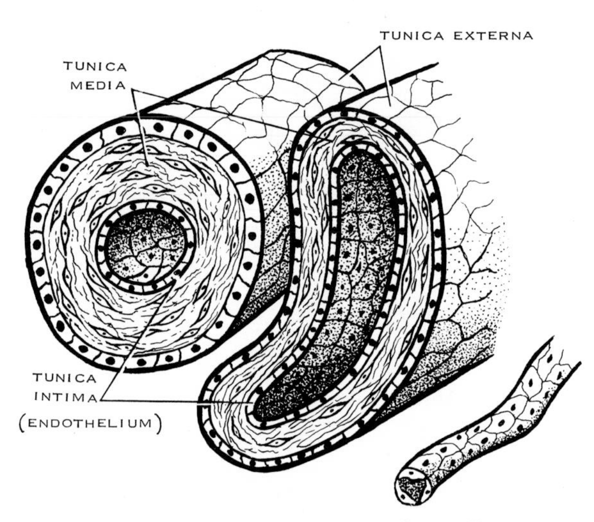

Fig. 26–3. Artery, vein, and capillary.
(After LeGros Clark, Tissues of the Body, 1939, by permission of Oxford University Press, Inc.)

The layers of the arteries and veins are developed slowly during fetal life and youth, and remain rudimentary in small vertebrates. Presumably their formation is a direct reaction of the cells to the tensions produced by blood pressure. Large veins (particularly the pulmonaries) are structurally much like arteries. The wall of a piece of vein grafted into an arterial trunk soon becomes arterial, i.e., develops a thick tunica media.

The walls of the larger arteries and veins are nourished by small arteries, veins and capillaries ("vasa vasorum") which penetrate the tunica externa. Nerves also grow into the tunica media, and the blood pressure and speed of blood flow can be adapted to the needs of the whole animal by the relaxation or contraction of the arterial musculature.

The smallest arteries usually intergrade with capillaries, losing their muscular and special fibrous layers as they branch and become smaller. The capillaries have only the thinnest lining of flattened endothelial cells, though they may be somewhat reinforced by other cells or by reticular fibers around them. They form incredibly profuse networks that penetrate almost all parts of the body, adapting their pattern to the local cellular structure. Apparently, gaps do not normally occur between the cells of their endothelial lining, yet the blood fluid diffuses through to become the lymph or general tissue juice, and white blood corpuscles worm their way out into the tissues and back again without difficulty. Though so small and delicate as to be invisible in dissection, the capillaries are the locus of all the indispensable physiological functions of the blood vascular system which were described in the introduction to this chapter.

Capillaries are normally tubular but are easily collapsed by pressure, which temporarily stops the blood flow. Observations of living capillaries in mammalian tissues also show that they are capable of contraction by themselves. In fact, circulation is normally stopped in many tiny arteries, capillaries, and veins for hours at a time and then opened up again. The total mileage of these vessels is apparently great enough so that in quiet moments parts of it are idled in rotation and the whole is held in readiness for times of stress. Direct arteriovenous connections are not uncommon in certain tissues, and the dilation of these would encourage an idling of circulation in the surrounding capillary bed.

C. Rete Mirabile

In some parts of some vertebrates, either arteries or veins may be found in the remarkable pattern known as **rete mirabile.** The stem vessel divides within a short space into a multitude of parallel ones, which may then either re-collect as a single vessel or pass over into capillaries. Some rete formations involve only one artery by itself in loose tissue, or one vein. In other cases, small arteries or veins may form a rete over the surface of a larger artery. These are biological applications of an engineering principle widely used in industry, namely counter-current exchange. The red gland associated with the teleost gas bladder is usually provided with an elaborate double rete mirabile (Fig. 23–3). The arteries approaching the gas bladder break into huge numbers of parallel arterioles which are spaced alternately with parallel venules derived from the drainage vein, so that each arteriole is surrounded by venules and vice versa [3].

Such patterns are conducive to the complete diffusion of substances from the blood, or complete absorption of substances from the tissues, as required in the placenta (Fig. 11–12), the liver, the kidneys, or gills. They may also serve for heat conservation. For instance, in the legs of birds and various mammals the returning venous blood trickles in rete formations over the surface of arteries, and is warmed by taking the heat from the arterial blood. Thus the center of the body may be maintained at high temperature without too much loss of heat into the ground, even when the animal is standing on ice.

A whale diving a mile or so deep in the ocean could not afford to have its ribs crushed in by the pressure. Since the air in its lungs is compressed to perhaps a tenth of its normal surface volume during a deep dive, the thoracic space must somehow be occupied. Huge mats of rete mirabile tissue line the pleura, and there is a very high proportion of blood per unit of body weight. Space occupied by the lungs while the whale is cruising at the surface is more and more occupied by blood which swells the rete tissue as he dives deeper and deeper [4].

Sinusoids are a variant of capillaries. Instead of being tubular and having a relatively uniform bore adjusted to the size of the erythrocytes, they are irregularly enlarged so as to wrap over the surfaces of neighboring tissues (Fig. 22–8 B). Instead of being completely lined with endothelium they may harbor large phagocytic cells in their delicate walls. They are found in the spleen, the liver, and a few other tissues.

IV. DEVELOPMENT OF THE ARTERIAL PATTERN

A. Dorsal Aorta

In the anamniotes the dorsal aorta appears before the onset of circulation as a single midline tube, but in the amniotes a pair of provisional aortae are formed, one on each side below the notochord (Fig. 26–2 A). The pair of them gradually fuse together to form the definitive dorsal aorta after the circulation of blood has commenced. Even after the fusion has taken place at the head end, the posterior part of the embryo shows for a time the gradual development of paired aortae out of the diffuse network of preliminary capillaries (Fig. 26–2 B).

In reptiles, the dorsal aorta secondarily undergoes a splitting into right and left aortae backwards from the head and in some cases well beyond stomach level in the mid-fetal stages. The plane of this split is shifted from sagittal to oblique, in such a way that the originally symmetrical subclavian arteries which spring from its dorsal surface are assigned to the right aorta, while the main visceral arteries which spring from its ventral surface are assigned to the left (Fig. 26–4). This has some physiological significance, because of the way the heart is partitioned (page 520). Fresh blood is available only on the left-dorsal side of the ventricle, where the right aorta arises. Therefore, the forelimbs, like the brain and special sense organs, receive fresh blood. The left aorta draws stale blood, but this seems to satisfy the requirements of the digestive viscera to which it flows. The anterior part of the dorsal aorta is secondarily split in anura also, but here the division takes place symmetrically.

B. Segmental Arteries

Pairs of segmental arteries are given off to the body wall from the dorsal aorta or its paired precursors (Fig. 17–28). In the metameric adults of the fishes, the series may remain complete, or

follow the boundaries between the oblique and the rectus muscles. Originally continuous vessels (Fig. 26–6) come to receive most of their blood anteriorly from the subclavians and posteriorly from the external iliacs, the two flows dwindling as they approach each other at umbilical level. The anterior sections are called **internal thoracic arteries** in adult anatomy, and the abdominal parts are called **epigastric arteries** (Figs. 26–6, 26–7).

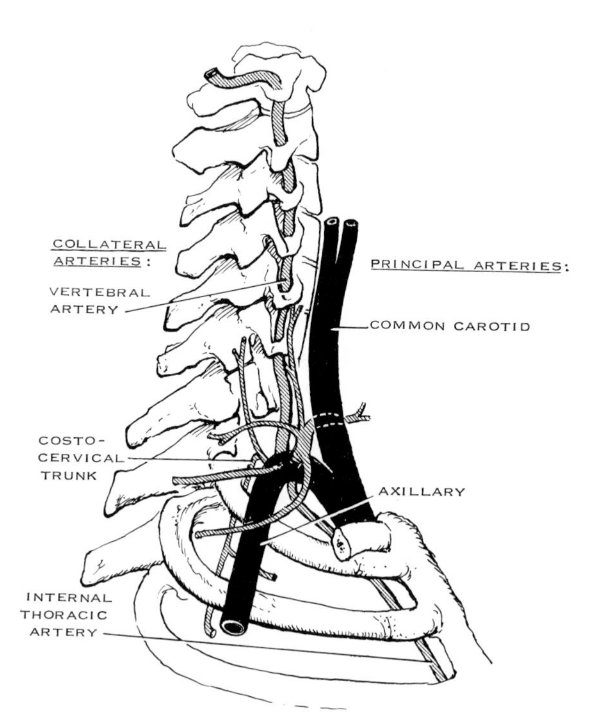

Fig. 26–7. Main and collateral arteries in man.
(After Sobotta-Uhlenhuth, Atlas of Human Anatomy, 7th edition, 1957, by permission of Hafner Publishing Co., Inc.)

D. Visceral Arteries

Besides the paired somatic arteries to the body wall, the dorsal aorta gives off variable numbers of **paired visceral arteries** to the intermediate mesoderm and **unpaired visceral arteries** across the dorsal mesentery to the intestinal tract (Fig. 5–14). The former category includes the **vitelline arteries** to the yolk sac or its equivalent, and the **allantoic** or **umbilical arteries** of amniotes, which carry blood to the allantois, the chorioallantois or the placenta as the case may be. Although these are lost with the scaffold tissues, other paired visceral arteries persist in the adult as supply lines to the kidneys, gonads and urogenital ducts. They are as variable as the organs they supply.

In some tetrapods the paired pulmonary arteries send twigs to serve parts of the anterior esophagus, but with this exception the entire digestive tract posterior to the pharynx, together with the great glands, spleen, and gas bladder, are served by the unpaired visceral arteries. In bony fishes, the gas bladder may intrude between the dorsal aorta and the whole dorsal mesentery, so that the entire intestine has to be served by a single trunk artery that arises from the anterior end of the dorsal aorta. In other vertebrates, a small number of arteries are given off at variable levels of the aorta, bearing such names as the **coeliac trunk** (PNA), **superior** and **inferior mesenteric arteries, rectal artery,** etc. The pattern is relatively stable for a species, but not at all so among the orders and classes.

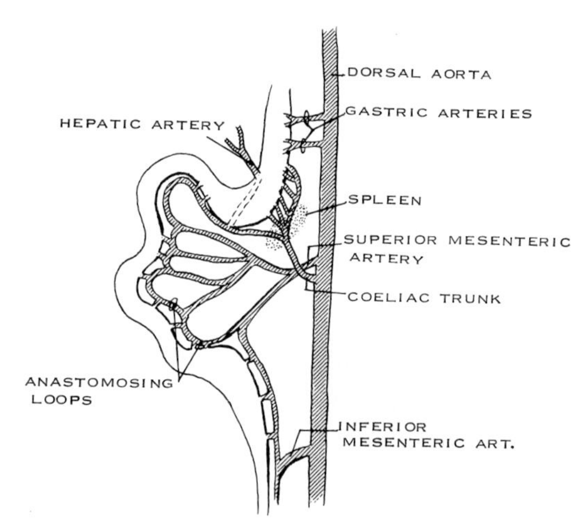

Fig. 26–8. Unpaired visceral arteries of a lizard, *Anolis*.
(After F. Hochstetter, 1898.)

One meets collateral pathways among the visceral arteries also (Fig. 26–8). Those that approach the intestine frequently make anastomosing loops in the dorsal mesentery, so that there are alternative paths by which blood can reach a particular point in case the normal line is impeded by pressure developing from unusual postures or injuries. There are some curious and unexplained overlappings of arteries in the mesenteries of reptiles (cf. coeliac trunk and superior mesenteric artery, Fig. 26–8), which might arise by reconstruction of trunk arteries through such anastomosing loops, or they might arise by the drifting of their origins along the dorsal aorta because of different rates of growth in different sectors of its walls. The locus of origin of the human coeliac trunk from the dorsal aorta is known to drift eleven segments caudad during the second month of gestation, past the origins of a series of fixed segmental arteries.

V. DEVELOPMENT OF VEIN PATTERNS

A. Inconstancy

Once the arterial system is set up in relation to the principal organs its pattern has a certain constancy, except for the late transformations of the aortic arches and the elimination of paths to the scaffold tissues. Not so the venous pattern, whose main vessels continue to be radically altered as late as the mid-fetal stage. None of the principal veins of the mammalian pharyngula (Fig. 5–15) persist in recognizable form in the adult. The venous transformations are different in the amniotes from what they are in the anamniotes, and are even very different in the separate orders of anamniotes.

This long drawn out and rather casual process finally yields a relatively predictable venous pattern for any given species. Nevertheless, gross individual anomalies are far commoner within the venous system than in the arterial. This may be because the selection of major pathways from the pervasive capillary bed is dominated by blood pressure from the heart on the arterial side, whereas on the venous side the pressure is low, giving control over to local factors produced by the growing and shifting organs and tissues.

B. Main Veins

Anterior and **posterior cardinal veins** are set up in uniform style in the young embryos of all vertebrates. The posterior cardinals trail along the sides of the dorsal aorta and are fed by **segmental veins** that parallel the segmental arteries. Single or multiple members of this series specialize as **subclavian** and **iliac veins** at the levels of the limb buds.

A single **caudal vein** develops in most vertebrates ventral to the caudal artery (continuation of the dorsal aorta in the tail). In anamniotes this makes a loop around the cloaca and continues craniad for a time as a subintestinal vein (Fig. 22–12), or a pair of vitelline veins, but is later connected with the posterior cardinals. The remodeling of the caudal vein and parts of the posterior cardinal system to form a renal portal system will be described in the next chapter. The remodeling of the subintestinal vein or the vitelline veins to form a hepatic portal vein has already been described (page 468).

The anterior cardinal veins, and anterior parts of the posterior cardinals, persist in many adult fishes and amphibia, but may be extensively augmented or reworked. In amniotes they are transformed almost unrecognizably. The development of a new belly vein, the **postcava,** to be described in the next chapter, captures most of the segmental drainage of the posterior cardinals including the iliacs, and they dwindle correspondingly.

Collateral veins establish a gridwork like that of the arteries in the trunk region, but with contrasts between amniotes and fishes. In the amniotes, **vertebral veins** are formed by longitudinal anastomoses between the segmental veins, paralleling the vertebral arteries. **Thoraco-epigastric veins** (PNA) parallel the internal thoracic and epigastric arteries. In the fishes the segmental veins are connected in a grid by two pairs of quite different longitudinal vessels: **lateral veins** and **abdominal veins.** The former accompany the lateral-line nerves of their own sides in the plane separating epaxial and hypaxial muscles; they empty craniad usually in the subclavian veins. The latter arise in the ventrolateral walls of the belly and drain toward the common cardinal veins.

The venous grid in the bellies of amphibia may include all four of these longitudinal systems, the two mentioned for amniotes and the two found in fishes. Their abdominal veins are formed as a pair but then fuse into a single midline vein which crosses the falciform ligament to the liver, joining the hepatic portal system. Somewhat similar abdominal veins form in amniotes as extensions of the allantoic veins, but usually disappear with these at birth or hatching.

All these variations and transformations, including those of the renal portal and postcaval systems (see next chapter), rather imply that the arrangement of the great veins is not very important in an animal so long as the blood can find its way back to the heart without undue delay. Surgical experiments have shown that there is no single vein in the body which cannot be successfully eliminated, if the throttling of it is done by slow enough stages so that the collateral routes can develop the capacity needed to replace it.

VI. PATTERNS OF LYMPHATIC VESSELS

The lymphatic channels arise by the local organization of mesenchymal cells into delicate endothelial tubes in the tissue spaces, which subsequently coalesce and organize into a drainage system. There is a highly developed pattern of functional veins in the embryo before the first lymphatics are detectable. In lower vertebrates, the principal lymphatic trunks run close by veins, and in all cases the lymph is finally emptied into veins.

Some investigators have decided that the cyclostomes and most elasmobranchs have no independent lymphatic system of vessels, but that there are hemolymph spaces in which both venous and lymphatic functions are carried on together. Others, not denying the difficulty of demonstration, find sinuous spaces in the lampreys and hagfishes, and definite channels in elasmobranchs, which are strictly lymphatic, wrapping over or forming networks around principal veins and emptying into them through openings guarded by valves [5].

In bony fishes and amphibian tadpoles, some of the veins are so thoroughly wrapped in these lymphatic networks that injection of ink or dyes into the lymph stream completely conceals them, giving the false impression that the veins themselves have been filled. In other places the lymphatics form more definite ducts which run parallel to the veins (Fig. 26–9). Separate lymph ducts occur in the dorsal and ventral midline at the base of the tailfin. A swamp of lymph capillaries encases the spinal cord, amounting to another longitudinal lymph trunk in the neural canal of the vertebral column. Extensive lymphatics in the tissue layers of the digestive system are drained across the dorsal mesentery to subvertebral trunks that follow the course of the posterior cardinal veins. More of the lymph flows in channels following the venous gridwork of the trunk.

In teleosts, the main longitudinal lymph channels empty into a neck-band of storage chambers or sinuses as they approach the heart. Rather similar subscapular or axillary lymph sinuses occur in lizards. These animals also have subvertebral trunks which occupy the position of

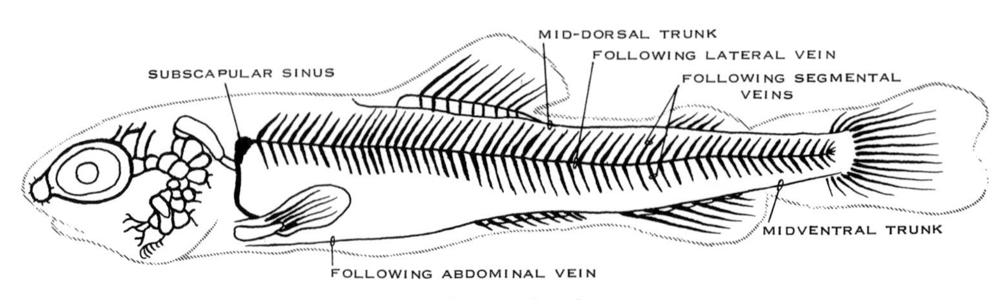

Fig. 26–9. Lymph vessels of a young trout.
(After Hoyer and Michalski, 1922.)

the obliterated posterior cardinal veins and join in a large midline sinus in the belly region, from which a pair of lymph vessels called **thoracic ducts** lead toward the veins entering the heart. A similar **lymphatic cistern** (cisterna chyli, PNA) and a single thoracic duct survive in mammals.

Frogs have intersegmental and longitudinal lymph vessels of the usual sort at the tadpole stage, but in the adult these expand into an extraordinary collection of enormous sinuses which lift most of the skin free from the underlying tissues, penetrate fascia planes between the principal muscle groups in the head and appendages, and wrap around certain of the viscera. The black lines in Figure 26–10 represent only strips along which the skin is attached to the body; between these lines the skin literally floats on lymph sinuses.

Tiny **lymph hearts** assist the flow of the lymph in a few groups of teleosts, and in all amphibia, all reptiles, and some birds. Urodele larvae show them in fairly segmental series on each side of the trunk and tail, where they rhythmically pump the lymph from subcutaneous and intermuscular channels directly into the lateral veins. Each of these little organs is a muscular sac fitted with a simple valve at the intake and another at the exit to the vein. The lymph hearts may be reduced in number as the individual matures.

Frogs usually have two pairs of lymph hearts, one under the skin at the base of the tail or (after metamorphosis) lateral to the cloaca near the tip of the urostyle, and the other deep under the vertebrae at the level of the scapulae. The posterior pair pump into the iliac veins, and the anterior ones into vertebral veins, just before these meet the internal jugular veins. It is the posterior pair that persist in reptiles and a few birds.

A number of new features sharply contrast the lymphatic system of birds and mammals from those of all lower vertebrates.

(a) The larger drainage ducts, instead of being irregular flabby nets wrapped over the surface of blood vessels, become definite though delicate tubes, visible by themselves in dissection without the use of colored injections.

(b) Superficial longitudinal ducts are replaced by deeper connections so that in the trunk most of the flow toward the heart is inward and craniad through the paired or single **thoracic duct** below the vertebral column. Lymphatics of

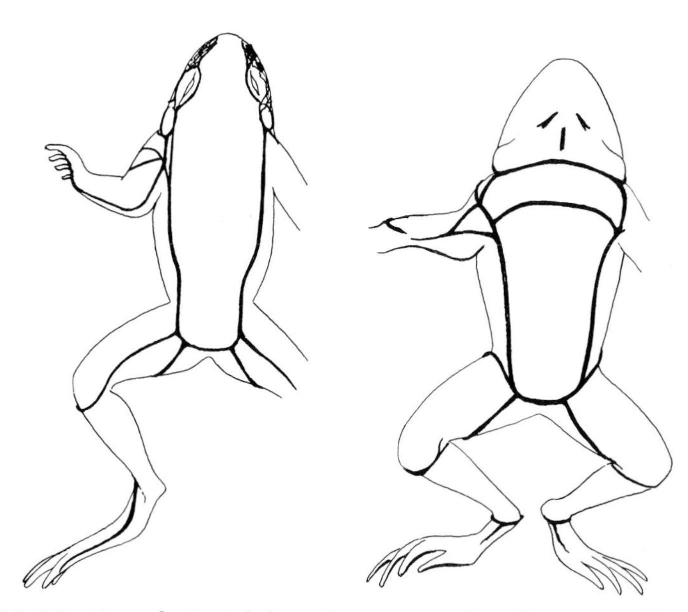

Fig. 26–10. Boundaries of the subcutaneous lymph sinuses of a frog.
(After E. Gaupp, 1896.)

the head, neck, and pectoral appendages approach the heart more or less directly and end in the great veins nearby.

(c) The larger lymph ducts have valves which permit flow only in the direction of the receiving veins, thus making use of the massaging effect of bodily movements, to press the lymph on its way.

(d) Lymph hearts often become non-functional in birds and are never developed in mammals.

(e) Lymph nodes (already discussed on page 529) are interposed in the course of the principal ducts.

Birds have only two pairs of lymph nodes, one at the base of the neck and the other deep in the lumbar region on the subvertebral trunks that lead to the thoracic duct, just anterior to the kidneys. Aside from quite problematic structures reported in frogs and crocodilia, these are the only true lymph nodes found in non-mammalian vertebrates. They are located at points where lower animals tend to have lymph sinuses. Here also are the great concentrations of the lymph nodes that are scattered over the bodies of mammals: at both ends of the neck, in the axilla, in the pelvis, and near the cistern of the subvertebral drainage path. The development of very large numbers of lymph nodes is one of the numerous new evolutionary steps taken by mammals.

REFERENCES

1. Colle-Vandevelde, A., 1961. *J. Embryol. Exptl. Morphol.* 9: 68.

2. Mayersbach, H., 1956. *Anat. Anz.* 102: 333.

3. Scholander, P. F., 1957. *Sci. American* 196: 96. Rete mirabile.

4. Walmsley, R., 1938. *Carnegie Inst. Wash. Publ.* 496, *Contrib. Embryol.* 27: 107.

5. Hoyer, H., 1938. *In* H. G. Bronn, *Klassen und Ordnungen des Tierreichs,* Bd. VI, 1 Abt., 2 Buch, Teil 2. No more detailed summary of the lymphatic system of lower vertebrates has appeared since this one.

27

The Urinary System

I. INTRODUCTION

The function of the urinary apparatus is to help control the total water content of the animal, and to remove nitrogenous and other wastes from the blood stream. Many other mechanisms in the body cooperate with the kidneys in maintaining the constancy of the watery environment within which all the cells must function, and other organs help with the excretion products too, in special cases: placentas, gills, lungs, salt glands, sweat glands, etc. But every vertebrate has kidneys and ducts for this purpose, and sends some sort of urinary excretion to a vent at the end of the trunk.

This urinary apparatus was seen in working order at the pharyngula stage of the embryo (page 83; Fig. 5–18), and consisted of a localized mass of tubules on each side, each of which drained into its own primitive kidney duct which led to the cloaca. The tubule masses lay mostly above the coelomic mesoderm and mostly below the epimeric mesoderm. The individual tubules had a close relation with the blood stream, often through both arterial capillaries and venous sinuses. This made it possible to transfer substances, either by diffusion or by active transport, from the blood to the urine that the tubule cells were secreting.

Since this primitive urinary apparatus sustains the pharyngula, it might be supposed that the needs of the adult animal could simply be taken care of by a suitable multiplication of the tubular elements without changes in design or position. In further growth, however, each individual vertebrate so transforms its urinary apparatus that the adult arrangement can be compared with the embryonic one only in the most general terms. Not only this, each vertebrate class handles the later transformation in its own special way.

All vertebrate embryos develop a pair of kidney strips from the intermediate mesoderm, and a *wave of differentiation* of urinary tubules and other structures sweeps down the strips in an anteroposterior progression (pages 83, 148). This wave takes a considerable amount of time, extending through the embryonic and fetal period in most cases, and in some animals long into the larval or juvenile stages in the life history. Neither the design of the successively appearing tubules themselves, nor their relationship with the blood stream, remains fixed during the wave of differentiation. The changes may occur gradually, or in one or more sudden jumps. Associated with such sudden alterations of design, space gaps or time gaps may occur.

An example of a coincident space-and-time

differentiate tubules if the ureter bud is included, but not without [4].

The type of tubules produced by such inductions is at least partly determined by local factors, perhaps by the quality of the mesenchyme into which the tubular epithelium is growing. Prospective mesonephric or metanephric tissue when transplanted into the pronephric end of the kidney strip will form tubules of the pronephric type. Under the influence of certain abnormal inductors in tissue cultures, metanephric blastema has been observed to form tubules of a generalized or mesonephric type.

III. KIDNEY HISTOLOGY

The sparseness or thickness of mesenchyme in the intermediate mesoderm strip is correlated with differences in early differentiation. If there is little mesenchyme, as is the case in lampreys, sharks, and the limbless amphibia, the kidney strip shares in the segmentation of the epimere medial to it and also in the coelomic split of the hypomere lateral to it (Fig. 8–14). The segmentation carves the strip into successive **nephrotomes,** and the splitting provides each nephrotome with a small cavity called a **nephrocoel** from which a segmental tubule buds by epithelial invagination. Such nephrotomes, nephrocoels, and segmentally disposed tubules appear only fleetingly at the very anterior ends of the kidney strips of bird and mammal embryos. In urodeles and anura, there are no nephrocoels or nephrotomes and only in the first few segments does one see a single kidney tubule forming below each myotome.

The greatest range in kidney tubule histology occurs in the first few segments, i.e., at the pronephric end of the strip. Leading embryologists of the previous century hoped to find here clues to the evolutionary origin of vertebrate kidneys, but no simple theory emerged from the wealth of variation discovered. The relations with the coelom are not standardized. There may be an opening of the tubule directly in the coelom (Fig. 27–1 A, nephrostome), or into a nephrocoel (Fig. 27–1 B, nephocoelostome), or none at all (Fig. 27–1 C), etc., etc. The relations with the circulatory system are even more varied. Tufts of arterial capillaries (called **glomus** if large, and **glomerulus** if small) may intrude into the coelom near a nephrostome, or into a nephrocoel, or into a glomerular capsule produced from the tubule itself (Figs. 27–1, 8–20). Dozens of variations are recorded, often several in one embryo, in successive parts of the kidney strip. It may be recalled that the most anterior members of other series, for instance vertebrae and myotomes, also exhibit peculiarities, before the pattern stabilizes farther back in the trunk.

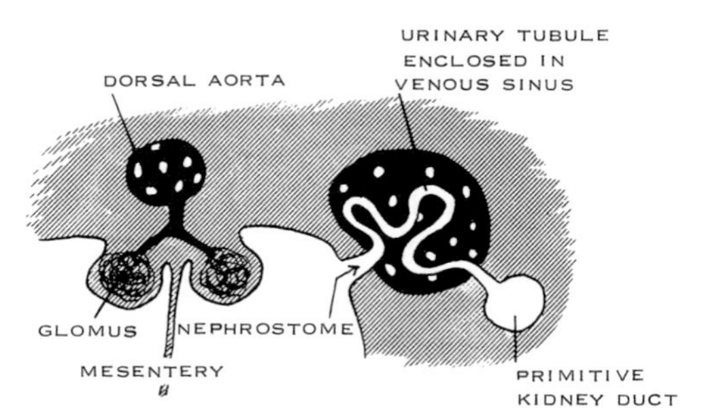

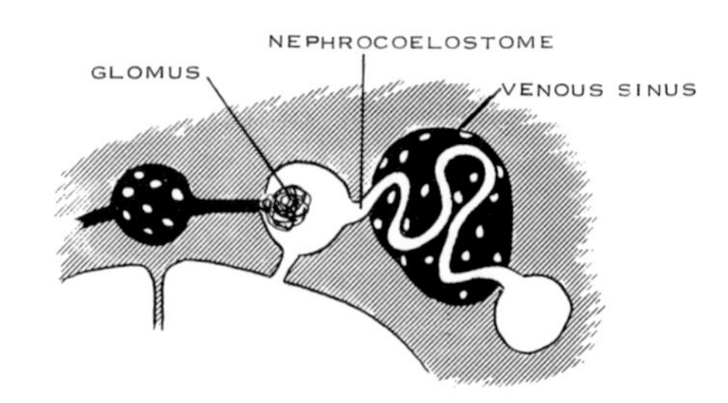

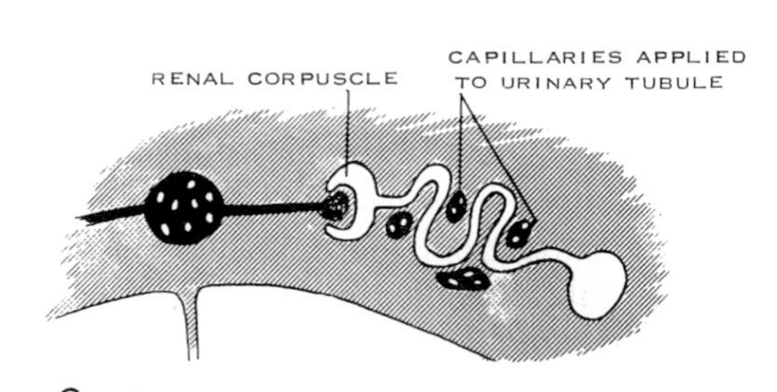

Fig. 27–1. Variations in the relationships of kidney tubules.

Usually the urinary tubules acquire relationships, with both arteries and veins. In the amblystoma embryo, the dorsal aorta produces a

glomus on each side of the midline, dangling in the roof of the coelom at pronephros level. Waste materials discharged from these into the coelomic fluid can no doubt be wafted into the pronephric tubules by the cilia which line their nephrostomes (Figs. 5–18 B, 27–1 A) and then moved along the tubules to the primitive kidney ducts. In embryos of some vertebrates such a glomus–nephrostome–tubule relationship is rendered more efficient by walling it off from the rest of the coelom, in a little pronephric chamber.

Farther posteriorly, however (in the amblystoma starting at once with the tubule in segment 10, the first formed after the time-and-space gap), a ball of arterial capillaries, the **glomerulus,** is intruded directly into an enlarged epithelial bulb, the **glomerular capsule,** near the medial end of the tubule (Figs. 8–20 E, 27–1 C). Glomerulus and capsule together form a characteristic element in kidney histology, the **renal corpuscle.**

Once kidney tubules with renal corpuscles have started to form, a repeating pattern becomes relatively stabilized for the rest of the kidney strip, varied chiefly in rates of multiplication and minor refinements. A single one of these nephric units is formed under the 10th myotome in the amblystoma kidney strip, but there are three or four in the 15th segment, and from five to seven in the 20th. Part of this multiplication represents independent tubule formation, but as one looks farther back, an increasing part comes from budding in the interior of the thickening kidney ridge. Secondary tubules sprout from, and empty into, the primary ones (Fig. 8–20 E), and develop their own renal corpuscles. Secondary tubules in turn may give off tertiary tubules, and so on tree-fashion up to six or more generations. In amniotes, by such profuse budding processes, the last one or two segments of the kidney strip give rise to enough tubules and renal corpuscles to form the entire surviving kidney of the adult.

As the individual tubule lengthens, it differentiates into special sections which may have different functions in urine production. In urodeles for instance (Fig. 27–2), a well developed tubule will have five sections: (a) a *neck* which leads from the opening of the glomerular capsule, and receives the nephrostome if there is one; (b) a *proximal convoluted part* composed of tall secretory cells; (c) a short and narrow *middle section,* which is ciliated; (d) a *distal convoluted part* lined by cuboidal cells; and (e) a comparatively straight *collecting duct* which empties laterally into the primitive kidney duct.

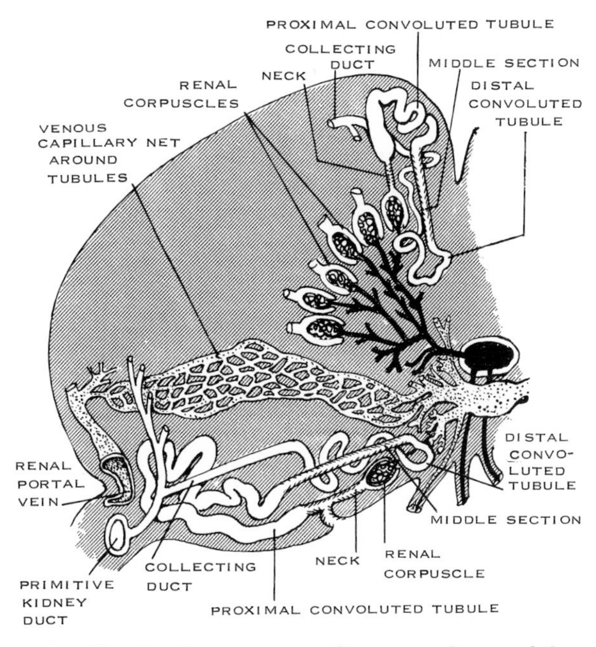

Fig. 27–2. Cross-section diagram of a urodele kidney, caudal part.
(After S. W. Chase, 1923.)

Analysis of the urine withdrawn from the sections of the tubule by micropipettes, and other experiments, indicate that the glomerulus acts as a simple filter with the pressure of blood behind it, and allows water and dissolved substances from the blood to enter the tubule in great quantity and with little discrimination. The convoluted parts restore to the blood much of the fluid and the useful food substances and salts, adding some other kinds of molecules to the urine by selective withdrawals from the blood, as well as concentrating the nitrogenous wastes. Most of what the cells of the convoluted parts do is accomplished by the cytoplasmic machinery against osmotic pressures. Research on this machinery so far has revealed only its complexity, and almost nothing of how it works [1]

The differentiation of the kidney tubules into sections is by no means constant; it has been modified many times in evolution. Efforts have been made to correlate such changes with functional needs. Unless the blood and tissue fluids of a fish are isotonic with the surrounding water, as is found to be the case only in certain hagfishes, there must be a continual adjustment of the bodily store of water and salts. Most freshwater fishes need to save salts and pump out water. In comparison with marine teleosts they are apt to show a better development of glomeruli and their kidney tubules are longer. Marine teleosts on the other hand are in constant danger of osmotic dehydration. They restore the fluid lost in their sparse urine by drinking sea water. This loads them up with superfluous salt, but they have acquired the ability to excrete both salt and nitrogenous waste through their gills. Under these circumstances, kidney reductions are possible that might wipe out other kinds of vertebrates. The number of tubules may be much reduced. The tubules themselves may be shortened and much simplified by inclusion of only one convoluted section or none. A few species of marine teleosts not only show these reductions, they have also gotten rid of the glomeruli [5].

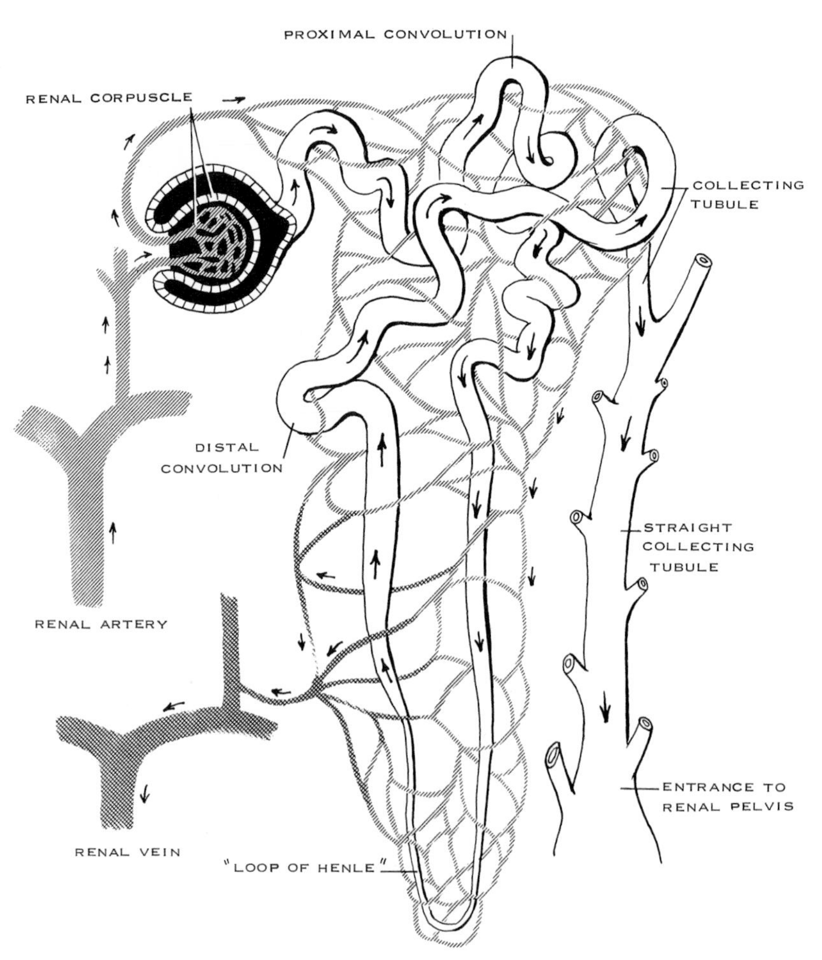

Fig. 27–3. Diagram of a mammalian urinary tubule.
(After H. W. Smith, The Kidney, 1951, by permission of Oxford University Press, Inc.)

In birds and mammals the proximal and distal convoluted sections of the kidney tubule are further subdivided into coiled and straight parts. Those of the mammalian metanephros are so arranged that the coiled parts characteristically lie in a cortical layer, and the straight parts, augmented by a greatly lengthened narrow middle section, run far down into the center or medulla of the organ, and back out again. This elaborate device, called the "loop of Henle," is involved in the reabsorption of water. The glomerulus actually allows more than a hundred times as much water to filter from its blood as will be excreted in the urine that leaves the other end of the tubule. All this extra water must be pushed back into the blood by the activity of the tubule cells, while they are at the same time transporting other substances in the opposite direction, toward the urine.

The salvaging of some elements in the glomerular filtrate, and the concentrating of others as the urine passes along the kidney tubule, requires that the blood stream be closely associated not only with the glomeruli, but with the main sections of the tubules also. Adaptable as usual, vertebrate kidneys accept whatever blood comes handy, tubules in the anterior parts of the kidney strips being supplied in different ways than are those in the posterior parts. Glomeruli and tubules of mammalian kidneys are both supplied with arterial blood. In other vertebrates, the tubules are chiefly or wholly supplied with venous blood (see page 551).

IV. DEGENERATIONS AND TRANSFORMATIONS IN THE KIDNEY STRIP

The primary wave of tubule differentiation has not even reached the pelvic region before the secondary wave of degenerations and transformations begins. The determining factors in the second wave are totally unknown. The tubules which are diagnosed as pronephric in the amniotes make a very perfunctory appearance, and may never have a real urinary function. They and a number of more posterior tubules disappear completely at a very early stage. On the other hand the pronephroi of the amblystoma persist halfway through the larval stage, and are essential for life until the more posterior tubules become functional. But at the proper time they too disappear, and so do the rest of the tubules in the anterior half of the trunk.

In the amniotes, the wave of degeneration is arrested for a variable time during the fetal period when the middle kidney, **mesonephros,** is functioning. At a later time (variable with species) this too degenerates, leaving the **metanephros** to carry on through youth and maturity.

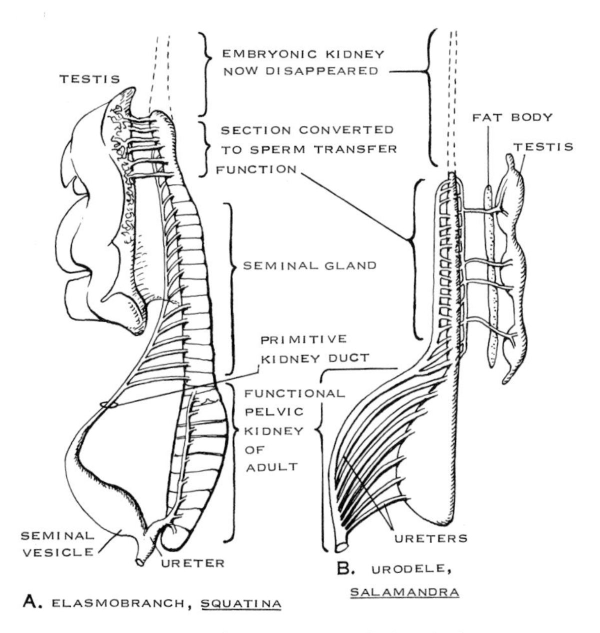

Fig. 27–4. Transformations of the kidney strip. (A after Borcea, 1906.)

The mesonephros is drained of its urine through the primitive kidney duct, the metanephros through the ureter. The two organs are dissectable as separate organs in the late fetus, being wrapped in separate connective tissue envelopes.

There is a comparable but less clearcut situation in amphibia. The part of the kidney strip back of the first major zone of tubule obliteration usually consists of a thin *cranial* part and a robust *caudal* part, a trunk kidney and a pelvic kidney, the former being served by the primitive kidney duct, the latter (usually, and with sexual differences) by a bundle of ureters (Fig. 27–4 B). As will be detailed in Chapter 29, the cranial part acquires a sperm-transfer function in males and loses most of its urinary tubules; the same is true of the mesonephros in male amniotes. In both the amphibia and the amniotes, the major part of the urine-forming function, if not all of it, is transferred to the pelvic or metanephric part of the kidney ridge.

Since the continuous kidney strip in the trunk and pelvic region of an amphibian is not carved up into a meso- and a metanephros by connective tissue envelopes, it is usually described as a unit, the posterior kidney or **opisthonephros.** The conversion of some of its anterior tubules to sexual functions in males, and the transfer of most of its urinary functions toward the pelvic end, are peculiarities that are also found in the kidneys of elasmobranchs and some other fishes.

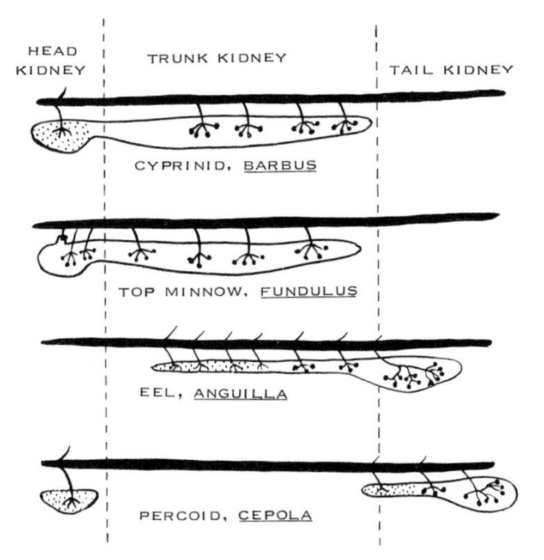

Fig. 27–5. Some kidney patterns in teleosts. (After Audigé, 1910.)

In male elasmobranchs (Fig. 27–4 A) and holocephals, a considerable length of the kidney strip, between the anterior part converted to sperm transfer and the posterior part which takes over most of the urinary function, is transformed into a **seminal gland.** In females it either remains as a minor adjunct of the functional kidney, i.e., a cranial opisthonephros, or disappears, according to the custom of the species. It retains a kidney function also in male sharks and holocephals before the stage of sexual maturity, but in the rays it is apparently specialized from the start. In any case, when its adult structure has been completed, no trace remains of the renal corpuscles, and the tubules secrete a substance into the primitive kidney duct which mixes with and favors the sperm. The part of the original kidney strip which is taken over by this quite non-urinary structure may be more extensive than the pelvic section which remains in urinary function.

In the teleosts the secondary alterations of the kidney-strip derivatives are often profound, and do not seem to fall into types that correlate sensibly with the taxonomic groups (Fig. 27–5). The newly hatched larvae commonly show only one glomus-containing pronephric tubule on each side, connecting with its own primitive kidney duct which runs to the base of the tail in the usual position, embedded in lymphoid tissue. There the two ducts meet and achieve an opening to the outside. Such single-nephron kidneys are actually found in the adults of some teleost species, all the rest of the kidney strips having been pre-empted by the lymphoid tissue.

"Head kidneys" are common in teleosts. They take the form of two pyramidal masses anterior to the main body cavity, dorsal to the septum transversum. Their embryonic development is known in only a few species. Although they may lie at pronephric levels, they are apt not to be urinary in function, but composed mostly of lymphoid tissue. Anomalous but apparently genuine thyroid tissue has been found in head kidneys of a number of bony fishes.

Opisthonephroi may persist the entire length of the trunk in other teleosts, either in contact with pronephroi or head kidneys, or slightly separated from them. Masses of urinary tubules may be found only in the middle of the trunk, either fused into a single column engulfing the main trunk vein, or forming bilobed masses, or multiple segmental ladder-like contacts; or they may form separate right and left kidneys, applied to the sides of the vertebral centra. However they may appear in dissection, the microscope often reveals that they contain more lymphoid than renal tissue (stippled in the diagrams of Fig. 27–5).

Quite commonly the vents of a bony fish are

placed well forward on the belly, so that the coelom is described as being prolonged into the tail. In such a case it is common to find that there is also a "tail kidney" which projects as an unpaired mass a considerable distance along the dorsal wall of this coelomic pocket. It is usually drained by a single "ureter" of its own.

There are teleosts which show head, trunk, *and* tail kidneys, all in line, at the adult stage. Others combine head and trunk kidneys only, or trunk and tail kidneys only. Probably the majority of teleosts have one or another variant of the trunk kidney alone. The coelacanth *Latimeria* has only a single fused mass of tail kidney, but it is drained by a pair of ducts.

The primitive kidney ducts of teleosts show versatility themselves. Often they fuse and form an enlarged sac or urinary bladder before they end posteriorly. In a few species with degenerated urinary tubules the primitive kidney ducts become enlarged and filled with villi, perhaps as substitute urine-secreting organs. The male stickleback constructs a nest at the breeding season, in which he induces the female to lay eggs. The nest consists of sticks and leaves put together with a sort of glue which is secreted by his primitive kidney ducts and some of the collecting tubules of his kidneys.

V. RISE OF THE AMNIOTE METANEPHROS

No really satisfactory distinction can be made between the metanephroi of amniotes and the caudal parts of the opisthonephroi of elmasmobranchs and amphibia. They all arise in the segments closest to the pelvis, at the end of the wave of differentiation. In amniotes, the origin of the pair of ureters from the posterior ends of the primitive kidney ducts (Fig. 27–6) and their growth forward into metanephrogenic blastema,

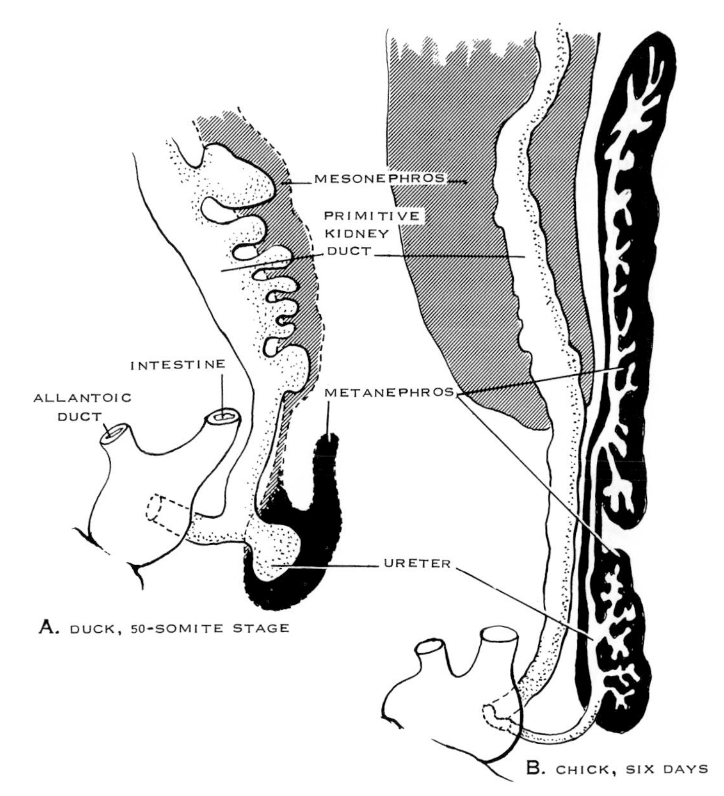

Fig. 27–6. Ureter formation in bird embryos.
(After K. D. Schreiner, 1902.)

mesenteric vein and vitelline veins, i.e., the hepatic portal system. Meanwhile, the primitive cardinal vein of each side proceeds to separate into two parallel vessels (Fig. 27–8 B, C). One of these shifts to the dorsolateral side of the primitive kidney duct, and is the **posterior cardinal vein** of later stages (V). The other lies ventromedial to it, and is the **subcardinal vein** (VI). These two on each side remain interconnected by a capillary net, and the two subcardinals are similarly interconnected below the dorsal aorta. In effect, this whole axial area around and between the kidney strips has become enveloped in a disorderly swamp of venous channels through which sets of parallel longitudinal paths can be traced. These paths become extensively remodeled during the lengthy period of differentiation of the kidney strips, as the next several paragraphs will show.

The posterior cardinal and subcardinal veins, extending caudad, finally reach the level of the cloaca. Here they come in contact with the **caudal vein** (VII) and at once they join to capture its entire flow, cutting it off from the subintestinal or vitelline veins that had previously been in its direct line.

The anterior parts of the subcardinals become obliterated down through the trunk levels in which the kidney strips themselves are degenerating, and their posterior parts, having from the first been interconnected, combine to form a single midline vein below the dorsal aorta (Fig. 27–8 D). Eventually also, they become cut off from the caudal vein.

Meanwhile, the posterior cardinals have become interrupted in mid-trunk (Fig. 27–8 D, E). Their posterior parts, now receiving the full flow from the caudal vein (augmented by segmental veins from the flanks, and by iliac veins from the hindlegs), become **renal portal veins** (VIII), sending all this blood into a spongelike sinusoidal matrix enveloping the kidney tubules, whence it is drained by the single subcardinal vein.

In most urodeles there develop two paths by which this subcardinal blood can reach the heart. One, which is standard among sharks and some other fishes, is produced by a juncture between the subcardinal and the free ends of the anterior sections of the two posterior cardinal veins, or at least one of them. The other path to the heart, which is standard among all the tetrapods, and is found also in the dipnoi and *Latimeria,* is quickly developed as a backward extension from the hepatic vein along the dorsal surface of the liver, the right lateral mesentery, and the dorsal midline mesentery. It joins the subcardinal sinus, completing a major new vein, called the **postcava** (inferior vena cava, PNA) (Fig. 27–8 E).

This great vein is characteristically made up in amphibia and amniotes from a patchwork of paired veins in the posterior trunk, collected by the unpaired vein which grows back from the hepatic vein on the right side. Perhaps because of this right-sided anterior connection, it is mostly from the right members of the posterior paired veins, and from anastomoses across the midline, that the components of the posterior part of the postcava are selected. In mammals, these selections vary somewhat with the species, and include not only parts of the posterior cardinal and subcardinal veins but also **supracardinal veins** which parallel them dorsomedial to the kidneys and directly dorsal to the subcardinals, bordering the dorsal aorta. The supracardinals are not found in lower vertebrates, nor are they conspicuous in other amniotes.

In most tetrapods, the venous flow from the hindlimbs has a choice of paths toward the heart (see below). In mammals however, it is all gathered into the great postcaval vein.

The growing liver usually engulfs the anterior element of the postcava, i.e., the part that grows caudad from the hepatic vein. It will be recalled that when the liver engulfed the vitelline and umbilical veins at an earlier stage it interrupted and dispersed them in hepatic sinusoids. It has no such effect on the postcava.

VII. FURTHER VENOUS CHANGES IN THE PELVIS

A. Venous Anastomoses

Considering how the somatic trunk veins link themselves in a gridwork, and how the longitudinal trunks of the kidney strip regions are interlaced with each other by capillary nets, it is not surprising to find that veins of the visceral and the somatic sets become interconnected in the pelvic region. Marked differences in venous flow found here in adult vertebrates are to be explained by the selection of different elements from the complex of pathways that become available through these pelvic anastomoses.

Veins of the cloaca and rectum of elasmobranchs may drain either into the iliac veins, and so through the somatic grid to the heart (specifically through the abdominal veins in the belly wall), or they may drain along the hindgut to the hepatic portal vein. The hindlimbs of tetrapods, according to the species, send their blood to an abdominal vein in the ventral belly wall, or to the postcava, or to both of them. Epigastric (belly wall) veins often empty into iliac veins which may lead to the renal portal veins, or to the postcava directly. A connection quite regularly remains between the abdominal vein and the renal portal system in adult amphibia, reptiles, and birds. In some of these species (Fig. 27–9) part of the blood from the hindlimbs may go to the heart by way of the abdominal and hepatic portal veins, and part by way of the renal portal and postcaval veins. Clinically important communications occur between the hepatic portal and postcaval systems in the pelvic viscera of adult humans. Venous blood from the tail fills the renal portal system in many lower vertebrates, but once the frog tadpole has lost its tail, its kidneys receive blood chiefly from the hind legs. In bony fishes, much of the blood from the tail, and in some species all of it, bypasses the kidneys; it may enter the hepatic portal system, or the posterior cardinal vein of one side, or there may be a direct shunt around the kidney to the subcardinal, depending on the species.

B. Fates of the Renal Portal System

These pelvic venous anastomoses provide detours around the renal portal system in the adults of a great many kinds of vertebrates. Species of teleosts can be found to illustrate almost any degree of elimination of this system. In amphibia and reptiles, the ventral abdominal vein provides a substantial bypass (Fig. 27–9). In adult birds, though there is a permanent renal portal vein with the possibility of inflow from the hindleg, belly wall, and hingut, a large venous shunt also develops around the kidney from the renal portal to the postcava (Fig. 27–10). A complicated muscular valve at the parting of the ways may possibly manipulate the flow, either away from the kidney or through it.

In mammals, by the time the caudal end of the kidney strip is beginning to differentiate metanephric tubules, the hindlimb blood is bypassed through the supracardinal veins to the developing postcava. Though traces of a renal portal system are found in fetal marsupials, no higher mammals ever form one, their kidneys being entirely supplied through arteries.

The question may well be asked, what advantage is served by the renal portal system? Lampreys never develop one, no mammals retain one if indeed they ever show traces of it in development, and some teleosts get rid of it entirely.

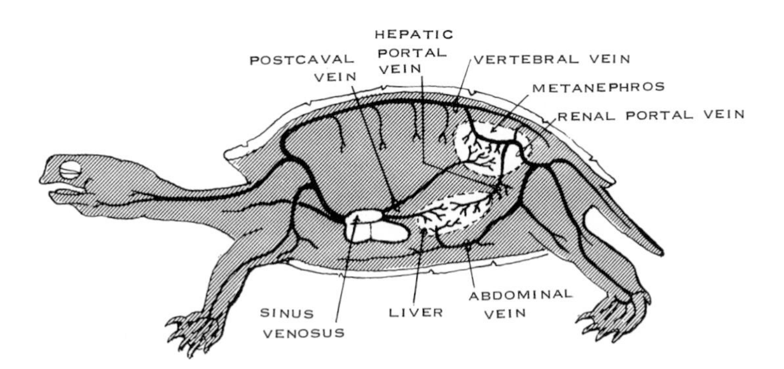

Fig. 27–9. Pelvic venous anastomoses in a turtle.

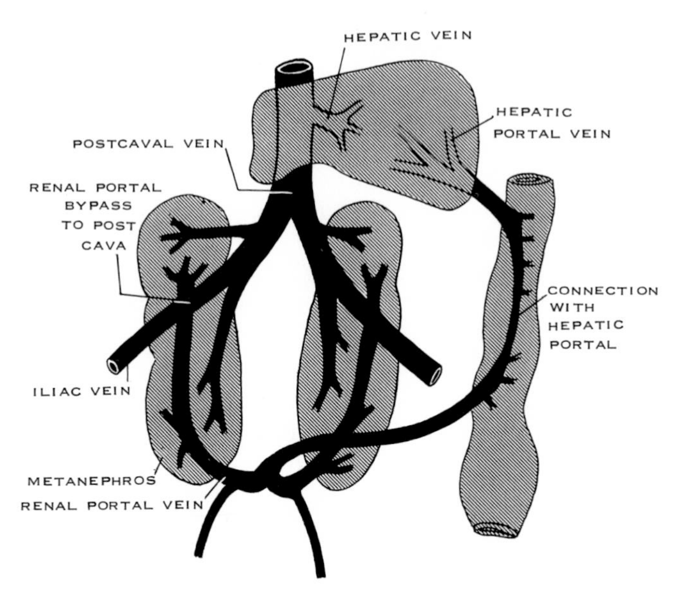

Fig. 27–10. Pelvic venous anastomoses in a bird.
(After R. Spanner, 1925.)

The kidneys always receive arterial blood in addition to what they get from renal portal veins, and in frogs there is sufficient interconnection between the renal arteries and veins that interruption of the blood supply through either one of the two paths is not fatal.

VIII. URINARY BLADDERS

One might guess that urinary bladders are not of great importance in the survival effort or in the evolution of species. They are lacking in hagfishes, a few bony fishes, some reptiles, and all but a few species of birds.

There are two main types of urinary bladders in the phylum. Fishes in general develop mesodermal bladders which lie dorsal to the gut, and tetrapods have endodermal bladders which derive from the cloaca and lie ventral to the gut.

A. Fish Bladders

In the elasmobranchs and holocephals there is no doubt that the bladders are mesodermal and they lie dorsal to the cloaca, but there are two sorts, one for males and the other for females. In males, the bladders are formed by simple enlargement of the cloacal ends of the ureters which drain the caudal mesonephroi. They occasionally remain paired, but in most elasmobranch species they meet in the midline and fuse to form a Y-shaped or bilobed bladder.

In the females of these same species, the caudal mesonephroi are developed more feebly, and the ureters remain simple. Normally the bladders are paired structures formed by enlargement of the cloacal ends of the primitive kidney ducts.

Teleost urinary bladders vary endlessly in size and shape. From their adult arrangement it might be guessed that they arise by a simple swelling of the fused posterior ends of the primitive kidney ducts. But in some teleost embryos, and also in lampreys and ganoid fishes, it is known that the ephemeral cloaca is divided by a more or less horizontal urorectal fold of its walls so as to separate a ventral rectum, into which the gut empties, from a dorsal urinary or urogenital part. This latter, if enlarged, constitutes a bladder which may be partly mesodermal (from the primitive kidney ducts) and partly endodermal (from the cloaca). Since the bladder is usually removed somewhat from the outside, the contribution of endoderm may be negligible. The tail-kidney, when one is present, sends a third urine duct, the so-called ureter, into the bladder. Its mode of origin is unknown. The tube which drains the bladder is fitted with a sphincter muscle, and empties to the outside through a separate opening posterior to the anus.

B. Bladders of Tetrapods

In amphibia the urinary bladder arises at a late stage by the evagination of a simple pocket from the endodermal anterior wall of the cloaca in the midventral line, below the gut. This evagination is contained at all times within the coelom, there being no umbilical opening in the wall of the belly. Since all the kidney ducts empty into the cloaca, the urine which is normally found filling the bladder must get there by force of gravity and pressure of the cloacal walls. The periodic act of urination is accomplished by the contraction of a lacy network of smooth-muscle fibers that develop in the bladder wall. The urine passes backward, traversing the cloaca for the second time, before reaching the outside.

In amniotes, the bladder is associated with a new structure, the allantois. The cloaca gives off an anteroventral evagination as before, but in these embryos the belly wall is wide open and there is nothing to prevent the outgrowth from spreading into the extraembryonic coelom. Mesonephric urine that gets to it by way of the cloaca usually inflates it into a balloon-like **allantoic sac** which spreads far beyond the body of the embryo and applies itself against the inside of the chorion (Figs. 11–2, 11–6).

After the allantois has served its important functions in the fetus, the parts of it that lie outside the umbilical opening are cast off with other fetal membranes (page 194). In many reptiles, the part that remains inside the closed body wall enlarges as a urinary bladder and continues to receive urine by way of the cloaca. On the other hand, none of it survives the fetal period in the snakes or crocodilia, or most birds or some families of lizards, which thus come to lack urinary bladders.

In mammals, the allantois is developed to widely different degrees, in apparent correlation with the efficiency of the placenta as an excretory organ. It appears at an extremely early stage, even before the body axis has formed. Most of it is discarded with the placenta at birth, but the inner end of the stalk always remains as a urinary bladder.

For some time the prospective bladder cavity and that of the cloaca are one continuous space, into which the primitive kidney ducts open. As soon as the ureters have developed from the lower ends of these ducts a series of characteristically mammalian transformations occur in this region (Fig. 27–7):

(a) The cloaca-bladder chamber enlarges itself, and opens out the bases of the primitive kidney ducts, adding their tissues to its walls, up to and beyond the points of origin of the ureters. The result is that these four urine tubes then open separately into it. (Only those of the right side are shown in Fig. 27–7).

(b) A narrowing waist begins to separate the cloaca part of the chamber from the bladder part. This constriction finally narrows to a tube, the **urethra,** which remains as the drainage path for the adult bladder.

(c) While this is happening, the ureter and primitive kidney duct of each side shift somewhat in position relative to each other. The result of this shift is that the ureters come to empty directly through the dorsal wall of the bladder part, while their parents, the primitive kidney ducts, continue to open farther down, below the urethra (Fig. 27–7 C). Only now, and uniquely in mammals, can urine flow directly from the ureters into the bladder.

IX. FATES OF CLOACAS

The cloaca is part of the basic pattern of the vertebrates. It has at least momentary existence at the pharyngula stage in known representatives of all the major groups. Persisting without much change in adult elasmobranchs and holocephals, it gives rise to a urinary bladder in amphibia, and to a bladder-allantois complex in sauropsida. Nevertheless in all these groups it continues throughout life to receive the products of the intestine, the urinary ducts, and the genital ducts.

Members of the different sauropsidan groups develop quite a variety of cloacal subdivisions.

The most primitive of the surviving reptiles (the sphenodon) and the most advanced ones (crocodilia) both retain a large cloacal chamber uncomplicated by divisions. In other reptiles and in birds, the lateral cloacal walls project folds inward, sometimes boldly and sometimes vaguely marking a boundary between the part which receives the feces and that which receives the genital products. Before the cloacal membrane ruptures in the early embryo, it has sunk inward to some degree, producing at least a token inpocketing of proctodeal ectoderm. As a result, in theory at least, the finished cloaca may consist of two endodermal parts, a dorsoanterior **coprodeum** and a ventroanterior **urodeum,** and one ectodermal part, the more posterior **proctodeum.**

There are numerous departures from this simple scheme. Many turtles for instance not only have an enormous bilobed allantoic urinary bladder, but develop a pair of "accessory bladders" as outpouchings from the urodeum. In both turtles and crocodilia the ventral wall of the cloaca is modified into a penis-like structure (cf. Chapter 29). In some lizards and snakes an imitation bladder is produced anterodorsally from the urodeum, and birds also usually develop a single blind **cloacal sac** (page 468) in this position. The muscular ring-folds that separate hindgut, coprodeum, urodeum, and proctodeum may merely be suggested, or they may be strongly developed. The semi-solid "urine" is generally stored in a urodeal compartment but is excreted with the feces in a single mass.

The monotremes (as their name implies) preserve a large simple cloaca throughout life (Fig. 29–7). The rest of the mammals have adopted quite a new style. The early formation and fusion of right and left **urorectal folds** in the frontal plane quite eliminates their embryonic cloaca by dividing it into a dorsal **rectum** and a ventral **urogenital sinus.** (Fig. 27–7 B). The primitive kidney ducts, after their separation from the ureters by the growth and tissue modeling that was described above, are found to empty into the urogenital sinus after the closure of the urorectal folds. The urinary bladder also empties into the urogenital sinus through its narrowing and elongating urethra.

In the mammalian pharyngula, the cloaca has not yet been completely subdivided, but the endoderm of its cavity is in contact externally with the slightly intruded ectoderm of the proctodeum, forming a cloacal membrane. Complete separation of the rectum from the urogenital sinus takes place before the cloacal membrane has thinned out to the point of rupturing. As a result, independent anal and urogenital apertures are eventually formed, separated by a zone of ectoderm and mesoderm which is defined as the **perineum.** The musculature of this area, which in other amniotes is laid down in the form of a rather simple **cloacal sphincter** (Fig. 29–11), becomes somewhat distorted by the separation of the two apertures. Its dorsal parts become specialized in relation to the anus, and its ventral parts in relation to the external genital organs which develop around the urogenital aperture (see Chapters 28, 29).

In the lampreys and most of the bony fishes, the cloaca is also eliminated quite early, by subdivision. In these, however, it is the dorsal part which receives the kidney and sex ducts, leading to a single **urogenital aperture,** usually on a slightly projecting papilla, at the base of the tail. The ventral part receives the feces and empties through a separate anus. Some teleosts show three openings, a further subdivision having segregated a genital pore, lying between the anterior anus and the posterior urinary pore. Only a few teleost species preserve the embryonic cloaca relationship in the adult stage.

REFERENCES

Homer Smith's book is a classic and highly readable summary and interpretation of all aspects of the biology of kidneys. More recent advances are summarized by Forster as part of a great new monograph on cellular biology. Experimental work on the embryonic intermediate mesoderm, out of which the kidneys and their ducts arise, is summarized to 1955 by Burns.

1. Forster, R. P., 1961. *In* J. Brachet and A. E. Mirsky (eds.), *The cell,* Vol. 5. Academic Press, Inc., New York.
2. Burns, R. K., 1955. *In* B. H. Willier, P. A. Weiss, and V. Hamburger (eds.), *Analysis of development.* W. B. Saunders Co., Philadelphia.
3. Holtfreter, J., 1944. *Rev. can. biol.* 3: 220.
4. Grobstein, C., 1955. *J. Exptl. Zool.* 130: 319.
5. Smith, H. W., 1951. *The kidney.* Oxford University Press, Fair Lawn, N. J.
6. Grodzinski, Z., 1925. *Bull. intern. acad. polon. sci.,* Sér. B., 196.

28

The Genital System: I

At the pharyngula stage, vertebrates show only traces of genital differentiation, and there is not enough sex anatomy established to tell males from females. How males and females acquire their characteristic differences is too big a story for this chapter, which will focus only on femaleness, leaving maleness for the next chapter. But the first question to be raised is how it is decided what the sex of a given individual shall be? [1]

I. SEX DETERMINATION

Sexuality takes many forms in plants and animals. Sometimes, as in earthworms and corn, both maleness and femaleness may reside in a single hermaphroditic individual. Sometimes, as in various protozoa, there may be multiple mating types without sharp sexual contrasts in their structure. In higher animals, both the accidents of nature and experiments in the laboratory show the existence of such curious phenomena as superfemales and supermales, gynandromorphs, intersexes, and sterile hybrids. All these conditions have to be explained in a single theoretical framework along with the familiar male–female dichotomy.

Certain worms and molluscs are known in which sex is regularly determined, and may later even be reversed, by environmental circumstances. So far as is now known, this does not regularly happen in any vertebrate species, but the sex ratio in a population of amphibian embryos can sometimes be sharply changed by the operation of extrinsic factors. Temperatures higher than normal may tip the scale toward maleness, and low temperatures toward femaleness. Overripeness of eggs may increase the percentage of males. Much has been learned about the role of sex hormones in accentuating or repressing the processes of sexual development. Nevertheless, the stability of sex ratios in natural populations does imply that the normal mechanism for determining sex has a high degree of insulation from environmental factors. Indeed a device adequate for this purpose, namely the chance recombination of sex chromosomes, has usually acted at fertilization with sufficient authority to override the usual range of subsequent environmental effects.

It is not always possible to distinguish the regular chromosomes or *autosomes* from special *sex chromosomes* in cytological preparations, though the inheritance of sex-linked characters may show that the distinction exists. However, in some species of plants and many of animals including some vertebrates, sex chromosomes can be picked out on the metaphase plates of dividing cells because in one sex or other they appear unpaired or their partners are of smaller size. Whichever sex this is will produce two classes of gametes, half of them carrying a normal sex chromosome and the other half the small one or none at all.

If this heterogametic sex is male (as in man and various other mammals, the common frogs, etc.) the male individual carries in every cell a pair of sex chromosomes conventionally called X and Y, or a single unmated X. The female carries two X chromosomes in every cell. If the heterogametic sex is female (as in salamanders, some primitive anura, birds, etc.) the like pair of sex chromosomes of the male are traditionally designated ZZ, the unlike pair of the female, W and Z. The distinction between the XY combination and the WZ combination is purely conventional, to facilitate certain genetic discussions.

The question as to which is the heterogametic sex is not of great significance except in certain special patterns of inheritance, and possibly a single mutation could transform the one condition into the other. Both male and female heterogamety occur in the teleost group, and both conditions have even been reported in different geographic races of a single species of platyfish.

It seems likely that in all vertebrates, and in many other animals and plants, a genetic balance is maintained, such that if two X or Z chromosomes are brought together in fertilization, the resulting zygote is predisposed toward one sex, and if it receives only one X or one Z (the Y or W being in this respect less potent) it is predisposed toward the other sex. This does not imply that the X or the Z chromosomes are the exclusive carriers of sex-determining genes. No single Mendelian factor or chromosome locus has been found in any organism that determines sex by itself. The function of the double dose of X or Z genes is to override a very slight tendency of autosomal genes to work in the other direction, a single X or Z being insufficient for this purpose.

In man and other primates, and representatives of several other orders of mammals, non-mitotic cells of many adult tissues (neurons, epithelial cells, etc.) may be marked in correlation with sex. The majority of these cells carry small chromatin bodies against the nuclear membrane in females, and very few do in males. If these "nuclear satellites" are reliable indicators of genetic sex, then the population of humans contains some genetic females who have become male and vice versa, though most of them have been unable to differentiate perfectly and remain in sterile and intersexual condition [2].

It is suggested that the nuclear satellites are the form taken by material from the XX chromosome pair during the intermitotic period. However, similar markers are reported to be ten times more common in the cells of hens (WZ) than in those of roosters (ZZ) [3].

In spite of the genic mechanisms for establishing sex, environmental or other controllable factors may still alter the balance. *Sex hormones* for instance have specific and striking effects on the growth and differentiation of parts of the genital apparatus. These biochemical substances are found in the tissues and body fluids of all adult vertebrates. The hormones which in general encourage the differentiation of male characters are called *androgens,* those which bring out femaleness are called *estrogens.* Numerous androgenic and estrogenic chemicals are known, some of them isolated from nature and others synthesized in the laboratory.

Androgens not only encourage the differentiation and growth of characteristically male genital parts, they may also exert a rather specific inhibitory action on female parts. Estrogens also may inhibit the development of male parts. The effects of these chemicals do not always follow this neat pattern. Various experiments have produced "paradoxical effects": heavy doses of estrogens may cause over-stimulation of male parts, etc. The theories to account for these paradoxical effects are still not satisfactory [1]. For that matter, there is not yet *any* knowledge as to how the sex hormones produce their effects upon the cells of susceptible growing tissues.

Estrogens have been used successfully to force genetically male salamanders (of ZZ constitution) to become females and lay fertilizable eggs. Androgens have also forced genetically female frogs (of XX constitution) to become male and breed with normal females. In both cases the sex reversal may be interpreted as an inhibition of the dominating factors carried by the X or Z chromosomes, releasing the capacities of the autosomes. In various other vertebrates, dosing the developing males with estrogens, or the developing females with androgens, has usually repressed the full development of the genetic sexuality without complete reversal of sex. In such cases, intermediate conditions result, such as gonads which take the form of ovotestes.

At present, known methods of assay are not good enough to decide when the sex hormones first appear in the embryo, though there is good evidence from transplantations and from the fusion of embryos together ("parabiosis"), and from extirpation of gonad rudiments, that such influences are at work very early. Perhaps these embryonic sex hormones are chemicaly different from those found in later stages.

With rare exceptions it is only in very early stages of development that the cue which the individual has taken from his genes can be countermanded by other influences. All kinds of vertebrates pass through a juvenile or larval stage in which sex is difficult to diagnose, but this does not necessarily mean that sex determination is not complete. In most cases it can be established indirectly that long before the definitive sexual anatomy appears, or before a ripening process like that of puberty ushers in the actively sexual period of the life history, the individual's developmental capacity has become limited to one sex, and attempts at reversal then only succeed in preventing him or her from becoming ripe. Some of the exceptional cases of successful reversal will be mentioned below.

II. EARLY GONAD DEVELOPMENT

Gonads of vertebrates are assembled from two different sources, distinguished as structural and germinal elements. Materials from both sources are necessary for the completion of sexual development.

The *structural elements* of the gonads are parts of the intermediate mesoderm lying on each side between the dorsal aorta and the kidney strip. These mesodermal cells condense into slightly raised gonad ridges which project into the coelom at or slightly posterior to the pectoral level soon after the pharyngula stage. The *germinal elements* are primordial germ cells which migrate into the gonad ridges.

The **primordial germ cells** are large distinctive cells which appear in all vertebrate embryos soon after the germ layers have been defined, usualy in paired lateral or extraembryonic endodermal areas. Special metabolic properties allow them to be selectively stained [4]. They are rather scattered at first, but in later stages they concentrate toward the gonad ridges, apparently by active migration (Fig. 8–12). Large numbers of them disappear on the way.

The eventual fate of the primordial germ cells has been much discussed. Direct evidence that they form gametes has recently become available [10], but not to the exclusion of the possibility that gametes may also come from other sources, perhaps induced by them. Embryos surgically deprived of all their primordial germ cells do retain an ability to form gonad ridges, but the gonads which develop from these remain sterile. Certain genes which produce sterility are correlated with sparse appearance of them [5]. If the primordial germ cells are sex-determining agents they are not the only ones, and it has been shown in anuran embryos by transplantation experiments that the sex of the gonad has been determined in labile form even before they reach it. Nevertheless, it seems clear that normal sex development requires their presence.

It is rare for the whole gonad ridge to be converted into a gonad. Anterior and posterior parts of it may disappear or may form non-sexual structures, for example the fat-bodies which accompany the gonads of amphibia (Fig. 27–4 B). The part which differentiates into a real gonad usually lifts itself away from the kidney and develops its own mesentery.

While this is happening, the epithelium of its surface thickens and sends trains of cells called **sex cords** into the connective tissue stroma of its interior (Fig. 28–1 A, B). The primordial germ cells accompany the sex cords, but thereafter their history becomes difficult to follow.

In amniotes and amphibia some investigators have reported two main immigrations of sex cords, the first destined to form seminiferous and rete tubules in males but degenerating in females, and the second breaking up into egg follicles in females. Human embryos show only one immigration [6], but a sharp distinction can be made between developments in the **cortex** and the **medulla** of the gonad, the former involved in the transformation to femaleness (Fig. 28–1 C), the latter to maleness (Fig. 28–1 D).

The result of the establishment of a medulla and a cortex is a double gonad, which is potentially hermaphroditic or bisexual, but is actually in a non-functional, immature condition. This state of affairs constitutes a neuter or **indifferent period** of sexual development. In some kinds of animals there is evidence of a competition during this period between factors favorable to maleness and factors favorable to femaleness, ending in the establishment of a clear dominance leading to a visible **declaration of sex.** If the individual is to be female, the cortical component thickens and the cords to which it gives rise break up into cell nests or follicles. If it is to be male, semniferous tubules are differentiated from the cords in the medulla and the cortex produces a stout connective tissue sheath, the **tunica albuginea.** This further development requires gonadotrophic hormones from the pituitary gland. If the pituitary is removed, the gonad remains, or becomes, sterile.

Declaration of sex is not coincident with sexual maturation or puberty, but long precedes it. The indifferent stage may last through a larval period of a year or more in some amphibia, during which time the gonad has an immature but frankly hermaphroditic appearance. In hagfishes, and in common eels (*Anguilla*), the individuals may reach an advanced age and nearly full size before sex is declared. On the other hand, the indifferent period may be compressed into the first quarter of the pregnancy time in mammals, and it is finished in the third day of incubation of the chick embryo.

In many teleosts, differentiation toward maleness or femaleness is so early and direct that no histologic appearance of potential bisexuality can be found [7]. On the other hand there are certain teleost groups which normally develop true hermaphroditic gonads, i.e., organs producing both eggs and sperm simultaneously [8]. An isolated individual of one of these species can fertilize "her" eggs with "his" own sperm.

A number of lines of evidence indicate that it is actually a competition of factors for maleness and factors for femaleness which decides the individual's sex. For instance, when twins of

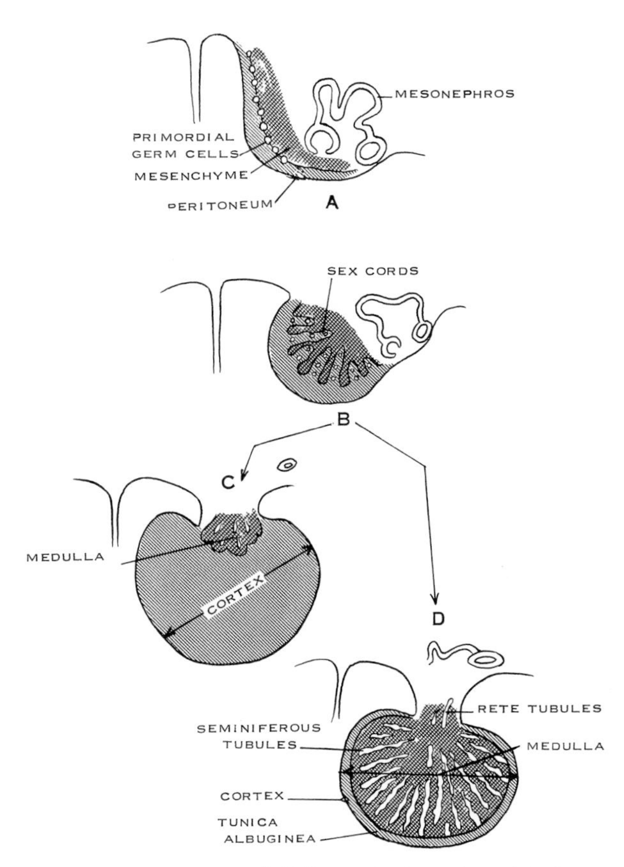

Fig. 28–1. Gonad differentiation. A and B. Indifferent stages. C. Female. D. Male.

opposite sex are produced in cattle, their placental circulations often mix, and the female twin becomes a **freemartin,** intermediate in her sexual anatomy, and sterile. It is suspected that the cause may be the balanced effects of competing hormones, but a puzzle remains: similar circumstances occur in other species *without* the formation of freemartins.

In toads, a small suppressed mass of cortical material is normally segregated from the gonad ridge. It has no name except **Bidder's organ.** When a male toad is castrated, the tissue of this organ is apparently released from the repressive action of testis hormones, for it slowly transforms into a functional ovary.

Also, when salamander embryos are grafted together in the siamese-twin arrangement called parabiosis, about half of the cases turn out, according to expectation, to be male-female combinations. In these, usually the ovaries are inhibited, and this is supposed to be the result of hormones passing from the male to the female through their conjoined circulatory systems.

All the above cases show factors for maleness winning the competition, but something like the reverse of this may occur in the domestic hen which normally has a functional left ovary and a vestigial right gonad consisting mostly of medullary material. If the left ovary is removed from a female at hatching, or if it regresses during her old age, the medullary tissue of her rudimentary right gonad is released from dominance and may then transform into a testis. In some cases it not only produces functional spermatozoa but also enough of a change in the hormone balance to convert the hen's appearance and behavior into that of a cock, and she may become a father.

In all these cases cited above, both kinds of gonads are capable of differentiating completely, except that one kind suppresses the other. It is a reasonable guess that the natural dominance of testes over ovaries in some animals, and the reverse in others, has a genetic basis. The dominant sex is usually the one with the XY or WZ pair of sex chromosomes. Nevertheless, the genetic bias can be either temporarily or permanently thwarted, and sex can be reversed by hormone administration or grafting procedures at early sensitive stages, at least in amphibia and birds.

It is not yet understood how this competition between sexual tendencies is bypassed in the development of the few teleost species which normally become completely hermaphroditic. A condition very close to complete hermaphroditism (functional testes accompanying almost functional ovaries for instance) has been described in individuals or families of various other vertebrates, including man.

III. STRUCTURE OF OVARIES

Although the ovaries arise from paired gonad-ridge anlagen, they do not always develop sym-

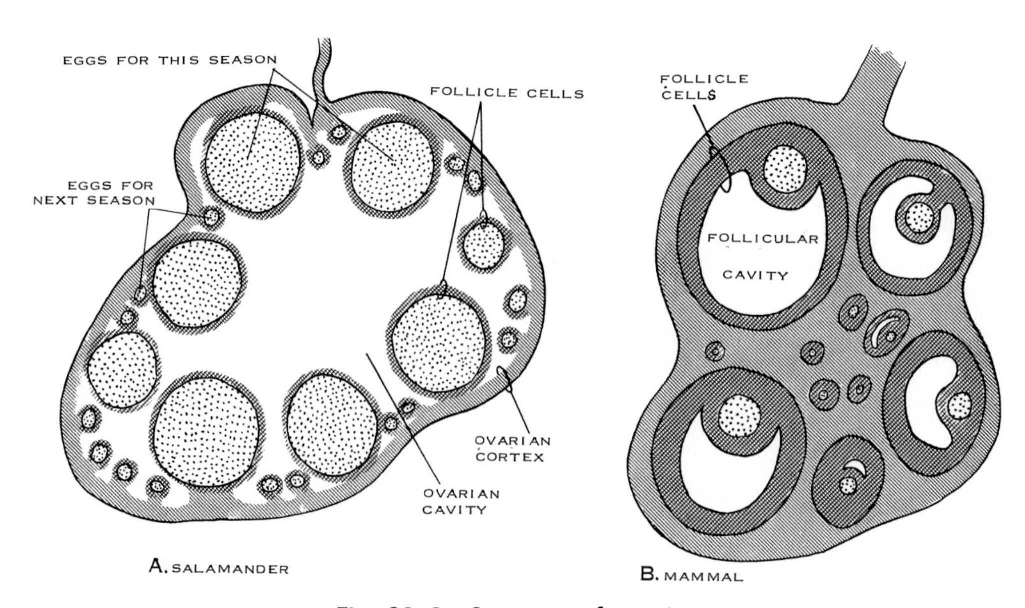

Fig. 28–2. Structure of ovaries.

metrically. One of them may lie somewhat anterior to the other, or as in some fishes and most birds, one of them may be suppressed. The two sometimes fuse into a midline mass, and when this happens the dorsal aorta is buried and the dorsal mesentery seems to spring from the ventral surface of the fused ovarian mass. There are many examples of this among the kinds of fishes which produce enormous numbers of eggs.

As with many abdominal viscera, the shapes of ovaries are unpredictable. In different species they may be compact, elongate, leaflike, or baggy, and in a single individual they may vary grossly in appearance and size according to the seasons of the year. If either a small number of large eggs or a large number of small eggs is produced, the ovary may fill the coelom to bursting just before the breeding time, and may collapse to a very small percentage of its maximum size after ovulation. The ovaries of sharks and birds produce very large eggs, those of mammals and some teleosts produce eggs of minute size.

The female sex cords, penetrating into the connective tissue stroma of the ovary, break up into nests of **follicle cells,** in the center of each of which a single **oogonium** presently becomes prominent. As the follicles become larger each acquires a connective tissue capsule, the **theca folliculi.** Blood and lymph channels penetrate the ovary and lace the surfaces of the follicles. In fishes and amphibia, the connective tissue stroma is an insignificant fraction of the ovarian mass, but in amniotes, especially in the placental mammals, it becomes cell-rich and complex. As the oogonia enlarge into **primary oocytes,** the follicle cells that surround them become more numerous and more definitely segregated.

In amphibian ovaries, the follicles dangle for some months by narrow threads in a central cavity that was created when the medulla of the indifferent gonad degenerated (Fig. 28–2 A). Later the eggs, coated thinly by their follicle cells, move again to the outside, so that when they finally ripen they break out into the coelomic cavity. In the ovaries of reptiles and monotremes the young follicles have similar relations with large lymph spaces that develop in the interior of the ovary. In none of these do cavities appear within the follicles themselves. But in mammals (Fig. 28–2 B) the many-layered follicles do develop cavities into which the eggs, covered by their satellite cells, project. The follicles lie in unbroken connective tissue, but as in all the other cases they move to the exterior of the ovary at last and discharge their eggs into the coelom.

The usual arrangement in the teleosts is quite different. While there are some species in which ovulation takes place through the outer wall of the ovary into the coelom, in most cases it oc-

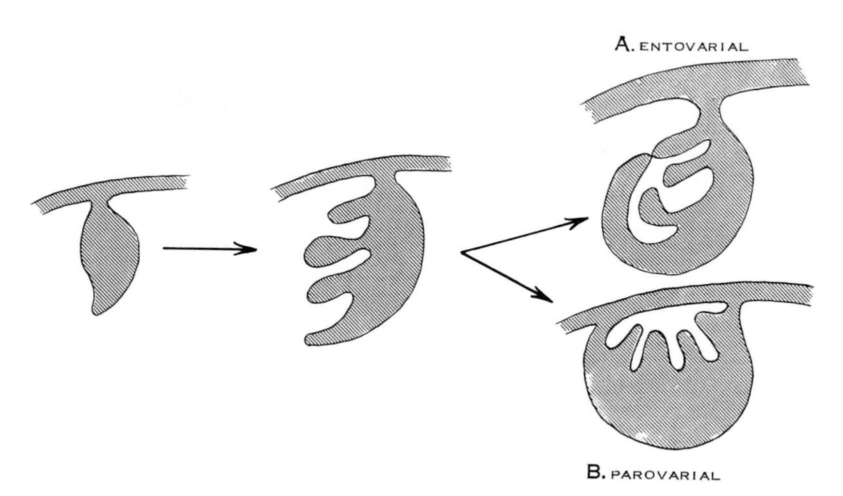

Fig. 28–3. Ovisacs of teleosts.

curs internally. The ovary develops leaflike expansions which fold over and either fuse with the organ itself, forming an **entovarial ovisac,** or with the nearby coelomic wall, forming a **parovarial ovisac** (Fig. 28–3). In either case, the eggs are discharged into the ovisac when they mature.

The germ cells and their follicles are formed in great excess, and seasonal or cyclical crops of them are allowed to mature at intervals characteristic of the species. What selects the ones to mature at any one time and what controls their numbers is unknown. It has been demonstrated in many vertebrates that eggs will not mature in the ovary without certain hormones from the pituitary, and that when they are mature the pituitary reacts either to ovarian influences or to nervous stimuli by releasing other hormones which trigger off the ovulation process. The details are apparently different in different vertebrates (cf. Chapter 30).

When ovulation takes places, some of the follicle cells are dragged away with the maturing egg, but the rest of them remain behind, inside the collapsed theca. In certain lower vertebrates they are lost without further ado, but in others, including representatives of all the major groups, they persist for some time and multiply, taking on the histologic attributes of secretory cells. The same appearance is achieved in all groups of vertebrates also by the so-called **atretic follicles,** i.e., follicles whose oocytes degenerate instead of maturing.

For most of the non-mammalian vertebrates, it is not yet known what these pre-ovulatory or post-ovulatory glandular masses do. Obviously however, they have been involved in a bold evolutionary advance in the marsupials and placental mammals. Here, the cells of the post-ovulatory follicle condense into a conspicuous mass of endocrine tissue called the **corpus luteum** (Fig. 4–19), which liberates a steroid hormone into the blood stream. This hormone, called progesterone, is essential for the attachment or implantation of the blastocyst in the uterus, and for the maintenance of pregnancy. Similar progestins have been obtained from other kinds of vertebrates (and even tunicates), but the tissues which give rise to them are often in doubt.

IV. EGG PATH

Irrespective of whether it is fertilized inside the body of the female or not, the egg after ovulation (or the embryo derived from its fertilization) is carried to the outside by one means or another. Three contrasting types of provision for this may now be described.

A. Absence of Oviducts

In hagfishes and lampreys the provision for transportation of eggs outside the body is hardly more elaborate than what one can find in coelenterates. There are no oviducts at all. The eggs are shed into the body cavity, and under the pressure of belly musculature they find their way out through a pair of pores in the body wall that lead to a urogenital sinus which empties behind the anus. Some of the bony fishes have arrangements almost as simple.

B. Teleost Sacs and Ducts

As already mentioned, teleost eggs are shed into the ovisacs rather than into the coelom, except in a few primitive or supposedly degenerate species which may not even produce ovisacs. These ovarian spaces are prolonged posteriorly as tubes which follow the mesenteries of the gonad ridges and meet to empty by a single median pore between the anus and the urinary papilla. The posterior parts of this very simple oviduct system may arise separately by folding or excavation of the mesenteries either before or after the ovisacs have arisen. Particularly in species with parovarial ovisacs, they may not connect with the ovaries at all. In such cases, the shed eggs pass from the ovisacs to the coelom at the posterior ends of the ovaries, and are then picked up through the free funnels of a pair of oviducts, or a single one in the midline, for transfer to the genital pore.

The teleost egg path structures are subject to a good many variations, but it should be noted that parts are fabricated from the gonad itself, and the more posterior ducts have no relation to the kidney duct system at all. In these respects teleosts differ from the rest of the vertebrates. Also, as will be seen, there is another odd thing about these species: their egg path and their sperm path are directly comparable.

C. Paramesonephric Oviducts

In a third assemblage of vertebrates, including the elasmobranchs, the amphibia, and the amniotes, the oviducts are in close developmental relation to the primitive kidney ducts, and usually have no direct contact with the ovaries at all. They form on each side by direct aggregation of cells from the coelomic lining to form a ridge which grows backward along the kidney strip. A funnel quite like a nephrostome opens into the ridge at its anterior end, and as the cord of cells is spun out posteriorly it is converted into a tube which eventually reaches the cloaca. It is entirely unlike a teleost oviduct, either in development or in anatomical relationships, and may be distinguished as a **paramesonephric duct** (PNA). It forms after the pharyngula stage, and in anura even as late as the stage of metamorphosis from the tadpole. The primitive kidney duct, which it follows, was already complete and functional before the pharyngula stage.

There is no suggestion of any relationship between the paramesonephric duct and its *ovary* at embryonic stages. Rather illogically, in elasmobranchs and many amniotes the growing tip of this kind of oviduct is inseparable from the *primitive kidney duct,* so that it may be described as a pinched-off product of the latter. Experimental removal of the primitive kidney duct is followed by the failure of formation of the oviduct on that side.

The evolutionary relationship or homology between the teleost oviduct and the paramesonephric duct has been much debated and remains uncertain. Some of the archaic living fishes, for instance the garpikes, follow the teleost pattern precisely. Others, such as sturgeons, and the bowfin *Amia,* have short paired oviducts ending anteriorly in open funnels which can be compared either with the paramesonephric type or with the uncompleted parovarial teleost type.

Paramesonephric oviducts normally develop to a rudimentary condition equally well in the young embryos of both sexes, or for that matter in embryos castrated at very young stages. Normally in males they remain rudimentary or disappear more or less completely in late fetal stages, but many adult male amphibia continue to carry rudimentary oviducts along with their male genitals. Experimentally it has been shown that if embryos are flooded with androgens or have testes grafted into them before oviduct anlagen appear, no oviducts will form at all. Once these are established, however, the sensitivity disappears and they are able to maintain themselves as in normal circumstances.

At first the paramesonephric ducts take the shape of simple straight tubes. If the ovaries are removed from an embryo or a young female, her oviducts remain rudimentary. On the other hand if estrogens are administered a precocious differentiation can be produced. If ovaries are grafted into male chick embryos in the first third of the incubation period, the oviducts do not disappear but are partially retained and much enlarged. (Paradoxically, enlargement of paramesonephric ducts has been brought about in some vertebrates by experimental administration of progestins and androgens. These effects are not necessarily direct ones. The treatment may shock the recipient's own endocrine system into a strong and abnormal behavior.)

In normal females, the normal supply of estrogens at the end of the juvenile period produces dramatic effects on the paramesonephric ducts. The two oviducts of a frog increase their length four times, and their diameter correspondingly, and become richly glandular in preparation for the breeding season. A hen's single oviduct (the right one is normally inhibited) enlarges to thirty times its former size when she becomes old enough to start laying. When this maturation process is completed, the paramesonephric oviduct may show as many as five regions, each with its own function, and none of them showing any resemblance to the parts of the simple teleostean oviduct. The parts are, in order, the **infundibulum,** the **tube** (uterine tube, PNA), the **isthmus,** the **uterus,** and the **vagina** (Fig. 28–4).

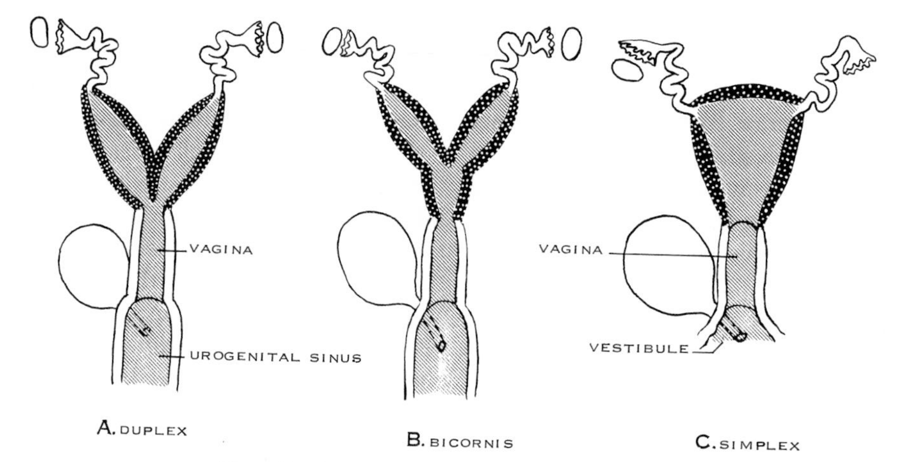

Fig. 28–5. Types of mammalian uterus.
(After A. Portmann, Einführung in die Vergleichende Morphologie der Wirbeltiere, 1948, by permission of Benno Schwabe & Co.)

tial fusion of the two uteri so that the right and left "horns of the uterus" lead posteriorly into a midline "body of the uterus" which in turn opens into the vagina (Fig. 28–5 B). According to the relative sizes of the body and the horns, these uteri are called *bipartite* (large horns) or *bicornuate* (small horns). The ultimate condition is illustrated in man and a few other placental mammals, which have small uterine tubes emptying at the upper corners of a single massive *uterus simplex* (Fig. 28–5 C).

While any given mammalian species has its normal uterine type, there is wide variation within orders and suborders of the class. Double, bipartite, bicornuate, and simplex uteri are each found in particular species of bats, for instance. Individual variations may also occur within a species. All the mammalian types of uterus have turned up as anomalous developmental variations in women.

The differentiation of the mammalian vagina has its special peculiarities. When the two oviducts have grown backward, met, and transformed into tubular structures, the posterior vaginal region remains as a solid cell mass connected with the uterine space (or spaces) by an epithelial strand. Its appearance varies with species. It usually opens up as a vaginal space late in development, but in guinea pigs and moles it may remain as an epithelial cord except during heat or pregnancy, and may even close up again between breeding seasons. The uterus–vagina boundary remains vague until late in development but usually then becomes marked by a sharp diminution of the muscular thickness and glandular lining of the uterine wall (Fig. 28–4 B). In many mammals the lower uterus eventually bulges into the upper part of the vagina, and sometimes, as in the human, the two parts meet at a sharp angle. In ungulates, rodents and primates, the boundary between the vagina and the urogenital sinus may be marked by a mucous membrane fold, the **hymen.**

These vaginal developments can be repressed in female embryos of various mammals by early administration of androgens, and the male pattern of urogenital sinus development can be shifted toward that of normal females by administration of estrogens, or by castration of early embryos. After its differentiation has gotten well under way the vagina will maintain itself in at least rudimentary and recognizable condition whatever hormones reach it, but both uterus and vagina continue through life to be highly sensitive to the normal cyclic changes of the female sexual rhythm.

Marsupials have indulged in a number of peculiar evolutionary experiments with the vagina.

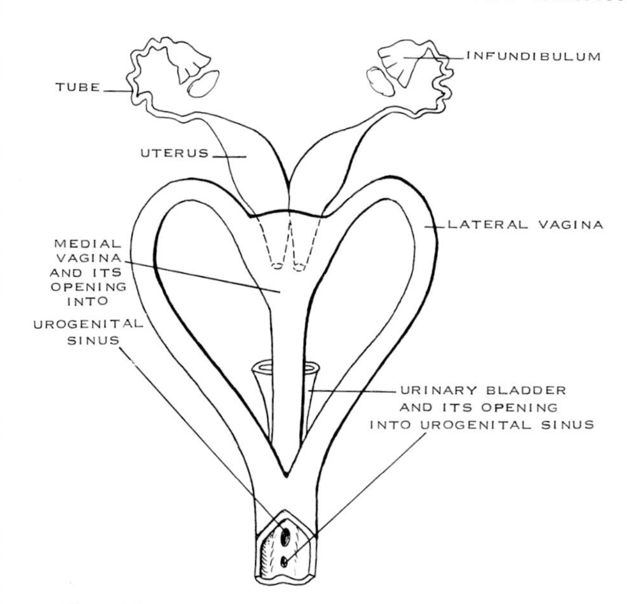

Fig. 28–6. Genital tract of female kangaroo.
(After A. Portmann, Einführung in die Vergleichende Morphologie der Wirbeltiere, 1948, by permission of Benno Schwabe & Co.)

Whereas monotremes and their non-mammalian ancestors have a pair of vaginae, one for each paramesonephric duct, and the placental mammals have fused these into a single one, most marsupials have three (Fig. 28–6). One lies in the midline and seems to be the normal mammalian vagina. It is actually used as part of the birth canal in some marsupials. The other two are arched tubes which grow out anterolaterally from the midline vagina and swing posteriorly, either to empty separately into the urogenital sinus or to join the midline vagina again. In some of these marsupials the lateral vaginae serve as birth canals and the median one never opens up; in others the median one opens temporarily to serve as the birth canal and then closes up without having acquired a permanent lining; or in still others it opens at the time of birth of the first litter and remains open thereafter.

Normally the posterior ends of paramesonephric oviducts empty into the cloaca. This relation holds in monotremes, but in other mammals the completion of the urorectal fold places the opening of the vagina in the urogenital sinus. As the female individual continues to grow, this sinus is usually transformed into a long tubular space (Fig. 28–4 B). In moles and man, however, its space becomes very much shortened anteroposteriorly and at the same time elongated dorsoventrally so that it is transformed into a narrow space between lateral lips ("labia minora"), and the vaginal and urethral orifices are brought close to the surface (Fig. 28–5 C). Either in this shortened version or the more usual tubular form, the opening of the vagina into it overshadows the opening of the urethra, so that the urogenital sinus of the mammalian fetus is customarily renamed the **vaginal vestibule** in the adult female.

As another variation, seen in some rodents, the tubular urogenital sinus is divided lengthwise by still another partition, so that the urethra

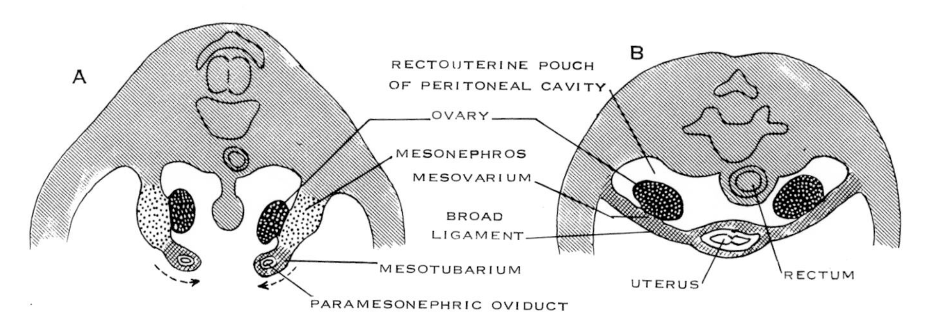

Fig. 28–7. Formation of a uterine broad ligament. A. Mesotubaria moving toward midline. B. Juncture of mesotubaria and oviducts.
(Redrawn from B. M. Patten, Foundations of Embryology, 1958, by permission of McGraw-Hill Book Co., Inc.)

and the vagina each acquire their own openings on the surface.

E. Mesenteries

In the vertebrates that develop paramesonephric oviducts the ovaries generally come to be suspended by their own **mesovaria,** the oviducts by their own **mesotubaria** (Fig. 28–4). In mammals the whole oviduct apparatus and the ovaries as well generally recede posteriorly during development, whether from active descent or the passive effects of relative growth rates. As the mesonephric parts of the kidney strips vanish, the roots of the mesovaria come to be transferred to the roots of the mesotubaria (Fig. 28–7). If at the same time the posterior parts of the mesotubaria are swung together with the fusing of the uteri in the pelvic region, a uniquely mammalian **broad ligament of the uterus** is produced from the two of them, crossing the body cavity in a frontal plane. The mesenteric attachments of the ovaries and the tubal sections of the two oviducts come to be subordinate to this highly developed broad ligament. The posterior part of the peritoneal cavity is divided by the ligament into a dorsal **rectouterine pouch** and a ventral **vesicouterine pouch.**

REFERENCES

1. Dodd, J. M., 1960. *Mem. Soc. Endocrinol.* 7: 17.
2. Lennox, B., D. M. Serr, and M. A. Ferguson-Smith, 1960. *Mem. Soc. Endocrinol.* 7: 123.
3. Kosin, I. L., and H. Iohzaki, 1959. *Science* 130: 43.
4. McKay, D. G., A. T. Hertig, E. C. Adams, and L. Danziger, 1953. *Anat. Record* 117: 201.
5. Mintz, B., 1957. *J. Embryol. Exptl. Morphol.* 5: 396.
6. Gillman, J., 1948. *Carnegie Inst. Wash. Publ.* 575, *Contrib. Embryol.* 32: 81.
7. Anteunis, A., 1959. *Arch. biol.* (*Liége*) 70: 783.
8. Bertin, L., 1958. *In* P.-P. Grassé (ed.), *Traité de zoologie,* Tome XIII (2). Masson, Paris.
9. Matthews, L. H., 1955. *Mem. Soc. Endocrinol.* 4: 129.
10. Blackler, A. W., and M. Fischberg, 1961. *J. Embryol. Exptl. Morphol.* 9: 634.

29

The Genital System: II

I. TESTIS DIFFERENTIATION

If the embryo at fertilization receives a set of genes which predisposes to maleness, and the balance is not changed by environmental or experimental circumstances, then the same germinal and structural elements that would otherwise differentiate into the eggs, their follicles, and an ovarian stroma, begin to develop into the tissues characteristic of a testis.

In males as in females, events are histologically comparable between tetrapods and elasmobranchs, in contrast with many other fishes. In this main cluster of vertebrates, cords of cells extend inward from the germinal epithelium toward the center of the gonad ridge carrying primordial germ cells with them (Fig. 28–1 B). If the germinal epithelium becomes obviously thinned out in this process, and if the mesenchyme thickens just underneath it, foreshadowing the differentiation of a stout fibrous layer, the **tunica albuginea,** then one is seeing the first structural evidence of the declaration of male sex (Fig. 28–1 D). The tunica albuginea becomes the connective tissue capsule of the testis. The inwandering cords of cells become **seminiferous tubules,** instead of breaking up into follicles or disintegrating.

Simultaneously, the mesenchyme of the center of the gonad and bordering the kidney strip is thickening and beginning to condense into another network of cords. These, like the inwandering testis cords, subsequently become a system of tubules. They usually form a network or **rete testis,** which eventually interconnects with the seminiferous tubules on the one hand, and with a group of kidney tubules on the other. No such arrangement of rete and kidney tubules develops in cyclostomes or teleosts, which acquire quite different means of delivering their sperm (see below).

Some fishes are known which have only one seminiferous tubule per testis, but in most vertebrates there are dozens or hundreds, multiplied by branching. The tubules may be short and blunt so that they could more appropriately be called lobules, or they may be very long, contorted, and threadlike (Fig. 4–20). Each develops a basement membrane and an inner germinal epithelium. In late embryonic stages the primordial germ cells in this epithelium divide and become smaller so that they are no longer distinguishable. As sexual maturity approaches, large nucleated cell-like masses appear at intervals along the tubule walls, firmly planted against the basement membrane. They are called **nurse cells,** because in the ripe testis the heads of large numbers of maturing spermatids are found plugged

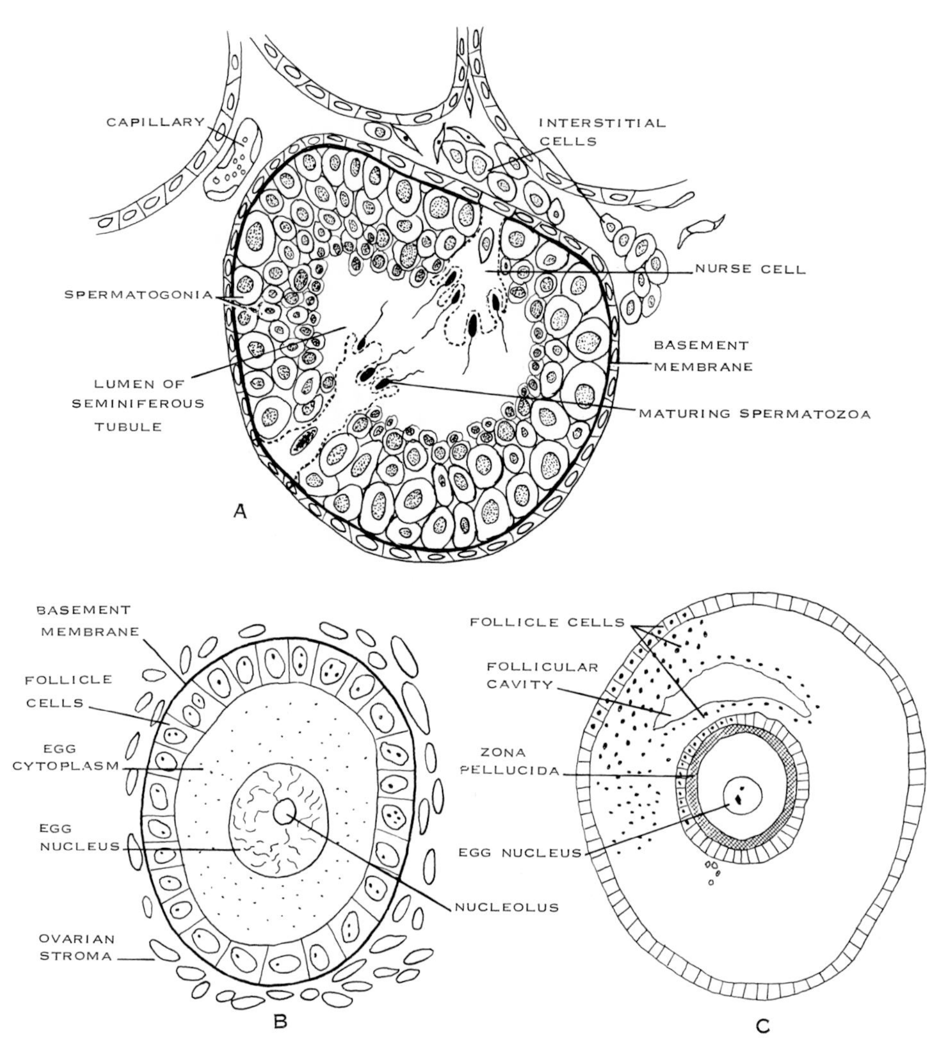

Fig. 29–1. Elements of gonad histology. A. Cross-section of a seminiferous tubule. B and C. Young and maturing ovarian follicles.

(After Hamilton, Boyd, and Mossman, Human Embryology, 2d edition, 1952, by permission of W. Heffer & Sons, Ltd.)

into sockets on their surfaces, the sperm tails dangling in the tubule lumen (Fig. 29–1 A).

These nurse cells of the testis and the follicle cells of the ovary are alike in being products of the sex cords of the gonad anlage. It has been suggested that they also carry on similar functions of secreting estrogens and of providing food materials for their growing or transforming gametes. In sharp contrast, many follicle cells attend one ovum (Fig. 29–1 B) but many sperm cells hang onto one nurse cell.

In mammals the mesenchyme of the gonad ridge not only forms the stout tunica albuginea just inside the coelomic epithelium, it may also form numbers of partitions in the interior, walling off groups of seminiferous tubules. In most other vertebrates, the latter are simply embedded in a general loose stroma of connective tissue through which blood vessels, lymph vessels, and nerves wander.

Special groups of these connective tissue cells differentiate in the angular spaces between the seminiferous tubules, as nests of **interstitial cells** (Fig. 29–1 A). Reports of their absence in some species may be due to the fact that their bulk fluctuates enormously with the seasons when there is a sharply localized breeding period. Comparable interstitial elements have been described in the ovaries of some vertebrates but are not common. Since the main source of androgenic hormones in the male is the testis, and since this supply is maintained after the seminiferous tubules are destroyed by heat or X-rays, it is assumed that the androgens come mainly from the interstitial cells.

II. SPERM PATH

Three or four types of vertebrates can be distinguished in respect of the devices by which sperm delivery to the outside is accomplished.

A. Absence of Sperm Ducts

The seminiferous lobules of lampreys and hagfishes void themselves to the coelomic cavity, and the sperm-filled coelom is then emptied through simple posterior abdominal pores by pressure from muscles of the belly wall. In these animals the paths for sperm cells and eggs are essentially alike, and there are no ducts.

B. Teleost Sperm Sacs and Ducts

The sex anatomy of teleost males is strictly comparable, down to its species variations, with that of the females. The sperm tubules may shed their contents into the coelom, as may the egg follicles, but in most species they open inward, to a central testis cavity like the ovisac of the female. A duct usually forms posterior to each gonad along the peritoneal wall, tapping the contents of the testis cavity and emptying to the outside. As with the oviduct of the teleost female, this **sperm duct** may form before, simultaneously with, later than, or quite independently of the testis cavity, and it may more or less fuse with its antimere. Such a fusion may extend also to the two gonads.

Neither the anterior part of the teleostean sperm path, inside the testis, nor the posterior part, have anything to do with the kidney apparatus, in development or otherwise.

In different kinds of teleosts the sperm ducts may empty separately between an anus and a urinary papilla, or into the urinary bladder, or into the urinary duct, or into an anus, or into a cloaca. Enlargements of the sperm ducts may serve as storage vesicles, and other variations of this system are numerous in teleosts.

C. Kidney Ducts Converted to Sperm Ducts

The commonest and certainly the most elaborate sperm path is that found in the same group of vertebrates whose females develop paramesonephric oviducts, namely the elasmobranchs, amphibia and amniotes. In these, the seminiferous tubules are connected through a rete testis to certain of the kidney tubules, and much of the primitive kidney duct is transformed into a **ductus deferens** in the adult male (Fig. 29–2 A), leading the sperm to the cloaca or to a urogenital sinus derived from it.

It will be recalled that in practically all the vertebrates the center of urinary function becomes progressively transferred to more posterior sections of the kidney strip. Anterior tubules degenerate while more posterior ones are multiplying. A reprieve from this degeneration comes to those few kidney tubules which acquire connections through rete tubules to a developing testis. They remain as **efferent ductules.**

In urodeles, a sharp distinction thus emerges between a **pars cranialis** or pars sexualis of the kidney strip, which tends to degenerate in females and is more or less occupied with sperm-transfer in males, and a **pars caudalis** which becomes the center of urine production. Much the same thing happens in elasmobranchs and in all the amniotes. In the latter, it has become customary to call the pars cranialis the mesonephros. When the tubules of this part of the kidney strip lose their urinary function they all disappear except for the ones connected with the rete testis. These latter undergo some reduction, losing their glomeruli if not also their glomerular capsules, but keep the path open to the primitive kidney duct. Such efferent ductules, together with an

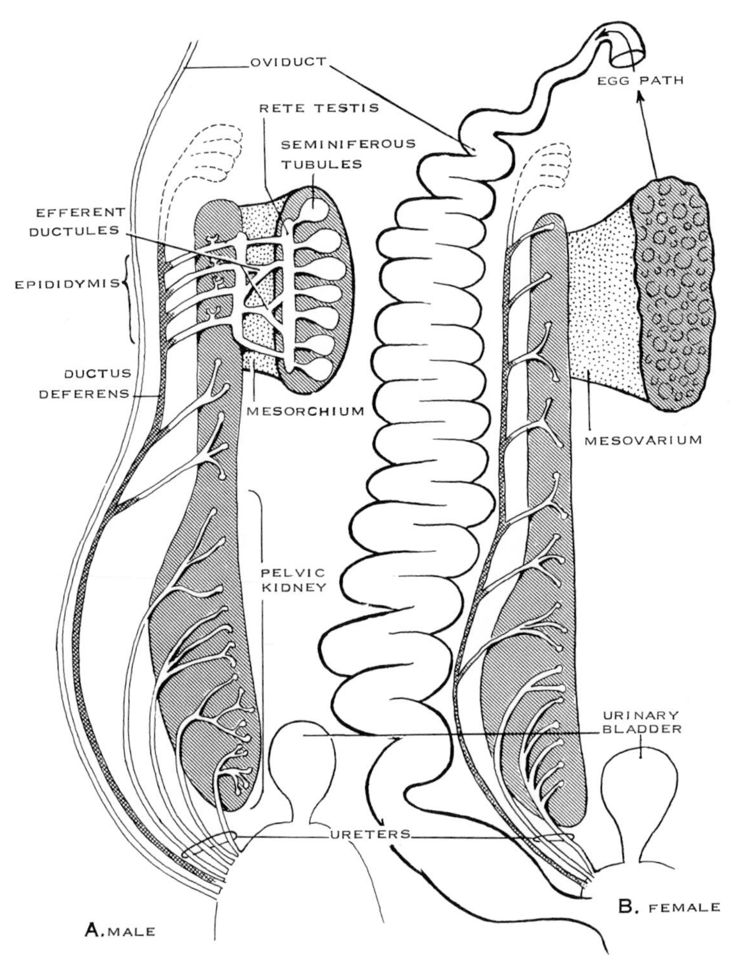

Fig. 29–2. Urogenital tract of a urodele, right side. Diagrammatic, based on the amblystoma.

(After A. Portmann, Einführung in die Vergleichende Morphologie der Wirbeltiere, 1948, by permission of Benno Schwabe & Co.)

adjacent part of the primitive kidney duct—which may form a bulky and highly contorted mass—constitute a new functional unit, the **epididymis** (Figs. 4–20, 29–3).

Not uncommonly, degenerate and detached remnants of other non-sexual mesonephric tubules may linger in the mesentery nearby as a useless mass called the **paradidymis** (Fig. 29–3 B). All this apparatus was present as an anlage in the female while her sex was being declared, and may still linger in the mesentery of the ovary of adult female amniotes. In the female, the homolog of the epididymis is called the **epoöphoron,** that of the paradidymis the **paroöphoron** (Fig. 29–3 C).

The mammalian epididymis has two functions, to store the masses of completed spermatozoa after they drop away from their nurse cells and cross the rete, and also to secrete a substance which maintains and nourishes them until they are ejaculated. The same may be true in some other amniotes but certainly not in all. The bird epididymis for instance is much too small to be a principal storage depot. The testis and ductus themselves increase their bulk several hundredfold in preparation for the breeding sea-

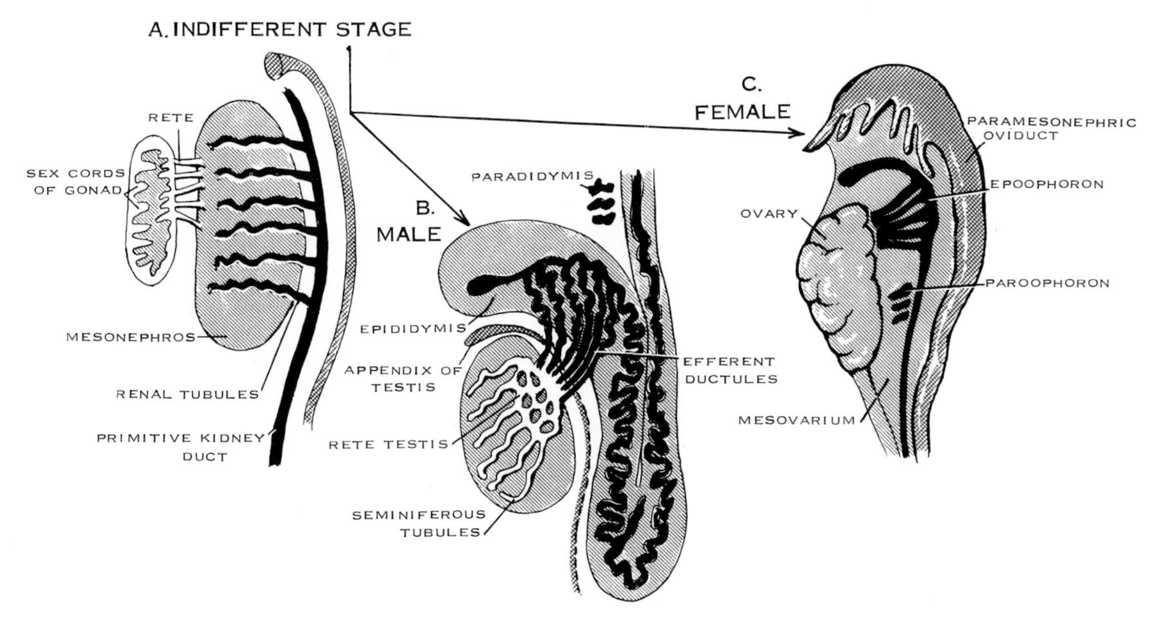

Fig. 29–3. Remnants of the mesonephric tubule system and the paramesonephric oviduct in male and female human.

son, the ductus being thrown into a mass of coils at its posterior end and serving as storehouse.

Cyclostomes and teleosts of course do not have an epididymis, since they do not use any kidney apparatus for sperm transfer. In dipnoan fishes, the kidney tubules taken over for sperm transfer may be scattered throughout the whole adult kidney, as in the Australian species, or may be confined to the posterior end of it (the "hypodidymis") in the other species.

Both testis and epididymis may be drawn far back toward the pelvis during development in the amniotes, but usually remain close to the permanent kidney mass. In mammals, however, they become separated from the metanephros in a process described below as "descent of the testis." The part of the primitive kidney duct into which the efferent ductules empty then contracts into a tightly coiled **ductus epididymidis** which forms most of the bulk of the epididymis. The rest of the primitive kidney duct, relieved of urinary function by the development of the metanephros and its ureter, is renamed the **ductus deferens.** It continues to maintain an exit into the cloaca in birds and reptiles, but becomes involved in new developments in mammals (see page 583).

The posterior part of the ductus deferens is commonly enlarged, or sends out a diverticulum, in the sexually mature individual. All male elasmobranchs show such chambers, called **seminal vesicles** (Fig. 27–4 A), which are homologous with the urinary bladders of their females. The seminal vesicles may be honeycombed internally with folds of a secretory membrane. Similar structures are known in the males of some anuran amphibia and birds, and are common and often highly elaborated in mammals. All these structures have to be carefully distinguished by embryologic study from posterior vestiges of the paramesonephric oviducts, which may be present side by side with them.

III. HORMONES AND THE DEVELOPMENT OF THE SPERM PATH

In normal females, and in members of either sex which have been castrated during early embryonic stages, the epididymis and ductus deferens remain rudimentary [1]. With a proper supply of androgens however, they finish their growth and differentiation with striking vigor. This has been demonstrated in many species, by administration of either natural or synthetic androgens to castrated young males, or for that matter to young females. When female frogs are experimentally forced to reverse their sex, ductus deferens enlargement follows as a consequence of the activity of their newly functional testes. Estrogens typically have no effect on the epididymis or the ductus deferens, though paradoxical stimulations have been reported sometimes in experiments involving heavy dosages.

Stimulation of the epididymis and ductus deferens can be noted in the intact male after injection of certain pituitary extracts. This effect is not obtainable after castration, which shows that the pituitary hormones are not acting directly. What happens is that gonad-stimulating or **gonadotropic hormones** from the pituitary stimulate the production of androgens in the host's own testes, which in turn act upon the epididymis and ductus. Hypophysectomy causes regression of these latter organs if they have been fully formed, or inhibition of their development in the juvenile period, because the consequent deprivation of gonadotropins prevents the testes from forming androgens. How any of these hormones achieve their effects in their own particular target organs is unknown [2].

IV. DESCENT OF TESTIS AND EPIDIDYMIS IN MAMMALS

A. Preliminary Gonad Shift

If the trunk of an embryo increases in length ten times as fast as the gonads, and if the gonads remain anchored to the region of the septum transversum, then the latter must become passively separated from the pelvis by increasing lengths. This happens in the great majority of elasmobranchs. But there are others in which the gonads remain in mid-trunk during development, or drift toward the pelvis. In mammals, the gonads, whether testes or ovaries, are always tied more securely at their pelvic ends, and they always shift posteriorly during the time that the mesonephros is undergoing regression.

B. Ligamentous Connections of the Testis

The mammalian gonad first appears as a lump or ridge on the surface of the mesonephric section of the kidney strip (Fig. 27–7). Later the metanephros becomes prominent, and the mesonephros, bearing its tiny gonad, acquires a sort of mesentery of its own by pinching away from the dorsal coelomic wall. In still later stages the testis continues to grow, but all of the mesonephros except the parts salvaged for the epididymis undergoes sharp regression. This reverses the size relation between testis and mesonephros. Finally the testis is described as being supported by its own mesentery, the **mesorchium,** most of which it took over from the epididymis that now lies on its border (Fig. 29–3).

The mesorchium (Fig. 29–4 A), extending posteriorly along the inside of the flank, reaches into the pelvic part of the coelom. Here it comes into contact with a conical mound of the ventrolateral body wall called the **inguinal cone.** Condensations of connective tissue form in both the mesentery and the cone; they join and extend posteriorly toward the skin of a **genital swelling** at the side of the opening to the urogenital sinus. The resulting ligament, called the **gubernaculum testis,** can later be described as tying the testis to the skin of the scrotum. This whole process takes place in the female also, the gubernaculum tying the ovary to the skin of a comparable swelling which usually subsides, but which remains in the human female as the labium major at the side of the vaginal vestibule.

C. Active Descent of the Testis

The mammalian testis now usually becomes involved in a much more spectacular descent toward its scrotal sac accompanied by its epididymis and part of the ductus deferens. This process is not even suggested in normal females.

A **hernia** is defined as the protrusion of an organ or tissue through an abnormal opening. The opening itself may be made by rupture of the normal retaining wall, or the herniating organ may stretch and push the wall before it, coming thus to lie in a hernial sac. The active descent of the mammalian testis may be considered as a

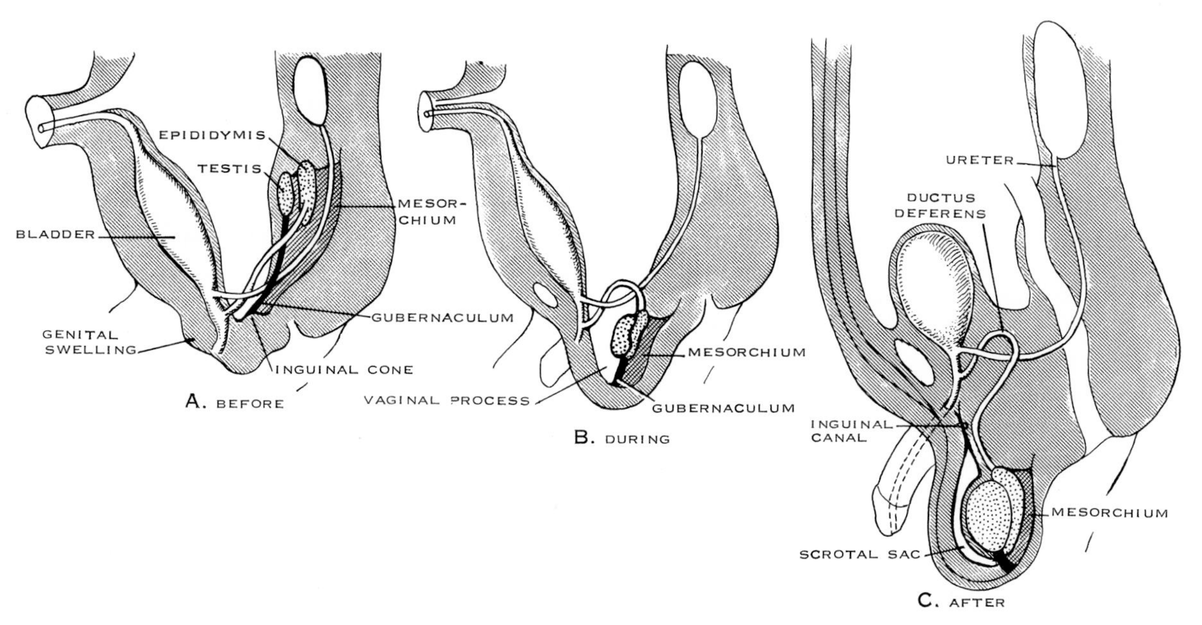

Fig. 29–4. Factors in the descent of the human testis.

normally occuring hernia without rupture. The scrotal sac is a *normal* structure precisely comparable to a hernial sac. The process of descent has been thoroughly described but the mechanics of it are not understood. The gubernaculum testis was once thought to be an active agent which pulled the testis down, but there is now general agreement that it plays an insignificant role.

As soon as the gubernaculum has differentiated, the peritoneal region embracing its posterior end begins to expand toward the outside, carrying it and the inguinal cone into a pocket called the **vaginal process** (Fig. 29–4 B). All the layers of the body wall are represented in the wall of this pocket. The whole fetus is rapidly enlarging at this time but the gubernaculum testis fails to keep pace with the deepening vaginal process of the peritoneum, and even shortens itself. Then the testis and its mesorchium, together with the epididymis and a loop of the ductus deferens, are tipped into the vaginal process and no longer lie in the main abdominal cavity. (Of course the testis, like any other coelomic organ, does not actually lie within the cavity that surrounds it, but hangs on its mesentery and is clothed by the visceral layer of the original coelomic lining. When the testis reaches the vaginal process this visceral layer is no longer called peritoneum but **tunica vaginalis.**)

The communication between the vaginal process and the main peritoneal cavity may narrow at a later stage, forming an **inguinal canal,** and this may eventually close itself completely so that the testis and its accompanying organs are permanently trapped (Fig. 29–4 C).

This active descent of the testes fails to take place in some mammals. Within the class all degrees may be found, between permanent normal retention of testes in the abdominal cavity and permanent location in closed dangling scrotal sacs. In monotremes and some insectivores the anlage of a gubernaculum appears (as it may in some reptiles) but later disappears; no vaginal process is formed and the testis remains in the abdomen. The gubernaculum and the vaginal process form in whales and armadillos, but the testis does not follow. In elephants, sea-cows, and various edentates the testes are restrained from descending because a broad ligament like that of the females (Fig. 28–7) is formed by the two mesorchia across the midline.

In the species whose testes do reach the vaginal processes of the peritoneum, the further active growth of the body wall in these areas may produce either slight, or considerable, **scrotal sacs.** Each of the principal layers of the body wall (peritoneum, transversus abdominis, the internal and external oblique muscles or their tendinous sheets, and the dermal and epidermal skin layers) can usually be traced by dissection, down into the wall of a scrotal sac. The continuity is clearest in the mammals which show the more primitive kinds of scrota, consisting of modest bulges of the body wall just beyond the pubic bones.

The two scrotal sacs may stay separate, but more commonly they are much prolonged and swing together to form a single scrotum with a midline partition. This usually lies posterior to the penis in placental mammals, but remains anterior to it in many marsupials. In most male humans, the two sacs have received their testes and swung together before birth, but the inguinal canals remain open for some months or years thereafter. Imperfect descent of testes is common among boys up to the age of puberty, and the anomaly of **cryptorchism,** in which one or both of the testes remain in the abdominal cavity, is usually reported to occur in more than one out of five hundred men.

Such cryptorchid testes are sterile. One sufficient reason for this (though other factors may be involved) is that human spermatogenesis cannot take place at the high temperature of the body cavity. Even in the cooler scrotum, human spermatogenesis may be interrupted for weeks as the aftermath of a temporary fever. The mammalian species which are normally cryptorchid usually have lower body temperatures. Bats and many rodents retain wide communications between their scrotal sacs and the abdominal cavity, and the testes descend through the inguinal canals only during the breeding season, returning to the abdomen during hibernation or cold weather. Male birds, which have very high blood temperatures but are invariably cryptorchid, presumably keep their testes cool by an air stream brought directly to the abdominal air sacs that wrap around them.

V. ACCESSORY GENITAL APPARATUS

A. Internal Fertilization and Viviparity

The great majority of vertebrates breed successfully without any other apparatus than the gonads and the structures of the egg path or sperm path that have already been described. Most representatives of the largest single class, the teleostomes, as well as the cyclostomes and the lungfishes, merely congregate in a group dance and shed their eggs and sperm together in the water. Frogs clasp in pairs and do the same. Most representatives of the second largest class, the birds, accomplish internal fertilization by no more elaborate procedure than the smearing of sperm from the male cloaca upon the opening of the female cloaca, whereupon the sperm cells swim up the oviduct and meet the egg near the infundibulum. Thus, even copulation does not require external genitals.

Nevertheless there is a conspicuous minority of other vertebrates which have developed quite elaborate accessory devices for the purpose of depositing sperm inside the female. At least six different patterns of such devices have been evolved independently, each in abundant variety. Two groups of fishes use modified fins in their copulation (*1* and *2* below), but the tetrapods (*3–8* below) use organs developed out of the cloaca or its external margins.

Both sexes of a species inherit the potential for producing this accessory genital apparatus, but the female is spared the effort of developing it since she need serve only as a receptacle, and her unadorned cloaca or urogenital sinus will do. There are two ways in which this economy has been contrived. One is for the parts needed by the male to be developed automatically unless they are repressed by the action of estrogens, as in certain birds. The other and more common arrangement is for them not to be developed at all unless specifically stimulated to do so by androgens, as in male mammals [1]. In the first case, castration of young embryos leads invariably to the male form of genitals, and the second case invariably to the female form.

Viviparity of the usual sort, namely development of the young within the female genital tract, requires internal fertilization. But since many kinds of fishes and reptiles practice internal fertilization and then proceed to lay eggs, it has been suggested that the initial advantage of the practice was the conservation of sperm [3]. Although practically all the viviparous lines of vertebrates have acquired some sort of special copulatory apparatus for depositing sperm inside the female, many non-viviparous ones have made equally spectacular progress along this line. Perhaps viviparity follows as a sort of evolutionary afterthought, once the more important trick of internal fertilization has been accomplished.

B. Devices for Copulation

It is necessary now to consider a number of independent developments in different stocks of vertebrates, which have in common only their adaptation for internal fertilization.

1. Elasmobranchs and Holocephals. In the males of all these fishes, **claspers** are normally developed from the medial borders of the paired pelvic fins (Fig. 21–13). The fact that all the members of these ancient classes have copulatory organs implies that experiments in internal fertilization, and perhaps even internal development of the young, were undertaken by vertebrates as early as Devonian times.

Claspers are developed in great variety in different species, though the basic pattern is easily recognized. No corresponding structures are formed from the pelvic fins of the females. It may be guessed, but it is not known, that their development is controlled by sex hormones.

The long basal cartilages of the clasper shafts are furnished with muscles so that they can be swung down and forward from their normally posterior position. Small cartilages at their tips are equipped with dilator muscles so that once the male has intruded one clasper (or both of them?) into the cloaca of his female they can be spread and anchored in. There are even species in which one of the terminal cartilages of the clasper is provided with a recurved erectile claw that can be set like a fishhook in the female's cloacal wall. Dorsal and ventral folds of skin, stiffened with cartilage, develop on the medial surface of the clasper in such a way that when the whole organ is swung forward the grooves between them can serve as a sperm guide from his cloaca to hers.

In many elasmobranchs, siphon sacs grow forward into the tissue of the pelvic fins from the bases of the claspers. They are very large and equipped with stout muscles and special gland masses in certain species, but in others they may be rudimentary or absent. The siphon sacs have not been found to contain spermatozoa, but the possibility has been suggested that they act as syringes to pump a current of sea water along the medial grooves, helping to direct semen from the male to the female. There is still not much information available on the mating behavior of elasmobranchs.

2. Viviparous Teleosts. Quite independently, a few bony fishes of at least four different orders have become viviparous. Most of these are cyprinodonts, including such familiar aquarium fishes as top minnows, mollies, swordtails, and guppies. In these the copulatory organ of the male is fashioned not from paired pelvic fins but from the unpaired anal fin. The anatomy of this **gonopodium** is too varied for a generalized description. It may be merely a furrowed lance-like object supported by fin-rays and equipped with muscles that can turn it forward and to one side or the other, or it may be a tube which the male can swing into position so that it makes contact with and continues the tube of his own genital aperture. Its tip, which may be armed with teeth or spines, is momentarily intruded into the genital aperture of the female and the organ serves as a guide for inserting within her little packets of spermatozoa, called **spermatophores.** It has been shown experimentally in a number of these species that the unspecialized anal fins of females can be transformed into gonopodia by treatment with androgens.

3. Urodeles. Some kinds of salamanders exhibit a sex play which resembles the clasping of frogs, but fertilization is accomplished in an entirely different way. The males deposit **spermatophores** on twigs or stones under the water, and the females take these up into their cloacas some time before egg-laying starts. Thus in some species (the amblystoma for instance) fertilization may occur in the oviduct of a female who has not been in physical contact with a male at all. In other species, spermatophores are passed directly from male to female by cloacal contact during the sex play.

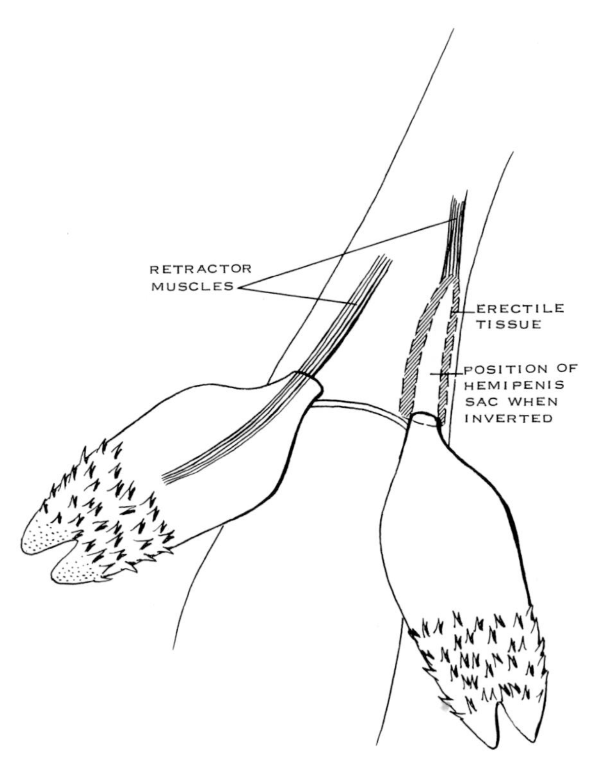

Fig. 29–5. Ventral view of the hemipenes of a snake, *Lachesis*.
(After J. Vellard, 1928.)

The spermatophores are packets of sperm cells coated with a tough glairy secretion which is derived from glands in the walls of the cloaca. At the approach of the breeding season, males of urodele species are readily distinguishable from females because the maturing of these glands causes their whole cloacal region to swell. In the females, the homologous glands remain rudimentary, but certain other ones in the cloacal roof may be specialized to serve as seminal receptacles. The females of some urodele species carry a supply of fertile sperm with them from one season to the next, and even in isolation will continue to lay fertilized eggs. While this curious behavior does not involve copulatory apparatus or even necessarily a copulation, it accomplishes the same purpose, i.e., internal fertilization. It has opened the way for at least one species of European salamander to become viviparous.

The cloacal glands characteristic of the adult male salamander are inhibited from development by castration. In either sex they are stimulated to develop by administration of androgens.

4. *Gymnophiona*. In all the burrowing blindworms of this tropical amphibian group, the cloaca of the male is very much longer than that of the female. It is equipped with special retractor muscles and apparently may be turned partly inside out and extruded by abdominal pressure. Internal fertilization is known to occur in these species, and it is an easy assumption, though not confirmed by direct observation, that the whole male cloaca serves as an organ of copulation by being everted into the cloaca of the female. The American tailed frog *Ascaphus* has invented a similar device.

5. *Squamata*. In the snakes and lizards, copulation is always practiced and the eggs are fertilized high in the oviduct before the albumen and eggshells are laid on. Viviparity is common. The agents of copulation are a pair of **hemipenes**, unlike anything found elsewhere in the phylum (Fig. 29–5).

These structures first arise in both sexes as bulges of the body wall just lateral to the cloaca on each side. They are not cloacal derivatives. They remain everted during most of the gestation period, and in fetuses of limbless lizards and snakes have been mistaken more than once for rudimentary hindlimb buds. Before birth or hatching they are pulled outside in and become subcutaneous penis pockets on each side of the base of the tail, their external orifices at the corners of the transverse slit-like cloacal aperture, and their blind ends directed posteriorly. Thereupon, in females they cease to grow and are more or less obliterated while in males they increase until they may form externally detectable ventrolateral bulges at the base of the tail. The sex of snakes and lizards can be diagnosed by probing for the penis pockets with a toothpick.

Each fully developed hemipenis in its invaginated state consists of a cavity lined by epidermis with several muscles attached to it, all embedded in loose blood-filled connective tissue. A long and a short **retractor muscle** take origin on tail vertebrae and insert respectively at the blind tip and the open end of the epidermal sac. The bed of blood sinuses through which they run is fed by several arteries and veins but drained only by a pair of rather small portal veins. If the inflow of blood is increased, blood piles up in the sinuses and inflates them; that is, the tissue is erectile. The retractor muscles, the erectile tissue, and a scent gland which drains through a duct to the surface near the cloaca, are all enclosed in a curved sheet of **propulsor muscle** whose fibers run dorsoventrally, attaching to vertebrae above and to a midline raphe ventrally. The right and the left propulsor muscles enclose the two hemipenes like parentheses in cross-section, like a corset in three dimensions. Therefore, when the retractors are relaxed and the blood-sinus tissue is erected, the epithelial sacs are forced by the pressure of these muscles behind them to turn inside out and extend as a pair of finger-like balloons at the sides of the cloaca.

When thus erected, each hemipenis bears a rather deep medial groove on its dorsal surface (not shown in Fig. 29–5), which forms a lateral continuation of the cloacal lumen. It may also be deeply cleft or double, and is usually studded with scales or tiny teeth. When the male seizes a female and brings his cloaca to hers, he erects and intrudes one hemipenis or the other into her, as an anchor and a dilator. In this position, its dorsal groove can serve as a sperm guide. When copulation is finished, the erectile tissue drains itself of blood and the retractor muscles pull the hemipenes outside-in again.

6. Turtles, Crocodilia, Birds. In sharp contrast to the paired extracloacal hemipenes of the squamate reptiles, the turtles, the crocodilia, and a very few species of birds develop an unpaired intracloacal **penis.** It is not known whether the penes of these groups are independent developments or divergent ends of a much-branched evolutionary effort.

The roomy turtle cloaca develops a midven-

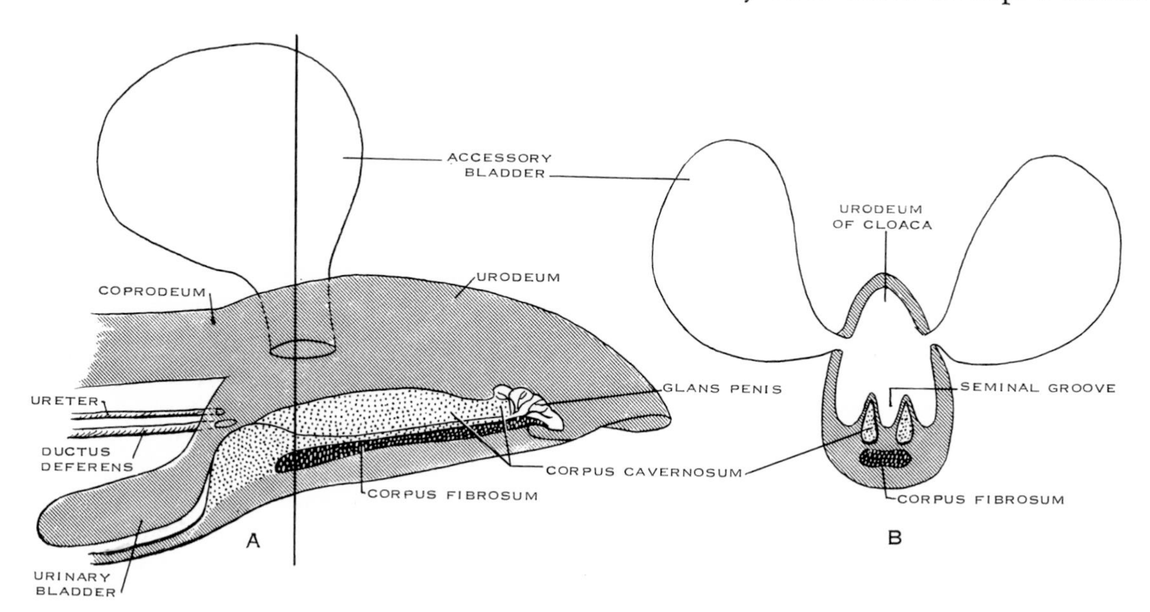

Fig. 29–6. Diagrams of a turtle penis. A. Dissection to the sagittal plane from the left side. B. Cross-section in the plane of the transverse line in A.
(After N. L. Wilbaut-Isebree Moens, 1911.)

tral linear pad of special mucous membrane which is scored by a sharp midline furrow and underlaid by a pair of fibrous bodies (**corpora fibrosa**) which practically always fuse to one around the base of the furrow and enlarge distally into a swelling called the **glans.** Above them, and forming the walls of a shallow groove, are two parallel **corpora cavernosa** (Fig. 29–6). As the animal matures, the corpora fibrosa and cavernosa become spongy with wide blood lacunae so that they are converted into erectile tissue. During sexual excitement of the adult male, this special apparatus swells enormously with blood, the midline groove is converted temporarily into a seminal tube, and for lack of room inside, the whole thing blossoms out through the cloacal aperture, glans first. The inner end of the temporary tube is at the place where the two ductus deferens empty into his cloaca, so that when the penis is inserted into his partner's cloaca it can transfer sperm directly to her. When this has been accomplished, blood drains from the sinuses, the penish shrinks back to its flaccid condition, and special **retractor muscles** pull it back inside, where it rests on the floor of the cloaca as before.

The erected penis of a male turtle may be nearly as large as its hindleg. A miniature replica of it, called the **clitoris,** is formed in the female, complete with groove and retractor muscles, but cannot be everted and has no function. The penis of an alligator is similar to that of a turtle in structure and function, but is set apart more sharply from the rest of the cloacal wall in the flaccid condition.

Among birds, only the flightless ratites, the ducks, and a few others develop a definite penis. In the ostrich, the penis is unpaired and has the same basic structure as that of the turtle. There are rods of erectile tissue, a seminal groove, and retractor muscles. However, the organ is asymmetric and more elaborate in detail. It lies in a special **penis pocket** on the ventral floor of the cloaca, from which it is rolled out during excretory acts as well as in copulation. In other ratites and in ducks the raised ridge in the ventral cloaca has the same parts as in the ostrich, but in addition there is a long **blind sac** entering its external end. During erection, not only does the entire penis swell and elongate and emerge from the cloacal cavity, but also the blind sac turns inside out, adding greatly to the length of the erected organ. A spiraled **seminal groove** on the everted blind sac connects with the groove on the outside of the main penis to form an uninterrupted channel from the deferent ducts to the outer tip.

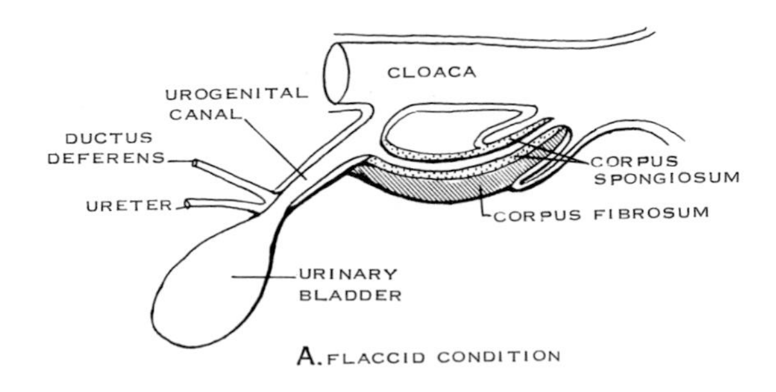

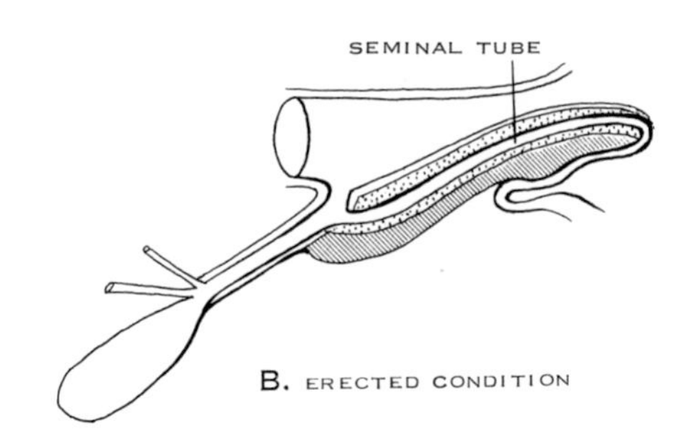

Fig. 29–7. Diagrams of a monotreme penis.
(After J. E. V. Boas, 1891.)

7. *Monotreme Mammals.* The penis of the monotremes is intermediate in form between those of turtles and the placental mammals, but has its own peculiarities as well (Fig. 29–7). It lies in a ventral penis pocket partly walled off from the rest of the cloaca. Internal to it there is an elongated urogenital sinus which connects the deferent ducts and the urinary bladder with the main cloacal chamber. The penis has a tube running through its length, communicating internally with the urogenital sinus and emptying externally through the glans. It is called a **seminal tube,** but one does not know whether semen actually traverses it during copulation. A soft mass of erectile tissue, the **corpus spongiosum,**

surrounds the seminal tube and extends into the glans, and the rest of the penis is filled with erectile tissue which may represent the corpus fibrosum. There is a retractor muscle for pulling the penis back into its cloacal pocket.

8. *Placental Mammals.* Except in monotremes, a urorectal fold cuts into the embryonic mammalian cloaca in the frontal plane, dividing it into a ventral urogenital sinus and a dorsal rectum (page 556; Figs. 27–7, 29–8). The urogenital sinus, which received urine first from the mesonephroi by way of the primitive kidney ducts, later receives urine from the ureters by way of the bladder, and then sexual products by way of the primitive kidney ducts in males, or the paramesonephric oviducts in females. The subsequent history of the urogenital sinus is not only spectacularly different in the two sexes, it demonstrates that there are two different meanings for the name urethra in mammalian anatomy (see page 584).

In the female, the products are a **vaginal vestibule** and some diminutive and imperfect replicas of the external genitals of the male (Fig. 29–8 C). The urogenital sinus of the male on the other hand does not long retain its original wide external aperture but becomes converted into a narrow tube whose distal end is secondarily prolonged down the length of the penis (Fig. 29–8 D).

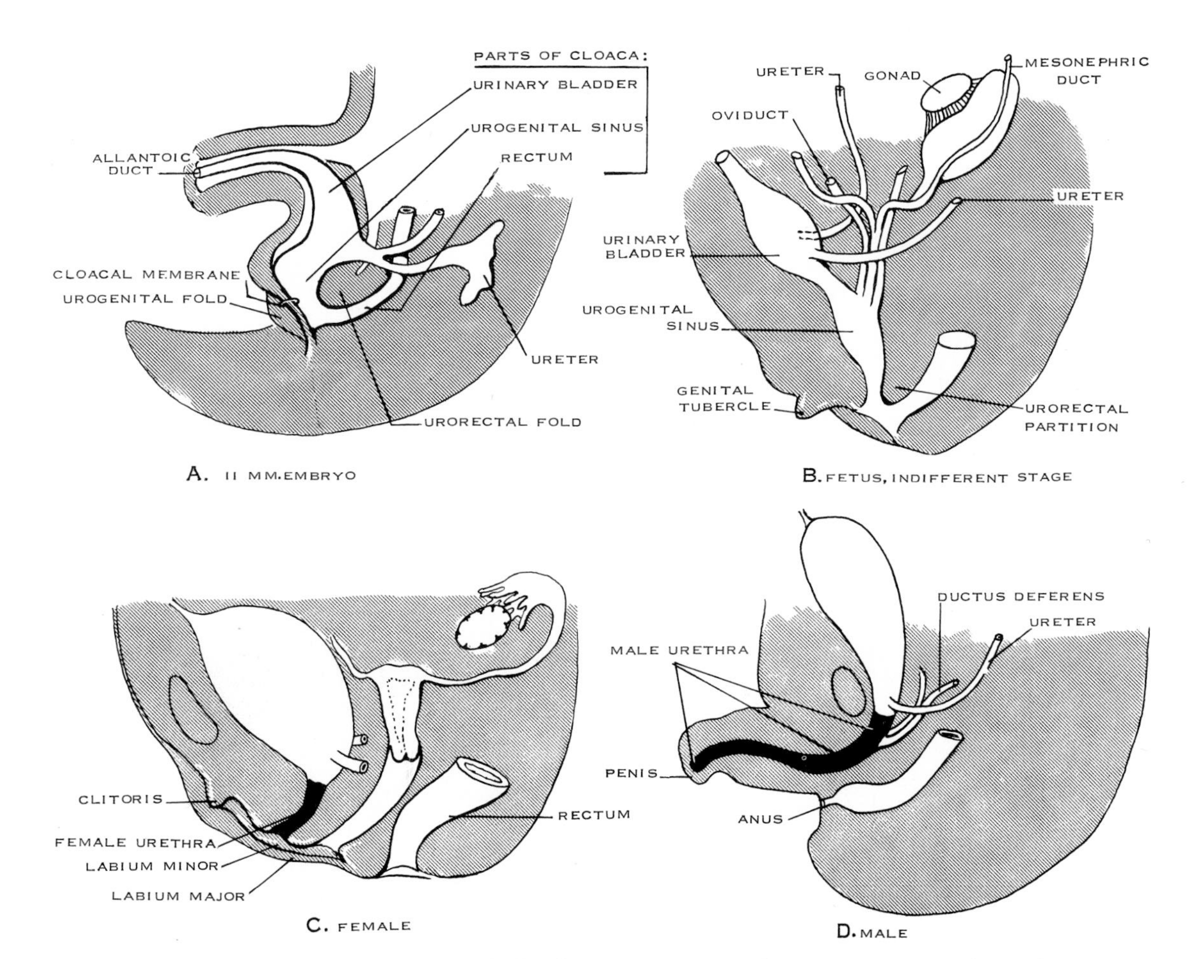

Fig. 29–8. Development of the human urogenital sinus. Diagramed as dissections to the sagittal plane.
(After F. Keibel, 1896.)

The penis itself arises from ridges that flank the original cloacal membrane; it is thus primarily an extracloacal structure in contrast with those of monotremes and turtles, alligators and birds. The ridges, called **urogenital folds** (Fig. 29–9 B), grow rapidly in the male so that they override and bury the urogenital part of the cloacal membrane and meet each other in the midline. In the human female they do not close together but remain as the **labia minora** at the sides of the vestibule (Fig. 29–9 D).

The penis of the male simultaneously lengthens to a considerable degree, and acquires a lumen, the **penile part of the urethra** which extends the cavity of the urogenital sinus to a new aperture at the distal **glans** (Fig. 29–8 D). In some mammals this penis tube is derived from the original groove between the two urogenital folds, in others it is an excavation of an epithelial cord that extends down the penis shaft. Irregularities in these developments may create, or leave, one or more openings on the underside of the penis. This inconvenient anomaly, called **hypospadias,** occurs in two to five cases out of a thousand men.

The difficulty with the word *urethra* mentioned above, comes from the fact that the urogenital sinus of the male becomes involved in penis development while that of the female is rather simply becoming a vaginal vestibule. By definitions established many generations before the developmental story became known, the ducts that lead urine from the bladder to the outside were called urethras in both male and female mammals. Only a small upper section of the **male urethra,** from the bladder down to the point where the entrance of the ductus deferens marks the beginning of the urogenital

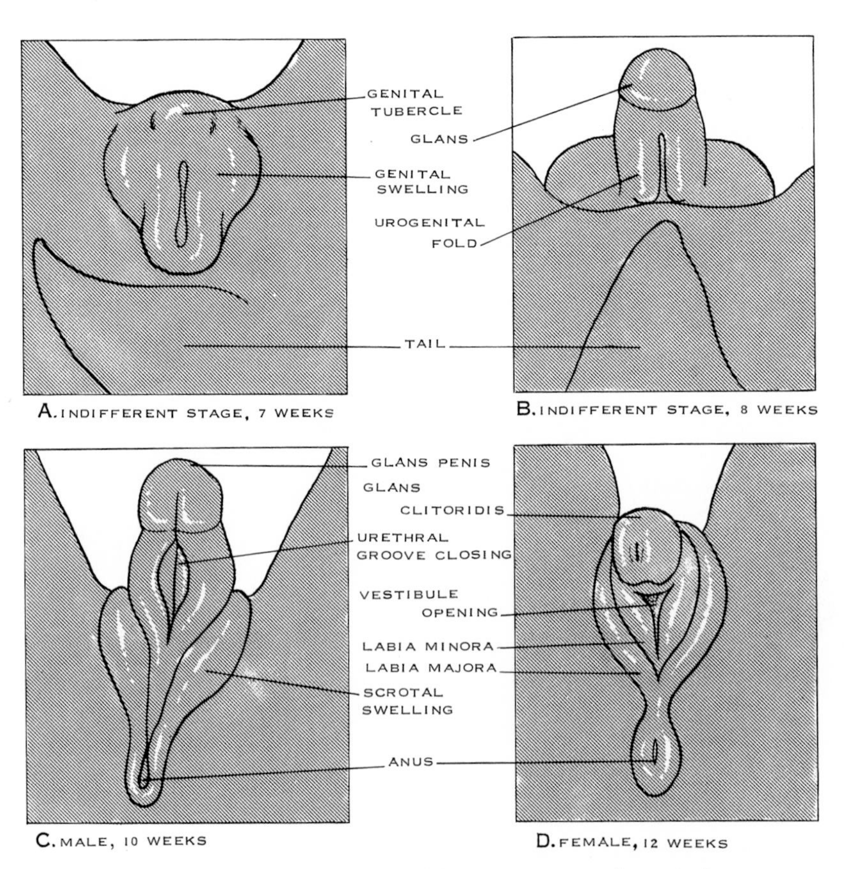

Fig. 29–9. Development of human external genitals.
(After M. H. Spaulding, 1921.)

sinus, is homologous with the **female urethra.** The middle section of the male urethra, being the persistent urogenital sinus, is homologous with the female vestibule. The outer section of the male urethra, which traverses the glans penis and part of its shaft, has no counterpart in the female (Fig. 29–8 C, D).

The connective tissue of the urogenital folds is partly converted into soft erectile tissue. In human females this is repressed by estrogen action, surviving only as small rudiments in the labia minora of the vestibule, converging ventrally on a midline protrusion called the **clitoris,** the homolog of the glans penis of the male (Fig. 29–9 D). Androgens actively stimulate the development of the erectile tissues in the male, and the entire tube of the penis is surrounded by a cylinder of it, called the **corpus spongiosum penis** (PNA), which is swollen proximally where the urethra enters it (forming the **bulbus penis**) (PNA) and swollen also distally around the outer end of the urethra (forming the **glans**) (Fig. 29–10). In some mammals the glans may be absent or appear as a separate mass of erectile tissue.

On the opposite side of the penis from the corpus spongiosum (i.e., on the upper side of it when in the erected position) the connective tissue also forms right and left rods of erectile tissue called the **corpora cavernosa.** These acquire all degrees of fusion into a single midline corpus caverosum in different species. Proximally, except in marsupials, the corpora cavernosa diverge as the **crura** or the legs of the penis, each crus being bound firmly to the ischium bone of its own side (Fig. 29–10 B). This gives the penis a firm anchorage on the skeleton, an advantage shared with the claspers and gonopodia of fishes but lacking in the intromittent organs of other tetrapods. In the partition between the two unfused corpora cavernosa, or in the sheath of the fused corpus near the glans, a penis bone or **baculum** usually forms. It is absent in man, ungulates and some others, and is highly variable but species-specific in shape and size.

Although one can recognize a basic pattern in comparing the penis structure of mammals, there are innumerable variations, even within single orders or families. The penis of a sloth is short and normally hypospadic, its tip lying very close

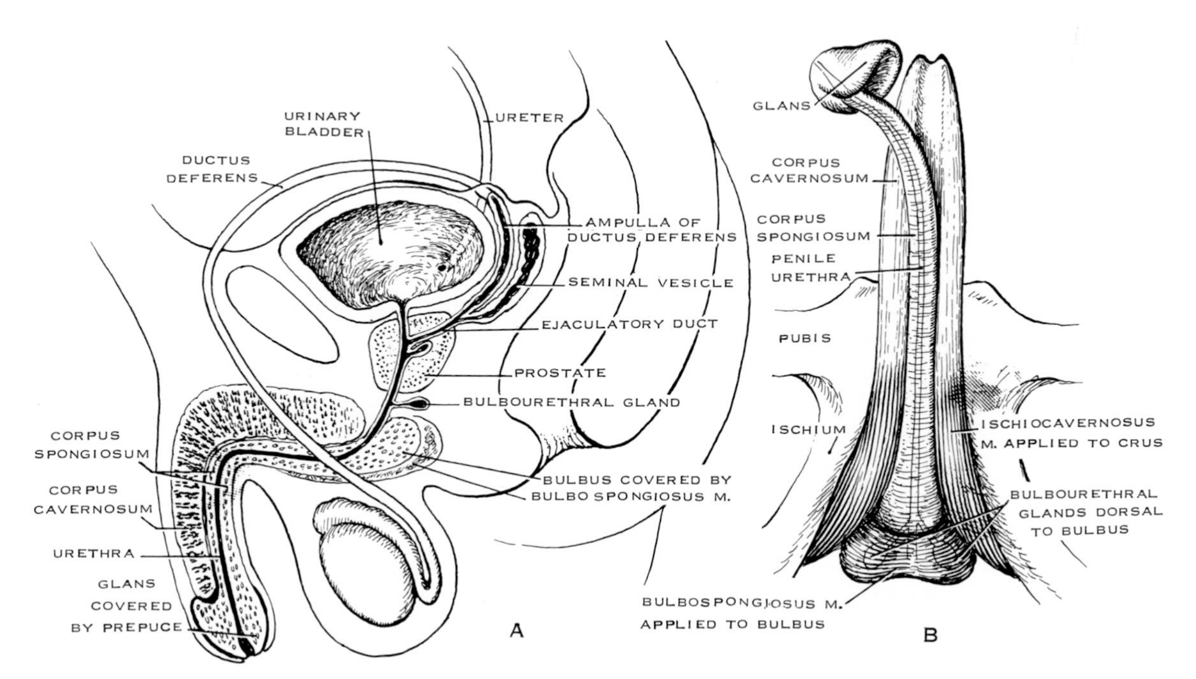

Fig. 29–10. Parts and relations of the human penis. A. Dissection to sagittal plane. B. Dissection, ventral view.

to the anus. The armadillo penis is one-third the length of the body. Whereas the early penis rudiments are entirely on the surface, a skin fold, the **prepuce** usually grows out over it in late fetal development so that it is more or less enclosed except during erection. The preputial cavity may lie quite concealed within the body wall (bull, boar) or in a loose dangling fold of skin (dog), or the prepuce may be entirely free of the body wall, out on a pendulous penis (bats, most primates). Its restriction to the region of the glans is almost an unique arrangement in the human. Male horses, whales, and elephants have such an extremely elongated penis that they have to pull it back into the preputial sac by special retractor muscles, where it lies in an S-coil when flaccid.

C. Derivatives of the Cloacal Sphincter

Monotremes retain a cloaca throughout life, and its opening is surrounded by a rather simple sphincter muscle. When the cloaca is subdivided by the urorectal fold in higher mammals (Fig. 29–11), thus acquiring two apertures, the sphincter cloacae is necessarily divided into a **sphincter ani** and a more ventral sphincter for the urogenital aperture. These are skeletal muscles, not to be confused with more intimate sphincters which develop from smooth muscle internally, in the walls of the rectum and the urogenital sinus or vagina. The sphincter ani usually spreads to the pelvic girdle and the vertebral column, appearing in human anatomy as the "levator ani" complex, with attachments on the pubis, the ilium and the coccyx. The muscles surrounding the aperture of the urogenital sinus become specialized in the service of the external genitals.

In the placental mammals, the derivatives of this urogenital sphincter are as variable as the penis itself. Commonly a pair of **ischiocavernosus muscles** form around the crura of the corpus cavernosum and help to tie them to the pelvic girdle (Fig. 29–10). Another derivative, the **bulbospongiosus muscle,** wraps itself around the enlarged bulb at the proximal end of the corpus spongiosum. It may become a massive structure, and its function is suggested in the older alternative names ejaculator muscle and accelerator urinae. These muscles are also found in females, but in vestigial condition.

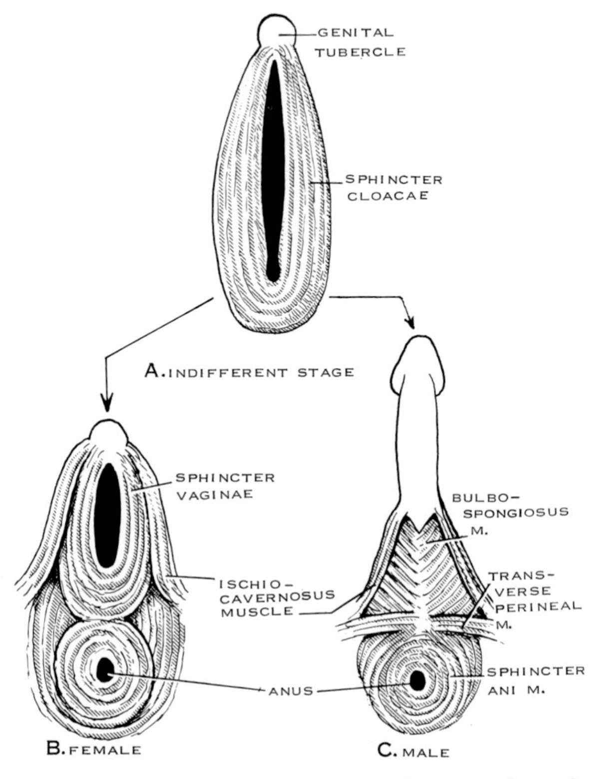

Fig. 29–11. Development of human cloacal muscles.
(After J. S. Popowsky, 1899.)

D. Accessory Slime Glands

Only a fraction of one per cent of the semen which male mammals ejaculate into their females consists of spermatozoa. The rest is a complex mixture of slime with nutrient and protecting chemicals produced by special glands of the lower male urogenital tract. Some species have only one macroscopic pair of such glands, others have numerous and elaborate sets of them. There is so much variation among mammals in this respect that the terminology of human anatomy is inadequate to describe them and homologies are often not clear. Even the obviously homologous sets do not have constant products or functions. It is not clear that in a given species any one set of them is essential for the maintenance of fertility. Typically these glands fail to appear in females or else they remain rudimentary, but they can be experimentally induced with androgens. They undergo regression in castrated males.

Seminal vesicles (PNA) are distinguished by their embryonic outgrowth as evaginations from the epithelium of the lower end of each ductus deferens, just proximal to the entrance of these into the urogenital sinus (Fig. 29–10 A). They are large, multiple and fancy in some rodents. In some other mammals they remain rudimentary.

The walls of the upper urogenital sinus usually give off other glands. In the human male there thus arises the **prostate,** an encapsulated mass of 15 to 30 branched tubules which empty separately into the sinus (i.e., into the male urethra) from all sides. Other smaller urethral glands which open farther down the tube are left outside the capsule. In other mammals such glands may be produced in profusion but not bound in a capsule (a "disseminated prostate"); or the encapsulated mass may be confined to the dorsal side of the tube. The horse has an enormous prostate, the pig a very small one. Often, as in man, a **prostatic utricle** (PNA) or male vagina can be located, embedded in the encapsulated prostate (Fig. 29–10 A). It is a vestige of the lower end of the paramesonephric oviduct system, left over from the indifferent stage of sexual development. It may be stimulated to grow larger by estrogen treatment.

Almost constantly in mammals, a pair of **bulbourethral glands** develop by evagination from the lower end of the urogenital sinus at the point where the crura of the corpus cavernosum diverge. Unlike the prostate and upper urethral glands and seminal vesicles, they may be found in females as well as males, serving a lubricatory function.

E. Erection, Emission, and Ejaculation

Erection of the mammalian penis resembles the tightening of an automobile tire by inflation of its inner tube. Connective tissue sheaths, like the shoe of the tire, give the whole organ its shape and rigidity, and the inflation is accomplished by blood pouring into the erectile tissues. The stimulation of certain autonomic nerves connected with the sacral part of the spinal cord causes the arteries leading into the erectile tissue to dilate from a normally relaxed state of partial obstruction, and the increased flow fills the cavernous blood sinuses to the extent allowed by the arterial blood pressure. This expands their surrounding connective tissue capsules to a limit set by their elasticity. The relatively fixed drainage capacity of the penis veins and the pressure put upon them by the cavernous tissue against the inside of the sheaths is also a factor in the maintenance of the erect state.

The sheath of connective tissue containing the corpus spongiosum and the glans is weaker and less resistant, and there are compensating venous outflow mechanisms which keep this part of the penis spongy rather than hard during its erection. The whole penis returns to its flaccid state when other autonomic nerves cause the arteries to shrink down again so that the veins can catch up on drainage of the blood accumulated in the cavernous spaces of the erectile tissue.

Emission of spermatozoa from the epididymis and ductus deferens into the urethra and their *ejaculation* together with the other components of the semen are accomplished by a separate nervous reflex from that producing the erection of the penis. Erection is a usual but not a necessary precursor for ejaculation. The smooth muscles which line the ductus deferens and the urethra, and the striated bulbospongiosus muscle, are the immediate agents in ejaculation.

REFERENCES

1. Jost, A., 1960. *Mem. Soc. Endocrinol.* 7: 49.
2. Watterson, R. L. (ed.), 1959. *Symposium on endocrines in development.* University of Chicago Press, Chicago.
3. Matthews, L. H., 1955. *Mem. Soc. Endocrinol.* 4: 129.

30

Integration Apparatus

There is a special fitness to an ending with some of the integration apparatus. Most of the previous chapters have necessarily narrowed the attention to particular periods of the life history, or to particular organs or body regions. One must at last bring some of the pieces together in the dimensions of time and space, and recall that the activity of the whole vertebrate animal must be meaningfully coordinated at every moment from fertilization to death.

The integration apparatus includes elements of the most diverse embryonic origins and anatomical structures. It is not a homogeneous "organ system" like the skeletal, the muscular, or the urogenital. It is necessarily involved in all the physiological and behavioral processes, and growth and differentiation as well. Its most important element, the **central nervous system,** was discussed in an elementary way in Chapter 18. Other parts, the **sense organs,** the **peripheral somatic nerves,** and the **blood and its vessels,** have been considered in their turn. Processes which integrate growth and differentiation have been hinted at from time to time, but knowledge of them is still very scanty. We now concentrate on two other parts of the integration apparatus, the **autonomic divisions of the nervous system** and certain **endocrine glands** which could not have been discussed meaningfully until the organs and tissues with which they deal had been taken up.

This chapter will also have the broader objective of showing ways in which the parts of the integrative apparatus interact with each other in a kaleidoscopically beautiful harmony, regulating the constancies of the body and mediating the slow and the quick changes that keep a fish in the swim or a land vertebrate in the running. In anatomical and physiological ways, the parts all work together.

I. THE AUTONOMIC NERVOUS SYSTEM

Only for teaching purposes is this part of the nervous apparatus given a separate name and description. It consists of certain ganglionic masses of nervous tissue placed outside the central nervous system, but serving through its axons and dendrites as an intermediate between this and the viscera of the whole body.

The autonomic ganglia are slowly assembled, mostly from neural-crest cells that migrate outward from the dorsolateral parts of the embryonic neural plate. They share this manner of origin with some parts of the ganglia of the cranial nerves and all the dorsal-root ganglia of the spinal nerves. Special experimental tech-

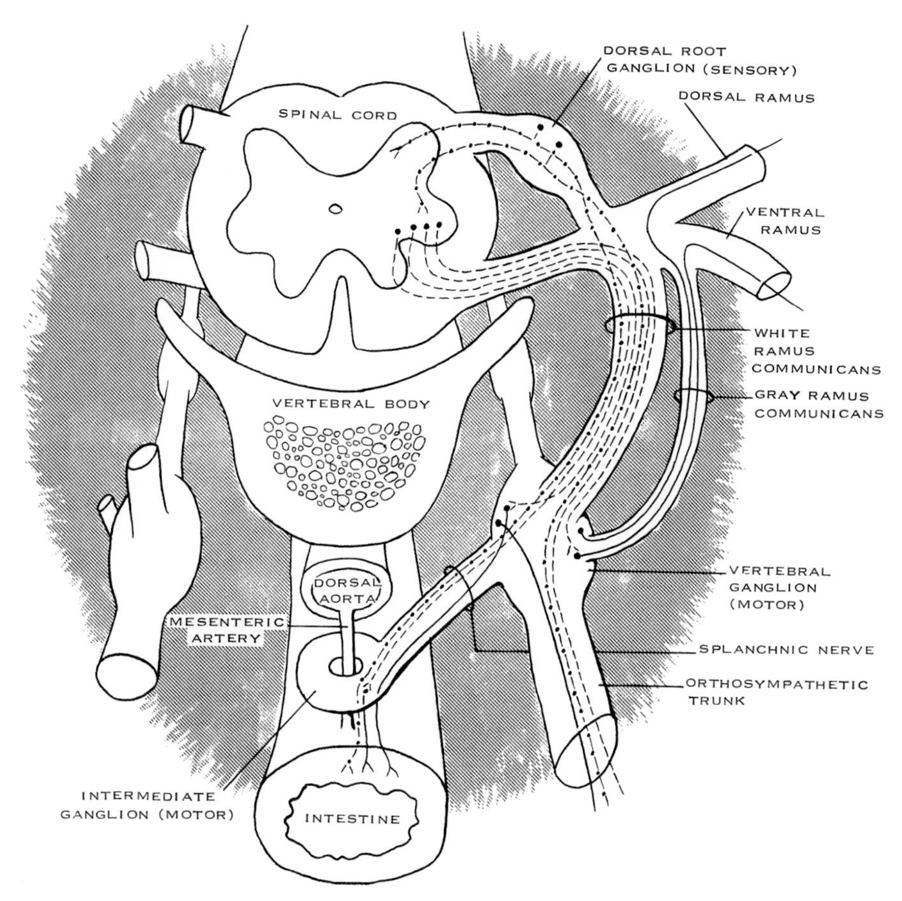

Fig. 30–1. Cross-section diagram to show relationships of the orthosympathetic elements.

niques available for certain amphibia have shown that the neural-crest cells are joined at later stages by other cells that migrate out from the ventral half of the spinal cord [1].

It should be specially noted that whereas the dorsal-root ganglia of the spinal nerves are part of the sensory system, the autonomic ganglia are part of the visceral motor apparatus. It is not known why some of these neural-crest cells become motor and others sensory, or why still others, which may remain in actual contact with the motor ganglia, differentiate into suprarenal or chromaffin tissue (see page 597).

Most of the axons which grow out from the autonomic ganglia differentiate quite late, long after the pioneer fibers of the spinal nerves have laid down the somatic segmental pattern. Some of them rejoin the dorsal and ventral rami of the spinal nerves and distribute segmentally, but the majority take irregular paths, perhaps in response to the more highly differentiated milieu through which they are sprouting. The result is a most disorderly pattern, with plexuses and mats of fibers as well as discrete nerves. Many of the axons find a way to their destinations by following the walls of blood vessels.

The first autonomic motor ganglia to be established in the trunk region take up their positions segmentally on either side of the dorsal aorta or the bodies of the vertebrae (**vertebral ganglia,** PNA) (Figs. 20–18, 30–1). Cells that migrate farther toward the viscera may come to rest around the bases of visceral arteries or in the mesenteries (**intermediate ganglia,** PNA), or even in the tissue layers of the viscera themselves (**terminal ganglia,** PNA).

A. Divisions of the Autonomic in Mammals

The parts of the mammalian autonomic system that have their most direct connections with the brain and the sacral part of the spinal cord are distinguished as **parasympathetic.** The parts directly connected with the thoracic and lumbar parts of the spinal cord are called **orthosympathetic** (Fig. 30–2).

Both these divisions include sensory and motor components. The sensory components have axons which stream toward the central nervous system from their dendritic zones in viscera, pass directly through the autonomic motor ganglia to their somata in the sensory dorsal-root ganglia, and spray their transmitting tips into the gray substance of brain or dorsal spinal cord (Fig. 30–1). The sensory autonomic components (they were merely called visceral sensory on page 293) need not be considered further.

B. Special Features of Motor Autonomic Components in Mammals

There are two peculiarities about the motor innervation of mammalian viscera that are not found in the somatic motor supply, or even in the nerves that supply the striated muscles of the pharynx segment series. (1) The motor stimulus, whether to smooth muscles or to gland cells, is delivered from the central nervous system through a two-neuron relay, the first neuron arising in the central nervous system and the second in an autonomic motor ganglion (Figs. 30–1, 30–2). (2) The viscera will accept nerve connections from both the ortho- and the parasympathetic divisions (Fig. 30–2).

1. Two-Neuron Relays. Since the two axons of the visceral effector relay extend respectively toward, and beyond, their mutual synapse in the autonomic ganglion, their neurons are called respectively **preganglionic** and **postganglionic.** The somata of preganglionic neurons lie within the central nervous system, and their axons, though varying considerably in size, are generally well myelinated so that bundles of them appear white in dissection. Bundles of the sparsely myelinated postganglionic fibers, by contrast, appear gray.

Thus, anatomists many generations ago distinguished between two sets of nervous connections or rami communicantes between the spinal nerves and the segmental vertebral ganglia, the white and the gray ones. **White rami communicantes** are bundles of preganglionic motor fibers (dashed lines in Figs. 30–1 and 30–2) which pass from the spinal cord to the autonomic motor ganglia. **Gray rami communicantes** are bundles of postganglionic fibers (solid lines in Fig. 30–1) which arise in the motor ganglia but pass dorsomesad to join the dorsal and ventral rami of the spinal nerves. Most of the fibers in the gray rami have endings in the smooth muscles of the blood vessels in the trunk musculature and skin. Their function is vasoconstriction.

In the parasympathetic division of the autonomic (Fig. 30–2, left side), the preganglionic fibers are characteristically long (particularly the ones in the vagus nerve), and they find their way to terminal ganglia that lie within their viscera. Postganglionic parasympathetic fibers, since they arise in the terminal ganglia, are generally very short. By contrast, most of the preganglionic fibers of the orthosympathetic division (Fig. 30–2, right) end in vertebral or intermediate ganglia at no great distance from where they leave the spinal cord, while the postganglionic fibers run considerable distances across the mesenteries to their endings in the gut muscle or digestive glands. They may casually increase their length by wandering up or (principally) down through the chain- or ladderlike sequence of nerve strands that interconnect the segmental vertebral ganglia in orthosympathetic trunks. Also, they are collected from a number of the segmental ganglia in descending **splanchnic nerves** (visceral nerves) that follow the peritoneum or cross the mesenteries on the way to intermediate ganglia and particular viscera.

2. Double Innervation. (Fig 30–2). The *heart,* like many other viscera, receives both parasympathetic motor innervation through the most posterior ramus of the vagus nerve, and orthosympathetic fibers from motor ganglia in the trunk.

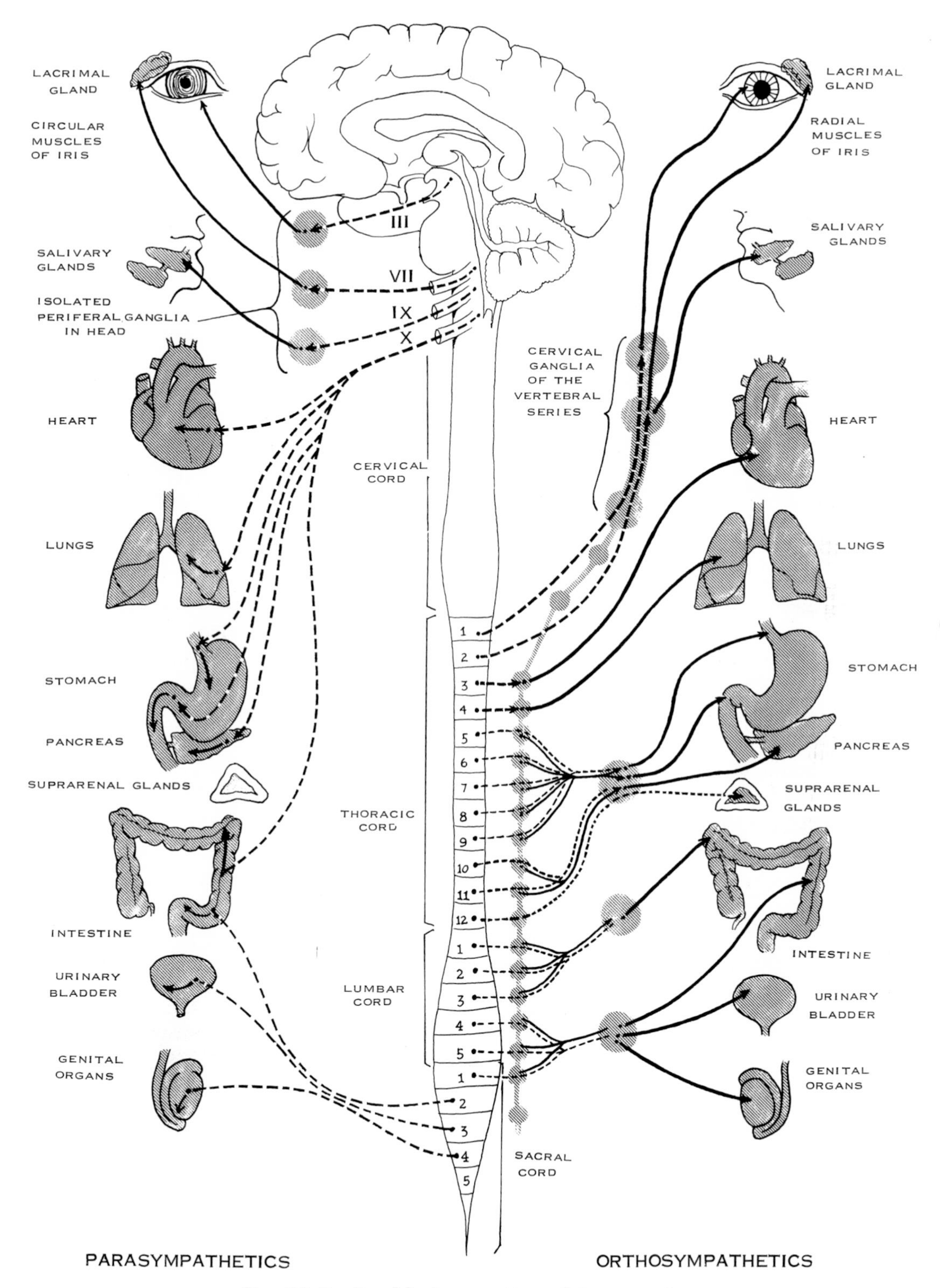

Fig. 30–2. Double innervation of human viscera.

(After C. D. Turner, General Endocrinology, 3d edition, 1960, by permission of W. B. Saunders Co.)

Stimulation through the former makes the heart beat slower, and stimulation through the latter accelerates it.

The *submandibular salivary gland* receives parasympathetic innervation from preganglionic VII nerve fibers by way of postganglionics arising in a special submandibular autonomic ganglion. Stimulation through this relay causes an abundant flow of watery saliva. The gland also receives orthosympathetic innervation by a relay from a vertebral ganglion high in the neck, the postganglionic fibers following branches of the external carotid artery to their destination. Responding to this nerve supply, the gland delivers a thick ropy saliva rich in organic materials.

The mammalian *penis* can be caused to erect itself by stimulation of a parasympathetic relay from the sacral part of the spinal cord. What happens is that arterial musculature which ordinarily restricts the volume of blood entering the cavernous bodies becomes relaxed, allowing the sinuses to become engorged. Vasoconstrictor stimuli to these same arteries through an orthosympathetic relay subsequently diminish the inflow, so that the sinuses can be drained. This returns the penis to its flaccid condition.

The *pupil* of the mammalian eye is constricted by a parasympathetic relay which causes the circular muscles of the iris to contract. The preganglionic fibers emerge in the orbit from the III nerve and find a special ciliary ganglion from which the postganglionic fibers arise. Widening of the pupil is accomplished by radially disposed iris muscles, whose postganglionic nerve supply comes all the way from a vertebral ganglion high in the neck, first along appropriate branches of the carotid artery system, and then along one of the orbital nerves-of-passage that skirts the eyeball.

These few examples, chosen from many, indicate not only that the mammalian viscera will accept innervation from both the ortho- and the parasympathetic divisions of the autonomic, but that opposed effects can be achieved within a single organ: stimulation or inhibition, contraction or relaxation, or the selective activation of different kinds of muscle or gland cells. The visceral life of a mammal is partly determined by the balance of these two nerve supplies, and this in turn may be influenced by chemical messengers in the blood, and all these by the central nervous system.

Many of the postganglionic orthosympathetic nerves are adrenergic; i.e., they secrete an adrenaline-like substance at their synaptic endings, and produce effects such as vasoconstriction, which can be imitated by injection of adrenalin into the blood stream. It was at one time popularly supposed that the orthosympathetic apparatus presides over emergencies, preparing the individual for massive "fight or flight" reactions. A more recent view is that such exciting physiological transformations are brought about predominantly by endocrine glands, particularly the medulla of the suprarenal gland (see below). Nevertheless, in the intact animal, there is an inseparable interplay between these endocrine and nervous functions.

Two types of adrenaline-like substances are known, epinephrine and norepinephrine, whose effects are somewhat different. The orthosympathetic postganglionics apply norepinephrine at highly localized sites, regulating the tone of blood vessels and making other regional adjustments that adapt the body to changes in posture, temperature, motor activity, etc., by exciting smooth muscles and constricting the arteries. The secretion of the suprarenal medulla, principally epinephrine, is broadcast throughout the body by the blood stream, and is more effective in speeding the heartbeat, stimulating the central nervous system, inhibiting smooth muscle and adjusting a variety of metabolic processes, producing the thoroughly aroused state.

C. Relation to the Central Nervous System

The sensory component of the autonomic, like all other afferent sources, continually reports its coded information into reticular areas of the spinal cord and brain. These poorly defined areas carry on the analysis, the choice of strategy, and the organization of patterned responses which keep the opposed capacities of the viscera in balance. Much of the visceral sensory inflow is of a feedback nature, keeping the central mechanism informed of the changing internal situation, instant by instant.

The hypothalamic region of the diencephalon has long been recognized as the "head ganglion of the sympathetic." Modern techniques of functional analysis show that many of its localized nuclei are specialized for the control of particular functions, such as blood pressure, heartbeat, respiratory rhythm, excretion, reproductive cycles and behavior, etc. Some of them are predominantly associated with the parasympathetic, and some with the orthosympathetic division of the peripheral distribution. This extraordinary region also exerts controls over, and even participates in, endocrine activities that help integrate the physiology of the whole individual (see below).

D. Autonomic System, Comparative

Knowledge of even the anatomy of the autonomic apparatus of lower vertebrates is scanty. Only the most superficial exploration has been made of its physiology [2].

The cranial (parasympathetic) part can be recognized even in primitive fishes. An outflow through the oculomotor nerve finds one or more tiny ganglia in the orbit, from which postganglionic fibers enter the eyeball through ciliary nerves. Tiny ganglia and postganglionic fibers can also be found on the post-trematic branches of cranial nerves VII, IX, and X. The great ramus intestinalis of the vagus only rarely extends beyond the pylorus of the stomach, but in a number of fishes is known to have motor functions through the foregut region. In teleosts and elasmobranchs, as in higher vertebrates, it also sends inhibitory nerve endings into the muscle of the heart. The lowly hagfishes have an extraordinary development of this ramus intestinalis, reaching along the gut as far as the cloaca, but its function is unknown. In some teleosts, the refilling of an emptied gas bladder is controlled by cranial parasympathetic fibers by way of the vagus.

All the lower vertebrates also have elements of the orthosympathetic division, in the form of segmental vertebral ganglia. In elasmobranchs these are only vaguely interconnected in longitudinal trunks, and they do not send gray rami back to the dorsal and ventral rami of the spinal nerves. They do, however, supply the entire intestine with splanchnic nerves.

Nothing much is added to the orthosympathetic of urodeles, but in both teleosts and anura the apparatus is much more highly organized, approaching that of the amniotes in complexity. Gray rami are sent out from the vertebral ganglia, and are vasoconstrictor in function. Strong commissures bind the vertebral ganglia together in longitudinal trunks. In the teleosts the trunks even extend into the head as far as the orbits. The preganglionic fibers wander widely from their segmental origins, synapsing in the motor ganglia which lie more anteriorly, more posteriorly, or even on the other side of the dorsal aorta.

Double innervation of viscera by both parasympathetic and orthosympathetic divisions is demonstrated for the esophagus and stomach of these anamniotes, but the actions of the two sets of nerves are additive, not opposed. Double innervation, with opposed effects, is known for the iris of at least one teleost, and for the gas bladders of others. It is known for the hearts of anura, but not for those of fishes. Parasympathetic nerves reach the bladder and rectum of the frog from the posterior end of the spinal cord, but do not oppose the action of the orthosympathetic there.

Among reptiles and birds, the anatomical development of the autonomic system is often more elaborate than for mammals, with double sets of orthosympathetic ganglion chains, following both the dorsal aorta and the vertebral artery on each side. The chains, with strictly segmental ganglia, extend into the head. (Mammals have only two or three ganglia for the seven cervical segments, and no extension of the trunks into the head.) The cranial and the sacral components of the parasympathetic division are more strongly developed in birds and reptiles, and broad overlaps of para- and orthosympathetic innervation occur. Opposed function is well known for the heart and some other viscera, but exploration in this area is far from complete.

II. ENDOCRINE GLANDS

It is impossible to draw a line between the autonomic nerve cells and endocrine cells, in either a structural or a functional sense. The heart of a frog, with its vagus nerves dangling from it, can be kept beating rhythmically for some time in salt solution, and if the nerves are stimulated electrically they will slow the beat. In the process they will release into the culture fluid a substance (identified as acetylcholine) which will have the same effect as vagus stimulus, upon any heart placed in this same fluid (the Loewi experiment). In other words, the vagus nerve is an endocrine gland, secreting the hormone acetylcholine. This substance does not travel far in the blood stream, being destroyed quickly by enzymes. However, there are no durability requirements in the definition of a hormone.

A. Neurosecretory Apparatus

In the epithalamic and hypothalamic parts of the diencephalon of all vertebrates there occur certain **neurosecretory cells** which are exactly intermediate in structure between normal gland cells and neurons. They have the general shape of nerve cells, but like gland cells they only receive synaptic stimuli, they do not transmit them. Also, like gland cells, they contain secretory granules in their cytoplasm. They actually may be seen in the process of giving out droplets of material (Fig. 30–3).

Those in the hypothalamus are the best known. They lie rather close to the midline funnel that leads down to the pituitary gland in the floor of the diencephalon, near the optic chiasma. Their secretions are elaborated in response to nervous stimulation from other tracts in the brain, and are passed along their axons in the direction of the pituitary. Some of these substances exert their effects directly on pituitary gland cells after a very short journey (page 595). Others may be transported to quite distant target organs after release from storage in that gland. These include the hormone oxytocin, which produces contractions of the uterus, and vasopressin, which adjusts the process of urine formation in such a way as to conserve water.

Many teleosts, particularly species which migrate between fresh and salt water, have a highly differentiated mass at the caudal end of the spinal cord called the **urohypophysis** [3], whose structure is closely comparable to the neurosecretory tissue associated with the pituitary in the hypothalamus. It is thought to be concerned with osmoregulatory or salt-regulatory activities.

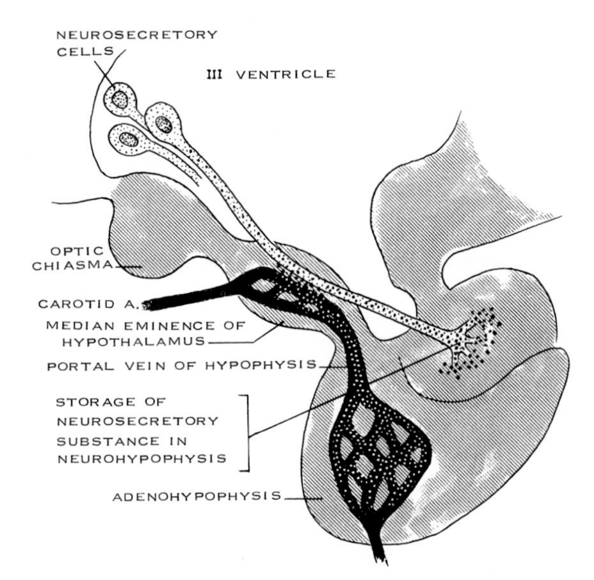

Fig. 30–3. Diagram of amniote hypothalamic neurosecretory apparatus.

B. Hypophysis

The pituitary gland or **hypophysis** is found throughout the vertebrates, and always has a double origin. The infundibulum, a downgrowth from the floor of the diencephalon posterior to the optic chiasma, produces one part. An ectodermal placode or pouch growing in from the surface of the embryo across the roof of the mouth contributes the other (Figs. 9–2, 18–16). These two parts of the finished gland enclose a bit of mesoderm between them but come into very intimate contact, though in the most diverse spatial relationships. The part from the brain is best called the **neurohypophysis.** Though it is the *posterior lobe* (PNA) of the hypophysis in human anatomy, it may lie mostly posterior, mostly anterior, or mostly dorsal to the part from the surface ectoderm in other species (Fig. 30–4).

The part derived from the ectodermal placode forms the primarily glandular areas of the hypophysis, and is hence called **adenohypophysis.** It is histologically divisible into several regions [4, 5]. The principal one of these is called the *anterior lobe* (PNA) of the human hypophysis, but this same part takes a posterior position in amphibia.

The adenohypophysis secretes a whole drugstore of potent regulatory chemicals into the blood stream. There are growth hormones, and specific hormones for stimulating the activity of the suprarenal cortex ("adrenocorticotropic hormone," or ACTH) and of the thyroid (thyrotropin, or thyroid-stimulating hormone, TSH). There is a family of gonadotropins, one of which stimulates the growth of ovarian follicles (FSH), another of which works on the corpus luteum of females or on the interstitial cells of males (LH or ICSH). A third gonadotropin, called prolactin (among many synonyms), stimulates milk production in female mammals, the maturing of the crop glands in pigeons, and the driving of newts back to water for their second metamorphosis [6]. These hormones are proteins or large peptide molecules and show species-specific differences in each category. Nevertheless it is not so much new categories of hormones that evolution has produced as new uses for the old categories. Still another type of hormone liberated by all vertebrate adenohypophyses, MSH, has bold stimulatory effects on melanophores in many lower vertebrates, but seems not to have been put to any significant use in normal healthy mammals.

A curiously localized method of hormone transportation has been developed to bring the hypophysis under the control of the hypothalamic neurosecretory cells (Fig. 30–3). Blood vessels from the carotid arteries merely skirt the surface of the neurohypophysis before ramifying in the adenohypophysis of fishes, but in anura and the amniotes they form a system of capillaries in a "median eminence" of brain tissue just posterior to the optic chiasma, and the venules which drain these then form a second set of capillaries in the adenohypophysis. This hypophyseal portal vein system apparently picks up substances from the neurosecretory cells and delivers them to the adenohypophysis. Without these essential stimuli (or supply of these precursor materials?) the adenohypophysis is unable to give out the gonadotropic hormones required by the sexual rhythms (pages 598, 599).

Other neurosecretions (oxytocin, vasopressin) probably flow to their storage depots in the neurohypophysis directly along the "axons" of the neurosecretory cells. It is not clear that the neurohypophysis synthesizes any hormones by itself.

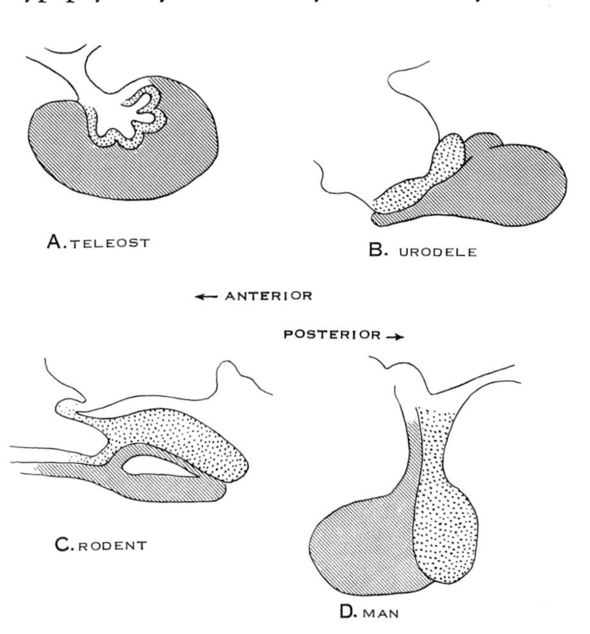

Fig. 30–4. Forms taken by the vertebrate pituitary gland (sagittal diagrams).

(After Green and Maxwell, 1959, in Comparative Endocrinology, by permission of John Wiley & Sons, Inc.)

Most if not all of the true nerve fibers that enter the adenohypophysis are assumed to end on blood vessels, not on endocrine gland cells. If the organ is removed and replanted to a new site, its production of gonadotropins stops at once. Replanted to the old site, it resumes this production as soon as the hypophyseal portal vein connections have been re-established and before there has been time for the regeneration of nerves [7, 8].

C. The Steroid Glands

The potent role of the steroid hormones classed as androgens and estrogens has already been discussed in relation to the differentiation of sexual characters (page 559, etc.). Androgens, though they have generally masculinizing effects, are produced in females as well as males. Estrogens likewise occur in both sexes. The testes of stallions are a rich source of "female sex hormones," and human testes continue to produce estrogens long after their output of androgens has declined with age. Furthermore, another characteristic mammalian endocrine apparatus, the **cortex of the suprarenal gland,** is also a producer of both androgens and estrogens.

There must thus be recognized a family of glands which produce these steroid hormones of sex [9]. An individual deprived of gonads is not deprived of "sex hormones" so long as the suprarenal cortex tissue is present. In fact, a considerable amount of sexual pathology is traceable not to the gonads themselves but to disorders of the suprarenal cortex.

The endocrine apparatus of this group of three "steroid glands" all has a common origin in the mesenchyme of the intermediate mesoderm along the kidney strip.

It is a peculiarity of mammals (Fig. 30–5 C) that the suprarenal cortex tissue should be associated so neatly with a medulla of tissue derived from a totally different source and having totally different functions (see below). In other tetrapods, the homologs of the cortical and medullary tissues are spread upon the kidneys in a disordered mixture. In the fishes (Fig. 30–5 A) they are quite separate. Their **interrenal bodies,** which lie below the dorsal aorta between the pelvic kidneys, are homologous with the mammalian suprarenal cortex.

Not only androgens and estrogens come from the suprarenal cortex. This tissue also produces progesterones like those liberated from the corpus luteum after ovulation. It is also a chief source of many other steroid hormones (cortisone and its relatives) which have potent metabolic effects that are only beginning to be understood [7]. They are essential for normal active life in mammals, regulating the responses by which the individual survives the stresses of injury, infection, exposure to heat or cold, lack of food, muscular exhaustion, etc.

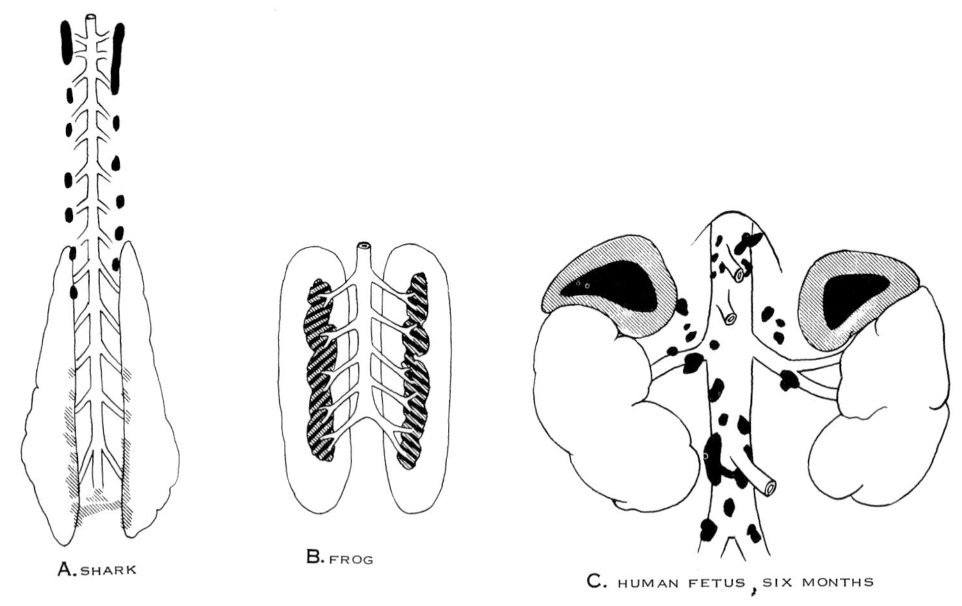

Fig. 30–5. Forms taken by the suprarenal cortex and medulla in various vertebrates.

(A and B after A. Portmann, Einführung in die Vergleichende Morphologie der Wirbeltiere, 1948, by permission of Benno Schwabe & Co. C after L. B. Arey, Developmental Anatomy, 6th edition, 1954, by permission of W. B. Saunders Co.)

The activity of the cortical cells is regulated in part by ACTH from the adenohypophysis. But release of ACTH in turn is regulated by the hypothalamus, either in response to hormonal feedbacks, or to stimuli brought up the brainstem by nerve tracts. Thus a vital sector of the animal's visceral life is regulated through a three-cornered balance of interactions between the suprarenal cortex, the hypothalamus and the hypophysis, maintained both through the blood stream and the autonomic and central nervous apparatus.

D. The Suprarenal Medulla

Migrating hordes of neural-crest cells not only produce motor ganglia of the orthosympathetic trunks, they form clumps of glandlike cells associated with these but called **chromaffin tissue** because of their affinity for certain dyes. Much of this material (shown black in Fig. 30–5) is collected on or near the kidneys in tetrapods and most of it is concentrated as the **medulla of the suprarenal gland** in mammals. The logic of this uniquely mammalian arrangement is obscure. In fishes and urodeles the chromaffin tissue remains associated with the orthosympathetic ganglia of the vertebral series, or perched on the stems of segmental blood vessels.

The suprarenal medulla cells are not only closely related to the postganglionic orthosympathetic neurons in origin and in location, they also resemble these in their ability to secrete an adrenaline-like substance. Preganglionic fibers are cholinergic; i.e., they transmit excitation across the synapse at the motor ganglion by means of acetylcholine. On the other hand their postganglionic fibers are mostly adrenergic, transferring their stimuli by means of norepinephrine. The suprarenal medulla, receiving cholinergic *preganglionic* fibers (unlike any other viscera) and responding by massive discharge of adrenaline-like compounds (mostly epinephrine, some norepinephrine) might then be interpreted as a massive orthosympathetic ganglion which has metamorphosed into an endocrine gland so that it can influence the whole body instead of a few localized spots.

While the suprarenal medulla can be mobilized for a total emergency reaction with the delay of only a few seconds, it is more normally involved in a self-regulating feedback interplay with the hypothalamus, the hypophysis, and the suprarenal cortex, in the minor adjustments of blood pressure and metabolism required by normal living.

E. Regulatory Actions of the Thyroid

The ontogenetic origin of the thyroid gland was considered earlier (page 328). Thyroxine-like substances are found in various other phyla of animals, and the evolution of the gland itself took place in such remote ancestors of vertebrates that the record has been lost. Since then, new uses have been discovered for the thyroid hormone as newly developed sensitivities to it have brought old organs and tissues into its group of targets. Throughout the surviving groups of vertebrates, the thyroid glands are control agents in both differentiation and behavior. In tetrapods, but not appreciably in the fishes, they have also become important regulators of respiratory and other metabolic rates.

An important cyclic interaction has developed between the thyroid and the pituitary glands. High levels of thyroid hormone in the blood depress TSH productivity in the adenohypophysis, which in turn holds the thyroid in check. But the adenohypophysis releases more TSH when the thyroid has reached too low a level of activity, correcting this situation also. This feedback cycle may be manipulated experimentally by hormone injections and various surgical techniques, and it can be diagrammed as though it were mediated by hormones alone; nevertheless there are some indications that a hypothalamic neural-neurohumeral link may be interposed in the circuit [7].

III. SOME EXAMPLES OF INTEGRATIVE SEQUENCES

The ways in which the central nervous system directs and integrates behavior, minute by minute and second by second, toward selected goals, have been explored by neurologists for several generations. In addition, in the last few decades, an impressive mass of information has been acquired about how particular hormones from endocrine glands regulate physiological states and produce slower changes in their target organs. Still more recently, the interactions of the nervous and endocrine systems have begun to be appreciated.

A. Amphibian Metamorphosis

The revolutionary changes of amphibian metamorphosis have previously been catalogued (page 337). It is now known that each tissue and organ and region of the tadpole develops its sensitivity to thyroid hormones at its own time and to its own degree, and that the thyroid itself changes the rate and the quality of its hormone production with time. All these variables are affected by a number of external influences, temperature for instance. Experimentally, ways have been found for repressing or exaggerating or throwing out of step some of the elements in what is normally a precisely coordinated symphony of metamorphic processes [10].

It has been proved that the thyroid hormones are the principal triggers, and that the thyroid gland is powerless to act without receiving proper amounts of TSH from the adenohypophysis. The reason for neoteny, i.e., the failure of a species to metamorphose, is an inadequate supply of thyroxine in the case of the tiger amblystomas of the high plains ("Colorado axolotls"). On the other hand it is an insensitivity of the tissues to an otherwise adequate supply of thyroxine in the case of the *Necturus*. In most amphibia, when the shifting balance of tissue sensitivities and thyroxine concentrations comes right, the metamorphic process is started and carried through. The missing elements in the picture are knowledge of the factors that throw the TSH production of the hypophysis into gear, and knowledge of what thyroxine does to the sensitive cells, and why.

If the adenohypophysis of a frog embryo is transplanted to a new site where it is out of contact with the neurohypophysis, it continues to produce hormones but at abnormal rates. The tadpole turns black, probably because of too much MSH, and may get to be ten times the normal maximum weight, probably because of excess growth hormone. At the same time there are hints of deficiency in TSH production [11]. This suggests that the adenohypophysis is normally under some sort of control by the neurohypophysis or by the hypothalamus.

Metamorphosis in a given species of amphibian tends to occur at a particular time of year, at a particular size. What triggers the hypophysis, so that it triggers the thyroid, so that this triggers the metamorphosis? Once the apparatus for the chain reaction has been set in place and tuned up by maturing processes in its various parts, the final push of the starting button might come from any one of a number of factors, possibly by skin sensations relayed through the central nervous system.

B. Ovulation

The ovaries of all vertebrates undergo regressive changes and become sterile after removal of the adenohypophysis. It is the release of FSH from this gland which stimulates the growth and the semifinal stages of the maturation of eggs. The ovocytes of frogs grow rapidly in late summer and are in a constant state of readiness to be ovulated all during the period of winter hibernation, but they are not shed. The trigger to ovulation is the release of another hormone, LH, from storage in the hypophysis. In some hibernating frogs, merely crushing the hypophysis *in situ* will release enough LH to cause many of the eggs to be shed. Complete ovulation can easily be secured by injecting extra hypophyseal gland materials from other frogs, male or female.

What normally brings about the release of this LH? In some frog species, ovulation takes place seasonally, in correlation with temperature, rainfall, or other environmental factors. In others it takes place rhythmically throughout the year, whether males are present or not. Cortisone from the suprarenal cortex tissue is known to facilitate frog ovulation [12]. Theoretically, somatic sensory stimulation could engage the adenohypophyseal apparatus for secretion of both gonadotropin (LH) and suprarenal cortex stimulators (ACTH) by way of the hypothalamus; or direct hormone feedbacks from the ovary could do it. The mechanisms by which the whole sexual behavior of the individual are brought into balance and onto a schedule certainly vary with the species.

The participation of neurohumors from the hypothalamus in these events is conclusively demonstrated for various birds and mammals, with striking species differences. In both rabbits and hens, ovulation is prevented by damage to the hypothalamus even when the hypophysis is untouched. It is possible to discover which particular hypothalamic nuclei secrete the material that stimulates LH release from the adenohypophysis. Interrupting the hypophyseal portal-vein system is enough to prevent this material from getting there. Electrical stimulation of the adenohypophysis itself does not cause ovulation in a rodent, but similar pulses delivered to the special hypothalamic centers, or to the amygdala, a forebrain region which has connectives with the hypothalamus, do cause ovulation.

Females of some species of mammals are like hibernating frogs in maintaining themselves in readiness for ovulation but waiting for a trigger-stimulus from outside (rabbits, ferrets, cats, mink, etc.). Others (women, cows, rats, and mice) ovulate spontaneously at rhythmically recurring periods in estrous cycles correlated with particular hormone fluctuations. In the former group, ovulation is provoked by the sensory stimulus of copulation or a mechanical disturbance of the genital tract, and prevented by surgical interruption of the flow of stimuli to the hypothalamus. Chemical substances which block the action of acetylcholine or adrenaline, and hence stop the transmission of nerve impulses at synapses, can block ovulation in a rabbit if injected into her blood stream within a minute of copulation.

In the spontaneously ovulating mammals, similar pharmacological devices, when precisely timed, can also delay or prevent ovulation. Although one of the factors that sets off the ovulatory process is the rise in the amount of estrogen given off by the ovary as the egg follicle is maturing, it does not seem that the estrogen stimulates LH production in the adenohypophysis directly, but by way of estrogen-sensitive elements in the hypothalamus, with a further relay through neurons, neurosecretory cells, and the little portal-vein system.

In birds also, the neurosecretory apparatus can be controlled through sensory stimuli, spinal cord, and brainstem. A hen will not ovulate her next egg while the last one is still stretching the walls of her upper oviduct. She ceases her egg-laying rhythm and becomes broody when the pattern of skin sensation sends information to her brain that there are enough eggs in her nest. The rhythm of egg-laying, and in fact the egg-laying season, are partly controlled by illumination. An isolated pigeon will not ovulate spontaneously, but the sight of herself in a mirror may be enough of a stimulus.

C. Estrous Cycles and Pregnancy in Mammals

The female sex cycles of mammals (**estrous cycles**) are more complex than those of birds, the oviparous reptiles, and anamniotes. They include not only a follicular phase, but also a new luteal phase and a regressive phase.

In the **follicular phase**, quite as in other vertebrates, the hypophyseal hormones FSH and LH stimulate the growth and maturation of eggs, and bring about ovulation. Just then the cells remaining in the collapsed ovarian follicle suddenly proliferate as a powerful endocrine gland, the corpus luteum (page 197; Fig. 4–19). The mammalian uterus has developed a high sensitivity to the luteal hormone, progesterone, in combination with the high output of estrogen from the follicular phase. This brings on the **luteal phase** of the sex cycle, in which the endometrial lining of the uterus thickens markedly, as though in preparation for the implantation of an embryo (Fig. 11–4).

The corpus luteum, however, cannot maintain itself without a combination of hormones from the hypophysis: LH and prolactin (the latter also called luteotropic hormone, LTH). A few days after ovulation, this support from the hypophysis is withdrawn, and the corpus luteum ceases to produce its progesterone. This initiates the **regression phase,** one result of which is that the uterus returns to its former condition by the shrinkage and sloughing of the endometrium, or, as in some primates, by a sharp breakdown and hemorrhage called **menstruation.** After a short period of healing, the follicular phase of a new cycle is started.

Corpora lutea and hormones like progesterone are by no means unique to mammals. Since progesterone quiets uterine muscle, it has been suggested that an earlier use for the corpus luteum was to put the uterus in such a state that it could be used as a reservoir in which a whole clutch of fertilized eggs could be accumulated before the necessity of laying them; this custom persists in many reptiles.

Two new developments led on from there. The first was that the mammalian uterine endometrium developed such a sensitivity to progesterone that it became soft and thick in the luteal phase (page 197), to the point that it could be penetrated by a developing embryo reaching it in the blastocyst stage (Fig. 6–9). The other was that the sprouting chorion of the little embryo became an endocrine gland in its turn, liberating into the pregnant mother's blood stream certain hormones (chorionic gonadotropins) which would prevent the decline of the corpus luteum and maintain it in secretory condition. This insured, first, the capacity of the uterus to support its endometrium in the pregnancy state, and second, the suppression of succeeding ovulatory cycles by inhibiting the production of new FSH from the hypophysis.

All the mammals that still live share the inheritance of these traits except the monotremes, which lay eggs. But those that undergo a pregnancy vary greatly in the extent to which they have taken the next step, the evolution of a placenta (page 203). They also have developed different tricks for the maintenance of the pregnancy. In some mammals, removal of the corpus luteum at any time results in abortion of the fetus and the resumption of estrous cycles. In others, the corpus luteum is necessary only in the early phases of pregnancy because the placenta in its turn becomes an endocrine gland, replacing the luteal cells as a source of progesterone.

These interacting hormonal and other devices that integrate the life of the fetus with that of the mother, i.e., the endocrine activities of the embryonic chorion and the placenta, are wholly new in mammals.

IV. FINAL COMMENTS ON INTEGRATIVE ACTIVITY

The above examples of the interplay of one organ upon another in events that happen only once in the life history (metamorphosis was discussed but puberty would have served as well), or in rhythms such as ovulation, the estrous cycle and pregnancy, have been selected to make a point. Many other examples could have been used: the apparatus coordinating the digestive sequences in the intestine, or the control of water balance and salt concentrations in the tissues, or the regulation of surface color patterns, the adjustment of metabolism and behavior to external demands, etc.

An individual vertebrate is not a collection of organs and tissues, it is a complex and coordinated entity. Only the student who knows the animal as it lives in its habitat, who has watched it develop from the egg, who has seen its architecture in dissection and under the microscope, and pursued the sources of its adjustability through physiology to biochemistry and biophysics, can get the beginnings of a comprehension of its beauty.

> "Our life contains a thousand springs
> And dies if one be gone
> Strange that a harp of thousand strings
> Should keep in tune so long."
>
> —Dr. Watts, "The Continental Harmony," 1794.

REFERENCES

The autonomic nervous system of man and laboratory animals is discussed in numerous texts of anatomy, neurology, and physiology. Specific information on lower vertebrates has to be dug out of the original literature, which has not been reviewed since 1952 (Nicol).

A remarkably condensed and well-organized summary of endocrine gland functions is available in Turner (1960), whose text reflects the fact that most research in this field focuses on mammals. Further comparative information can be found in various chapters of *The Physiology of Fishes*, 1957, M. E. Brown (ed.), Academic Press, Inc., New York, and in Pickford and Atz (1957). See also the 1959 symposium, *Comparative endocrinology*, A. Gorbman (ed.), John Wiley & Sons, Inc., New York, and the symposia published as *Memoirs of the Society for Endocrinology*, Cambridge University Press, London.

1. TRIPLETT, E. L., 1958. *J. Exptl. Zool.* 138: 283.
2. NICOL, J. A. C., 1952. *Biol. Revs.* 27: 1.
3. ENAMI, M., 1959. *In* A. GORBMAN (ed.), *Comparative endocrinology.* John Wiley & Sons, Inc., New York.
4. PICKFORD, G. E., and J. W. ATZ, 1957. *The physiology of the pituitary gland of fishes.* New York Zoological Society, New York.
5. GREEN, J. D., and D. S. MAXWELL, 1959. *In* A. GORBMAN (ed.); see Ref. 3.
6. GRANT, W. C., and J. A. GRANT, 1958. *Biol. Bull.* 114: 1.
7. TURNER, C. D., 1960. *General endocrinology.* 3d ed. W. B. Saunders Co., Philadelphia.
8. EVERETT, J. W., 1959. *In* A. GORBMAN (ed.); see Ref. 3.
9. SEGAL, S. J., 1959. *In* A. GORBMAN (ed.); see Ref. 3.
10. KOLLROS, J. J., 1961. *Am. Zoologist* 1: 107. Also, ETKIN, W., 1963. *Science* 139: 810.
11. ETKIN, W., and R. LEHRER, 1960. *Endocrinology* 67: 457.
12. WITSCHI, E., and C. Y. CHANG, 1959. *In* A. GORBMAN (ed.); see Ref. 3.

Index

Page references for definitions appear in **boldface** type, and page references for illustrations in *italics; **boldface italics*** indicate pages where both definition and illustration are found.

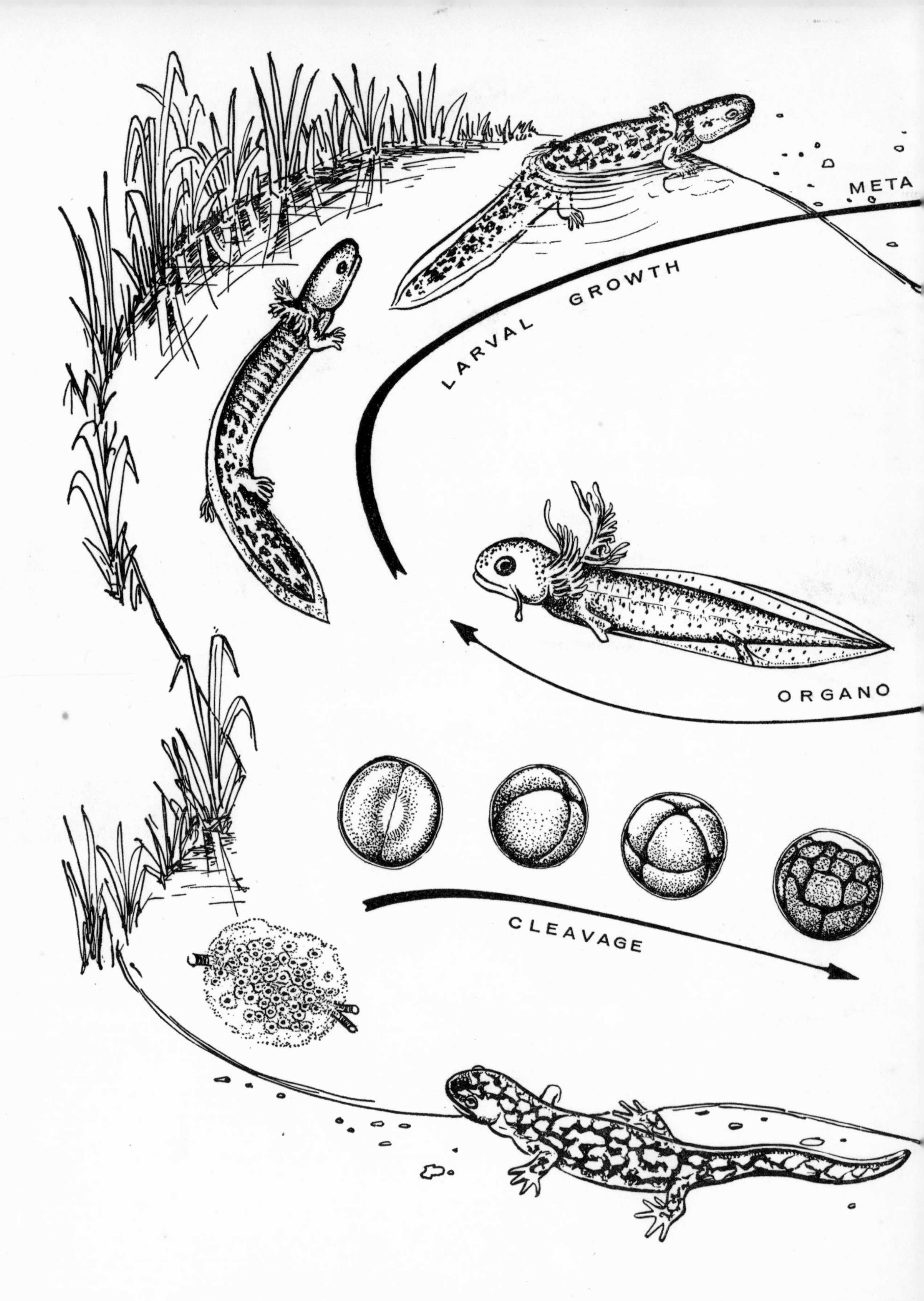

LIFE HISTORY OF